McGraw Hill Education **create**™

Course	**Introduction to Discrete Logic & Digital System**
Course Number	**ECE 225**
Instructor	**Dr. Dimitrios Kagaris**
	Southern Illinois University Carbondale
	ELECTRICAL AND COMPUTER ENGINEERING

http://create.mheducation.com

ISBN-10: 0390525863   ISBN-13: 9780390525864

Contents

Credits

C H A P T E R

1

The Foundations: Logic and Proof, Sets, and Functions

This chapter reviews the foundations of discrete mathematics. Three important topics are covered: logic, sets, and functions. The rules of logic specify the meaning of mathematical statements. For instance, these rules help us understand and reason with statements such as "There exists an integer that is not the sum of two squares," and "For every positive integer n the sum of the positive integers not exceeding n is $n(n + 1)/2$." Logic is the basis of all mathematical reasoning, and it has practical applications to the design of computing machines, to system specifications, to artificial intelligence, to computer programming, to programming languages, and to other areas of computer science, as well as to many other fields of study.

To understand mathematics, we must understand what makes up a correct mathematical argument, that is, a proof. Moreover, to learn mathematics, a person needs to actively construct mathematical arguments and not just read exposition. In this chapter, we explain what makes up a correct mathematical argument and introduce tools to construct these arguments. Proofs are important not only in mathematics, but also in many parts of computer science, including program verification, algorithm correctness, and system security. Furthermore, automated reasoning systems have been constructed that allow computers to construct their own proofs.

Much of discrete mathematics is devoted to the study of discrete structures, which are used to represent discrete objects. Many important discrete structures are built using sets, which are collections of objects. Among the discrete structures built from sets are combinations, which are unordered collections of objects used extensively in counting; relations, which are sets of ordered pairs that represent relationships between objects; graphs, which consist of sets of vertices and of edges that connect vertices; and finite state machines, which are used to model computing machines.

The concept of a function is extremely important in discrete mathematics. A function assigns to each element of a set precisely one element of a set. Useful structures such as sequences and strings are special types of functions. Functions play important roles throughout discrete mathematics. They are used to represent the computational complexity of algorithms, to study the size of sets, to count objects of different kinds, and in a myriad of other ways.

1.1 Logic

INTRODUCTION

The rules of logic give precise meaning to mathematical statements. These rules are used to distinguish between valid and invalid mathematical arguments. Since a major goal of this book is to teach the reader how to understand and how to construct correct mathematical arguments, we begin our study of discrete mathematics with an introduction to logic.

In addition to its importance in understanding mathematical reasoning, logic has numerous applications in computer science. These rules are used in the design of computer circuits, the construction of computer programs, the verification of the correctness of programs, and in many other ways. We will discuss each of these applications in the upcoming chapters.

PROPOSITIONS

Our discussion begins with an introduction to the basic building blocks of logic—propositions. A **proposition** is a declarative sentence that is either true or false, but not both.

EXAMPLE 1
All the following declarative sentences are propositions.

1. Washington, D.C., is the capital of the United States of America.
2. Toronto is the capital of Canada.
3. $1 + 1 = 2$.
4. $2 + 2 = 3$.

Propositions 1 and 3 are true, whereas 2 and 4 are false. ◀

Some sentences that are not propositions are given in the next example.

EXAMPLE 2
Consider the following sentences.

1. What time is it?
2. Read this carefully.

ARISTOTLE (384 B.C.E.–322 B.C.E.) Aristotle was born in Stargirus in northern Greece. His father was the personal physician of the King of Macedonia. Because his father died when Aristotle was young, Aristotle could not follow the custom of following his father's profession. Aristotle became an orphan at a young age when his mother also died. His guardian who raised him taught him poetry, rhetoric, and Greek. At the age of 17, his guardian sent him to Athens to further his education. Aristotle joined Plato's Academy where for 20 years he attended Plato's lectures, later presenting his own lectures on rhetoric. When Plato died in 347 B.C.E., Aristotle was not chosen to succeed him because his views differed too much from those of Plato. Instead, Aristotle joined the court of King Hermeas where he remained for three years, and married the niece of the King. When the Persians defeated Hermeas, Aristotle moved to Mytilene and, at the invitation of King Philip of Macedonia, he tutored Alexander, Philip's son, who later became Alexander the Great. Aristotle tutored Alexander for five years and after the death of King Philip, he returned to Athens and set up his own school, called the Lyceum.

Aristotle's followers were called the peripatetics, which means "to walk about," because Aristotle often walked around as he discussed philosophical questions. Aristotle taught at the Lyceum for 13 years where he lectured to his advanced students in the morning and gave popular lectures to a broad audience in the evening. When Alexander the Great died in 323 B.C.E., a backlash against anything related to Alexander led to trumped-up charges of impiety against Aristotle. Aristotle fled to Chalcis to avoid prosecution. He only lived one year in Chalcis, dying of a stomach ailment in 322 B.C.E.

Aristotle wrote three types of works: those written for a popular audience, compilations of scientific facts, and systematic treatises. The systematic treatises included works on logic, philosophy, psychology, physics, and natural history. Aristotle's writings were preserved by a student and were hidden in a vault where a wealthy book collector discovered them about 200 years later. They were taken to Rome, where they were studied by scholars and issued in new editions, preserving them for posterity.

3. $x + 1 = 2$.
4. $x + y = z$.

Sentences 1 and 2 are not propositions because they are not declarative sentences. Sentences 3 and 4 are not propositions because they are neither true nor false, since the variables in these sentences have not been assigned values. Various ways to form propositions from sentences of this type will be discussed in Section 1.3. ◀

Letters are used to denote propositions, just as letters are used to denote variables. The conventional letters used for this purpose are $p, q, r, s, \ldots$. The **truth value** of a proposition is true, denoted by T, if it is a true proposition and false, denoted by F, if it is a false proposition.

The area of logic that deals with propositions is called the **propositional calculus** or **propositional logic.** It was first developed systematically by the Greek philosopher Aristotle more than 2300 years ago.

We now turn our attention to methods for producing new propositions from those that we already have. These methods were discussed by the English mathematician George Boole in 1854 in his book *The Laws of Thought*. Many mathematical statements are constructed by combining one or more propositions. New propositions, called **compound propositions,** are formed from existing propositions using logical operators.

Links

DEFINITION 1

Let p be a proposition. The statement

"It is not the case that p"

is another proposition, called the *negation* of p. The negation of p is denoted by $\neg p$. The proposition $\neg p$ is read "not p."

EXAMPLE 3 Find the negation of the proposition

"Today is Friday."

Extra
Examples

and express this in simple English.

Solution: The negation is

"It is not the case that today is Friday."

This negation can be more simply expressed by

"Today is not Friday,"

or

"It is not Friday today." ◀

TABLE 1 The Truth Table for the Negation of a Proposition.

p	$\neg p$
T	F
F	T

Remark: Strictly speaking, sentences involving variable times such as those in Example 3 are not propositions unless a fixed time is assumed. The same holds for variable places unless a fixed place is assumed and for pronouns unless a particular person is assumed.

A **truth table** displays the relationships between the truth values of propositions. Truth tables are especially valuable in the determination of the truth values of propositions constructed from simpler propositions. Table 1 displays the two possible truth values of a proposition p and the corresponding truth values of its negation $\neg p$.

The negation of a proposition can also be considered the result of the operation of the **negation operator** on a proposition. The negation operator constructs a new proposition from a single existing proposition. We will now introduce the logical operators that are used to form new propositions from two or more existing propositions. These logical operators are also called **connectives.**

DEFINITION 2

Let p and q be propositions. The proposition "p and q," denoted $p \wedge q$, is the proposition that is true when both p and q are true and is false otherwise. The proposition $p \wedge q$ is called the *conjunction* of p and q.

The truth table for $p \wedge q$ is shown in Table 2. Note that there are four rows in this truth table, one row for each possible combination of truth values for the propositions p and q.

EXAMPLE 4   Find the conjunction of the propositions p and q where p is the proposition "Today is Friday" and q is the proposition "It is raining today."

Solution: The conjunction of these propositions, $p \wedge q$, is the proposition "Today is Friday and it is raining today." This proposition is true on rainy Fridays and is false on any day that is not a Friday and on Fridays when it does not rain. ◄

DEFINITION 3

Let p and q be propositions. The proposition "p or q," denoted $p \vee q$, is the proposition that is false when p and q are both false and true otherwise. The proposition $p \vee q$ is called the *disjunction* of p and q.

The truth table for $p \vee q$ is shown in Table 3.

The use of the connective *or* in a disjunction corresponds to one of the two ways the word *or* is used in English, namely, in an inclusive way. A disjunction is true when at least one of the two propositions is true. For instance, the inclusive or is being used in the statement

"Students who have taken calculus or computer science can take this class."

GEORGE BOOLE (1815–1864)   George Boole, the son of a cobbler, was born in Lincoln, England, in November 1815. Because of his family's difficult financial situation, Boole had to struggle to educate himself while supporting his family. Nevertheless, he became one of the most important mathematicians of the 1800s. Although he considered a career as a clergyman, he decided instead to go into teaching and soon afterward opened a school of his own. In his preparation for teaching mathematics, Boole—unsatisfied with textbooks of his day—decided to read the works of the great mathematicians. While reading papers of the great French mathematician Lagrange, Boole made discoveries in the calculus of variations, the branch of analysis dealing with finding curves and surfaces optimizing certain parameters.

In 1848 Boole published *The Mathematical Analysis of Logic,* the first of his contributions to symbolic logic. In 1849 he was appointed professor of mathematics at Queen's College in Cork, Ireland. In 1854 he published *The Laws of Thought,* his most famous work. In this book Boole introduced what is now called *Boolean algebra* in his honor. Boole wrote textbooks on differential equations and on difference equations that were used in Great Britain until the end of the nineteenth century. Boole married in 1855; his wife was the niece of the professor of Greek at Queen's College. In 1864 Boole died from pneumonia, which he contracted as a result of keeping a lecture engagement even though he was soaking wet from a rainstorm.

TABLE 2 The Truth Table for the Conjunction of Two Propositions.		
p	q	$p \wedge q$
T	T	T
T	F	F
F	T	F
F	F	F

TABLE 3 The Truth Table for the Disjunction of Two Propositions.		
p	q	$p \vee q$
T	T	T
T	F	T
F	T	T
F	F	F

Here, we mean that students who have taken both calculus and computer science can take the class, as well as the students who have taken only one of the two subjects. On the other hand, we are using the exclusive or when we say

"Students who have taken calculus or computer science, but not both, can enroll in this class."

Here, we mean that students who have taken both calculus and a computer science course cannot take the class. Only those who have taken exactly one of the two courses can take the class.

Similarly, when a menu at a restaurant states, "Soup or salad comes with an entrée," the restaurant almost always means that customers can have either soup or salad, but not both. Hence, this is an exclusive, rather than an inclusive, or.

EXAMPLE 5   What is the disjunction of the propositions p and q where p and q are the same propositions as in Example 4?

Solution: The disjunction of p and q, $p \vee q$, is the proposition

"Today is Friday or it is raining today."

This proposition is true on any day that is either a Friday or a rainy day (including rainy Fridays). It is only false on days that are not Fridays when it also does not rain.   ◀

As was previously remarked, the use of the connective *or* in a disjunction corresponds to one of the two ways the word *or* is used in English, namely, in an inclusive way. Thus, a disjunction is true when at least one of the two propositions in it is true. Sometimes, we use *or* in an exclusive sense. When the exclusive or is used to connect the propositions p and q, the proposition "p or q (but not both)" is obtained. This proposition is true when p is true and q is false, and when p is false and q is true. It is false when both p and q are false and when both are true.

Extra
Examples

DEFINITION 4   Let p and q be propositions. The *exclusive or* of p and q, denoted by $p \oplus q$, is the proposition that is true when exactly one of p and q is true and is false otherwise.

The truth table for the exclusive or of two propositions is displayed in Table 4.

TABLE 4 The Truth Table for the Exclusive Or of Two Propositions.		
p	*q*	$p \oplus q$
T	T	F
T	F	T
F	T	T
F	F	F

TABLE 5 The Truth Table for the Implication $p \rightarrow q$.		
p	*q*	$p \rightarrow q$
T	T	T
T	F	F
F	T	T
F	F	T

IMPLICATIONS

We will discuss several other important ways in which propositions can be combined.

DEFINITION 5

Assessment

Let *p* and *q* be propositions. The *implication* $p \rightarrow q$ is the proposition that is false when *p* is true and *q* is false, and true otherwise. In this implication *p* is called the *hypothesis* (or *antecedent* or *premise*) and *q* is called the *conclusion* (or *consequence*).

The truth table for the implication $p \rightarrow q$ is shown in Table 5. An implication is sometimes called a **conditional statement.**

Because implications play such an essential role in mathematical reasoning, a variety of terminology is used to express $p \rightarrow q$. You will encounter most if not all of the following ways to express this implication:

Extra Examples

"if *p*, then *q*"   "*p* implies *q*"
"if *p*, *q*"   "*p* only if *q*"
"*p* is sufficient for *q*"   "a sufficient condition for *q* is *p*"
"*q* if *p*"   "*q* whenever *p*"
"*q* when *p*"   "*q* is necessary for *p*"
"a necessary condition for *p* is *q*"   "*q* follows from *p*"

The implication $p \rightarrow q$ is false only in the case that *p* is true, but *q* is false. It is true when both *p* and *q* are true, and when *p* is false (no matter what truth value *q* has).

A useful way to understand the truth value of an implication is to think of an obligation or a contract. For example, the pledge many politicians make when running for office is:

"If I am elected, then I will lower taxes."

If the politician is elected, voters would expect this politician to lower taxes. Furthermore, if the politician is not elected, then voters will not have any expectation that this person will lower taxes, although the person may have sufficient influence to cause those in power to lower taxes. It is only when the politician is elected but does not lower taxes that voters can say that the politician has broken the campaign pledge. This last scenario corresponds to the case when *p* is true, but *q* is false in $p \rightarrow q$.

Similarly, consider a statement that a professor might make:

"If you get 100% on the final, then you will get an A."

If you manage to get a 100% on the final, then you would expect to receive an A. If you do not get 100% you may or may not receive an A depending on other factors. However, if you do get 100%, but the professor does not give you an A, you will feel cheated.

Many people find it confusing that "p only if q" expresses the same thing as "if p then q." To remember this, note that "p only if q" says that p cannot be true when q is not true. That is, the statement is false if p is true, but q is false. When p is false, q may be either true or false, because the statement says nothing about the truth value of q. A common error is for people to think that "q only if p" is a way of expressing $p \rightarrow q$. However, these statements have different truth values when p and q have different truth values.

The way we have defined implications is more general than the meaning attached to implications in the English language. For instance, the implication

"If it is sunny today, then we will go to the beach."

is an implication used in normal language, since there is a relationship between the hypothesis and the conclusion. Further, this implication is considered valid unless it is indeed sunny today, but we do not go to the beach. On the other hand, the implication

"If today is Friday, then $2 + 3 = 5$."

is true from the definition of implication, since its conclusion is true. (The truth value of the hypothesis does not matter then.) The implication

"If today is Friday, then $2 + 3 = 6$."

is true every day except Friday, even though $2 + 3 = 6$ is false.

We would not use these last two implications in natural language (except perhaps in sarcasm), since there is no relationship between the hypothesis and the conclusion in either implication. In mathematical reasoning we consider implications of a more general sort than we use in English. The mathematical concept of an implication is independent of a cause-and-effect relationship between hypothesis and conclusion. Our definition of an implication specifies its truth values; it is not based on English usage.

The if-then construction used in many programming languages is different from that used in logic. Most programming languages contain statements such as **if** p **then** S, where p is a proposition and S is a program segment (one or more statements to be executed). When execution of a program encounters such a statement, S is executed if p is true, but S is not executed if p is false, as illustrated in Example 6.

EXAMPLE 6   What is the value of the variable x after the statement

if $2 + 2 = 4$ **then** $x := x + 1$

if $x = 0$ before this statement is encountered? (The symbol $:=$ stands for assignment. The statement $x := x + 1$ means the assignment of the value of $x + 1$ to x.)

Solution: Since $2 + 2 = 4$ is true, the assignment statement $x := x + 1$ is executed. Hence, x has the value $0 + 1 = 1$ after this statement is encountered. ◀

CONVERSE, CONTRAPOSITIVE, AND INVERSE There are some related implications that can be formed from $p \rightarrow q$. The proposition $q \rightarrow p$ is called the **converse** of $p \rightarrow q$. The **contrapositive** of $p \rightarrow q$ is the proposition $\neg q \rightarrow \neg p$. The proposition $\neg p \rightarrow \neg q$ is called the **inverse** of $p \rightarrow q$.

The contrapositive, $\neg q \rightarrow \neg p$, of an implication $p \rightarrow q$ has the same truth value as $p \rightarrow q$. To see this, note that the contrapositive is false only when $\neg p$ is false and $\neg q$ is true, that is, only when p is true and q is false. On the other hand, neither the converse, $q \rightarrow p$, nor the inverse, $\neg p \rightarrow \neg q$, has the same truth value as $p \rightarrow q$ for all possible truth values of p and q. To see this, note that when p is true and q is false, the original implication is false, but the converse and the inverse are both true. When two compound propositions always have the same truth value we call them **equivalent,** so that an implication and its contrapositive are equivalent. The converse and the inverse of an implication are also equivalent, as the reader can verify. (We will study equivalent propositions in Section 1.2.) One of the most common logical errors is to assume that the converse or the inverse of an implication is equivalent to this implication.

We illustrate the use of implications in Example 7.

EXAMPLE 7

Extra Examples

What are the contrapositive, the converse, and the inverse of the implication

"The home team wins whenever it is raining."?

Solution: Because "q whenever p" is one of the ways to express the implication $p \rightarrow q$, the original statement can be rewritten as

"If it is raining, then the home team wins."

Consequently, the contrapositive of this implication is

"If the home team does not win, then it is not raining."

The converse is

"If the home team wins, then it is raining."

The inverse is

"If it is not raining, then the home team does not win."

Only the contrapositive is equivalent to the original statement. ◀

We now introduce another way to combine propositions.

DEFINITION 6

Let p and q be propositions. The *biconditional* $p \leftrightarrow q$ is the proposition that is true when p and q have the same truth values, and is false otherwise.

The truth table for $p \leftrightarrow q$ is shown in Table 6. Note that the biconditional $p \leftrightarrow q$ is true precisely when both the implications $p \rightarrow q$ and $q \rightarrow p$ are true. Because of this, the terminology

"p if and only if q"

is used for this biconditional and it is symbolically written by combining the symbols $\rightarrow$ and $\leftarrow$. There are some other common ways to express $p \leftrightarrow q$:

TABLE 6 The Truth Table for the Biconditional $p \leftrightarrow q$.		
p	q	$p \leftrightarrow q$
T	T	T
T	F	F
F	T	F
F	F	T

"p is necessary and sufficient for q"

"if p then q, and conversely"

"p if q".

The last way of expressing the biconditional uses the abbreviation "iff" for "if and only if." Note that $p \leftrightarrow q$ has exactly the same truth value as $(p \to q) \wedge (q \to p)$.

EXAMPLE 8   Let p be the statement "You can take the flight" and let q be the statement "You buy a ticket." Then $p \leftrightarrow q$ is the statement

"You can take the flight if and only if you buy a ticket."

This statement is true if p and q are either both true or both false, that is, if you buy a ticket and can take the flight or if you do not buy a ticket and you cannot take the flight. It is false when p and q have opposite truth values, that is, when you do not buy a ticket, but you can take the flight (such as when you get a free trip) and when you buy a ticket and cannot take the flight (such as when the airline bumps you). ◀

The "if and only if" construction used in biconditionals is rarely used in common language. Instead, biconditionals are often expressed using an "if, then" or an "only if" construction. The other part of the "if and only if" is implicit. For example, consider the statement in English "If you finish your meal, then you can have dessert." What is really meant is "You can have dessert if and only if you finish your meal." This last statement is logically equivalent to the two statements "If you finish your meal, then you can have dessert" and "You can have dessert, only if you finish your meal." Because of this imprecision in natural language, we need to make an assumption whether a conditional statement in natural language implicitly includes its converse. Because precision is essential in mathematics and in logic, we will always distinguish between the conditional statement $p \to q$ and the biconditional statement $p \leftrightarrow q$.

PRECEDENCE OF LOGICAL OPERATORS

We can construct compound propositions using the negation operator and the logical operators defined so far. We will generally use parentheses to specify the order in which logical operators in a compound proposition are to be applied. For instance, $(p \vee q) \wedge (\neg r)$ is the conjunction of $p \vee q$ and $\neg r$. However, to reduce the number of parentheses, we specify that the negation operator is applied before all other logical operators. This means that $\neg p \wedge q$ is the conjunction of $\neg p$ and q, namely, $(\neg p) \wedge q$, not the negation of the conjunction of p and q, namely $\neg (p \wedge q)$.

TABLE 7 Precedence of Logical Operators.	
Operator	**Precedence**
$\neg$	1
$\wedge$	2
$\vee$	3
$\rightarrow$	4
$\leftrightarrow$	5

Another general rule of precedence is that the conjunction operator takes precedence over the disjunction operator, so that $p \wedge q \vee r$ means $(p \wedge q) \vee r$ rather than $p \wedge (q \vee r)$. Because this rule may be difficult to remember, we will continue to use parentheses so that the order of the disjunction and conjunction operators is clear.

Finally, it is an accepted rule that the conditional and biconditional operators $\rightarrow$ and $\leftrightarrow$ have lower precedence than the conjunction and disjunction operators, $\wedge$ and $\vee$. Consequently, $p \vee q \rightarrow r$ is the same as $(p \vee q) \rightarrow r$. We will use parentheses when the order of the conditional operator and biconditional operator is at issue, although the conditional operator has precedence over the biconditional operator. Table 7 displays the precedence levels of the logical operators, $\neg, \wedge, \vee, \rightarrow$, and $\leftrightarrow$.

TRANSLATING ENGLISH SENTENCES

There are many reasons to translate English sentences into expressions involving propositional variables and logical connectives. In particular, English (and every other human language) is often ambiguous. Translating sentences into logical expressions removes the ambiguity. Note that this may involve making a set of reasonable assumptions based on the intended meaning of the sentence. Moreover, once we have translated sentences from English into logical expressions we can analyze these logical expressions to determine their truth values, we can manipulate them, and we can use rules of inference (which are discussed in Section 1.5) to reason about them.

To illustrate the process of translating an English sentence into a logical expression, consider Examples 9 and 10.

EXAMPLE 9 How can this English sentence be translated into a logical expression?

"You can access the Internet from campus only if you are a computer science major or you are not a freshman."

Solution: There are many ways to translate this sentence into a logical expression. Although it is possible to represent the sentence by a single propositional variable, such as p, this would not be useful when analyzing its meaning or reasoning with it. Instead, we will use propositional variables to represent each sentence part and determine the appropriate logical connectives between them. In particular, we let a, c, and f represent "You can access the Internet from campus," "You are a computer science major," and "You are a freshman," respectively. Noting that "only if" is one way an implication can be expressed, this sentence can be represented as

$$a \rightarrow (c \vee \neg f).$$ ◄

EXAMPLE 10 How can this English sentence be translated into a logical expression?

"You cannot ride the roller coaster if you are under 4 feet tall unless you are older than 16 years old."

Solution: There are many ways to translate this sentence into a logical expression. The simplest but least useful way is simply to represent the sentence by a single propositional variable, say, p. Although this is not wrong, doing this would not assist us when we try to analyze the sentence or reason using it. More appropriately, what we can do is to use propositional variables to represent each of the sentence parts and to decide on the appropriate logical connectives between them. In particular, we let q, r, and s represent

"You can ride the roller coaster," "You are under 4 feet tall," and "You are older than 16 years old," respectively. Then the sentence can be translated to

$$(r \wedge \neg s) \rightarrow \neg q.$$

Of course, there are other ways to represent the original sentence as a logical expression, but the one we have used should meet our needs. ◄

SYSTEM SPECIFICATIONS

Translating sentences in natural language (such as English) into logical expressions is an essential part of specifying both hardware and software systems. System and software engineers take requirements in natural language and produce precise and unambiguous specifications that can be used as the basis for system development. Example 11 shows how propositional expressions can be used in this process.

EXAMPLE 11

Extra Examples

Express the specification "The automated reply cannot be sent when the file system is full" using logical connectives.

Solution: One way to translate this is to let p denote "The automated reply can be sent" and q denote "The file system is full." Then $\neg p$ represents "It is not the case that the automated reply can be sent," which can also be expressed as "The automated reply cannot be sent." Consequently, our specification can be represented by the implication $q \rightarrow \neg p$. ◄

System specifications should not contain conflicting requirements. If they did there would be no way to develop a system that satisfies all specifications. Consequently, propositional expressions representing these specifications need to be **consistent.** That is, there must be an assignment of truth values to the variables in the expressions that makes all the expressions true.

EXAMPLE 12

Determine whether these system specifications are consistent:

"The diagnostic message is stored in the buffer or it is retransmitted."
"The diagnostic message is not stored in the buffer."
"If the diagnostic message is stored in the buffer, then it is retransmitted."

Extra Examples

Solution: To determine whether these specifications are consistent, we first express them using logical expressions. Let p denote "The diagnostic message is stored in the buffer" and let q denote "The diagnostic message is retransmitted." The specifications can then be written as $p \vee q, \neg p$, and $p \rightarrow q$. An assignment of truth values that makes all three specifications true must have p false to make $\neg p$ true. Since we want $p \vee q$ to be true but p must be false, q must be true. Because $p \rightarrow q$ is true when p is false and q is true, we conclude that these specifications are consistent since they are all true when p is false and q is true. We could come to the same conclusion by use of a truth table to examine the four possible assignments of truth values to p and q. ◄

EXAMPLE 13

Do the system specifications in Example 12 remain consistent if the specification "The diagnostic message is not retransmitted" is added?

Solution: By the reasoning in Example 12, the three specifications from that example are true only in the case when p is false and q is true. However, this new specification is $\neg q$, which is false when q is true. Consequently, these four specifications are inconsistent. ◄

BOOLEAN SEARCHES

Logical connectives are used extensively in searches of large collections of information, such as indexes of Web pages. Because these searches employ techniques from propositional logic, they are called **Boolean searches.**

In Boolean searches, the connective *AND* is used to match records that contain both of two search terms, the connective *OR* is used to match one or both of two search terms, and the connective *NOT* (sometimes written as *AND NOT*) is used to exclude a particular search term. Careful planning of how logical connectives are used is often required when Boolean searches are used to locate information of potential interest. Example 14 illustrates how Boolean searches are carried out.

EXAMPLE 14 **Web Page Searching.** Most Web search engines support Boolean searching techniques, which usually can help find Web pages about particular subjects. For instance, using Boolean searching to find Web pages about universities in New Mexico, we can look for pages matching NEW *AND* MEXICO *AND* UNIVERSITIES. The results of this search will include those pages that contain the three words NEW, MEXICO, and UNIVERSITIES. This will include all of the pages of interest, together with others such as a page about new universities in Mexico. Next, to find pages that deal with universities in New Mexico or Arizona, we can search for pages matching (NEW *AND* MEXICO *OR* ARIZONA) *AND* UNIVERSITIES. (*Note:* Here the *AND* operator takes precedence over the *OR* operator.) The results of this search will include all pages that contain the word UNIVERSITIES and either both the words NEW and MEXICO or the word ARIZONA. Again, pages besides those of interest will be listed. Finally, to find Web pages that deal with universities in Mexico (and not New Mexico), we might first look for pages matching MEXICO *AND* UNIVERSITIES, but since the results of this search will include pages about universities in New Mexico, as well as universities in Mexico, it might be better to search for pages matching (MEXICO *AND* UNIVERSITIES) *NOT* NEW. The results of this search include pages that contain both the words MEXICO and UNIVERSITIES but do not contain the word NEW. ◄

LOGIC PUZZLES

Puzzles that can be solved using logical reasoning are known as **logic puzzles.** Solving logic puzzles is an excellent way to practice working with the rules of logic. Also, computer programs designed to carry out logical reasoning often use well-known logic puzzles to illustrate their capabilities. Many people enjoy solving logic puzzles, which are published in books and periodicals as a recreational activity.

We will discuss two logic puzzles here. We begin with a puzzle that was originally posed by Raymond Smullyan, a master of logic puzzles, who has published more than a dozen books containing challenging puzzles that involve logical reasoning.

EXAMPLE 15 In [Sm78] Smullyan posed many puzzles about an island that has two kinds of inhabitants, knights, who always tell the truth, and their opposites, knaves, who always lie. You encounter two people A and B. What are A and B if A says "B is a knight" and B says "The two of us are opposite types"?

Solution: Let p and q be the statements that A is a knight and B is a knight, respectively, so that $\neg p$ and $\neg q$ are the statements that A is a knave and that B is a knave, respectively.

We first consider the possibility that A is a knight; this is the statement that p is true. If A is a knight, then he is telling the truth when he says that B is a knight, so that q is true, and A and B are the same type. However, if B is a knight, then B's statement that A and B are of opposite types, the statement $(p \wedge \neg q) \vee (\neg p \wedge q)$, would have to be true, which it is not, because A and B are both knights. Consequently, we can conclude that A is not a knight, that is, that p is false.

If A is a knave, then because everything a knave says is false, A's statement that B is a knight, that is, that q is true, is a lie, which means that q is false and B is also a knave. Furthermore, if B is a knave, then B's statement that A and B are opposite types is a lie, which is consistent with both A and B being knaves. We can conclude that both A and B are knaves.   ◄

We pose more of Smullyan's puzzles about knights and knaves in Exercises 51–55 at the end of this section. Next, we pose a puzzle known as the **muddy children puzzle** for the case of two children.

EXAMPLE 16 A father tells his two children, a boy and a girl, to play in their backyard without getting dirty. However, while playing, both children get mud on their foreheads. When the children stop playing, the father says "At least one of you has a muddy forehead," and then asks the children to answer "Yes" or "No" to the question: "Do you know whether you have a muddy forehead?" The father asks this question twice. What will the children answer each time this question is asked, assuming that a child can see whether his or her sibling has a muddy forehead, but cannot see his or her own forehead? Assume that both children are honest and that the children answer each question simultaneously.

Solution: Let s be the statement that the son has a muddy forehead and let d be the statement that the daughter has a muddy forehead. When the father says that at least

RAYMOND SMULLYAN (BORN 1919) Raymond Smullyan dropped out of high school. He wanted to study what he was really interested in and not standard high school material. After jumping from one university to the next, he earned an undergraduate degree in mathematics at the University of Chicago in 1955. He paid his college expenses by performing magic tricks at parties and clubs. He obtained a Ph.D. in logic in 1959 at Princeton, studying under Alonzo Church. After graduating from Princeton, he taught mathematics and logic at Dartmouth College, Princeton University, Yeshiva University, and the City University of New York. He joined the philosophy department at Indiana University in 1981 where he is now an emeritus professor.

Smullyan has written many books on recreational logic and mathematics, including *Satan, Cantor, and Infinity; What Is the Name of This Book?; The Lady or the Tiger?; Alice in Puzzleland; To Mock a Mockingbird; Forever Undecided;* and *The Riddle of Scheherazade: Amazing Logic Puzzles, Ancient and Modern.* Because his logic puzzles are challenging, entertaining, and thought-provoking, he is considered to be a modern-day Lewis Carroll. Smullyan has also written several books about the application of deductive logic to chess, three collections of philosophical essays and aphorisms, and several advanced books on mathematical logic and set theory. He is particularly interested in self-reference and has worked on extending some of Godel's results that show that it is impossible to write a computer program that can solve all mathematical problems. He is also particularly interested in explaining ideas from mathematical logic to the public.

Smullyan is a talented musician and often plays piano with his wife, who is a concert-level pianist. Making telescopes is one of his hobbies. He is also interested in optics and stereo photography. He states "I've never had a conflict between teaching and research as some people do because when I'm teaching, I'm doing research."

x	y	$x \vee y$	$x \wedge y$	$x \oplus y$
0	0	0	0	0
0	1	1	0	1
1	0	1	0	1
1	1	1	1	0

TABLE 8 Table for the Bit Operators *OR*, *AND*, and *XOR*.

one of the two children has a muddy forehead he is stating that the disjunction $s \vee d$ is true. Both children will answer "No" the first time the question is asked because each sees mud on the other child's forehead. That is, the son knows that d is true, but does not know whether s is true, and the daughter knows that s is true, but does not know whether d is true.

After the son has answered "No" to the first question, the daughter can determine that d must be true. This follows because when the first question is asked, the son knows that $s \vee d$ is true, but cannot determine whether s is true. Using this information, the daughter can conclude that d must be true, for if d were false, the son could have reasoned that because $s \vee d$ is true, then s must be true, and he would have answered "Yes" to the first question. The son can reason in a similar way to determine that s must be true. It follows that both children answer "Yes" the second time the question is asked.   ◀

LOGIC AND BIT OPERATIONS

Truth Value	Bit
T	1
F	0

Links

Computers represent information using bits. A **bit** has two possible values, namely, 0 (zero) and 1 (one). This meaning of the word bit comes from *b*inary dig*it*, since zeros and ones are the digits used in binary representations of numbers. The well-known statistician John Tukey introduced this terminology in 1946. A bit can be used to represent a truth value, since there are two truth values, namely, *true* and *false.* As is customarily done, we will use a 1 bit to represent true and a 0 bit to represent false. That is, 1 represents T (true), 0 represents F (false). A variable is called a **Boolean variable** if its value is either true or false. Consequently, a Boolean variable can be represented using a bit.

Computer **bit operations** correspond to the logical connectives. By replacing true by a one and false by a zero in the truth tables for the operators $\wedge$, $\vee$, and $\oplus$, the tables shown in Table 8 for the corresponding bit operations are obtained. We will also use the notation *OR, AND,* and *XOR* for the operators $\vee$, $\wedge$, and $\oplus$, as is done in various programming languages.

Information is often represented using bit strings, which are sequences of zeros and ones. When this is done, operations on the bit strings can be used to manipulate this information.

DEFINITION 7   A *bit string* is a sequence of zero or more bits. The *length* of this string is the number of bits in the string.

EXAMPLE 17   101010011 is a bit string of length nine.   ◀

We can extend bit operations to bit strings. We define the **bitwise *OR*, bitwise *AND*,** and **bitwise *XOR*** of two strings of the same length to be the strings that have as their bits the *OR*, *AND*, and *XOR* of the corresponding bits in the two strings, respectively. We use the symbols $\vee$, $\wedge$, and $\oplus$ to represent the bitwise *OR*, bitwise *AND*, and bitwise *XOR* operations, respectively. We illustrate bitwise operations on bit strings with Example 18.

EXAMPLE 18   Find the bitwise *OR*, bitwise *AND*, and bitwise *XOR* of the bit strings 01 1011 0110 and 11 0001 1101. (Here, and throughout this book, bit strings will be split into blocks of four bits to make them easier to read.)

Solution: The bitwise *OR*, bitwise *AND*, and bitwise *XOR* of these strings are obtained by taking the *OR*, *AND*, and *XOR* of the corresponding bits, respectively. This gives us

$$
\begin{array}{l}
\text{01 1011 0110} \\
\text{11 0001 1101} \\
\hline
\text{11 1011 1111} \quad \text{bitwise } OR \\
\text{01 0001 0100} \quad \text{bitwise } AND \\
\text{10 1010 1011} \quad \text{bitwise } XOR
\end{array}
$$

◀

Exercises

1. Which of these sentences are propositions? What are the truth values of those that are propositions?
   a) Boston is the capital of Massachusetts.
   b) Miami is the capital of Florida.
   c) $2 + 3 = 5$.   **d)** $5 + 7 = 10$.
   e) $x + 2 = 11$.   **f)** Answer this question.
   g) $x + y = y + x$ for every pair of real numbers x and y.

2. Which of these are propositions? What are the truth values of those that are propositions?
   a) Do not pass go.   **b)** What time is it?
   c) There are no black flies in Maine.
   d) $4 + x = 5$.
   e) $x + 1 = 5$ if $x = 1$.
   f) $x + y = y + z$ if $x = z$.

Links

JOHN WILDER TUKEY (1915–2000)   Tukey, born in New Bedford, Massachusetts, was an only child. His parents, both teachers, decided home schooling would best develop his potential. His formal education began at Brown University, where he studied mathematics and chemistry. He received a master's degree in chemistry from Brown and continued his studies at Princeton University, changing his field of study from chemistry to mathematics. He received his Ph.D. from Princeton in 1939 for work in topology, when he was appointed an instructor in mathematics at Princeton. With the start of World War II, he joined the Fire Control Research Office, where he began working in statistics. Tukey found statistical research to his liking and impressed several leading statisticians with his skills. In 1945, at the conclusion of the war, Tukey returned to the mathematics department at Princeton as a professor of statistics, and he also took a position at AT&T Bell Laboratories. Tukey founded the Statistics Department at Princeton in 1966 and was its first chairman. Tukey made significant contributions to many areas of statistics, including the analysis of variance, the estimation of spectra of time series, inferences about the values of a set of parameters from a single experiment, and the philosophy of statistics. However, he is best known for his invention, with J. W. Cooley, of the fast Fourier transform.

Tukey contributed his insight and expertise by serving on the President's Science Advisory Committee. He chaired several important committees dealing with the environment, education, and chemicals and health. He also served on committees working on nuclear disarmament. Tukey received many awards, including the National Medal of Science.

HISTORICAL NOTE   There were several other suggested words for a binary digit, including *binit* and *bigit*, that never were widely accepted. The adoption of the word *bit* may be due to its meaning as a common English word. For an account of Tukey's coining of the word *bit*, see the April 1984 issue of *Annals of the History of Computing*.

3. What is the negation of each of these propositions?

   a) Today is Thursday.
   b) There is no pollution in New Jersey.
   c) $2 + 1 = 3$.
   d) The summer in Maine is hot and sunny.

4. Let p and q be the propositions

   p : I bought a lottery ticket this week.
   q : I won the million dollar jackpot on Friday.

Express each of these propositions as an English sentence.

   a) $\neg p$ **b)** $p \vee q$ **c)** $p \rightarrow q$
   d) $p \wedge q$ **e)** $p \leftrightarrow q$ **f)** $\neg p \rightarrow \neg q$
   g) $\neg p \wedge \neg q$ **h)** $\neg p \vee (p \wedge q)$

5. Let p and q be the propositions "Swimming at the New Jersey shore is allowed" and "Sharks have been spotted near the shore," respectively. Express each of these compound propositions as an English sentence.

   a) $\neg q$ **b)** $p \wedge q$ **c)** $\neg p \vee q$
   d) $p \rightarrow \neg q$ **e)** $\neg q \rightarrow p$ **f)** $\neg p \rightarrow \neg q$
   g) $p \leftrightarrow \neg q$ **h)** $\neg p \wedge (p \vee \neg q)$

6. Let p and q be the propositions "The election is decided" and "The votes have been counted," respectively. Express each of these compound propositions as an English sentence.

   a) $\neg p$ **b)** $p \vee q$ **c)** $\neg p \wedge q$
   d) $q \rightarrow p$ **e)** $\neg q \rightarrow \neg p$ **f)** $\neg p \rightarrow \neg q$
   g) $p \leftrightarrow q$ **h)** $\neg q \vee (\neg p \wedge q)$

7. Let p and q be the propositions

   p : It is below freezing.
   q : It is snowing.

Write these propositions using p and q and logical connectives.

   a) It is below freezing and snowing.
   b) It is below freezing but not snowing.
   c) It is not below freezing and it is not snowing.
   d) It is either snowing or below freezing (or both).
   e) If it is below freezing, it is also snowing.
   f) It is either below freezing or it is snowing, but it is not snowing if it is below freezing.
   g) That it is below freezing is necessary and sufficient for it to be snowing.

8. Let p, q, and r be the propositions

   p : You have the flu.
   q : You miss the final examination.
   r : You pass the course.

Express each of these propositions as an English sentence.

   a) $p \rightarrow q$ **b)** $\neg q \leftrightarrow r$
   c) $q \rightarrow \neg r$ **d)** $p \vee q \vee r$
   e) $(p \rightarrow \neg r) \vee (q \rightarrow \neg r)$
   f) $(p \wedge q) \vee (\neg q \wedge r)$

9. Let p and q be the propositions

   p : You drive over 65 miles per hour.
   q : You get a speeding ticket.

Write these propositions using p and q and logical connectives.

   a) You do not drive over 65 miles per hour.
   b) You drive over 65 miles per hour, but you do not get a speeding ticket.
   c) You will get a speeding ticket if you drive over 65 miles per hour.
   d) If you do not drive over 65 miles per hour, then you will not get a speeding ticket.
   e) Driving over 65 miles per hour is sufficient for getting a speeding ticket.
   f) You get a speeding ticket, but you do not drive over 65 miles per hour.
   g) Whenever you get a speeding ticket, you are driving over 65 miles per hour.

10. Let p, q, and r be the propositions

   p : You get an A on the final exam.
   q : You do every exercise in this book.
   r : You get an A in this class.

Write these propositions using p, q, and r and logical connectives.

   a) You get an A in this class, but you do not do every exercise in this book.
   b) You get an A on the final, you do every exercise in this book, and you get an A in this class.
   c) To get an A in this class, it is necessary for you to get an A on the final.
   d) You get an A on the final, but you don't do every exercise in this book; nevertheless, you get an A in this class.
   e) Getting an A on the final and doing every exercise in this book is sufficient for getting an A in this class.
   f) You will get an A in this class if and only if you either do every exercise in this book or you get an A on the final.

11. Let p, q, and r be the propositions

   p : Grizzly bears have been seen in the area.
   q : Hiking is safe on the trail.
   r : Berries are ripe along the trail.

Write these propositions using p, q, and r and logical connectives.

   a) Berries are ripe along the trail, but grizzly bears have not been seen in the area.
   b) Grizzly bears have not been seen in the area and hiking on the trail is safe, but berries are ripe along the trail.
   c) If berries are ripe along the trail, hiking is safe if and only if grizzly bears have not been seen in the area.

d) It is not safe to hike on the trail, but grizzly bears have not been seen in the area and the berries along the trail are ripe.

e) For hiking on the trail to be safe, it is necessary but not sufficient that berries not be ripe along the trail and for grizzly bears not to have been seen in the area.

f) Hiking is not safe on the trail whenever grizzly bears have been seen in the area and berries are ripe along the trail.

12. Determine whether these biconditionals are true or false.

a) $2 + 2 = 4$ if and only if $1 + 1 = 2$.

b) $1 + 1 = 2$ if and only if $2 + 3 = 4$.

c) It is winter if and only if it is not spring, summer, or fall.

d) $1 + 1 = 3$ if and only if pigs can fly.

e) $0 > 1$ if and only if $2 > 1$.

13. Determine whether each of these implications is true or false.

a) If $1 + 1 = 2$, then $2 + 2 = 5$.

b) If $1 + 1 = 3$, then $2 + 2 = 4$.

c) If $1 + 1 = 3$, then $2 + 2 = 5$.

d) If pigs can fly, then $1 + 1 = 3$.

e) If $1 + 1 = 3$, then God exists.

f) If $1 + 1 = 3$, then pigs can fly.

g) If $1 + 1 = 2$, then pigs can fly.

h) If $2 + 2 = 4$, then $1 + 2 = 3$.

14. For each of these sentences, determine whether an inclusive or an exclusive or is intended. Explain your answer.

a) Experience with C++ or Java is required.

b) Lunch includes soup or salad.

c) To enter the country you need a passport or a voter registration card.

d) Publish or perish.

15. For each of these sentences, state what the sentence means if the or is an inclusive or (that is, a disjunction) versus an exclusive or. Which of these meanings of or do you think is intended?

a) To take discrete mathematics, you must have taken calculus or a course in computer science.

b) When you buy a new car from Acme Motor Company, you get $2000 back in cash or a 2% car loan.

c) Dinner for two includes two items from column A or three items from column B.

d) School is closed if more than 2 feet of snow falls or if the wind chill is below -100.

16. Write each of these statements in the form "if p, then q" in English. (*Hint:* Refer to the list of common ways to express implications provided in this section.)

a) It is necessary to wash the boss's car to get promoted.

b) Winds from the south imply a spring thaw.

c) A sufficient condition for the warranty to be good is that you bought the computer less than a year ago.

d) Willy gets caught whenever he cheats.

e) You can access the website only if you pay a subscription fee.

f) Getting elected follows from knowing the right people.

g) Carol gets seasick whenever she is on a boat.

17. Write each of these statements in the form "if p, then q" in English. (*Hint:* Refer to the list of common ways to express implications provided in this section.)

a) It snows whenever the wind blows from the northeast.

b) The apple trees will bloom if it stays warm for a week.

c) That the Pistons win the championship implies that they beat the Lakers.

d) It is necessary to walk 8 miles to get to the top of Long's Peak.

e) To get tenure as a professor, it is sufficient to be world-famous.

f) If you drive more than 400 miles, you will need to buy gasoline.

g) Your guarantee is good only if you bought your CD player less than 90 days ago.

18. Write each of these statements in the form "if p, then q" in English. (*Hint:* Refer to the list of common ways to express implications provided in this section.)

a) I will remember to send you the address only if you send me an e-mail message.

b) To be a citizen of this country, it is sufficient that you were born in the United States.

c) If you keep your textbook, it will be a useful reference in your future courses.

d) The Red Wings will win the Stanley Cup if their goalie plays well.

e) That you get the job implies that you had the best credentials.

f) The beach erodes whenever there is a storm.

g) It is necessary to have a valid password to log on to the server.

19. Write each of these propositions in the form "p if and only if q" in English.

a) If it is hot outside you buy an ice cream cone, and if you buy an ice cream cone it is hot outside.

b) For you to win the contest it is necessary and sufficient that you have the only winning ticket.

c) You get promoted only if you have connections, and you have connections only if you get promoted.

d) If you watch television your mind will decay, and conversely.

e) The trains run late on exactly those days when I take it.

20. Write each of these propositions in the form "*p* if and only if *q*" in English.

 a) For you to get an A in this course, it is necessary and sufficient that you learn how to solve discrete mathematics problems.

 b) If you read the newspaper every day, you will be informed, and conversely.

 c) It rains if it is a weekend day, and it is a weekend day if it rains.

 d) You can see the wizard only if the wizard is not in, and the wizard is not in only if you can see him.

21. State the converse, contrapositive, and inverse of each of these implications.

 a) If it snows today, I will ski tomorrow.

 b) I come to class whenever there is going to be a quiz.

 c) A positive integer is a prime only if it has no divisors other than 1 and itself.

22. State the converse, contrapositive, and inverse of each of these implications.

 a) If it snows tonight, then I will stay at home.

 b) I go to the beach whenever it is a sunny summer day.

 c) When I stay up late, it is necessary that I sleep until noon.

23. Construct a truth table for each of these compound propositions.

 a) $p \wedge \neg p$ **b)** $p \vee \neg p$

 c) $(p \vee \neg q) \rightarrow q$ **d)** $(p \vee q) \rightarrow (p \wedge q)$

 e) $(p \rightarrow q) \leftrightarrow (\neg q \rightarrow \neg p)$

 f) $(p \rightarrow q) \rightarrow (q \rightarrow p)$

24. Construct a truth table for each of these compound propositions.

 a) $p \rightarrow \neg p$ **b)** $p \leftrightarrow \neg p$

 c) $p \oplus (p \vee q)$ **d)** $(p \wedge q) \rightarrow (p \vee q)$

 e) $(q \rightarrow \neg p) \leftrightarrow (p \leftrightarrow q)$

 f) $(p \leftrightarrow q) \oplus (p \leftrightarrow \neg q)$

25. Construct a truth table for each of these compound propositions.

 a) $(p \vee q) \rightarrow (p \oplus q)$

 b) $(p \oplus q) \rightarrow (p \wedge q)$

 c) $(p \vee q) \oplus (p \wedge q)$

 d) $(p \leftrightarrow q) \oplus (\neg p \leftrightarrow q)$

 e) $(p \leftrightarrow q) \oplus (\neg p \leftrightarrow \neg r)$

 f) $(p \oplus q) \rightarrow (p \oplus \neg q)$

26. Construct a truth table for each of these compound propositions.

 a) $p \oplus p$ **b)** $p \oplus \neg p$

 c) $p \oplus \neg q$ **d)** $\neg p \oplus \neg q$

 e) $(p \oplus q) \vee (p \oplus \neg q)$

 f) $(p \oplus q) \wedge (p \oplus \neg q)$

27. Construct a truth table for each of these compound propositions.

 a) $p \rightarrow \neg q$ **b)** $\neg p \leftrightarrow q$

 c) $(p \rightarrow q) \vee (\neg p \rightarrow q)$

 d) $(p \rightarrow q) \wedge (\neg p \rightarrow q)$

 e) $(p \leftrightarrow q) \vee (\neg p \leftrightarrow q)$

 f) $(\neg p \leftrightarrow \neg q) \leftrightarrow (p \leftrightarrow q)$

28. Construct a truth table for each of these compound propositions.

 a) $(p \vee q) \vee r$ **b)** $(p \vee q) \wedge r$

 c) $(p \wedge q) \vee r$ **d)** $(p \wedge q) \wedge r$

 e) $(p \vee q) \wedge \neg r$ **f)** $(p \wedge q) \vee \neg r$

29. Construct a truth table for each of these compound propositions.

 a) $p \rightarrow (\neg q \vee r)$

 b) $\neg p \rightarrow (q \rightarrow r)$

 c) $(p \rightarrow q) \vee (\neg p \rightarrow r)$

 d) $(p \rightarrow q) \wedge (\neg p \rightarrow r)$

 e) $(p \leftrightarrow q) \vee (\neg q \leftrightarrow r)$

 f) $(\neg p \leftrightarrow \neg q) \leftrightarrow (q \leftrightarrow r)$

30. Construct a truth table for $((p \rightarrow q) \rightarrow r) \rightarrow s$.

31. Construct a truth table for $(p \leftrightarrow q) \leftrightarrow (r \leftrightarrow s)$.

32. What is the value of x after each of these statements is encountered in a computer program, if $x = 1$ before the statement is reached?

 a) **if** $1 + 2 = 3$ **then** $x := x + 1$

 b) **if** $(1 + 1 = 3)$ *OR* $(2 + 2 = 3)$ **then** $x := x + 1$

 c) **if** $(2 + 3 = 5)$ *AND* $(3 + 4 = 7)$ **then** $x := x + 1$

 d) **if** $(1 + 1 = 2)$ *XOR* $(1 + 2 = 3)$ **then** $x := x + 1$

 e) **if** $x < 2$ **then** $x := x + 1$

33. Find the bitwise *OR*, bitwise *AND*, and bitwise *XOR* of each of these pairs of bit strings.

 a) 101 1110, 010 0001

 b) 1111 0000, 1010 1010

 c) 00 0111 0001, 10 0100 1000

 d) 11 1111 1111, 00 0000 0000

34. Evaluate each of these expressions.

 a) $1\ 1000 \wedge (0\ 1011 \vee 1\ 1011)$

 b) $(0\ 1111 \wedge 1\ 0101) \vee 0\ 1000$

 c) $(0\ 1010 \oplus 1\ 1011) \oplus 0\ 1000$

 d) $(1\ 1011 \vee 0\ 1010) \wedge (1\ 0001 \vee 1\ 1011)$

Fuzzy logic is used in artificial intelligence. In fuzzy logic, a proposition has a truth value that is a number between 0 and 1, inclusive. A proposition with a truth value of 0 is false and one with a truth value of 1 is true. Truth values that are between 0 and 1 indicate varying degrees of truth. For instance, the truth value 0.8 can be assigned to the statement "Fred is happy," since Fred is happy most of the time, and the truth value 0.4 can be assigned to the statement "John is happy," since John is happy slightly less than half the time.

35. The truth value of the negation of a proposition in fuzzy logic is 1 minus the truth value of the proposition. What are the truth values of the statements "Fred is not happy" and "John is not happy"?

36. The truth value of the conjunction of two propositions in fuzzy logic is the minimum of the truth values of the two propositions. What are the truth values of the statements "Fred and John are happy" and "Neither Fred nor John is happy"?

37. The truth value of the disjunction of two propositions in fuzzy logic is the maximum of the truth values of the two propositions. What are the truth values of the statements "Fred is happy, or John is happy" and "Fred is not happy, or John is not happy"?

*38. Is the assertion "This statement is false" a proposition?

*39. The nth statement in a list of 100 statements is "Exactly n of the statements in this list are false."

    a) What conclusions can you draw from these statements?

    b) Answer part (a) if the nth statement is "At least n of the statements in this list are false."

    c) Answer part (b) assuming that the list contains 99 statements.

40. An ancient Sicilian legend says that the barber in a remote town who can be reached only by traveling a dangerous mountain road shaves those people, and only those people, who do not shave themselves. Can there be such a barber?

41. Each inhabitant of a remote village always tells the truth or always lies. A villager will only give a "Yes" or a "No" response to a question a tourist asks. Suppose you are a tourist visiting this area and come to a fork in the road. One branch leads to the ruins you want to visit; the other branch leads deep into the jungle. A villager is standing at the fork in the road. What one question can you ask the villager to determine which branch to take?

42. An explorer is captured by a group of cannibals. There are two types of cannibals—those who always tell the truth and those who always lie. The cannibals will barbecue the explorer unless he can determine whether a particular cannibal always lies or always tells the truth. He is allowed to ask the cannibal exactly one question.

    a) Explain why the question "Are you a liar?" does not work.

    b) Find a question that the explorer can use to determine whether the cannibal always lies or always tells the truth.

43. Express these system specifications using the propositions p "The message is scanned for viruses" and q "The message was sent from an unknown system" together with logical connectives.

    a) "The message is scanned for viruses whenever the message was sent from an unknown system."

    b) "The message was sent from an unknown system but it was not scanned for viruses."

    c) "It is necessary to scan the message for viruses whenever it was sent from an unknown system."

    d) "When a message is not sent from an unknown system it is not scanned for viruses."

44. Express these system specifications using the propositions p "The user enters a valid password," q "Access is granted," and r "The user has paid the subscription fee" and logical connectives.

    a) "The user has paid the subscription fee, but does not enter a valid password."

    b) "Access is granted whenever the user has paid the subscription fee and enters a valid password."

    c) "Access is denied if the user has not paid the subscription fee."

    d) "If the user has not entered a valid password but has paid the subscription fee, then access is granted."

45. Are these system specifications consistent? "The system is in multiuser state if and only if it is operating normally. If the system is operating normally, the kernel is functioning. The kernel is not functioning or the system is in interrupt mode. If the system is not in multiuser state, then it is in interrupt mode. The system is not in interrupt mode."

46. Are these system specifications consistent? "Whenever the system software is being upgraded, users cannot access the file system. If users can access the file system, then they can save new files. If users cannot save new files, then the system software is not being upgraded."

47. Are these system specifications consistent? "The router can send packets to the edge system only if it supports the new address space, For the router to support the new address space it is necessary that the latest software release be installed, The router can send packets to the edge system if the latest software release is installed, The router does not support the new address space."

48. Are these system specifications consistent? "If the file system is not locked, then new messages will be queued. If the file system is not locked, then the system is functioning normally, and conversely. If new messages are not queued, then they will be sent to the message buffer. If the file system is not locked, then new messages will be sent to the message buffer. New messages will not be sent to the message buffer."

49. What Boolean search would you use to look for Web pages about beaches in New Jersey? What if you wanted to find Web pages about beaches on the isle of Jersey (in the English Channel)?

50. What Boolean search would you use to look for Web pages about hiking in West Virginia? What if you wanted to find Web pages about hiking in Virginia, but not in West Virginia?

Exercises 51–55 relate to inhabitants of the island of knights and knaves created by Smullyan, where knights always tell the truth and knaves always lie. You encounter two people, A and B. Determine, if possible, what A and B are if they address you in the ways described. If you cannot determine what these two people are, can you draw any conclusions?

51. A says "At least one of us is a knave" and B says nothing.

52. A says "The two of us are both knights" and B says "A is a knave."

53. A says "I am a knave or B is a knight" and B says nothing.

54. Both A and B say "I am a knight."

55. A says "We are both knaves" and B says nothing.

Exercises 56–61 are puzzles that can be solved by translating statements into logical expressions and reasoning from these expressions using truth tables.

56. The police have three suspects for the murder of Mr. Cooper: Mr. Smith, Mr. Jones, and Mr. Williams. Smith, Jones, and Williams each declare that they did not kill Cooper. Smith also states that Cooper was a friend of Jones and that Williams disliked him. Jones also states that he did not know Cooper and that he was out of town the day Cooper was killed. Williams also states that he saw both Smith and Jones with Cooper the day of the killing and that either Smith or Jones must have killed him. Can you determine who the murderer was if

a) one of the three men is guilty, the two innocent men are telling the truth, but the statements of the guilty man may or may not be true?

b) innocent men do not lie?

57. Steve would like to determine the relative salaries of three coworkers using two facts. First, he knows that if Fred is not the highest paid of the three, then Janice is. Second, he knows that if Janice is not the lowest paid, then Maggie is paid the most. Is it possible to determine the relative salaries of Fred, Maggie, and Janice from what Steve knows? If so, who is paid the most and who the least? Explain your reasoning.

58. Five friends have access to a chat room. Is it possible to determine who is chatting if the following information is known? Either Kevin or Heather, or both, are chatting. Either Randy or Vijay, but not both, are chatting. If Abby is chatting, so is Randy.

Vijay and Kevin are either both chatting or neither is. If Heather is chatting, then so are Abby and Kevin. Explain your reasoning.

59. A detective has interviewed four witnesses to a crime. From the stories of the witnesses the detective has concluded that if the butler is telling the truth then so is the cook; the cook and the gardener cannot both be telling the truth; the gardener and the handyman are not both lying; and if the handyman is telling the truth then the cook is lying. For each of the four witnesses, can the detective determine whether that person is telling the truth or lying? Explain your reasoning.

60. Four friends have been identified as suspects for an unauthorized access into a computer system. They have made statements to the investigating authorities. Alice said "Carlos did it." John said "I did not do it." Carlos said "Diana did it." Diana said "Carlos lied when he said that I did it."

a) If the authorities also know that exactly one of the four suspects is telling the truth, who did it? Explain your reasoning.

b) If the authorities also know that exactly one is lying, who did it? Explain your reasoning.

*61. Solve this famous logic puzzle, attributed to Albert Einstein, and known as the **zebra puzzle.** Five men with different nationalities and with different jobs live in consecutive houses on a street. These houses are painted different colors. The men have different pets and have different favorite drinks. Determine who owns a zebra and whose favorite drink is mineral water (which is one of the favorite drinks) given these clues: The Englishman lives in the red house. The Spaniard owns a dog. The Japanese man is a painter. The Italian drinks tea. The Norwegian lives in the first house on the left. The green house is on the right of the white one. The photographer breeds snails. The diplomat lives in the yellow house. Milk is drunk in the middle house. The owner of the green house drinks coffee. The Norwegian's house is next to the blue one. The violinist drinks orange juice. The fox is in a house next to that of the physician. The horse is in a house next to that of the diplomat. (*Hint:* Make a table where the rows represent the men and columns represent the color of their houses, their jobs, their pets, and their favorite drinks and use logical reasoning to determine the correct entries in the table.)

1.2 Propositional Equivalences

INTRODUCTION

An important type of step used in a mathematical argument is the replacement of a statement with another statement with the same truth value. Because of this, methods that produce propositions with the same truth value as a given compound proposition are used extensively in the construction of mathematical arguments.

We begin our discussion with a classification of compound propositions according to their possible truth values.

DEFINITION 1

A compound proposition that is always true, no matter what the truth values of the propositions that occur in it, is called a *tautology*. A compound proposition that is always false is called a *contradiction*. Finally, a proposition that is neither a tautology nor a contradiction is called a *contingency*.

Tautologies and contradictions are often important in mathematical reasoning. The following example illustrates these types of propositions.

EXAMPLE 1

We can construct examples of tautologies and contradictions using just one proposition. Consider the truth tables of $p \lor \neg p$ and $p \land \neg p$, shown in Table 1. Since $p \lor \neg p$ is always true, it is a tautology. Since $p \land \neg p$ is always false, it is a contradiction. ◄

LOGICAL EQUIVALENCES

Demo

Compound propositions that have the same truth values in all possible cases are called **logically equivalent.** We can also define this notion as follows.

DEFINITION 2

The propositions p and q are called *logically equivalent* if $p \leftrightarrow q$ is a tautology. The notation $p \equiv q$ denotes that p and q are logically equivalent.

Remark: The symbol $\equiv$ is not a logical connective since $p \equiv q$ is not a compound proposition, but rather is the statement that $p \leftrightarrow q$ is a tautology. The symbol $\Leftrightarrow$ is sometimes used instead of $\equiv$ to denote logical equivalence.

Extra Examples

One way to determine whether two propositions are equivalent is to use a truth table. In particular, the propositions p and q are equivalent if and only if the columns giving their truth values agree. The following example illustrates this method.

EXAMPLE 2

Show that $\neg(p \lor q)$ and $\neg p \land \neg q$ are logically equivalent. This equivalence is one of *De Morgan's laws* for propositions, named after the English mathematician Augustus De Morgan, of the mid-nineteenth century.

TABLE 1 Examples of a Tautology and a Contradiction.			
p	$\neg p$	$p \lor \neg p$	$p \land \neg p$
T	F	T	F
F	T	T	F

TABLE 2 **Truth Tables for** $\neg(p \vee q)$ **and** $\neg p \wedge \neg q$.						
p	q	$p \vee q$	$\neg(p \vee q)$	$\neg p$	$\neg q$	$\neg p \wedge \neg q$
T	T	T	F	F	F	F
T	F	T	F	F	T	F
F	T	T	F	T	F	F
F	F	F	T	T	T	T

TABLE 3 **Truth Tables for** $\neg p \vee q$ **and** $p \rightarrow q$.				
p	q	$\neg p$	$\neg p \vee q$	$p \rightarrow q$
T	T	F	T	T
T	F	F	F	F
F	T	T	T	T
F	F	T	T	T

Solution: The truth tables for these propositions are displayed in Table 2. Since the truth values of the propositions $\neg(p \vee q)$ and $\neg p \wedge \neg q$ agree for all possible combinations of the truth values of p and q, it follows that $\neg(p \vee q) \leftrightarrow (\neg p \wedge \neg q)$ is a tautology and that these propositions are logically equivalent. ◄

EXAMPLE 3   Show that the propositions $p \rightarrow q$ and $\neg p \vee q$ are logically equivalent.

Solution: We construct the truth table for these propositions in Table 3. Since the truth values of $\neg p \vee q$ and $p \rightarrow q$ agree, these propositions are logically equivalent. ◄

EXAMPLE 4   Show that the propositions $p \vee (q \wedge r)$ and $(p \vee q) \wedge (p \vee r)$ are logically equivalent. This is the *distributive law* of disjunction over conjunction.

Solution: We construct the truth table for these propositions in Table 4. Since the truth values of $p \vee (q \wedge r)$ and $(p \vee q) \wedge (p \vee r)$ agree, these propositions are logically equivalent. ◄

Remark: A truth table of a compound proposition involving three different propositions requires eight rows, one for each possible combination of truth values of the three propositions. In general, 2^n rows are required if a compound proposition involves n propositions.

Table 5 contains some important equivalences.* In these equivalences, **T** denotes any proposition that is always true and **F** denotes any proposition that is always false. We also display some useful equivalences for compound propositions involving implications and biconditionals in Tables 6 and 7, respectively. The reader is asked to verify the equivalences in Tables 5–7 in the exercises at the end of the section.

---

*These identities are a special case of identities that hold for any Boolean algebra. Compare them with set identities in Table 1 in Section 1.7 and with Boolean identities in Table 5 in Section 10.1.

TABLE 4 A Demonstration That $p \vee (q \wedge r)$ and $(p \vee q) \wedge (p \vee r)$ Are Logically Equivalent.

p	q	r	$q \wedge r$	$p \vee (q \wedge r)$	$p \vee q$	$p \vee r$	$(p \vee q) \wedge (p \vee r)$
T	T	T	T	T	T	T	T
T	T	F	F	T	T	T	T
T	F	T	F	T	T	T	T
T	F	F	F	T	T	T	T
F	T	T	T	T	T	T	T
F	T	F	F	F	T	F	F
F	F	T	F	F	F	T	F
F	F	F	F	F	F	F	F

The associative law for disjunction shows that the expression $p \vee q \vee r$ is well defined, in the sense that it does not matter whether we first take the disjunction of p and q and then the disjunction of $p \vee q$ with r, or if we first take the disjunction of q and r and then take the disjunction of p and $q \vee r$. Similarly, the expression $p \wedge q \wedge r$ is well defined. By extending this reasoning, it follows that $p_1 \vee p_2 \vee \cdots \vee p_n$ and $p_1 \wedge p_2 \wedge \cdots \wedge p_n$ are well defined whenever $p_1, p_2, \ldots, p_n$ are propositions. Furthermore, note that De Morgan's laws extend to

$$\neg(p_1 \vee p_2 \vee \cdots \vee p_n) \equiv (\neg p_1 \wedge \neg p_2 \wedge \cdots \wedge \neg p_n)$$

and

$$\neg(p_1 \wedge p_2 \wedge \cdots \wedge p_n) \equiv (\neg p_1 \vee \neg p_2 \vee \cdots \vee \neg p_n).$$

(Methods for proving these identities will be given in Section 3.3.)

Links

AUGUSTUS DE MORGAN (1806–1871) Augustus De Morgan was born in India, where his father was a colonel in the Indian army. De Morgan's family moved to England when he was 7 months old. He attended private schools, where he developed a strong interest in mathematics in his early teens. De Morgan studied at Trinity College, Cambridge, graduating in 1827. Although he considered entering medicine or law, he decided on a career in mathematics. He won a position at University College, London, in 1828, but resigned when the college dismissed a fellow professor without giving reasons. However, he resumed this position in 1836 when his successor died, staying there until 1866.

De Morgan was a noted teacher who stressed principles over techniques. His students included many famous mathematicians, including Ada Augusta, Countess of Lovelace, who was Charles Babbage's collaborator in his work on computing machines (see page 25 for biographical notes on Ada Augusta). (De Morgan cautioned the countess against studying too much mathematics, since it might interfere with her childbearing abilities!)

De Morgan was an extremely prolific writer. He wrote more than 1000 articles for more than 15 periodicals. De Morgan also wrote textbooks on many subjects, including logic, probability, calculus, and algebra. In 1838 he presented what was perhaps the first clear explanation of an important proof technique known as *mathematical induction* (discussed in Section 3.3 of this text), a term he coined. In the 1840s De Morgan made fundamental contributions to the development of symbolic logic. He invented notations that helped him prove propositional equivalences, such as the laws that are named after him. In 1842 De Morgan presented what was perhaps the first precise definition of a limit and developed some tests for convergence of infinite series. De Morgan was also interested in the history of mathematics and wrote biographies of Newton and Halley.

In 1837 De Morgan married Sophia Frend, who wrote his biography in 1882. De Morgan's research, writing, and teaching left little time for his family or social life. Nevertheless, he was noted for his kindness, humor, and wide range of knowledge.

TABLE 5 Logical Equivalences.	
Equivalence	*Name*
$p \wedge \mathbf{T} \equiv p$ $p \vee \mathbf{F} \equiv p$	Identity laws
$p \vee \mathbf{T} \equiv \mathbf{T}$ $p \wedge \mathbf{F} \equiv \mathbf{F}$	Domination laws
$p \vee p \equiv p$ $p \wedge p \equiv p$	Idempotent laws
$\neg(\neg p) \equiv p$	Double negation law
$p \vee q \equiv q \vee p$ $p \wedge q \equiv q \wedge p$	Commutative laws
$(p \vee q) \vee r \equiv p \vee (q \vee r)$ $(p \wedge q) \wedge r \equiv p \wedge (q \wedge r)$	Associative laws
$p \vee (q \wedge r) \equiv (p \vee q) \wedge (p \vee r)$ $p \wedge (q \vee r) \equiv (p \wedge q) \vee (p \wedge r)$	Distributive laws
$\neg(p \wedge q) \equiv \neg p \vee \neg q$ $\neg(p \vee q) \equiv \neg p \wedge \neg q$	De Morgan's laws
$p \vee (p \wedge q) \equiv p$ $p \wedge (p \vee q) \equiv p$	Absorption laws
$p \vee \neg p \equiv \mathbf{T}$ $p \wedge \neg p \equiv \mathbf{F}$	Negation laws

TABLE 6 Logical Equivalences Involving Implications.
$p \rightarrow q \equiv \neg p \vee q$
$p \rightarrow q \equiv \neg q \rightarrow \neg p$
$p \vee q \equiv \neg p \rightarrow q$
$p \wedge q \equiv \neg(p \rightarrow \neg q)$
$\neg(p \rightarrow q) \equiv p \wedge \neg q$
$(p \rightarrow q) \wedge (p \rightarrow r) \equiv p \rightarrow (q \wedge r)$
$(p \rightarrow r) \wedge (q \rightarrow r) \equiv (p \vee q) \rightarrow r$
$(p \rightarrow q) \vee (p \rightarrow r) \equiv p \rightarrow (q \vee r)$
$(p \rightarrow r) \vee (q \rightarrow r) \equiv (p \wedge q) \rightarrow r$

TABLE 7 Logical Equivalences Involving Biconditionals.
$p \leftrightarrow q \equiv (p \rightarrow q) \wedge (q \rightarrow p)$
$p \leftrightarrow q \equiv \neg p \leftrightarrow \neg q$
$p \leftrightarrow q \equiv (p \wedge q) \vee (\neg p \wedge \neg q)$
$\neg(p \leftrightarrow q) \equiv p \leftrightarrow \neg q$

The logical equivalences in Table 5, as well as any others that have been established (such as those shown in Tables 6 and 7), can be used to construct additional logical equivalences. The reason for this is that a proposition in a compound proposition can be replaced by one that is logically equivalent to it without changing the truth value of the

Extra
Examples

compound proposition. This technique is illustrated in Examples 5 and 6, where we also use the fact that if p and q are logically equivalent and q and r are logically equivalent, then p and r are logically equivalent (see Exercise 50).

EXAMPLE 5   Show that $\neg(p \vee (\neg p \wedge q))$ and $\neg p \wedge \neg q$ are logically equivalent.

Solution: We could use a truth table to show that these compound propositions are equivalent. Instead, we will establish this equivalence by developing a series of logical equivalences, using one of the equivalences in Table 5 at a time, starting with $\neg(p \vee (\neg p \wedge q))$ and ending with $\neg p \wedge \neg q$. We have the following equivalences.

$$\begin{aligned}
\neg(p \vee (\neg p \wedge q)) &\equiv \neg p \wedge \neg(\neg p \wedge q) && \text{from the second De Morgan's law} \\
&\equiv \neg p \wedge [\neg(\neg p) \vee \neg q] && \text{from the first De Morgan's law} \\
&\equiv \neg p \wedge (p \vee \neg q) && \text{from the double negation law} \\
&\equiv (\neg p \wedge p) \vee (\neg p \wedge \neg q) && \text{from the second distributive law} \\
&\equiv \mathbf{F} \vee (\neg p \wedge \neg q) && \text{since } \neg p \wedge p \equiv \mathbf{F} \\
&\equiv (\neg p \wedge \neg q) \vee \mathbf{F} && \text{from the commutative law} \\
& && \text{for disjunction} \\
&\equiv \neg p \wedge \neg q && \text{from the identity law for } \mathbf{F}
\end{aligned}$$

Consequently $\neg(p \vee (\neg p \wedge q))$ and $\neg p \wedge \neg q$ are logically equivalent.   ◀

EXAMPLE 6   Show that $(p \wedge q) \rightarrow (p \vee q)$ is a tautology.

Solution: To show that this statement is a tautology, we will use logical equivalences to demonstrate that it is logically equivalent to $\mathbf{T}$. (*Note:* This could also be done using a truth table.)

$$\begin{aligned}
(p \wedge q) \rightarrow (p \vee q) &\equiv \neg(p \wedge q) \vee (p \vee q) && \text{by Example 3} \\
&\equiv (\neg p \vee \neg q) \vee (p \vee q) && \text{by the first De Morgan's law} \\
&\equiv (\neg p \vee p) \vee (\neg q \vee q) && \text{by the associative and commutative} \\
& && \text{laws for disjunction} \\
&\equiv \mathbf{T} \vee \mathbf{T} && \text{by Example 1 and the commutative} \\
& && \text{law for disjunction} \\
&\equiv \mathbf{T} && \text{by the domination law}
\end{aligned}$$
   ◀

A truth table can be used to determine whether a compound proposition is a tautology. This can be done by hand for a proposition with a small number of variables, but when the number of variables grows, this becomes impractical. For instance, there are $2^{20} = 1,048,576$ rows in the truth value table for a proposition with 20 variables. Clearly, you need a computer to help you determine, in this way, whether a compound proposition in

Links

ADA AUGUSTA, COUNTESS OF LOVELACE (1815–1852)   Ada Augusta was the only child from the marriage of the famous poet Lord Byron and Annabella Millbanke, who separated when Ada was 1 month old. She was raised by her mother, who encouraged her intellectual talents. She was taught by the mathematicians William Frend and Augustus De Morgan. In 1838 she married Lord King, later elevated to Earl of Lovelace. Together they had three children.

Ada Augusta continued her mathematical studies after her marriage, assisting Charles Babbage in his work on an early computing machine, called the Analytic Engine. The most complete accounts of this machine are found in her writings. After 1845 she and Babbage worked toward the development of a system to predict horse races. Unfortunately, their system did not work well, leaving Ada heavily in debt at the time of her death. The programming language Ada is named in honor of the Countess of Lovelace.

20 variables is a tautology. But when there are 1000 variables, can even a computer determine in a reasonable amount of time whether a compound proposition is a tautology? Checking every one of the 2^{1000} (a number with more than 300 decimal digits) possible combinations of truth values simply cannot be done by a computer in even trillions of years. Furthermore, no other procedures are known that a computer can follow to determine in a reasonable amount of time whether a compound proposition in such a large number of variables is a tautology. We will study questions such as this in Chapter 2, when we study the complexity of algorithms.

Exercises

1. Use truth tables to verify these equivalences.

a) $p \wedge \mathbf{T} \equiv p$ **b)** $p \vee \mathbf{F} \equiv p$

c) $p \wedge \mathbf{F} \equiv \mathbf{F}$ **d)** $p \vee \mathbf{T} \equiv \mathbf{T}$

e) $p \vee p \equiv p$ **f)** $p \wedge p \equiv p$

2. Show that $\neg(\neg p)$ and p are logically equivalent.

3. Use truth tables to verify the commutative laws

a) $p \vee q \equiv q \vee p$

b) $p \wedge q \equiv q \wedge p$

4. Use truth tables to verify the associative laws

a) $(p \vee q) \vee r \equiv p \vee (q \vee r)$

b) $(p \wedge q) \wedge r \equiv p \wedge (q \wedge r)$

5. Use a truth table to verify the distributive law
$p \wedge (q \vee r) \equiv (p \wedge q) \vee (p \wedge r)$.

6. Use a truth table to verify the equivalence
$\neg(p \wedge q) \equiv \neg p \vee \neg q$.

7. Show that each of these implications is a tautology by using truth tables.

a) $(p \wedge q) \rightarrow p$ **b)** $p \rightarrow (p \vee q)$

c) $\neg p \rightarrow (p \rightarrow q)$ **d)** $(p \wedge q) \rightarrow (p \rightarrow q)$

e) $\neg(p \rightarrow q) \rightarrow p$ **f)** $\neg(p \rightarrow q) \rightarrow \neg q$

8. Show that each of these implications is a tautology by using truth tables.

a) $[\neg p \wedge (p \vee q)] \rightarrow q$

b) $[(p \rightarrow q) \wedge (q \rightarrow r)] \rightarrow (p \rightarrow r)$

c) $[p \wedge (p \rightarrow q)] \rightarrow q$

d) $[(p \vee q) \wedge (p \rightarrow r) \wedge (q \rightarrow r)] \rightarrow r$

9. Show that each implication in Exercise 7 is a tautology without using truth tables.

10. Show that each implication in Exercise 8 is a tautology without using truth tables.

11. Use truth tables to verify the absorption laws.

a) $p \vee (p \wedge q) \equiv p$ **b)** $p \wedge (p \vee q) \equiv p$

12. Determine whether $(\neg p \wedge (p \rightarrow q)) \rightarrow \neg q$ is a tautology.

13. Determine whether $(\neg q \wedge (p \rightarrow q)) \rightarrow \neg p$ is a tautology.

Links

HENRY MAURICE SHEFFER (1883–1964) Henry Maurice Sheffer, born to Jewish parents in the western Ukraine, emigrated to the United States in 1892 with his parents and six siblings. He studied at the Boston Latin School before entering Harvard, where he completed his undergraduate degree in 1905, his master's in 1907, and his Ph.D. in philosophy in 1908. After holding a postdoctoral position at Harvard, Henry traveled to Europe on a fellowship. Upon returning to the United States, he became an academic nomad, spending one year each at the University of Washington, Cornell, the University of Minnesota, the University of Missouri, and City College in New York. In 1916 he returned to Harvard as a faculty member in the philosophy department. He remained at Harvard until his retirement in 1952.

Sheffer introduced what is now known as the Sheffer stroke in 1913; it became well known only after its use in the 1925 edition of Whitehead and Russell's *Principia Mathematica*. In this same edition Russell wrote that Sheffer had invented a powerful method that could be used to simplify the *Principia*. Because of this comment, Sheffer was something of a mystery man to logicians, especially because Sheffer, who published little in his career, never published the details of this method, only describing it in mimeographed notes and in a brief published abstract.

Sheffer was a dedicated teacher of mathematical logic. He liked his classes to be small and did not like auditors. When strangers appeared in his classroom, Sheffer would order them to leave, even his colleagues or distinguished guests visiting Harvard. Sheffer was barely five feet tall; he was noted for his wit and vigor, as well as for his nervousness and irritability. Although widely liked, he was quite lonely. He is noted for a quip he spoke at his retirement: "Old professors never die, they just become emeriti." Sheffer is also credited with coining the term "Boolean algebra" (the subject of Chapter 10 of this text). Sheffer was briefly married and lived most of his later life in small rooms at a hotel packed with his logic books and vast files of slips of paper he used to jot down his ideas. Unfortunately, Sheffer suffered from severe depression during the last two decades of his life.

14. Show that $p \leftrightarrow q$ and $(p \wedge q) \vee (\neg p \wedge \neg q)$ are equivalent.

15. Show that $(p \rightarrow q) \rightarrow r$ and $p \rightarrow (q \rightarrow r)$ are not equivalent.

16. Show that $p \rightarrow q$ and $\neg q \rightarrow \neg p$ are logically equivalent.

17. Show that $\neg p \leftrightarrow q$ and $p \leftrightarrow \neg q$ are logically equivalent.

18. Show that $\neg(p \oplus q)$ and $p \leftrightarrow q$ are logically equivalent.

19. Show that $\neg(p \leftrightarrow q)$ and $\neg p \leftrightarrow q$ are logically equivalent.

20. Show that $(p \rightarrow q) \wedge (p \rightarrow r)$ and $p \rightarrow (q \wedge r)$ are logically equivalent.

21. Show that $(p \rightarrow r) \wedge (q \rightarrow r)$ and $(p \vee q) \rightarrow r$ are logically equivalent.

22. Show that $(p \rightarrow q) \vee (p \rightarrow r)$ and $p \rightarrow (q \vee r)$ are logically equivalent.

23. Show that $(p \rightarrow r) \vee (q \rightarrow r)$ and $(p \wedge q) \rightarrow r$ are logically equivalent.

24. Show that $\neg p \rightarrow (q \rightarrow r)$ and $q \rightarrow (p \vee r)$ are logically equivalent.

25. Show that $p \leftrightarrow q$ and $(p \rightarrow q) \wedge (q \rightarrow p)$ are logically equivalent.

26. Show that $p \leftrightarrow q$ and $\neg p \leftrightarrow \neg q$ are logically equivalent.

27. Show that $\neg(p \leftrightarrow q)$ and $p \leftrightarrow \neg q$ are logically equivalent.

28. Show that $(p \vee q) \wedge (\neg p \vee r) \rightarrow (q \vee r)$ is a tautology.

29. Show that $(p \rightarrow q) \wedge (q \rightarrow r) \rightarrow (p \rightarrow r)$ is a tautology.

The **dual** of a compound proposition that contains only the logical operators $\vee$, $\wedge$, and $\neg$ is the proposition obtained by replacing each $\vee$ by $\wedge$, each $\wedge$ by $\vee$, each **T** by **F**, and each **F** by **T**. The dual of proposition s is denoted by s^*.

30. Find the dual of each of these propositions.
    a) $p \wedge \neg q \wedge \neg r$ **b)** $(p \wedge q \wedge r) \vee s$
    c) $(p \vee \mathbf{F}) \wedge (q \vee \mathbf{T})$

31. Show that $(s^*)^* = s$.

32. Show that the logical equivalences in Table 5, except for the double negation law, come in pairs, where each pair contains propositions that are duals of each other.

**33. Why are the duals of two equivalent compound propositions also equivalent, where these compound propositions contain only the operators $\wedge$, $\vee$, and $\neg$?

34. Find a compound proposition involving the propositions p, q, and r that is true when p and q are true and r is false, but is false otherwise. (*Hint:* Use a conjunction of each proposition or its negation.)

35. Find a compound proposition involving the propositions p, q, and r that is true when exactly two of p, q,

and r are true and is false otherwise. (*Hint:* Form a disjunction of conjunctions. Include a conjunction for each combination of values for which the proposition is true. Each conjunction should include each of the three propositions or their negations.)

36. Suppose that a truth table in n propositional variables is specified. Show that a compound proposition with this truth table can be formed by taking the disjunction of conjunctions of the variables or their negations, with one conjunction included for each combination of values for which the compound proposition is true. The resulting compound proposition is said to be in **disjunctive normal form.**

A collection of logical operators is called **functionally complete** if every compound proposition is logically equivalent to a compound proposition involving only these logical operators.

37. Show that $\neg$, $\wedge$, and $\vee$ form a functionally complete collection of logical operators. (*Hint:* Use the fact that every proposition is logically equivalent to one in disjunctive normal form, as shown in Exercise 36.)

*38. Show that $\neg$ and $\wedge$ form a functionally complete collection of logical operators. (*Hint:* First use De Morgan's law to show that $p \vee q$ is equivalent to $\neg(\neg p \wedge \neg q)$.)

*39. Show that $\neg$ and $\vee$ form a functionally complete collection of logical operators.

The following exercises involve the logical operators *NAND* and *NOR*. The proposition p *NAND* q is true when either p or q, or both, are false; and it is false when both p and q are true. The proposition p *NOR* q is true when both p and q are false, and it is false otherwise. The propositions p *NAND* q and p *NOR* q are denoted by $p \mid q$ and $p \downarrow q$, respectively. (The operators $\mid$ and $\downarrow$ are called the **Sheffer stroke** and the **Peirce arrow** after H. M. Sheffer and C. S. Peirce, respectively.)

40. Construct a truth table for the logical operator *NAND*.

41. Show that $p \mid q$ is logically equivalent to $\neg(p \wedge q)$.

42. Construct a truth table for the logical operator *NOR*.

43. Show that $p \downarrow q$ is logically equivalent to $\neg(p \vee q)$.

44. In this exercise we will show that $\{\downarrow\}$ is a functionally complete collection of logical operators.
    a) Show that $p \downarrow p$ is logically equivalent to $\neg p$.
    b) Show that $(p \downarrow q) \downarrow (p \downarrow q)$ is logically equivalent to $p \vee q$.
    c) Conclude from parts (a) and (b), and Exercise 39, that $\{\downarrow\}$ is a functionally complete collection of logical operators.

*45. Find a proposition equivalent to $p \rightarrow q$ using only the logical operator $\downarrow$.

46. Show that $\{\mid\}$ is a functionally complete collection of logical operators.

47. Show that $p \mid q$ and $q \mid p$ are equivalent.

48. Show that $p \mid (q \mid r)$ and $(p \mid q) \mid r$ are not equivalent, so that the logical operator $\mid$ is not associative.

*49. How many different truth tables of compound propositions are there that involve the propositions p and q?

50. Show that if p, q, and r are compound propositions such that p and q are logically equivalent and q and r are logically equivalent, then p and r are logically equivalent.

51. The following sentence is taken from the specification of a telephone system: "If the directory database is opened, then the monitor is put in a closed state, if the system is not in its initial state." This specification is hard to understand since it involves two implications. Find an equivalent, easier-to-understand specification that involves disjunctions and negations but not implications.

52. How many of the disjunctions $p \vee \neg q, \neg p \vee q, q \vee r$, $q \vee \neg r, \neg q \vee \neg r$ can be made simultaneously true by an assignment of truth values to p, q, and r?

53. How many of the disjunctions $p \vee \neg q \vee s, \neg p \vee \neg r \vee s, \neg p \vee \neg r \vee \neg s, \neg p \vee q \vee \neg s, q \vee r \vee \neg s,$ $q \vee \neg r \vee \neg s, \neg p \vee \neg q \vee \neg s, p \vee r \vee s, p \vee r \vee \neg s$ can be made simultaneously true by an assignment of truth values to p, q, r, and s?

A compound proposition is **satisfiable** if there is an assignment of truth values to the variables in the proposition that makes the compound proposition true.

54. Which of these compound propositions are satisfiable?

a) $(p \vee q \vee \neg r) \wedge (p \vee \neg q \vee \neg s) \wedge (p \vee \neg r \vee \neg s) \wedge (\neg p \vee \neg q \vee \neg s) \wedge (p \vee q \vee \neg s)$

b) $(\neg p \vee \neg q \vee r) \wedge (\neg p \vee q \vee \neg s) \wedge (p \vee \neg q \vee \neg s) \wedge (\neg p \vee \neg r \vee \neg s) \wedge (p \vee q \vee \neg r) \wedge (p \vee \neg r \vee \neg s)$

c) $(p \vee q \vee r) \wedge (p \vee \neg q \vee \neg s) \wedge (q \vee \neg r \vee s) \wedge (\neg p \vee r \vee s) \wedge (\neg p \vee q \vee \neg s) \wedge (p \vee \neg q \vee \neg r) \wedge (\neg p \vee \neg q \vee s) \wedge (\neg p \vee \neg r \vee \neg s)$

55. Explain how an algorithm for determining whether a compound proposition is satisfiable can be used to determine whether a compound proposition is a tautology. (*Hint:* Look at $\neg p$, where p is the proposition that is being examined.)

1.3	**Predicates and Quantifiers**

INTRODUCTION

Statements involving variables, such as

$$\text{``}x > 3\text{,''} \quad \text{``}x = y + 3\text{,''} \quad \text{and} \quad \text{``}x + y = z\text{,''}$$

are often found in mathematical assertions and in computer programs. These statements are neither true nor false when the values of the variables are not specified. In this section we will discuss the ways that propositions can be produced from such statements.

The statement "x is greater than 3" has two parts. The first part, the variable x, is the subject of the statement. The second part—the **predicate,** "is greater than 3"—refers to a property that the subject of the statement can have. We can denote the statement "x is greater than 3" by $P(x)$, where P denotes the predicate "is greater than 3" and x is the variable. The statement $P(x)$ is also said to be the value of the **propositional function** P at x. Once a value has been assigned to the variable x, the statement $P(x)$ becomes a proposition and has a truth value. Consider Example 1.

EXAMPLE 1 Let $P(x)$ denote the statement "$x > 3$." What are the truth values of $P(4)$ and $P(2)$?

Solution: We obtain the statement $P(4)$ by setting $x = 4$ in the statement "$x > 3$." Hence, $P(4)$, which is the statement "$4 > 3$," is true. However, $P(2)$, which is the statement "$2 > 3$," is false. ◄

We can also have statements that involve more than one variable. For instance, consider the statement "$x = y + 3$." We can denote this statement by $Q(x, y)$, where x and y are variables and Q is the predicate. When values are assigned to the variables x and y, the statement $Q(x, y)$ has a truth value.

EXAMPLE 2

Let $Q(x, y)$ denote the statement "$x = y + 3$." What are the truth values of the propositions $Q(1, 2)$ and $Q(3, 0)$?

Solution: To obtain $Q(1, 2)$, set $x = 1$ and $y = 2$ in the statement $Q(x, y)$. Hence, $Q(1, 2)$ is the statement "$1 = 2 + 3$," which is false. The statement $Q(3, 0)$ is the proposition "$3 = 0 + 3$," which is true. ◀

Similarly, we can let $R(x, y, z)$ denote the statement "$x + y = z$." When values are assigned to the variables x, y, and z, this statement has a truth value.

EXAMPLE 3

What are the truth values of the propositions $R(1, 2, 3)$ and $R(0, 0, 1)$?

Solution: The proposition $R(1, 2, 3)$ is obtained by setting $x = 1$, $y = 2$, and $z = 3$ in the statement $R(x, y, z)$. We see that $R(1, 2, 3)$ is the statement "$1 + 2 = 3$," which is true. Also note that $R(0, 0, 1)$, which is the statement "$0 + 0 = 1$," is false. ◀

In general, a statement involving the n variables $x_1, x_2, \ldots, x_n$ can be denoted by

$$P(x_1, x_2, \ldots, x_n).$$

A statement of the form $P(x_1, x_2, \ldots, x_n)$ is the value of the **propositional function** P at the n-tuple $(x_1, x_2, \ldots, x_n)$, and P is also called a **predicate.**

CHARLES SANDERS PEIRCE (1839–1914) Many consider Charles Peirce the most original and versatile intellect from the United States; he was born in Cambridge, Massachusetts. His father, Benjamin Peirce, was a professor of mathematics and natural philosophy at Harvard. Peirce attended Harvard (1855–1859) and received a Harvard master of arts degree (1862) and an advanced degree in chemistry from the Lawrence Scientific School (1863). His father encouraged him to pursue a career in science, but instead he chose to study logic and scientific methodology.

In 1861, Peirce became an aide in the United States Coast Survey, with the goal of better understanding scientific methodology. His service for the Survey exempted him from military service during the Civil War. While working for the Survey, Peirce carried out astronomical and geodesic work. He made fundamental contributions to the design of pendulums and to map projections, applying new mathematical developments in the theory of elliptic functions. He was the first person to use the wavelength of light as a unit of measurement. Peirce rose to the position of Assistant for the Survey, a position he held until he was forced to resign in 1891 when he disagreed with the direction taken by the Survey's new administration.

Although making his living from work in the physical sciences, Peirce developed a hierarchy of sciences, with mathematics at the top rung, in which the methods of one science could be adapted for use by those sciences under it in the hierarchy. He was also the founder of the American philosophical theory of pragmatism.

The only academic position Peirce ever held was as a lecturer in logic at Johns Hopkins University in Baltimore from 1879 to 1884. His mathematical work during this time included contributions to logic, set theory, abstract algebra, and the philosophy of mathematics. His work is still relevant today; some of his work on logic has been recently applied to artificial intelligence. Peirce believed that the study of mathematics could develop the mind's powers of imagination, abstraction, and generalization. His diverse activities after retiring from the Survey included writing for newspapers and journals, contributing to scholarly dictionaries, translating scientific papers, guest lecturing, and textbook writing. Unfortunately, the income from these pursuits was insufficient to protect him and his second wife from abject poverty. He was supported in his later years by a fund created by his many admirers and administered by the philosopher William James, his lifelong friend. Although Peirce wrote and published voluminously in a vast range of subjects, he left more than 100,000 pages of unpublished manuscripts. Because of the difficulty of studying his unpublished writings, scholars have only recently started to understand some of his varied contributions. A group of people is devoted to making his work available over the Internet to bring a better appreciation of Peirce's accomplishments to the world.

Propositional functions occur in computer programs, as Example 4 demonstrates.

EXAMPLE 4   Consider the statement

$$\textbf{if } x > 0 \textbf{ then } x := x + 1.$$

When this statement is encountered in a program, the value of the variable x at that point in the execution of the program is inserted into $P(x)$, which is "$x > 0$." If $P(x)$ is true for this value of x, the assignment statement $x := x + 1$ is executed, so the value of x is increased by 1. If $P(x)$ is false for this value of x, the assignment statement is not executed, so the value of x is not changed.   ◀

QUANTIFIERS

Assessment

When all the variables in a propositional function are assigned values, the resulting statement becomes a proposition with a certain truth value. However, there is another important way, called **quantification,** to create a proposition from a propositional function. Two types of quantification will be discussed here, namely, universal quantification and existential quantification. The area of logic that deals with predicates and quantifiers is called the **predicate calculus.**

THE UNIVERSAL QUANTIFIER   Many mathematical statements assert that a property is true for all values of a variable in a particular domain, called the **universe of discourse** or the **domain.** Such a statement is expressed using a universal quantification. The universal quantification of a propositional function is the proposition that asserts that $P(x)$ is true for all values of x in the universe of discourse. The universe of discourse specifies the possible values of the variable x.

DEFINITION 1   The *universal quantification* of $P(x)$ is the proposition

"$P(x)$ is true for all values of x in the universe of discourse."

The notation

$$\forall x \, P(x)$$

denotes the universal quantification of $P(x)$. Here $\forall$ is called the **universal quantifier.** The proposition $\forall x \, P(x)$ is read as

"for all $x \, P(x)$"   or   "for every $x \, P(x)$."

Remark: It is best to avoid using "for any x" since it is often ambiguous as to whether "any" means "every" or "some." In some cases, "any" is unambiguous, such as when it is used in negatives, for example, "there is not any reason to avoid studying."

We illustrate the use of the universal quantifier in Examples 5–10.

EXAMPLE 5   Let $P(x)$ be the statement "$x + 1 > x$." What is the truth value of the quantification $\forall x \, P(x)$, where the universe of discourse consists of all real numbers?

Solution: Since $P(x)$ is true for all real numbers x, the quantification

$$\forall x\, P(x)$$

is true. ◄

EXAMPLE 6 Let $Q(x)$ be the statement "$x < 2$." What is the truth value of the quantification $\forall x\, Q(x)$, where the universe of discourse consists of all real numbers?

Solution: $Q(x)$ is not true for every real number x, since, for instance, $Q(3)$ is false. Thus

$$\forall x\, Q(x)$$

is false. ◄

When all the elements in the universe of discourse can be listed—say, $x_1, x_2, \ldots,$ x_n—it follows that the universal quantification $\forall x\, P(x)$ is the same as the conjunction

$$P(x_1) \wedge P(x_2) \wedge \cdots \wedge P(x_n),$$

since this conjunction is true if and only if $P(x_1), P(x_2), \ldots, P(x_n)$ are all true.

EXAMPLE 7 What is the truth value of $\forall x\, P(x)$, where $P(x)$ is the statement "$x^2 < 10$" and the universe of discourse consists of the positive integers not exceeding 4?

Solution: The statement $\forall x\, P(x)$ is the same as the conjunction

$$P(1) \wedge P(2) \wedge P(3) \wedge P(4),$$

since the universe of discourse consists of the integers $1, 2, 3$, and 4. Since $P(4)$, which is the statement "$4^2 < 10$," is false, it follows that $\forall x\, P(x)$ is false. ◄

EXAMPLE 8 What does the statement $\forall x\, T(x)$ mean if $T(x)$ is "x has two parents" and the universe of discourse consists of all people?

Solution: The statement $\forall x\, T(x)$ means that for every person x, that person has two parents. This statement can be expressed in English as "Every person has two parents." This statement is true (except for clones). ◄

Specifying the universe of discourse is important when quantifiers are used. The truth value of a quantified statement often depends on which elements are in this universe of discourse, as Example 9 shows.

EXAMPLE 9 What is the truth value of $\forall x(x^2 \geq x)$ if the universe of discourse consists of all real numbers and what is its truth value if the universe of discourse consists of all integers?

Solution: Note that $x^2 \geq x$ if and only if $x^2 - x = x(x-1) \geq 0$. Consequently, $x^2 \geq x$ if and only if $x \leq 0$ or $x \geq 1$. It follows that $\forall x(x^2 \geq x)$ is false if the universe of discourse consists of all real numbers (since the inequality is false for all real numbers x with $0 < x < 1$). However, if the universe of discourse consists of the integers, $\forall x(x^2 \geq x)$ is true, since there are no integers x with $0 < x < 1$. ◄

To show that a statement of the form $\forall x\, P(x)$ is false, where $P(x)$ is a propositional function, we need only find one value of x in the universe of discourse for which $P(x)$ is false. Such a value of x is called a **counterexample** to the statement $\forall x\, P(x)$.

EXAMPLE 10   Suppose that $P(x)$ is "$x^2 > 0$." To show the statement $\forall x\, P(x)$ is false where the universe of discourse consists of all integers, we give a counterexample. We see that $x = 0$ is a counterexample since $x^2 = 0$ when $x = 0$ so that x^2 is not greater than 0 when $x = 0$.   ◀

Looking for counterexamples to universally quantified statements is an important activity in the study of mathematics, as we will see in subsequent sections of this book.

THE EXISTENTIAL QUANTIFIER Many mathematical statements assert that there is an element with a certain property. Such statements are expressed using existential quantification. With existential quantification, we form a proposition that is true if and only if $P(x)$ is true for at least one value of x in the universe of discourse.

DEFINITION 2   The *existential quantification* of $P(x)$ is the proposition

"There exists an element x in the universe of discourse such that $P(x)$ is true."

We use the notation

$\exists x\, P(x)$

for the existential quantification of $P(x)$. Here $\exists$ is called the **existential quantifier.** The existential quantification $\exists x\, P(x)$ is read as

"There is an x such that $P(x)$,"
"There is at least one x such that $P(x)$,"

or

"For some $x\, P(x)$."

We illustrate the use of the existential quantifier in Examples 11–13.

EXAMPLE 11   Let $P(x)$ denote the statement "$x > 3$." What is the truth value of the quantification $\exists x\, P(x)$, where the universe of discourse consists of all real numbers?

Extra Examples

Solution: Since "$x > 3$" is true—for instance, when $x = 4$—the existential quantification of $P(x)$, which is $\exists x\, P(x)$, is true.   ◀

EXAMPLE 12   Let $Q(x)$ denote the statement "$x = x + 1$." What is the truth value of the quantification $\exists x\, Q(x)$, where the universe of discourse consists of all real numbers?

Solution: Since $Q(x)$ is false for every real number x, the existential quantification of $Q(x)$, which is $\exists x\, Q(x)$, is false.   ◀

When all elements in the universe of discourse can be listed—say, $x_1, x_2, \ldots, x_n$—the existential quantification $\exists x\, P(x)$ is the same as the disjunction

$$P(x_1) \vee P(x_2) \vee \cdots \vee P(x_n),$$

since this disjunction is true if and only if at least one of $P(x_1), P(x_2), \ldots, P(x_n)$ is true.

TABLE 1 **Quantifiers.**		
Statement	*When True?*	*When False?*
$\forall x\, P(x)$	$P(x)$ is true for every x.	There is an x for which $P(x)$ is false.
$\exists x\, P(x)$	There is an x for which $P(x)$ is true.	$P(x)$ is false for every x.

EXAMPLE 13   What is the truth value of $\exists x\, P(x)$ where $P(x)$ is the statement "$x^2 > 10$" and the universe of discourse consists of the positive integers not exceeding 4?

Solution: Since the universe of discourse is $\{1, 2, 3, 4\}$, the proposition $\exists x\, P(x)$ is the same as the disjunction

$$P(1) \vee P(2) \vee P(3) \vee P(4).$$

Since $P(4)$, which is the statement "$4^2 > 10$," is true, it follows that $\exists x\, P(x)$ is true. ◀

Table 1 summarizes the meaning of the universal and the existential quantifiers.

It is sometimes helpful to think in terms of looping and searching when determining the truth value of a quantification. Suppose that there are n objects in the universe of discourse for the variable x. To determine whether $\forall x\, P(x)$ is true, we can loop through all n values of x to see if $P(x)$ is always true. If we encounter a value x for which $P(x)$ is false, then we have shown that $\forall x\, P(x)$ is false. Otherwise, $\forall x\, P(x)$ is true. To see whether $\exists x\, P(x)$ is true, we loop through the n values of x searching for a value for which $P(x)$ is true. If we find one, then $\exists x\, P(x)$ is true. If we never find such an x, we have determined that $\exists x\, P(x)$ is false. (Note that this searching procedure does not apply if there are infinitely many values in the universe of discourse. However, it is still a useful way of thinking about the truth values of quantifications.)

BINDING VARIABLES

When a quantifier is used on the variable x or when we assign a value to this variable, we say that this occurrence of the variable is **bound.** An occurrence of a variable that is not bound by a quantifier or set equal to a particular value is said to be **free.** All the variables that occur in a propositional function must be bound to turn it into a proposition. This can be done using a combination of universal quantifiers, existential quantifiers, and value assignments.

The part of a logical expression to which a quantifier is applied is called the **scope** of this quantifier. Consequently, a variable is free if it is outside the scope of all quantifiers in the formula that specifies this variable.

EXAMPLE 14   In the statement $\exists x\, Q(x, y)$, the variable x is bound by the existential quantification $\exists x$, but the variable y is free because it is not bound by a quantifier and no value is assigned to this variable.

In the statement $\exists x(P(x) \wedge Q(x)) \vee \forall x\, R(x)$, all variables are bound. The scope of the first quantifier, $\exists x$, is the expression $P(x) \wedge Q(x)$ because $\exists x$ is applied only to $P(x) \wedge Q(x)$, and not to the rest of the statement. Similarly, the scope of the second quantifier, $\forall x$, is the expression $R(x)$. That is, the existential quantifier binds the variable x in $P(x) \wedge Q(x)$ and the universal quantifier $\forall x$ binds the variable x in $R(x)$. Observe that we could have written our statement using two different variables x and y, as $\exists x(P(x) \land Q(x)) \lor \forall y R(y)$, because the scopes of the two quantifiers do not overlap. The reader should be aware that in common usage, the same letter is often used to represent variables bound by different quantifiers with scopes that do not overlap.   ◄

NEGATIONS

We will often want to consider the negation of a quantified expression. For instance, consider the negation of the statement

"Every student in the class has taken a course in calculus."

This statement is a universal quantification, namely,

$$\forall x\, P(x),$$

where $P(x)$ is the statement "x has taken a course in calculus." The negation of this statement is "It is not the case that every student in the class has taken a course in calculus." This is equivalent to "There is a student in the class who has not taken a course in calculus." And this is simply the existential quantification of the negation of the original propositional function, namely,

$$\exists x \, \neg P(x).$$

This example illustrates the following equivalence:

$$\neg \forall x\, P(x) \equiv \exists x \, \neg P(x).$$

Extra Examples

Suppose we wish to negate an existential quantification. For instance, consider the proposition "There is a student in this class who has taken a course in calculus." This is the existential quantification

$$\exists x \, Q(x),$$

where $Q(x)$ is the statement "x has taken a course in calculus." The negation of this statement is the proposition "It is not the case that there is a student in this class who has taken a course in calculus." This is equivalent to "Every student in this class has not taken calculus," which is just the universal quantification of the negation of the original propositional function, or, phrased in the language of quantifiers,

$$\forall x \, \neg Q(x).$$

This example illustrates the equivalence

$$\neg \exists x \, Q(x) \equiv \forall x \, \neg Q(x).$$

Negations of quantifiers are summarized in Table 2.

Remark: When the universe of discourse of a predicate $P(x)$ consists of n elements, where n is a positive integer, the rules for negating quantified statements are exactly the same as De Morgan's laws discussed in Section 1.2. This follows because $\neg \forall x\, P(x)$ is the same as $\neg(P(x_1) \land P(x_2) \land \cdots \land P(x_n))$, which is equivalent to $\neg P(x_1) \lor \neg P(x_2) \lor \cdots \lor \neg P(x_n)$ by De Morgan's laws, and this is the same as $\exists x \neg P(x)$. Similarly, $\neg \exists x\, P(x)$ is the same as $\neg(P(x_1) \lor P(x_2) \lor \cdots \lor P(x_n))$, which by De Morgan's laws is equivalent to $\neg P(x_1) \land \neg P(x_2) \land \cdots \land \neg P(x_n)$, and this is the same as $\forall x \neg P(x)$.

We illustrate the negation of quantified statements in Examples 15 and 16.

TABLE 2 **Negating Quantifiers.**

Negation	Equivalent Statement	When Is Negation True?	When False?
$\neg\exists x\,P(x)$	$\forall x\,\neg P(x)$	For every x, $P(x)$ is false.	There is an x for which $P(x)$ is true.
$\neg\forall x\,P(x)$	$\exists x\,\neg P(x)$	There is an x for which $P(x)$ is false.	$P(x)$ is true for every x.

EXAMPLE 15 What are the negations of the statements "There is an honest politician" and "All Americans eat cheeseburgers"?

Solution: Let $H(x)$ denote "x is honest." Then the statement "There is an honest politician" is represented by $\exists x\,H(x)$, where the universe of discourse consists of all politicians. The negation of this statement is $\neg\exists x\,H(x)$, which is equivalent to $\forall x\,\neg H(x)$. This negation can be expressed as "Every politician is dishonest." (*Note:* In English the statement "All politicians are not honest" is ambiguous. In common usage this statement often means "Not all politicians are honest." Consequently, we do not use this statement to express this negation.)

Let $C(x)$ denote "x eats cheeseburgers." Then the statement "All Americans eat cheeseburgers" is represented by $\forall x\,C(x)$, where the universe of discourse consists of all Americans. The negation of this statement is $\neg\forall x\,C(x)$, which is equivalent to $\exists x\,\neg C(x)$. This negation can be expressed in several different ways, including "Some American does not eat cheeseburgers" and "There is an American who does not eat cheeseburgers." ◀

EXAMPLE 16 What are the negations of the statements $\forall x(x^2 > x)$ and $\exists x(x^2 = 2)$?

Solution: The negation of $\forall x(x^2 > x)$ is the statement $\neg\forall x(x^2 > x)$, which is equivalent to $\exists x\,\neg(x^2 > x)$. This can be rewritten as $\exists x(x^2 \leq x)$. The negation of $\exists x(x^2 = 2)$ is the statement $\neg\exists x(x^2 = 2)$, which is equivalent to $\forall x\,\neg(x^2 = 2)$. This can be rewritten as $\forall x(x^2 \neq 2)$. The truth values of these statements depend on the universe of discourse. ◀

TRANSLATING FROM ENGLISH INTO LOGICAL EXPRESSIONS

Translating sentences in English (or other natural languages) into logical expressions is a crucial task in mathematics, logic programming, artificial intelligence, software engineering, and many other disciplines. We began studying this topic in Section 1.1, where we used propositions to express sentences in logical expressions. In that discussion, we purposely avoided sentences whose translations required predicates and quantifiers. Translating from English to logical expressions becomes even more complex when quantifiers are needed. Furthermore, there can be many ways to translate a particular sentence. (As a consequence, there is no "cookbook" approach that can be followed step by step.) We will use some examples to illustrate how to translate sentences from English into logical expressions. The goal in this translation is to produce simple and useful logical expressions. In this section, we restrict ourselves to sentences that can be translated into logical expressions using a single quantifier; in the next section, we will look at more complicated sentences that require multiple quantifiers.

EXAMPLE 17

Extra
Examples

Express the statement "Every student in this class has studied calculus" using predicates and quantifiers.

Solution: First, we rewrite the statement so that we can clearly identify the appropriate quantifiers to use. Doing so, we obtain:

"For every student in this class, that student has studied calculus."

Next, we introduce a variable x so that our statement becomes

"For every student x in this class, x has studied calculus."

Continuing, we introduce the predicate $C(x)$, which is the statement "x has studied calculus." Consequently, if the universe of discourse for x consists of the students in the class, we can translate our statement as $\forall x C(x)$.

However, there are other correct approaches; different universes of discourse and other predicates can be used. The approach we select depends on the subsequent reasoning we want to carry out. For example, we may be interested in a wider group of people than only those in this class. If we change the universe of discourse to consist of all people, we will need to express our statement as

"For every person x, if person x is a student in this class then x has studied calculus."

If $S(x)$ represents the statement that person x is in this class, we see that our statement can be expressed as $\forall x(S(x) \rightarrow C(x))$. [*Caution!* Our statement *cannot* be expressed as $\forall x(S(x) \wedge C(x))$ since this statement says that all people are students in this class and have studied calculus!]

Finally, when we are interested in the background of people in subjects besides calculus, we may prefer to use the two-variable quantifier $Q(x, y)$ for the statement "student x has studied subject y." Then we would replace $C(x)$ by $Q(x, \text{calculus})$ in both approaches we have followed to obtain $\forall x Q(x, \text{calculus})$ or $\forall x(S(x) \rightarrow Q(x, \text{calculus}))$. ◀

In Example 17 we displayed different approaches for expressing the same statement using predicates and quantifiers. However, we should always adopt the simplest approach that is adequate for use in subsequent reasoning.

EXAMPLE 18

Express the statements "Some student in this class has visited Mexico" and "Every student in this class has visited either Canada or Mexico" using predicates and quantifiers.

Solution: The statement "Some student in this class has visited Mexico" means that

"There is a student in this class with the property that the student has visited Mexico."

We can introduce a variable x, so that our statement becomes

"There is a student x in this class having the property x has visited Mexico."

We introduce the predicate $M(x)$, which is the statement "x has visited Mexico." If the universe of discourse for x consists of the students in this class, we can translate this first statement as $\exists x M(x)$.

However, if we are interested in people other than those in this class, we look at the statement a little differently. Our statement can be expressed as

"There is a person x having the properties that x is a student in this class and x has visited Mexico."

In this case, the universe of discourse for the variable x consists of all people. We introduce the predicate $S(x)$, "x is a student in this class." Our solution becomes $\exists x (S(x) \wedge M(x))$ since the statement is that there is a person x who is a student in this class and who has visited Mexico. [*Caution!* Our statement cannot be expressed as $\exists x (S(x) \rightarrow M(x))$, which is true when there is someone not in the class.]

Similarly, the second statement can be expressed as

"For every x in this class, x has the property that x has visited Mexico or x has visited Canada."

(Note that we are assuming the inclusive, rather than the exclusive, *or* here.) We let $C(x)$ be the statement "x has visited Canada." Following our earlier reasoning, we see that if the universe of discourse for x consists of the students in this class, this second statement can be expressed as $\forall x (C(x) \vee M(x))$. However, if the universe of discourse for x consists of all people, our statement can be expressed as

"For every person x, if x is a student in this class, then x has visited Mexico or x has visited Canada."

In this case, the statement can be expressed as $\forall x (S(x) \rightarrow (C(x) \vee M(x)))$.

Instead of using the predicates $M(x)$ and $C(x)$ to represent that x has visited Mexico and x has visited Canada, respectively, we could use a two-place predicate $V(x, y)$ to represent "x has visited country y." In this case, $V(x, \text{Mexico})$ and $V(x, \text{Canada})$ would have the same meaning as $M(x)$ and $C(x)$ and could replace them in our answers. If we are working with many statements that involve people visiting different countries, we might prefer to use this two-variable approach. Otherwise, for simplicity, we would stick with the one-variable predicates $M(x)$ and $C(x)$. ◀

EXAMPLES FROM LEWIS CARROLL

Lewis Carroll (really C. L. Dodgson writing under a pseudonym), the author of *Alice in Wonderland,* is also the author of several works on symbolic logic. His books contain many examples of reasoning using quantifiers. Examples 19 and 20 come from his book

CHARLES LUTWIDGE DODGSON (1832–1898) We know Charles Dodgson as *Lewis Carroll*— the pseudonym he used in his writings on logic. Dodgson, the son of a clergyman, was the third of 11 children, all of whom stuttered. He was uncomfortable in the company of adults and is said to have spoken without stuttering only to young girls, many of whom he entertained, corresponded with, and photographed (often in the nude). Although attracted to young girls, he was extremely puritanical and religious. His friendship with the three young daughters of Dean Liddell led to his writing *Alice in Wonderland,* which brought him money and fame.

Dodgson graduated from Oxford in 1854 and obtained his master of arts degree in 1857. He was appointed lecturer in mathematics at Christ Church College, Oxford, in 1855. He was ordained in the Church of England in 1861 but never practiced his ministry. His writings include articles and books on geometry, determinants, and the mathematics of tournaments and elections. (He also used the pseudonym Lewis Carroll for his many works on recreational logic.)

Symbolic Logic; other examples from that book are given in the exercise set at the end of this section. These examples illustrate how quantifiers are used to express various types of statements.

EXAMPLE 19   Consider these statements. The first two are called *premises* and the third is called the *conclusion.* The entire set is called an *argument.*

> "All lions are fierce."
> "Some lions do not drink coffee."
> "Some fierce creatures do not drink coffee."

(In Section 1.5 we will discuss the issue of determining whether the conclusion is a valid consequence of the premises. In this example, it is.) Let $P(x)$, $Q(x)$, and $R(x)$ be the statements "x is a lion," "x is fierce," and "x drinks coffee," respectively. Assuming that the universe of discourse is the set of all creatures, express the statements in the argument using quantifiers and $P(x)$, $Q(x)$, and $R(x)$.

Solution: We can express these statements as:

$$\forall x(P(x) \to Q(x)).$$
$$\exists x(P(x) \land \neg R(x)).$$
$$\exists x(Q(x) \land \neg R(x)).$$

Notice that the second statement cannot be written as $\exists x(P(x) \to \neg R(x))$. The reason is that $P(x) \to \neg R(x)$ is true whenever x is not a lion, so that $\exists x(P(x) \to \neg R(x))$ is true as long as there is at least one creature that is not a lion, even if every lion drinks coffee. Similarly, the third statement cannot be written as

$$\exists x(Q(x) \to \neg R(x)).$$ ◀

EXAMPLE 20   Consider these statements, of which the first three are premises and the fourth is a valid conclusion.

> "All hummingbirds are richly colored."
> "No large birds live on honey."
> "Birds that do not live on honey are dull in color."
> "Hummingbirds are small."

Let $P(x)$, $Q(x)$, $R(x)$, and $S(x)$ be the statements "x is a hummingbird," "x is large," "x lives on honey," and "x is richly colored," respectively. Assuming that the universe of discourse is the set of all birds, express the statements in the argument using quantifiers and $P(x)$, $Q(x)$, $R(x)$, and $S(x)$.

Solution: We can express the statements in the argument as

$$\forall x(P(x) \to S(x)).$$
$$\neg\exists x(Q(x) \land R(x)).$$
$$\forall x(\neg R(x) \to \neg S(x)).$$
$$\forall x(P(x) \to \neg Q(x)).$$

(Note we have assumed that "small" is the same as "not large" and that "dull in color" is the same as "not richly colored." To show that the fourth statement is a valid conclusion of the first three, we need to use rules of inference that will be discussed in Section 1.5.)   ◀

LOGIC PROGRAMMING

An important type of programming language is designed to reason using the rules of predicate logic. Prolog (from *Pro*gramming in *Log*ic), developed in the 1970s by computer scientists working in the area of artificial intelligence, is an example of such a language. Prolog programs include a set of declarations consisting of two types of statements, **Prolog facts** and **Prolog rules.** Prolog facts define predicates by specifying the elements that satisfy these predicates. Prolog rules are used to define new predicates using those already defined by Prolog facts. Example 21 illustrates these notions.

EXAMPLE 21 Consider a Prolog program given facts telling it the instructor of each class and in which classes students are enrolled. The program uses these facts to answer queries concerning the professors who teach particular students. Such a program could use the predicates *instructor*(p, c) and *enrolled*(s, c) to represent that professor p is the instructor of course c and that student s is enrolled in course c, respectively. For example, the Prolog facts in such a program might include:

```
instructor(chan,math273)
instructor(patel,ee222)
instructor(grossman,cs301)
enrolled(kevin,math273)
enrolled(juana,ee222)
enrolled(juana,cs301)
enrolled(kiko,math273)
enrolled(kiko,cs301)
```

(Lowercase letters have been used for entries because Prolog considers names beginning with an uppercase letter to be variables.)

A new predicate *teaches*(p, s), representing that professor p teaches student s, can be defined using the Prolog rule

```
teaches(P,S) :- instructor(P,C), enrolled(S,C)
```

which means that *teaches*(p, s) is true if there exists a class c such that professor p is the instructor of class c and student s is enrolled in class c. (Note that a comma is used to represent a conjunction of predicates in Prolog. Similarly, a semicolon is used to represent a disjunction of predicates.)

Prolog answers queries using the facts and rules it is given. For example, using the facts and rules listed, the query

```
?enrolled(kevin,math273)
```

produces the response

```
yes
```

since the fact *enrolled*(kevin, math273) was provided as input. The query

```
?enrolled(X,math273)
```

produces the response

```
kevin
kiko
```

To produce this response, Prolog determines all possible values of X for which *enrolled*$(X,$ math273$)$ has been included as a Prolog fact. Similarly, to find all the professors who are instructors in classes being taken by Juana, we use the query

```
?teaches(X,juana)
```

This query returns

```
patel
grossman
```

◀

Exercises

1. Let $P(x)$ denote the statement "$x \leq 4$." What are the truth values?

a) $P(0)$ **b)** $P(4)$ **c)** $P(6)$

2. Let $P(x)$ be the statement "the word x contains the letter a." What are the truth values?

a) P(orange)   **b)** P(lemon)
c) P(true)   **d)** P(false)

3. Let $Q(x, y)$ denote the statement "x is the capital of y." What are these truth values?

a) Q(Denver, Colorado)
b) Q(Detroit, Michigan)
c) Q(Massachusetts, Boston)
d) Q(New York, New York)

4. State the value of x after the statement **if** $P(x)$ **then** $x := 1$ is executed, where $P(x)$ is the statement "$x > 1$," if the value of x when this statement is reached is

a) $x = 0$.   **b)** $x = 1$.   **c)** $x = 2$.

5. Let $P(x)$ be the statement "x spends more than five hours every weekday in class," where the universe of discourse for x consists of all students. Express each of these quantifications in English.

a) $\exists x\, P(x)$ **b)** $\forall x\, P(x)$
c) $\exists x\, \neg P(x)$ **d)** $\forall x\, \neg P(x)$

6. Let $N(x)$ be the statement "x has visited North Dakota," where the universe of discourse consists of the students in your school. Express each of these quantifications in English.

a) $\exists x N(x)$ **b)** $\forall x N(x)$ **c)** $\neg \exists x N(x)$
d) $\exists x \neg N(x)$ **e)** $\neg \forall x N(x)$ **f)** $\forall x \neg N(x)$

7. Translate these statements into English, where $C(x)$ is "x is a comedian" and $F(x)$ is "x is funny" and the universe of discourse consists of all people.

a) $\forall x(C(x) \rightarrow F(x))$ **b)** $\forall x(C(x) \wedge F(x))$
c) $\exists x(C(x) \rightarrow F(x))$ **d)** $\exists x(C(x) \wedge F(x))$

8. Translate these statements into English, where $R(x)$ is "x is a rabbit" and $H(x)$ is "x hops" and the universe of discourse consists of all animals.

a) $\forall x(R(x) \rightarrow H(x))$ **b)** $\forall x(R(x) \wedge H(x))$
c) $\exists x(R(x) \rightarrow H(x))$ **d)** $\exists x(R(x) \wedge H(x))$

9. Let $P(x)$ be the statement "x can speak Russian" and let $Q(x)$ be the statement "x knows the computer language C++." Express each of these sentences in terms of $P(x)$, $Q(x)$, quantifiers, and logical connectives. The universe of discourse for quantifiers consists of all students at your school.

a) There is a student at your school who can speak Russian and who knows C++.

b) There is a student at your school who can speak Russian but who doesn't know C++.

c) Every student at your school either can speak Russian or knows C++.

d) No student at your school can speak Russian or knows C++.

10. Let $C(x)$ be the statement "x has a cat," let $D(x)$ be the statement "x has a dog," and let $F(x)$ be the statement "x has a ferret." Express each of these statements in terms of $C(x)$, $D(x)$, $F(x)$, quantifiers, and logical connectives. Let the universe of discourse consist of all students in your class.

a) A student in your class has a cat, a dog, and a ferret.

b) All students in your class have a cat, a dog, or a ferret.

c) Some student in your class has a cat and a ferret, but not a dog.

d) No student in your class has a cat, a dog, and a ferret.

e) For each of the three animals, cats, dogs, and ferrets, there is a student in your class who has one of these animals as a pet.

11. Let $P(x)$ be the statement "$x = x^2$." If the universe of discourse consists of the integers, what are the truth values?

a) $P(0)$ **b)** $P(1)$ **c)** $P(2)$
d) $P(-1)$ **e)** $\exists x P(x)$ **f)** $\forall x P(x)$

12. Let $Q(x)$ be the statement "$x + 1 > 2x$." If the universe of discourse consists of all integers, what are these truth values?

    a) $Q(0)$ **b)** $Q(-1)$ **c)** $Q(1)$

    d) $\exists x\, Q(x)$ **e)** $\forall x\, Q(x)$ **f)** $\exists x\, \neg Q(x)$

    g) $\forall x\, \neg Q(x)$

13. Determine the truth value of each of these statements if the universe of discourse consists of all integers.

    a) $\forall n(n + 1 > n)$ **b)** $\exists n(2n = 3n)$

    c) $\exists n(n = -n)$ **d)** $\forall n(n^2 \geq n)$

14. Determine the truth value of each of these statements if the universe of discourse consists of all real numbers.

    a) $\exists x(x^3 = -1)$ **b)** $\exists x(x^4 < x^2)$

    c) $\forall x((-x)^2 = x^2)$ **d)** $\forall x(2x > x)$

15. Determine the truth value of each of these statements if the universe of discourse for all variables consists of all integers.

    a) $\forall n(n^2 \geq 0)$ **b)** $\exists n(n^2 = 2)$

    c) $\forall n(n^2 \geq n)$ **d)** $\exists n(n^2 < 0)$

16. Determine the truth value of each of these statements if the universe of discourse of each variable consists of all real numbers.

    a) $\exists x(x^2 = 2)$ **b)** $\exists x(x^2 = -1)$

    c) $\forall x(x^2 + 2 \geq 1)$ **d)** $\forall x(x^2 \neq x)$

17. Suppose that the universe of discourse of the propositional function $P(x)$ consists of the integers 0, 1, 2, 3, and 4. Write out each of these propositions using disjunctions, conjunctions, and negations.

    a) $\exists x\, P(x)$ **b)** $\forall x\, P(x)$ **c)** $\exists x\, \neg P(x)$

    d) $\forall x\, \neg P(x)$ **e)** $\neg \exists x\, P(x)$ **f)** $\neg \forall x\, P(x)$

18. Suppose that the universe of discourse of the propositional function $Q(x)$ consists of the integers $-2, -1$, 0, 1, and 2. Write out each of these propositions using disjunctions, conjunctions, and negations.

    a) $\exists x\, P(x)$ **b)** $\forall x\, P(x)$ **c)** $\exists x\, \neg P(x)$

    d) $\forall x\, \neg P(x)$ **e)** $\neg \exists x\, P(x)$ **f)** $\neg \forall x\, P(x)$

19. Suppose that the universe of discourse of the propositional function $P(x)$ consists of the integers 1, 2, 3, 4, and 5. Express these statements without using quantifiers, instead using only negations, disjunctions, and conjunctions.

    a) $\exists x\, P(x)$ **b)** $\forall x\, P(x)$

    c) $\neg \exists x\, P(x)$ **d)** $\neg \forall x\, P(x)$

    e) $\forall x((x \neq 3) \to P(x)) \vee \exists x\, \neg P(x)$

20. Suppose that the universe of discourse of the propositional function $P(x)$ consists of $-5, -3, -1$, 1, 3, and 5. Express these statements without using quantifiers, instead using only negations, disjunctions, and conjunctions.

    a) $\exists x\, P(x)$ **b)** $\forall x\, P(x)$

    c) $\forall x((x \neq 1) \to P(x))$

    d) $\exists x((x \geq 0) \wedge P(x))$

    e) $\exists x(\neg P(x)) \wedge \forall x((x < 0) \to P(x))$

21. Translate in two ways each of these statements into logical expressions using predicates, quantifiers, and logical connectives. First, let the universe of discourse consist of the students in your class and second, let it consist of all people.

    a) Someone in your class can speak Hindi.

    b) Everyone in your class is friendly.

    c) There is a person in your class who was not born in California.

    d) A student in your class has been in a movie.

    e) No student in your class has taken a course in logic programming.

22. Translate in two ways each of these statements into logical expressions using predicates, quantifiers, and logical connectives. First, let the universe of discourse consist of the students in your class and second, let it consist of all people.

    a) Everyone in your class has a cellular phone.

    b) Somebody in your class has seen a foreign movie.

    c) There is a person in your class who cannot swim.

    d) All students in your class can solve quadratic equations.

    e) Some student in your class does not want to be rich.

23. Translate each of these statements into logical expressions using predicates, quantifiers, and logical connectives.

    a) No one is perfect.

    b) Not everyone is perfect.

    c) All your friends are perfect.

    d) One of your friends is perfect.

    e) Everyone is your friend and is perfect.

    f) Not everybody is your friend or someone is not perfect.

24. Translate each of these statements into logical expressions in three different ways by varying the universe of discourse and by using predicates with one and with two variables.

    a) Someone in your school has visited Uzbekistan.

    b) Everyone in your class has studied calculus and C++.

    c) No one in your school owns both a bicycle and a motorcycle.

    d) There is a person in your school who is not happy.

    e) Everyone in your school was born in the twentieth century.

25. Translate each of these statements into logical expressions in three different ways by varying the universe of discourse and by using predicates with one and with two variables.

    a) A student in your school has lived in Vietnam.

    b) There is a student in your school who cannot speak Hindi.

c) A student in your school knows Java, Prolog, and C++.

d) Everyone in your class enjoys Thai food.

e) Someone in your class does not play hockey.

26. Translate each of these statements into logical expressions using predicates, quantifiers, and logical connectives.

a) Something is not in the correct place.

b) All tools are in the correct place and are in excellent condition.

c) Everything is in the correct place and in excellent condition.

d) Nothing is in the correct place and is in excellent condition.

e) One of your tools is not in the correct place, but it is in excellent condition.

27. Express each of these statements using logical operators, predicates, and quantifiers.

a) Some propositions are tautologies.

b) The negation of a contradiction is a tautology.

c) The disjunction of two contingencies can be a tautology.

d) The conjunction of two tautologies is a tautology.

28. Suppose the universe of discourse of the propositional function $P(x, y)$ consists of pairs x and y, where x is 1, 2, or 3 and y is 1, 2, or 3. Write out these propositions using disjunctions and conjunctions.

a) $\exists x\, P(x, 3)$ b) $\forall y\, P(1, y)$

c) $\exists y \neg P(2, y)$ d) $\forall x \neg P(x, 2)$

29. Suppose that the universe of discourse of $Q(x, y, z)$ consists of triples x, y, z, where $x = 0, 1,$ or $2, y = 0$ or 1, and $z = 0$ or 1. Write out these propositions using disjunctions and conjunctions.

a) $\forall y\, Q(0, y, 0)$

b) $\exists x\, Q(x, 1, 1)$

c) $\exists z \neg Q(0, 0, z)$

d) $\exists x \neg Q(x, 0, 1)$

30. Express each of these statements using quantifiers. Then form the negation of the statement so that no negation is to the left of a quantifier. Next, express the negation in simple English. (Do not simply use the words "It is not the case that.")

a) All dogs have fleas.

b) There is a horse that can add.

c) Every koala can climb.

d) No monkey can speak French.

e) There exists a pig that can swim and catch fish.

31. Express each of these statements using quantifiers. Then form the negation of the statement, so that no negation is to the left of a quantifier. Next, express the negation in simple English. (Do not simply use the words "It is not the case that.")

a) Some old dogs can learn new tricks.

b) No rabbit knows calculus.

c) Every bird can fly.

d) There is no dog that can talk.

e) There is no one in this class who knows French and Russian.

32. Express the negation of these propositions using quantifiers, and then express the negation in English.

a) Some drivers do not obey the speed limit.

b) All Swedish movies are serious.

c) No one can keep a secret.

d) There is someone in this class who does not have a good attitude.

33. Find a counterexample, if possible, to these universally quantified statements, where the universe of discourse for all variables consists of all integers.

a) $\forall x(x^2 \geq x)$ b) $\forall x(x > 0 \vee x < 0)$

c) $\forall x(x = 1)$

34. Find a counterexample, if possible, to these universally quantified statements, where the universe of discourse for all variables consists of all real numbers.

a) $\forall x(x^2 \neq x)$ b) $\forall x(x^2 \neq 2)$

c) $\forall x(|x| > 0)$

35. Express each of these statements using predicates and quantifiers.

a) A passenger on an airline qualifies as an elite flyer if the passenger flies more than 25,000 miles in a year or takes more than 25 flights during that year.

b) A man qualifies for the marathon if his best previous time is less than 3 hours and a woman qualifies for the marathon if her best previous time is less than 3.5 hours.

c) A student must take at least 60 course hours, or at least 45 course hours and write a master's thesis, and receive a grade no lower than a B in all required courses, to receive a master's degree.

d) There is a student who has taken more than 21 credit hours in a semester and received all A's.

Exercises 36–40 deal with the translation between system specification and logical expressions involving quantifiers.

36. Translate these system specifications into English where the predicate $S(x, y)$ is "x is in state y" and where the universe of discourse for x and y consists of all systems and all possible states, respectively.

a) $\exists x\, S(x, \text{open})$

b) $\forall x(S(x, \text{malfunctioning}) \vee S(x, \text{diagnostic}))$

c) $\exists x\, S(x, \text{open}) \vee \exists x\, S(x, \text{diagnostic})$

d) $\exists x \neg S(x, \text{available})$

e) $\forall x \neg S(x, \text{working})$

37. Translate these specifications into English where $F(p)$ is "Printer p is out of service," $B(p)$ is "Printer p is busy," $L(j)$ is "Print job j is lost," and $Q(j)$ is "Print job j is queued."

a) $\exists p(F(p) \wedge B(p)) \rightarrow \exists j\, L(j)$

b) $\forall p\, B(p) \rightarrow \exists j\, Q(j)$
c) $\exists j\, (Q(j) \wedge L(j)) \rightarrow \exists p\, F(p)$
d) $(\forall p\, B(p) \wedge \forall j\, Q(j)) \rightarrow \exists j\, L(j)$

38. Express each of these system specifications using predicates, quantifiers, and logical connectives.

    a) When there is less than 30 megabytes free on the hard disk, a warning message is sent to all users.

    b) No directories in the file system can be opened and no files can be closed when system errors have been detected.

    c) The file system cannot be backed up if there is a user currently logged on.

    d) Video on demand can be delivered when there are at least 8 megabytes of memory available and the connection speed is at least 56 kilobits per second.

39. Express each of these system specifications using predicates, quantifiers, and logical connectives.

    a) At least one mail message can be saved if there is a disk with more than 10 kilobytes of free space.

    b) Whenever there is an active alert, all queued messages are transmitted.

    c) The diagnostic monitor tracks the status of all systems except the main console.

    d) Each participant on the conference call whom the host of the call did not put on a special list was billed.

40. Express each of these system specifications using predicates, quantifiers, and logical connectives.

    a) Every user has access to an electronic mailbox.

    b) The system mailbox can be accessed by everyone in the group if the file system is locked.

    c) The firewall is in a diagnostic state only if the proxy server is in a diagnostic state.

    d) At least one router is functioning normally if the throughput is between 100 kbps and 500 kbps and the proxy server is not in diagnostic mode.

41. Determine whether $\forall x(P(x) \rightarrow Q(x))$ and $\forall x\, P(x) \rightarrow \forall x\, Q(x)$ have the same truth value.

42. Show that $\forall x(P(x) \wedge Q(x))$ and $\forall x\, P(x) \wedge \forall x\, Q(x)$ have the same truth value.

43. Show that $\exists x(P(x) \vee Q(x))$ and $\exists x\, P(x) \vee \exists x\, Q(x)$ have the same truth value.

44. Establish these logical equivalences, where A is a proposition not involving any quantifiers.

    a) $(\forall x\, P(x)) \vee A \equiv \forall x(P(x) \vee A)$

    b) $(\exists x\, P(x)) \vee A \equiv \exists x(P(x) \vee A)$

45. Establish these logical equivalences, where A is a proposition not involving any quantifiers.

    a) $(\forall x\ P(x)) \wedge A \equiv \forall x(P(x) \wedge A)$

    b) $(\exists x\ P(x)) \wedge A \equiv \exists x(P(x) \wedge A)$

46. Show that $\forall x\, P(x) \vee \forall x\, Q(x)$ and $\forall x(P(x) \vee Q(x))$ are not logically equivalent.

47. Show that $\exists x\, P(x) \wedge \exists x\, Q(x)$ and $\exists x(P(x) \wedge Q(x))$ are not logically equivalent.

48. The notation $\exists! x\, P(x)$ denotes the proposition

    "There exists a unique x such that $P(x)$ is true."

If the universe of discourse consists of all integers, what are the truth values?

    a) $\exists! x(x > 1)$ **b)** $\exists! x(x^2 = 1)$

    c) $\exists! x(x + 3 = 2x)$ **d)** $\exists! x(x = x + 1)$

49. What are the truth values of these statements?

    a) $\exists! x\, P(x) \rightarrow \exists x\, P(x)$

    b) $\forall x\, P(x) \rightarrow \exists! x\, P(x)$

    c) $\exists! x\, \neg P(x) \rightarrow \neg \forall x\, P(x)$

50. Write out $\exists! x\, P(x)$, where the universe of discourse consists of the integers 1, 2, and 3, in terms of negations, conjunctions, and disjunctions.

51. Given the Prolog facts in Example 21, what would Prolog return given these queries?

    a) `?instructor(chan,math273)`

    b) `?instructor(patel,cs301)`

    c) `?enrolled(X,cs301)`

    d) `?enrolled(kiko,Y)`

    e) `?teaches(grossman,Y)`

52. Given the Prolog facts in Example 21, what would Prolog return when given these queries?

    a) `?enrolled(kevin,ee222)`

    b) `?enrolled(kiko,math273)`

    c) `?instructor(grossman,X)`

    d) `?instructor(X,cs301)`

    e) `?teaches(X,kevin)`

53. Suppose that Prolog facts are used to define the predicates *mother*(M, Y) and *father*(F, X), which represent that M is the mother of Y and F is the father of X, respectively. Give a Prolog rule to define the predicate *sibling*(X, Y), which represents that X and Y are siblings (that is, have the same mother and the same father).

54. Suppose that Prolog facts are used to define the predicates *mother*(M, Y) and *father*(F, X), which represent that M is the mother of Y and F is the father of X, respectively. Give a Prolog rule to define the predicate *grandfather*(X, Y), which represents that X is the grandfather of Y. (*Hint:* You can write a disjunction in Prolog either by using a semicolon to separate predicates or by putting these predicates on separate lines.)

Exercises 55–58 are based on questions found in the book *Symbolic Logic* by Lewis Carroll.

55. Let $P(x), Q(x)$, and $R(x)$ be the statements "x is a professor," "x is ignorant," and "x is vain," respectively. Express each of these statements using quantifiers; logical connectives; and $P(x)$, $Q(x)$, and $R(x)$, where the universe of discourse consists of all people.

    a) No professors are ignorant.

    b) All ignorant people are vain.

    c) No professors are vain.

d) Does (c) follow from (a) and (b)? If not, is there a correct conclusion?

56. Let $P(x)$, $Q(x)$, and $R(x)$ be the statements "x is a clear explanation," "x is satisfactory," and "x is an excuse," respectively. Suppose that the universe of discourse for x consists of all English text. Express each of these statements using quantifiers, logical connectives, and $P(x)$, $Q(x)$, and $R(x)$.

a) All clear explanations are satisfactory.
b) Some excuses are unsatisfactory.
c) Some excuses are not clear explanations.
* **d)** Does (c) follow from (a) and (b)? If not, is there a correct conclusion?

57. Let $P(x)$, $Q(x)$, $R(x)$, and $S(x)$ be the statements "x is a baby," "x is logical," "x is able to manage a crocodile," and "x is despised," respectively. Suppose that the universe of discourse consists of all people. Express each of these statements using quantifiers;

logical connectives; and $P(x)$, $Q(x)$, $R(x)$, and $S(x)$.

a) Babies are illogical.
b) Nobody is despised who can manage a crocodile.
c) Illogical persons are despised.
d) Babies cannot manage crocodiles.
* **e)** Does (d) follow from (a), (b), and (c)? If not, is there a correct conclusion?

58. Let $P(x)$, $Q(x)$, $R(x)$, and $S(x)$ be the statements "x is a duck," "x is one of my poultry," "x is an officer," and "x is willing to waltz," respectively. Express each of these statements using quantifiers; logical connectives; and $P(x)$, $Q(x)$, $R(x)$, and $S(x)$.

a) No ducks are willing to waltz.
b) No officers ever decline to waltz.
c) All my poultry are ducks.
d) My poultry are not officers.
* **e)** Does (d) follow from (a), (b), and (c)? If not, is there a correct conclusion?

1.4   Nested Quantifiers

INTRODUCTION

In Section 1.3 we defined the existential and universal quantifiers and showed how they can be used to represent mathematical statements. We also explained how they can be used to translate English sentences into logical expressions. In this section we will study **nested quantifiers**, which are quantifiers that occur within the scope of other quantifiers, such as in the statement $\forall x \exists y(x + y = 0)$. Nested quantifiers commonly occur in mathematics and computer science. Although nested quantifiers can sometimes be difficult to understand, the rules we have already studied in Section 1.3 can help us use them.

TRANSLATING STATEMENTS INVOLVING NESTED QUANTIFIERS

Complicated expressions involving quantifiers arise in many contexts. To understand these statements involving many quantifiers, we need to unravel what the quantifiers and predicates that appear mean. This is illustrated in Example 1.

EXAMPLE 1

Additional Steps

Assume that the universe of discourse for the variables x and y consists of all real numbers. The statement

$$\forall x \forall y(x + y = y + x)$$

says that $x + y = y + x$ for all real numbers x and y. This is the commutative law for addition of real numbers. Likewise, the statement

$$\forall x \exists y(x + y = 0)$$

says that for every real number x there is a real number y such that $x + y = 0$. This states that every real number has an additive inverse. Similarly, the statement

Extra Examples

$$\forall x \forall y \forall z(x + (y + z) = (x + y) + z)$$

is the associative law for addition of real numbers.   ◀

EXAMPLE 2   Translate into English the statement

$$\forall x \forall y ((x > 0) \wedge (y < 0) \rightarrow (xy < 0)),$$

where the universe of discourse for both variables consists of all real numbers.

Solution: This statement says that for every real number x and for every real number y, if $x > 0$ and $y < 0$, then $xy < 0$. That is, this statement says that for real numbers x and y, if x is positive and y is negative, then xy is negative. This can be stated more succinctly as "The product of a positive real number and a negative real number is a negative real number."   ◄

Expressions with nested quantifiers expressing statements in English can be quite complicated. The first step in translating such an expression is to write out what the quantifiers and predicates in the expression mean. The next step is to express this meaning in a simpler sentence. This process is illustrated in Examples 3 and 4.

EXAMPLE 3   Translate the statement

$$\forall x (C(x) \vee \exists y (C(y) \wedge F(x, y)))$$

into English, where $C(x)$ is "x has a computer," $F(x, y)$ is "x and y are friends," and the universe of discourse for both x and y consists of all students in your school.

Solution: The statement says that for every student x in your school x has a computer or there is a student y such that y has a computer and x and y are friends. In other words, every student in your school has a computer or has a friend who has a computer.   ◄

EXAMPLE 4   Translate the statement

$$\exists x \forall y \forall z ((F(x, y) \wedge F(x, z) \wedge (y \neq z)) \rightarrow \neg F(y,z))$$

into English, where $F(a,b)$ means a and b are friends and the universe of discourse for $x, y,$ and z consists of all students in your school.

Solution: We first examine the expression $(F(x, y) \wedge F(x, z) \wedge (y \neq z)) \rightarrow \neg F(y, z)$. This expression says that if students x and y are friends, and students x and z are friends, and furthermore, if y and z are not the same student, then y and z are not friends. It follows that the original statement, which is triply quantified, says that there is a student x such that for all students y and all students z other than y, if x and y are friends and x and z are friends, then y and z are not friends. In other words, there is a student none of whose friends are also friends with each other.   ◄

TRANSLATING SENTENCES INTO LOGICAL EXPRESSIONS

In Section 1.3 we showed how quantifiers can be used to translate sentences into logical expressions. However, we avoided sentences whose translation into logical expressions required the use of nested quantifiers. We now address the translation of such sentences.

EXAMPLE 5   Express the statement "If a person is female and is a parent, then this person is some-one's mother" as a logical expression involving predicates, quantifiers with a universe of discourse consisting of all people, and logical connectives.

Solution: The statement "If a person is female and is a parent, then this person is someone's mother" can be expressed as "For every person x, if person x is female and person x is a parent, then there exists a person y such that person x is the mother of person y." We introduce the predicates $F(x)$ to represent "x is female," $P(x)$ to represent "x is a parent," and $M(x, y)$ to represent "x is the mother of y." The original statement can be represented as

$$\forall x((F(x) \land P(x)) \to \exists y M(x, y)).$$

We can move $\exists y$ all the way to the left, because y does not appear in $F(x) \land P(x)$, to obtain an equivalent expression

$$\forall x \exists y((F(x) \land P(x)) \to M(x, y)). \qquad \blacktriangleleft$$

EXAMPLE 6 Express the statement "Everyone has exactly one best friend" as a logical expression involving predicates, quantifiers with a universe of discourse consisting of all people, and logical connectives.

Solution: The statement "Everyone has exactly one best friend" can be expressed as "For every person x, person x has exactly one best friend." Introducing the universal quantifier, we see that this statement is the same as "$\forall x$ (person x has exactly one best friend)" where the universe of discourse consists of all people.

To say that x has exactly one best friend means that there is a person y who is the best friend of x, and, furthermore, that for every person z, if person z is not person y, then z is not the best friend of x. When we introduce the predicate $B(x, y)$ to be the statement "y is the best friend of x," the statement that x has exactly one best friend can be represented as

$$\exists y(B(x, y) \land \forall z((z \neq y) \to \neg B(x, z))).$$

Consequently, our original statement can be expressed as

$$\forall x \exists y(B(x, y) \land \forall z((z \neq y) \to \neg B(x, z))).$$

(Note that we can write this statement as $\forall x \exists! y B(x, y)$, where $\exists!$ is the "uniqueness quantifier" defined in Exercise 48 of Section 1.3. However, the "uniqueness quantifier" is not really a quantifier; rather, it is a shorthand for expressing certain statements that can be expressed using the quantifiers $\forall$ and $\exists$. The "uniqueness quantifier" $\exists!$ can be thought of as a macro.) $\qquad \blacktriangleleft$

EXAMPLE 7 Use quantifiers to express the statement "There is a woman who has taken a flight on every airline in the world."

Solution: Let $P(w, f)$ be "w has taken f" and $Q(f, a)$ be "f is a flight on a." We can express the statement as

$$\exists w \forall a \exists f(P(w, f) \land Q(f, a)),$$

where the universes of discourse for w, f, and a consist of all the women in the world, all airplane flights, and all airlines, respectively.

The statement could also be expressed as

$$\exists w \forall a \exists f R(w, f, a),$$

where $R(w, f, a)$ is "w has taken f on a." Although this is more compact, it somewhat obscures the relationships among the variables. Consequently, the first solution is usually preferable. $\qquad \blacktriangleleft$

Mathematical statements expressed in English can be translated into logical expressions as Examples 8–10 show.

EXAMPLE 8   Translate the statement "The sum of two positive integers is positive" into a logical expression.

Additional Steps

Solution: To translate this statement into a logical expression, we first rewrite it so that the implied quantifiers are shown: "For every two positive integers, the sum of these integers is positive." Next, we introduce the variables x and y to obtain "For all positive integers x and y, $x + y$ is positive." Consequently, we can express this statement as

$$\forall x \forall y ((x > 0) \land (y > 0) \to (x + y > 0)),$$

where the universe of discourse for both variables consists of all integers.   ◀

EXAMPLE 9   Translate the statement "Every real number except zero has a multiplicative inverse."

Extra Examples

Solution: We first rewrite this as "For every real number x except zero, x has a multiplicative inverse." We can rewrite this as "For every real number x, if $x \neq 0$, then there exists a real number y such that $xy = 1$." This can be rewritten as

$$\forall x ((x \neq 0) \to \exists y (xy = 1)).$$ ◀

One example that you may be familiar with is the concept of limit, which is important in calculus.

EXAMPLE 10   **(Calculus required)** Express the definition of a limit using quantifiers.

Solution: Recall that the definition of the statement

$$\lim_{x \to a} f(x) = L$$

is: For every real number $\epsilon > 0$ there exists a real number $\delta > 0$ such that $|f(x) - L| < \epsilon$ whenever $0 < |x - a| < \delta$. This definition of a limit can be phrased in terms of quantifiers by

$$\forall \epsilon \exists \delta \forall x (0 < |x - a| < \delta \to |f(x) - L| < \epsilon),$$

where the universe of discourse for the variables δ and ϵ consists of all positive real numbers and for x consists of all real numbers.

This definition can also be expressed as

$$\forall \epsilon > 0 \ \exists \delta > 0 \ \forall x (0 < |x - a| < \delta \to |f(x) - L| < \epsilon)$$

when the universe of discourse for the variables ϵ and δ consists of all real numbers, rather than just the positive real numbers.   ◀

NEGATING NESTED QUANTIFIERS

Statements involving nested quantifiers can be negated by successively applying the rules for negating statements involving a single quantifier. This is illustrated in Examples 11–13.

EXAMPLE 11 Express the negation of the statement $\forall x \exists y (xy = 1)$ so that no negation precedes a quantifier.

Extra Examples

Solution: By successively applying the rules for negating quantified statements given in Table 2 of Section 1.3, we can move the negation in $\neg \forall x \exists y (xy = 1)$ inside all the quantifiers. We find that $\neg \forall x \exists y (xy = 1)$ is equivalent to $\exists x \neg \exists y (xy = 1)$, which is equivalent to $\exists x \forall y \neg (xy = 1)$. Since $\neg (xy = 1)$ can be expressed more simply as $xy \neq 1$, we conclude that our negated statement can be expressed as $\exists x \forall y (xy \neq 1)$. ◄

EXAMPLE 12 Use quantifiers to express the statement that "There does not exist a woman who has taken a flight on every airline in the world."

Solution: This statement is the negation of the statement "There is a woman who has taken a flight on every airline in the world" from Example 7. By Example 7, our statement can be expressed as $\neg \exists w \forall a \exists f (P(w, f) \wedge Q(f, a))$, where $P(w, f)$ is "w has taken f" and $Q(f, a)$ is "f is a flight on a." By successively applying the rules for negating quantified statements from Table 2 of Section 1.3 to move the negation inside successive quantifiers and by applying De Morgan's law in the last step, we find that our statement is equivalent to each of this sequence of statements:

$$\forall w \neg \forall a \exists f (P(w, f) \wedge Q(f, a)) \equiv \forall w \exists a \neg \exists f (P(w, f) \wedge Q(f, a))$$

$$\equiv \forall w \exists a \forall f \neg (P(w, f) \wedge Q(f, a))$$

$$\equiv \forall w \exists a \forall f (\neg P(w, f) \vee \neg Q(f, a)).$$

This last statement states "For every woman there is an airline such that for all flights, this woman has not taken that flight or that flight is not on this airline." ◄

EXAMPLE 13 Use quantifiers and predicates to express the fact that $\lim_{x \to a} f(x)$ does not exist.

Solution: To say that $\lim_{x \to a} f(x)$ does not exist means that for all real numbers L, $\lim_{x \to a} f(x) \neq L$. By using Example 10, the statement $\lim_{x \to a} f(x) \neq L$ can be expressed as

$$\neg \forall \epsilon > 0 \, \exists \delta > 0 \, \forall x (0 < |x - a| < \delta \to |f(x) - L| < \epsilon).$$

Successively applying the rules for negating quantified expressions, we construct this sequence of equivalent statements

$$\neg \forall \epsilon > 0 \, \exists \delta > 0 \, \forall x (0 < |x - a| < \delta \to |f(x) - L| < \epsilon)$$

$$\equiv \exists \epsilon > 0 \, \neg \exists \delta > 0 \, \forall x (0 < |x - a| < \delta \to |f(x) - L| < \epsilon)$$

$$\equiv \exists \epsilon > 0 \, \forall \delta > 0 \, \neg \forall x (0 < |x - a| < \delta \to |f(x) - L| < \epsilon)$$

$$\equiv \exists \epsilon > 0 \, \forall \delta > 0 \, \exists x \, \neg (0 < |x - a| < \delta \to |f(x) - L| < \epsilon)$$

$$\equiv \exists \epsilon > 0 \, \forall \delta > 0 \, \exists x (0 < |x - a| < \delta \wedge |f(x) - L| \geq \epsilon).$$

We use the equivalence $\neg (p \to q) \equiv p \wedge \neg q$, in the last step.

Because the statement $\lim_{x \to a} f(x)$ does not exist means for all real numbers L, $\lim_{x \to a} f(x) \neq L$. This statement can be expressed as

$$\forall L \exists \epsilon > 0 \, \forall \delta > 0 \, \exists x (0 < |x - a| < \delta \wedge |f(x) - L| \geq \epsilon).$$

This last statement says that for every real number L there is a real number $\epsilon > 0$ such that for every real number $\delta > 0$, there exists a real number x such that $0 < |x - a| < \delta$ and $|f(x) - L| \geq \epsilon$. ◄

THE ORDER OF QUANTIFIERS

Extra Examples

Many mathematical statements involve multiple quantifications of propositional functions involving more than one variable. It is important to note that the order of the quantifiers is important, unless all the quantifiers are universal quantifiers or all are existential quantifiers. These remarks are illustrated by Examples 14–16. In each of these examples the universe of discourse for each variable consists of all real numbers.

EXAMPLE 14 Let $P(x, y)$ be the statement "$x + y = y + x$." What is the truth value of the quantification $\forall x \forall y P(x, y)$?

Solution: The quantification

$$\forall x \forall y P(x, y)$$

denotes the proposition

"For all real numbers x and for all real numbers $y, x + y = y + x$."

Since $P(x, y)$ is true for all real numbers x and y, the proposition $\forall x \forall y P(x, y)$ is true. ◀

EXAMPLE 15 Let $Q(x, y)$ denote "$x + y = 0$." What are the truth values of the quantifications $\exists y \forall x Q(x, y)$ and $\forall x \exists y Q(x, y)$?

Solution: The quantification

$$\exists y \forall x Q(x, y)$$

denotes the proposition

"There is a real number y such that for every real number x, $Q(x, y)$."

No matter what value of y is chosen, there is only one value of x for which $x + y = 0$. Since there is no real number y such that $x + y = 0$ for all real numbers x, the statement $\exists y \forall x Q(x, y)$ is false.
     The quantification

$$\forall x \exists y Q(x, y)$$

denotes the proposition

"For every real number x there is a real number y such that $Q(x, y)$."

Given a real number x, there is a real number y such that $x + y = 0$; namely, $y = -x$. Hence, the statement $\forall x \exists y Q(x, y)$ is true. ◀

Example 15 illustrates that the order in which quantifiers appear makes a difference. The statements $\exists y \forall x P(x, y)$ and $\forall x \exists y P(x, y)$ are not logically equivalent. The statement $\exists y \forall x P(x, y)$ is true if and only if there is a y that makes $P(x, y)$ true for every x. So, for this statement to be true, there must be a particular value of y for which $P(x, y)$ is true regardless of the choice of x. On the other hand, $\forall x \exists y P(x, y)$ is true if and only if for every value of x there is a value of y for which $P(x, y)$ is true. So, for this statement to be true, no matter which x you choose, there must be a value of y (possibly depending on the x you choose) for which $P(x, y)$ is true. In other words, in the second case y can depend on x, whereas in the first case y is a constant independent of x.

TABLE 1 Quantifications of Two Variables.

Statement	When True?	When False?
$\forall x \forall y P(x, y)$ $\forall y \forall x P(x, y)$	$P(x, y)$ is true for every pair x, y.	There is a pair x, y for which $P(x, y)$ is false.
$\forall x \exists y P(x, y)$	For every x there is a y for which $P(x, y)$ is true.	There is an x such that $P(x, y)$ is false for every y.
$\exists x \forall y P(x, y)$	There is an x for which $P(x, y)$ is true for every y.	For every x there is a y for which $P(x, y)$ is false.
$\exists x \exists y P(x, y)$ $\exists y \exists x P(x, y)$	There is a pair x, y for which $P(x, y)$ is true.	$P(x, y)$ is false for every pair x, y.

From these observations, it follows that if $\exists y \forall x P(x, y)$ is true, then $\forall x \exists y P(x, y)$ must also be true. However, if $\forall x \exists y P(x, y)$ is true, it is not necessary for $\exists y \forall x P(x, y)$ to be true. (See Supplementary Exercises 14 and 16 at the end of this chapter.)

THINKING OF QUANTIFICATION AS LOOPS In working with quantifications of more than one variable, it is sometimes helpful to think in terms of nested loops. (Of course, if there are infinitely many elements in the universe of discourse of some variable, we cannot actually loop through all values. Nevertheless, this way of thinking is helpful in understanding nested quantifiers.) For example, to see whether $\forall x \forall y P(x, y)$ is true, we loop through the values for x, and for each x we loop through the values for y. If we find that $P(x, y)$ is true for all values for x and y, we have determined that $\forall x \forall y P(x, y)$ is true. If we ever hit a value x for which we hit a value y for which $P(x, y)$ is false, we have shown that $\forall x \forall y P(x, y)$ is false.

Similarly, to determine whether $\forall x \exists y P(x, y)$ is true, we loop through the values for x. For each x we loop through the values for y until we find a y for which $P(x, y)$ is true. If for all x we hit such a y, then $\forall x \exists y P(x, y)$ is true; if for some x we never hit such a y, then $\forall x \exists y P(x, y)$ is false.

To see whether $\exists x \forall y P(x, y)$ is true, we loop through the values for x until we find an x for which $P(x, y)$ is always true when we loop through all values for y. Once we find such an x, we know that $\exists x \forall y P(x, y)$ is true. If we never hit such an x, then we know that $\exists x \forall y P(x, y)$ is false.

Finally, to see whether $\exists x \exists y P(x, y)$ is true, we loop through the values for x, where for each x we loop through the values for y until we hit an x for which we hit a y for which $P(x, y)$ is true. The statement $\exists x \exists y P(x, y)$ is false only if we never hit an x for which we hit a y such that $P(x, y)$ is true.

Table 1 summarizes the meanings of the different possible quantifications involving two variables.

Quantifications of more than two variables are also common, as Example 16 illustrates.

EXAMPLE 16   Let $Q(x, y, z)$ be the statement "$x + y = z$." What are the truth values of the statements $\forall x \forall y \exists z Q(x, y, z)$ and $\exists z \forall x \forall y Q(x, y, z)$?

Solution: Suppose that x and y are assigned values. Then, there exists a real number z such that $x + y = z$. Consequently, the quantification

$$\forall x \forall y \exists z \, Q(x, y, z),$$

which is the statement

"For all real numbers x and for all real numbers y there is a real number z such that $x + y = z$,"

is true. The order of the quantification here is important, since the quantification

$$\exists z \forall x \forall y \, Q(x, y, z),$$

which is the statement

"There is a real number z such that for all real numbers x and for all real numbers y it is true that $x + y = z$,"

is false, since there is no value of z that satisfies the equation $x + y = z$ for all values of x and y.   ◄

Exercises

1. Translate these statements into English, where the universe of discourse for each variable consists of all real numbers.

a) $\forall x \exists y (x < y)$

b) $\forall x \forall y (((x \geq 0) \land (y \geq 0)) \rightarrow (xy \geq 0))$

c) $\forall x \forall y \exists z (xy = z)$

2. Translate these statements into English, where the universe of discourse for each variable consists of all real numbers.

a) $\exists x \forall y (xy = y)$

b) $\forall x \forall y (((x \geq 0) \land (y < 0)) \rightarrow (x - y > 0))$

c) $\forall x \forall y \exists z (x = y + z)$

3. Let $Q(x, y)$ be the statement "x has sent an e-mail message to y," where the universe of discourse for both x and y consists of all students in your class. Express each of these quantifications in English.

a) $\exists x \exists y \, Q(x, y)$ **b)** $\exists x \forall y \, Q(x, y)$

c) $\forall x \exists y \, Q(x, y)$ **d)** $\exists y \forall x \, Q(x, y)$

e) $\forall y \exists x \, Q(x, y)$ **f)** $\forall x \forall y \, Q(x, y)$

4. Let $P(x, y)$ be the statement "student x has taken class y," where the universe of discourse for x consists of all students in your class and for y consists of all computer science courses at your school. Express each of these quantifications in English.

a) $\exists x \exists y \, P(x, y)$ **b)** $\exists x \forall y \, P(x, y)$

c) $\forall x \exists y \, P(x, y)$ **d)** $\exists y \forall x \, P(x, y)$

e) $\forall y \exists x \, P(x, y)$ **f)** $\forall x \forall y \, P(x, y)$

5. Let $W(x, y)$ mean that student x has visited website y, where the universe of discourse for x consists of all students in your school and the universe of discourse

for y consists of all websites. Express each of these statements by a simple English sentence.

a) $W(\text{Sarah Smith}, \text{www.att.com})$

b) $\exists x \, W(x, \text{www.imdb.org})$

c) $\exists y \, W(\text{Jose Orez}, y)$

d) $\exists y (W(\text{Ashok Puri}, y) \land W(\text{Cindy Yoon}, y))$

e) $\exists y \forall z (y \neq (\text{David Belcher}) \land (W(\text{David Belcher}, z) \rightarrow W(y, z)))$

f) $\exists x \exists y \forall z ((x \neq y) \land (W(x, z) \leftrightarrow W(y, z)))$

6. Let $C(x, y)$ mean that student x is enrolled in class y, where the universe of discourse for x consists of all students in your school and the universe of discourse for y is the set of all classes being given at your school. Express each of these statements by a simple English sentence.

a) $C(\text{Randy Goldberg}, \text{CS } 252)$

b) $\exists x \, C(x, \text{Math } 695)$

c) $\exists y \, C(\text{Carol Sitea}, y)$

d) $\exists x (C(x, \text{Math } 222) \land C(x, \text{CS } 252))$

e) $\exists x \exists y \forall z ((x \neq y) \land (C(x, z) \rightarrow C(y, z)))$

f) $\exists x \exists y \forall z ((x \neq y) \land (C(x, z) \leftrightarrow C(y, z)))$

7. Let $T(x, y)$ mean that student x likes cuisine y, where the universe of discourse for x consists of all students at your school and the universe of discourse for y consists of all cuisines. Express each of these statements by a simple English sentence.

a) $\neg T(\text{Abdallah Hussein}, \text{Japanese})$

b) $\exists x \, T(x, \text{Korean}) \land \forall x \, T(x, \text{Mexican})$

c) $\exists y (T(\text{Monique Arsenault}, y) \lor T(\text{Jay Johnson}, y))$

d) $\forall x \forall z \exists y ((x \neq z) \rightarrow \neg(T(x, y) \land T(z, y)))$

e) $\exists x \exists z \forall y (T(x, y) \leftrightarrow T(z, y))$

f) $\forall x \forall z \exists y (T(x, y) \leftrightarrow T(z, y))$

8. Let $Q(x, y)$ be the statement "student x has been a contestant on quiz show y." Express each of these sentences in terms of $Q(x, y)$, quantifiers, and logical connectives, where the universe of discourse for x consists of all students at your school and for y consists of all quiz shows on television.

a) There is a student at your school who has been a contestant on a television quiz show.

b) No student at your school has ever been a contestant on a television quiz show.

c) There is a student at your school who has been a contestant on *Jeopardy* and on *Wheel of Fortune*.

d) Every television quiz show has had a student from your school as a contestant.

e) At least two students from your school have been contestants on *Jeopardy*.

9. Let $L(x, y)$ be the statement "x loves y," where the universe of discourse for both x and y consists of all people in the world. Use quantifiers to express each of these statements.

a) Everybody loves Jerry.

b) Everybody loves somebody.

c) There is somebody whom everybody loves.

d) Nobody loves everybody.

e) There is somebody whom Lydia does not love.

f) There is somebody whom no one loves.

g) There is exactly one person whom everybody loves.

h) There are exactly two people whom Lynn loves.

i) Everyone loves himself or herself.

j) There is someone who loves no one besides himself or herself.

10. Let $F(x, y)$ be the statement "x can fool y," where the universe of discourse consists of all people in the world. Use quantifiers to express each of these statements.

a) Everybody can fool Fred.

b) Evelyn can fool everybody.

c) Everybody can fool somebody.

d) There is no one who can fool everybody.

e) Everyone can be fooled by somebody.

f) No one can fool both Fred and Jerry.

g) Nancy can fool exactly two people.

h) There is exactly one person whom everybody can fool.

i) No one can fool himself or herself.

j) There is someone who can fool exactly one person besides himself or herself.

11. Let $S(x)$ be the predicate "x is a student," $F(x)$ the predicate "x is a faculty member," and $A(x, y)$ the predicate "x has asked y a question," where the universe of discourse consists of all people associated with your school. Use quantifiers to express each of these statements.

a) Lois has asked Professor Michaels a question.

b) Every student has asked Professor Gross a question.

c) Every faculty member has either asked Professor Miller a question or been asked a question by Professor Miller.

d) Some student has not asked any faculty member a question.

e) There is a faculty member who has never been asked a question by a student.

f) Some student has asked every faculty member a question.

g) There is a faculty member who has asked every other faculty member a question.

h) Some student has never been asked a question by a faculty member.

12. Let $I(x)$ be the statement "x has an Internet connection" and $C(x, y)$ be the statement "x and y have chatted over the Internet," where the universe of discourse for the variables x and y consists of all students in your class. Use quantifiers to express each of these statements.

a) Jerry does not have an Internet connection.

b) Rachel has not chatted over the Internet with Chelsea.

c) Jan and Sharon have never chatted over the Internet.

d) No one in the class has chatted with Bob.

e) Sanjay has chatted with everyone except Joseph.

f) Someone in your class does not have an Internet connection.

g) Not everyone in your class has an Internet connection.

h) Exactly one student in your class has an Internet connection.

i) Everyone except one student in your class has an Internet connection.

j) Everyone in your class with an Internet connection has chatted over the Internet with at least one other student in your class.

k) Someone in your class has an Internet connection but has not chatted with anyone else in your class.

l) There are two students in your class who have not chatted with each other over the Internet.

m) There is a student in your class who has chatted with everyone in your class over the Internet.

n) There are at least two students in your class who have not chatted with the same person in your class.

o) There are two students in the class who between them have chatted with everyone else in the class.

13. Let $M(x, y)$ be "x has sent y an e-mail message" and $T(x, y)$ be "x has telephoned y," where the universe of discourse consists of all students in your class. Use quantifiers to express each of these statements. (Assume that all e-mail messages that were sent are received, which is not the way things often work.)

a) Chou has never sent an e-mail message to Koko.

b) Arlene has never sent an e-mail message to or telephoned Sarah.

c) Jose has never received an e-mail message from Deborah.

d) Every student in your class has sent an e-mail message to Ken.

e) No one in your class has telephoned Nina.

f) Everyone in your class has either telephoned Avi or sent him an e-mail message.

g) There is a student in your class who has sent everyone else in your class an e-mail message.

h) There is someone in your class who has either sent an e-mail message or telephoned everyone else in your class.

i) There are two students in your class who have sent each other e-mail messages.

j) There is a student who has sent himself or herself an e-mail message.

k) There is a student in your class who has not received an e-mail message from anyone else in the class and who has not been called by any other student in the class.

l) Every student in the class has either received an e-mail message or received a telephone call from another student in the class.

m) There are at least two students in your class such that one student has sent the other e-mail and the second student has telephoned the first student.

n) There are two students in your class who between them have sent an e-mail message to or telephoned everyone else in the class.

14. Use quantifiers and predicates with more than one variable to express these statements.

a) There is a student in this class who can speak Hindi.

b) Every student in this class plays some sport.

c) Some student in this class has visited Alaska but has not visited Hawaii.

d) All students in this class have learned at least one programming language.

e) There is a student in this class who has taken every course offered by one of the departments in this school.

f) Some student in this class grew up in the same town as exactly one other student in this class.

g) Every student in this class has chatted with at least one other student in at least one chat group.

15. Use quantifiers and predicates with more than one variable to express these statements.

a) Every computer science student needs a course in discrete mathematics.

b) There is a student in this class who owns a personal computer.

c) Every student in this class has taken at least one computer science course.

d) There is a student in this class who has taken at least one course in computer science.

e) Every student in this class has been in every building on campus.

f) There is a student in this class who has been in every room of at least one building on campus.

g) Every student in this class has been in at least one room of every building on campus.

16. A discrete mathematics class contains 1 mathematics major who is a freshman, 12 mathematics majors who are sophomores, 15 computer science majors who are sophomores, 2 mathematics majors who are juniors, 2 computer science majors who are juniors, and 1 computer science major who is a senior. Express each of these statements in terms of quantifiers and then determine its truth value.

a) There is a student in the class who is a junior.

b) Every student in the class is a computer science major.

c) There is a student in the class who is neither a mathematics major nor a junior.

d) Every student in the class is either a sophomore or a computer science major.

e) There is a major such that there is a student in the class in every year of study with that major.

17. Express each of these system specifications using predicates, quantifiers, and logical connectives, if necessary.

a) Every user has access to exactly one mailbox.

b) There is a process that continues to run during all error conditions only if the kernel is working correctly.

c) All users on the campus network can access all websites whose url has a .edu extension.

* d) There are exactly two systems that monitor every remote server.

18. Express each of these system specifications using predicates, quantifiers, and logical connectives, if necessary.

a) At least one console must be accessible during every fault condition.

b) The e-mail address of every user can be retrieved whenever the archive contains at least one message sent by every user on the system.

c) For every security breach there is at least one mechanism that can detect that breach if and only if there is a process that has not been compromised.

d) There are at least two paths connecting every two endpoints on the network.

e) No one knows the password of every user on the system except for the system administrator.

19. Express each of these statements using mathematical and logical operators, predicates, and quantifiers, where the universe of discourse consists of all integers.

a) The sum of two negative integers is negative.

b) The difference of two positive integers is not necessarily positive.

c) The sum of the squares of two integers is greater than or equal to the square of their sum.

d) The absolute value of the product of two integers is the product of their absolute values.

20. Express each of these statements using predicates, quantifiers, logical connectives, and mathematical operators where the universe of discourse consists of all integers.

a) The product of two negative integers is positive.

b) The average of two positive integers is positive.

c) The difference of two negative integers is not necessarily negative.

d) The absolute value of the sum of two integers does not exceed the sum of the absolute values of these integers.

21. Use predicates, quantifiers, logical connectives, and mathematical operators to express the statement that every positive integer is the sum of the squares of four integers.

22. Use predicates, quantifiers, logical connectives, and mathematical operators to express the statement that there is a positive integer that is not the sum of three squares.

23. Express each of these mathematical statements using predicates, quantifiers, logical connectives, and mathematical operators.

a) The product of two negative real numbers is positive.

b) The difference of a real number and itself is zero.

c) Every positive real number has exactly two square roots.

d) A negative real number does not have a square root that is a real number.

24. Translate each of these nested quantifications into an English statement that expresses a mathematical fact. The universe of discourse in each case consists of all real numbers.

a) $\exists x \forall y (x + y = y)$

b) $\forall x \forall y (((x \geq 0) \wedge (y < 0)) \rightarrow (x - y > 0))$

c) $\exists x \exists y (((x \leq 0) \wedge (y \leq 0)) \wedge (x - y > 0))$

d) $\forall x \forall y ((x \neq 0) \wedge (y \neq 0) \leftrightarrow (xy \neq 0))$

25. Translate each of these nested quantifications into an English statement that expresses a mathematical fact. The universe of discourse in each case consists of all real numbers.

a) $\exists x \forall y (xy = y)$

b) $\forall x \forall y (((x < 0) \wedge (y < 0)) \rightarrow (xy > 0))$

c) $\exists x \exists y ((x^2 > y) \wedge (x < y))$

d) $\forall x \forall y \exists z (x + y = z)$

26. Let $Q(x, y)$ be the statement "$x + y = x - y$." If the universe of discourse for both variables consists of all integers, what are the truth values?

a) $Q(1, 1)$ **b)** $Q(2, 0)$ **c)** $\forall y Q(1, y)$

d) $\exists x Q(x, 2)$ **e)** $\exists x \exists y Q(x, y)$ **f)** $\forall x \exists y Q(x, y)$

g) $\exists y \forall x Q(x, y)$

h) $\forall y \exists x Q(x, y)$

i) $\forall x \forall y Q(x, y)$

27. Determine the truth value of each of these statements if the universe of discourse for all variables consists of all integers.

a) $\forall n \exists m (n^2 < m)$ **b)** $\exists n \forall m (n < m^2)$

c) $\forall n \exists m (n + m = 0)$ **d)** $\exists n \forall m (nm = m)$

e) $\exists n \exists m (n^2 + m^2 = 5)$ **f)** $\exists n \exists m (n^2 + m^2 = 6)$

g) $\exists n \exists m (n + m = 4 \wedge n - m = 1)$

h) $\exists n \exists m (n + m = 4 \wedge n - m = 2)$

i) $\forall n \forall m \exists p (p = (m + n)/2)$

28. Determine the truth value of each of these statements if the universe of discourse of each variable consists of all real numbers.

a) $\forall x \exists y (x^2 = y)$ **b)** $\forall x \exists y (x = y^2)$

c) $\exists x \forall y (xy = 0)$ **d)** $\exists x \exists y (x + y \neq y + x)$

e) $\forall x (x \neq 0 \rightarrow \exists y (xy = 1))$

f) $\exists x \forall y (y \neq 0 \rightarrow xy = 1)$

g) $\forall x \exists y (x + y = 1)$

h) $\exists x \exists y (x + 2y = 2 \wedge 2x + 4y = 5)$

i) $\forall x \exists y (x + y = 2 \wedge 2x - y = 1)$

j) $\forall x \forall y \exists z (z = (x + y)/2)$

29. Suppose the universe of discourse of the propositional function $P(x, y)$ consists of pairs x and y, where x is 1, 2, or 3 and y is 1, 2, or 3. Write out these propositions using disjunctions and conjunctions.

a) $\forall x \forall y P(x, y)$ **b)** $\exists x \exists y P(x, y)$

c) $\exists x \forall y P(x, y)$ **d)** $\forall y \exists x P(x, y)$

30. Rewrite each of these statements so that negations appear only within predicates (that is, so that no negation is outside a quantifier or an expression involving logical connectives).

a) $\neg \exists y \exists x P(x, y)$ **b)** $\neg \forall x \exists y P(x, y)$

c) $\neg \exists y (Q(y) \wedge \forall x \neg R(x, y))$

d) $\neg \exists y (\exists x R(x, y) \vee \forall x S(x, y))$

e) $\neg \exists y (\forall x \exists z T(x, y, z) \vee \exists x \forall z U(x, y, z))$

31. Express the negations of each of these statements so that all negation symbols immediately precede predicates.

a) $\forall x \exists y \forall z T(x, y, z)$

b) $\forall x \exists y P(x, y) \vee \forall x \exists y Q(x, y)$

c) $\forall x \exists y (P(x, y) \wedge \exists z R(x, y, z))$

d) $\forall x \exists y (P(x, y) \rightarrow Q(x, y))$

32. Express the negations of each of these statements so that all negation symbols immediately precede predicates.

a) $\exists z \forall y \forall x T(x, y, z)$
b) $\exists x \exists y P(x, y) \land \forall x \forall y Q(x, y)$
c) $\exists x \exists y (Q(x, y) \leftrightarrow Q(y, x))$
d) $\forall y \exists x \exists z (T(x, y, z) \lor Q(x, y))$

33. Rewrite each of these statements so that negations appear only within predicates (that is, so that no negation is outside a quantifier or an expression involving logical connectives).

a) $\neg \forall x \forall y P(x, y)$ **b)** $\neg \forall y \exists x P(x, y)$
c) $\neg \forall y \forall x (P(x, y) \lor Q(x, y))$
d) $\neg (\exists x \exists y \neg P(x, y) \land \forall x \forall y Q(x, y))$
e) $\neg \forall x (\exists y \forall z P(x, y, z) \land \exists z \forall y P(x, y, z))$

34. Express each of these statements using quantifiers. Then form the negation of the statement so that no negation is to the left of a quantifier. Next, express the negation in simple English. (Do not simply use the words "It is not the case that.")

a) No one has lost more than one thousand dollars playing the lottery.
b) There is a student in this class who has chatted with exactly one other student.
c) No student in this class has sent e-mail to exactly two other students in this class.
d) Some student has solved every exercise in this book.
e) No student has solved at least one exercise in every section of this book.

35. Express each of these statements using quantifiers. Then form the negation of the statement so that no negation is to the left of a quantifier. Next, express the negation in simple English. (Do not simply use the words "It is not the case that.")

a) Every student in this class has taken exactly two mathematics classes at this school.
b) Someone has visited every country in the world except Libya.
c) No one has climbed every mountain in the Himalayas.
d) Every movie actor has either been in a movie with Kevin Bacon or has been in a movie with someone who has been in a movie with Kevin Bacon.

36. Express the negations of these propositions using quantifiers, and in English.

a) Every student in this class likes mathematics.
b) There is a student in this class who has never seen a computer.
c) There is a student in this class who has taken every mathematics course offered at this school.
d) There is a student in this class who has been in at least one room of every building on campus.

37. Find a counterexample, if possible, to these universally quantified statements, where the universe of discourse for all variables consists of all integers.

a) $\forall x \forall y (x^2 = y^2 \rightarrow x = y)$
b) $\forall x \exists y (y^2 = x)$ **c)** $\forall x \forall y (xy \geq x)$

38. Find a counterexample, if possible, to these universally quantified statements, where the universe of discourse for all variables consists of all integers.

a) $\forall x \exists y (x = 1/y)$ **b)** $\forall x \exists y (y^2 - x < 100)$
c) $\forall x \forall y (x^2 \neq y^3)$

39. Use quantifiers to express the associative law for multiplication of real numbers.

40. Use quantifiers to express the distributive laws of multiplication over addition for real numbers.

41. Determine the truth value of the statement $\forall x \exists y (xy = 1)$ if the universe of discourse for the variables consists of

a) the nonzero real numbers.
b) the nonzero integers.
c) the positive real numbers.

42. Determine the truth value of the statement $\exists x \forall y (x \leq y^2)$ if the universe of discourse for the variables consists of

a) the positive real numbers.
b) the integers.
c) the nonzero real numbers.

43. Show that the two statements $\neg \exists x \forall y P(x, y)$ and $\forall x \exists y \neg P(x, y)$ have the same truth value.

*44. Show that $\forall x P(x) \lor \forall x Q(x)$ and $\forall x \forall y (P(x) \lor Q(y))$ are logically equivalent. (The new variable y is used to combine the quantifications correctly.)

*45. a) Show that $\forall x P(x) \land \exists x Q(x)$ is equivalent to $\forall x \exists y (P(x) \land Q(y))$.
b) Show that $\forall x P(x) \lor \exists x Q(x)$ is equivalent to $\forall x \exists y (P(x) \lor Q(y))$.

A statement is in **prenex normal form (PNF)** if and only if it is of the form

$$Q_1 x_1 Q_2 x_2 \cdots Q_k x_k P(x_1, x_2, \ldots, x_k),$$

where each $Q_i, i = 1, 2, \ldots, k$, is either the existential quantifier or the universal quantifier, and $P(x_1, \ldots, x_k)$ is a predicate involving no quantifiers. For example, $\exists x \forall y (P(x, y) \land Q(y))$ is in prenex normal form, whereas $\exists x P(x) \lor \forall x Q(x)$ is not (since the quantifiers do not all occur first).

Every statement formed from propositional variables, predicates, **T**, and **F** using logical connectives and quantifiers is equivalent to a statement in prenex normal form. Exercise 47 asks for a proof of this fact.

*46. Put these statements in prenex normal form. (*Hint:* Use logical equivalence from Tables 5 and 6 in Section 1.2, Table 2 in Section 1.3, Exercises 42–45 in Section 1.3, and Exercises 44 and 45 in this section.)

a) $\exists x P(x) \lor \exists x Q(x) \lor A$, where A is a proposition not involving any quantifiers.
b) $\neg (\forall x P(x) \lor \forall x Q(x))$
c) $\exists x P(x) \rightarrow \exists x Q(x)$

**47. Show how to transform an arbitrary statement to a statement in prenex normal form that is equivalent to the given statement.

48. A real number x is called an **upper bound** of a set S of real numbers if x is greater than or equal to every member of S. The real number x is called the **least upper bound** of a set S of real numbers if x is an upper bound of S and x is less than or equal to every upper bound of S; if the least upper bound of a set S exists, it is unique.

    a) Using quantifiers, express the fact that x is an upper bound of S.

    b) Using quantifiers, express the fact that x is the least upper bound of S.

*49. Express the quantification $\exists! x\, P(x)$ using universal quantifications, existential quantifications, and logical operators.

The statement $\lim_{n \to \infty} a_n = L$ means that for every positive real number ϵ there is a positive integer N such that $|a_n - L| < \epsilon$ whenever $n > N$.

50. (Calculus required) Use quantifiers to express the statement that $\lim_{n \to \infty} a_n = L$.

51. (Calculus required) Use quantifiers to express the statement that $\lim_{n \to \infty} a_n$ does not exist.

52. (Calculus required) Use quantifiers to express this definition: A sequence $\{a_n\}$ is a Cauchy sequence if for every real number $\epsilon > 0$ there exists a positive integer N such that $|a_m - a_n| < \epsilon$ for every pair of positive integers m and n with $m > N$ and $n > N$.

53. (Calculus required) Use quantifiers and logical connectives to express this definition: A number L is the **limit superior** of a sequence $\{a_n\}$ if for every real number $\epsilon > 0$, $a_n > L - \epsilon$ for infinitely many n and $a_n > L + \epsilon$ for only finitely many n.

1.5   Methods of Proof

INTRODUCTION

Two important questions that arise in the study of mathematics are: (1) When is a mathematical argument correct? (2) What methods can be used to construct mathematical arguments? This section helps answer these questions by describing various forms of correct and incorrect mathematical arguments.

    A **theorem** is a statement that can be shown to be true. (Theorems are sometimes called *propositions, facts,* or *results.*) We demonstrate that a theorem is true with a sequence of statements that form an argument, called a **proof.** To construct proofs, methods are needed to derive new statements from old ones. The statements used in a proof can include **axioms** or **postulates,** which are the underlying assumptions about mathematical structures, the hypotheses of the theorem to be proved, and previously proved theorems. The **rules of inference,** which are the means used to draw conclusions from other assertions, tie together the steps of a proof.

    In this section rules of inference will be discussed. This will help clarify what makes up a correct proof. Some common forms of incorrect reasoning, called **fallacies,** will also be described. Then various methods commonly used to prove theorems will be introduced.

    The terms *lemma* and *corollary* are used for certain types of theorems. A **lemma** (plural **lemmas** or **lemmata**) is a simple theorem used in the proof of other theorems. Complicated proofs are usually easier to understand when they are proved using a series of lemmas, where each lemma is proved individually. A **corollary** is a proposition that can be established directly from a theorem that has been proved. A **conjecture** is a statement whose truth value is unknown. When a proof of a conjecture is found, the conjecture becomes a theorem. Many times conjectures are shown to be false, so they are not theorems.

    The methods of proof discussed in this chapter are important not only because they are used to prove mathematical theorems, but also for their many applications to computer science. These applications include verifying that computer programs are correct, establishing that operating systems are secure, making inferences in the area of artificial intelligence, showing that system specifications are consistent, and so on. Consequently, understanding the techniques used in proofs is essential both in mathematics and in computer science.

RULES OF INFERENCE

We will now introduce rules of inference for propositional logic. These rules provide the justification of the steps used to show that a conclusion follows logically from a set of hypotheses. The tautology $(p \land (p \to q)) \to q$ is the basis of the rule of inference called **modus ponens,** or the **law of detachment.** This tautology is written in the following way:

$$\begin{array}{c} p \\ p \to q \\ \hline \therefore q \end{array}$$

Using this notation, the hypotheses are written in a column and the conclusion below a bar. (The symbol $\therefore$ denotes "therefore.") Modus ponens states that if both an implication and its hypothesis are known to be true, then the conclusion of this implication is true.

EXAMPLE 1   Suppose that the implication "if it snows today, then we will go skiing" and its hypothesis, "it is snowing today," are true. Then, by modus ponens, it follows that the conclusion of the implication, "we will go skiing," is true. ◀

EXAMPLE 2   Assume that the implication "if n is greater than 3, then n^2 is greater than 9" is true. Consequently, if n is greater than 3, then, by modus ponens, it follows that n^2 is greater than 9. ◀

Table 1 lists some important rules of inference. The verifications of these rules of inference can be found as exercises in Section 1.2. Here are some examples of arguments using these rules of inference.

EXAMPLE 3   State which rule of inference is the basis of the following argument: "It is below freezing now. Therefore, it is either below freezing or raining now."

Solution: Let p be the proposition "It is below freezing now" and q the proposition "It is raining now." Then this argument is of the form

$$\begin{array}{c} p \\ \hline \therefore p \lor q \end{array}$$

This is an argument that uses the addition rule. ◀

EXAMPLE 4   State which rule of inference is the basis of the following argument: "It is below freezing and raining now. Therefore, it is below freezing now."

Solution: Let p be the proposition "It is below freezing now," and let q be the proposition "It is raining now." This argument is of the form

$$\begin{array}{c} p \land q \\ \hline \therefore p \end{array}$$

This argument uses the simplification rule. ◀

EXAMPLE 5   State which rule of inference is used in the argument:

If it rains today, then we will not have a barbecue today. If we do not have a barbecue today, then we will have a barbecue tomorrow. Therefore, if it rains today, then we will have a barbecue tomorrow.

TABLE 1 Rules of Inference.

Rule of Inference	*Tautology*	*Name*
p $\therefore\ p \vee q$	$p \rightarrow (p \vee q)$	Addition
$p \wedge q$ $\therefore\ p$	$(p \wedge q) \rightarrow p$	Simplification
p q $\therefore\ p \wedge q$	$((p) \wedge (q)) \rightarrow (p \wedge q)$	Conjunction
p $p \rightarrow q$ $\therefore\ q$	$[p \wedge (p \rightarrow q)] \rightarrow q$	Modus ponens
$\neg q$ $p \rightarrow q$ $\therefore\ \neg p$	$[\neg q \wedge (p \rightarrow q)] \rightarrow \neg p$	Modus tollens
$p \rightarrow q$ $q \rightarrow r$ $\therefore\ p \rightarrow r$	$[(p \rightarrow q) \wedge (q \rightarrow r)] \rightarrow (p \rightarrow r)$	Hypothetical syllogism
$p \vee q$ $\neg p$ $\therefore\ q$	$[(p \vee q) \wedge \neg p] \rightarrow q$	Disjunctive syllogism
$p \vee q$ $\neg p \vee r$ $\therefore\ q \vee r$	$[(p \vee q) \wedge (\neg p \vee r)] \rightarrow (q \vee r)$	Resolution

Solution: Let p be the proposition "It is raining today," let q be the proposition "We will not have a barbecue today," and let r be the proposition "We will have a barbecue tomorrow." Then this argument is of the form

$$p \rightarrow q$$
$$\underline{q \rightarrow r}$$
$$\therefore p \rightarrow r$$

Hence, this argument is a hypothetical syllogism. ◀

VALID ARGUMENTS

An argument form is called **valid** if whenever all the hypotheses are true, the conclusion is also true. Consequently, showing that q logically follows from the hypotheses $p_1, p_2, \ldots, p_n$ is the same as showing that the implication

$$(p_1 \wedge p_2 \wedge \cdots \wedge p_n) \rightarrow q$$

is true. When all propositions used in a valid argument are true, it leads to a correct conclusion. However, a valid argument can lead to an incorrect conclusion if one or more false propositions are used within the argument. For example,

"If $\sqrt{2} > \frac{1}{2}$, then $\left(\sqrt{2}\right)^2 > \left(\frac{3}{2}\right)^2$. We know that $\sqrt{2} > \frac{3}{2}$. Consequently, $\left(\sqrt{2}\right)^2 = 2 > \left(\frac{3}{2}\right)^2 = \frac{9}{4}$."

is a valid argument form based on modus ponens. However, the conclusion of this argument is false, because $2 < \frac{9}{4}$. The false proposition "$\sqrt{2} > \frac{3}{2}$" has been used in the argument, which means that the conclusion of the argument may be false.

When there are many premises, several rules of inference are often needed to show that an argument is valid. This is illustrated by the following examples, where the steps of arguments are displayed step by step, with the reason for each step explicitly stated. These examples also show how arguments in English can be analyzed using rules of inference.

EXAMPLE 6 Show that the hypotheses "It is not sunny this afternoon and it is colder than yesterday," "We will go swimming only if it is sunny," "If we do not go swimming, then we will take a canoe trip," and "If we take a canoe trip, then we will be home by sunset" lead to the conclusion "We will be home by sunset."

Solution: Let p be the proposition "It is sunny this afternoon," q the proposition "It is colder than yesterday," r the proposition "We will go swimming," s the proposition "We will take a canoe trip," and t the proposition "We will be home by sunset." Then the hypotheses become $\neg p \wedge q$, $r \rightarrow p$, $\neg r \rightarrow s$, and $s \rightarrow t$. The conclusion is simply t.

We construct an argument to show that our hypotheses lead to the desired conclusion as follows.

Step	Reason
1. $\neg p \wedge q$	Hypothesis
2. $\neg p$	Simplification using Step 1
3. $r \rightarrow p$	Hypothesis
4. $\neg r$	Modus tollens using Steps 2 and 3
5. $\neg r \rightarrow s$	Hypothesis
6. s	Modus ponens using Steps 4 and 5
7. $s \rightarrow t$	Hypothesis
8. t	Modus ponens using Steps 6 and 7

◀

EXAMPLE 7 Show that the hypotheses "If you send me an e-mail message, then I will finish writing the program," "If you do not send me an e-mail message, then I will go to sleep early," and "If I go to sleep early, then I will wake up feeling refreshed" lead to the conclusion "If I do not finish writing the program, then I will wake up feeling refreshed."

Solution: Let p be the proposition "You send me an e-mail message," q the proposition "I will finish writing the program," r the proposition "I will go to sleep early," and s the proposition "I will wake up feeling refreshed." Then the hypotheses are $p \rightarrow q$, $\neg p \rightarrow r$, and $r \rightarrow s$. The desired conclusion is $\neg q \rightarrow s$.

This argument form shows that our hypotheses lead to the desired conclusion.

Step	Reason
1. $p \rightarrow q$	Hypothesis
2. $\neg q \rightarrow \neg p$	Contrapositive of Step 1
3. $\neg p \rightarrow r$	Hypothesis
4. $\neg q \rightarrow r$	Hypothetical syllogism using Steps 2 and 3
5. $r \rightarrow s$	Hypothesis
6. $\neg q \rightarrow s$	Hypothetical syllogism using Steps 4 and 5

◀

Extra
Examples

RESOLUTION

Computer programs have been developed to automate the task of reasoning and proving theorems. Many of these programs make use of a rule of inference known as **resolution.** This rule of inference is based on the tautology

$$((p \lor q) \land (\neg p \lor r)) \to (q \lor r).$$

(The verification that this is a tautology was addressed in Exercise 28 in Section 1.2.) The final disjunction in the resolution rule, $q \lor r$, is called the **resolvent.** When we let $q = r$ in this tautology, we obtain $(p \lor q) \land (\neg p \lor q) \to q$. Furthermore, when we let $r = \mathbf{F}$, we obtain $(p \lor q) \land (\neg p) \to q$ (because $q \lor \mathbf{F} \equiv q$), which is the tautology on which the rule of disjunctive syllogism is based.

EXAMPLE 8   Use resolution to show that the hypotheses "Jasmine is skiing or it is not snowing" and "It is snowing or Bart is playing hockey" imply that "Jasmine is skiing or Bart is playing hockey."

Solution: Let p be the proposition "It is snowing," q the proposition "Jasmine is skiing," and r the proposition "Bart is playing hockey." We can represent the hypotheses as $\neg p \lor q$ and $p \lor r$, respectively. Using resolution, the proposition $q \lor r$, "Jasmine is skiing or Bart is playing hockey," follows.   ◄

Resolution plays an important role in programming languages based on the rules of logic, such as Prolog (where resolution rules for quantified statements are applied). Furthermore, it can be used to build automatic theorem proving systems. To construct proofs in propositional logic using resolution as the only rule of inference, the hypotheses and the conclusion must be expressed as **clauses,** where a clause is a disjunction of variables or negations of these variables. We can replace a statement in propositional logic that is not a clause by one or more equivalent statements that are clauses. For example, suppose we have a statement of the form $p \lor (q \land r)$. Because $p \lor (q \land r) \equiv (p \lor q) \land (p \lor r)$, we can replace the single statement $p \lor (q \land r)$ by two statements $p \lor q$ and $p \lor r$, each of which is a clause. We can replace a statement of the form $\neg(p \lor q)$ by the two statements $\neg p$ and $\neg q$ because De Morgan's law tells us that $\neg(p \lor q) \equiv \neg p \land \neg q$. We can also replace an implication $p \to q$ with the equivalent disjunction $\neg p \lor q$.

EXAMPLE 9   Show that the hypotheses $(p \land q) \lor r$ and $r \to s$ imply the conclusion $p \lor s$.

Solution: We can rewrite the hypothesis $(p \land q) \lor r$ as two clauses, $p \lor r$ and $q \lor r$. We can also replace $r \to s$ by the equivalent clause $\neg r \lor s$. Using the two clauses $p \lor r$ and $\neg r \lor s$, we can use resolution to conclude $p \lor s$.   ◄

FALLACIES

Several common fallacies arise in incorrect arguments. These fallacies resemble rules of inference but are based on contingencies rather than tautologies. These are discussed here to show the distinction between correct and incorrect reasoning.

The proposition $[(p \to q) \land q] \to p$ is not a tautology, since it is false when p is false and q is true. However, there are many incorrect arguments that treat this as a tautology. This type of incorrect reasoning is called the **fallacy of affirming the conclusion.**

EXAMPLE 10   Is the following argument valid?

> If you do every problem in this book, then you will learn discrete mathematics. You learned discrete mathematics.

> Therefore, you did every problem in this book.

Solution: Let p be the proposition "You did every problem in this book." Let q be the proposition "You learned discrete mathematics." Then this argument is of the form: if $p \rightarrow q$ and q, then p. This is an example of an incorrect argument using the fallacy of affirming the conclusion. Indeed, it is possible for you to learn discrete mathematics in some way other than by doing every problem in this book. (You may learn discrete mathematics by reading, listening to lectures, doing some but not all the problems in this book, and so on.)   ◄

The proposition $[(p \rightarrow q) \wedge \neg p] \rightarrow \neg q$ is not a tautology, since it is false when p is false and q is true. Many incorrect arguments use this incorrectly as a rule of inference. This type of incorrect reasoning is called the **fallacy of denying the hypothesis.**

EXAMPLE 11   Let p and q be as in Example 10. If the implication $p \rightarrow q$ is true, and $\neg p$ is true, is it correct to conclude that $\neg q$ is true? In other words, is it correct to assume that you did not learn discrete mathematics if you did not do every problem in the book, assuming that if you do every problem in this book, then you will learn discrete mathematics?

Solution: It is possible that you learned discrete mathematics even if you did not do every problem in this book. This incorrect argument is of the form $p \rightarrow q$ and $\neg p$ imply $\neg q$, which is an example of the fallacy of denying the hypothesis.   ◄

RULES OF INFERENCE FOR QUANTIFIED STATEMENTS

We discussed rules of inference for propositions. We will now describe some important rules of inference for statements involving quantifiers. These rules of inference are used extensively in mathematical arguments, often without being explicitly mentioned.

Universal instantiation is the rule of inference used to conclude that $P(c)$ is true, where c is a particular member of the universe of discourse, given the premise $\forall x \, P(x)$. Universal instantiation is used when we conclude from the statement "All women are wise" that "Lisa is wise," where Lisa is a member of the universe of discourse of all women.

Universal generalization is the rule of inference that states that $\forall x \, P(x)$ is true, given the premise that $P(c)$ is true for all elements c in the universe of discourse. Universal generalization is used when we show that $\forall x \, P(x)$ is true by taking an arbitrary element c from the universe of discourse and showing that $P(c)$ is true. The element c that we select must be an arbitrary, and not a specific, element of the universe of discourse. Universal generalization is used implicitly in many proofs in mathematics and is seldom mentioned explicitly.

Existential instantiation is the rule that allows us to conclude that there is an element c in the universe of discourse for which $P(c)$ is true if we know that $\exists x \, P(x)$ is true. We cannot select an arbitrary value of c here, but rather it must be a c for which $P(c)$ is true. Usually we have no knowledge of what c is, only that it exists. Since it exists, we may give it a name (c) and continue our argument.

TABLE 2 Rules of Inference for Quantified Statements.	
Rule of Inference	**Name**
$\forall x\, P(x)$ $\therefore\ P(c)$	Universal instantiation
$P(c)$ for an arbitrary c $\therefore\ \forall x\, P(x)$	Universal generalization
$\exists x\, P(x)$ $\therefore\ P(c)$ for some element c	Existential instantiation
$P(c)$ for some element c $\therefore\ \exists x\, P(x)$	Existential generalization

Existential generalization is the rule of inference that is used to conclude that $\exists x\, P(x)$ is true when a particular element c with $P(c)$ true is known. That is, if we know one element c in the universe of discourse for which $P(c)$ is true, then we know that $\exists x\, P(x)$ is true.

We summarize these rules of inference in Table 2. We will illustrate how one of these rules of inference for quantified statements is used in Example 12.

EXAMPLE 12   Show that the premises "Everyone in this discrete mathematics class has taken a course in computer science" and "Marla is a student in this class" imply the conclusion "Marla has taken a course in computer science."

Solution: Let $D(x)$ denote "x is in this discrete mathematics class," and let $C(x)$ denote "x has taken a course in computer science." Then the premises are $\forall x(D(x) \rightarrow C(x))$ and $D(\text{Marla})$. The conclusion is $C(\text{Marla})$.

The following steps can be used to establish the conclusion from the premises.

Step	Reason
1. $\forall x(D(x) \rightarrow C(x))$	Premise
2. $D(\text{Marla}) \rightarrow C(\text{Marla})$	Universal instantiation from (1)
3. $D(\text{Marla})$	Premise
4. $C(\text{Marla})$	Modus ponens from (2) and (3)

◀

EXAMPLE 13   Show that the premises "A student in this class has not read the book," and "Everyone in this class passed the first exam" imply the conclusion "Someone who passed the first exam has not read the book."

Solution: Let $C(x)$ be "x is in this class," $B(x)$ be "x has read the book," and $P(x)$ be "x passed the first exam." The premises are $\exists x(C(x) \wedge \neg B(x))$ and $\forall x(C(x) \rightarrow P(x))$. The conclusion is $\exists x(P(x) \wedge \neg B(x))$. These steps can be used to establish the conclusion from the premises.

Step	Reason
1. $\exists x(C(x) \wedge \neg B(x))$	Premise
2. $C(a) \wedge \neg B(a)$	Existential instantiation from (1)
3. $C(a)$	Simplification from (2)
4. $\forall x(C(x) \rightarrow P(x))$	Premise

Step	Reason
5. $C(a) \rightarrow P(a)$	Universal instantiation from (4)
6. $P(a)$	Modus ponens from (3) and (5)
7. $\neg B(a)$	Simplification from (2)
8. $P(a) \land \neg B(a)$	Conjunction from (6) and (7)
9. $\exists x(P(x) \land \neg B(x))$	Existential generalization from (8)

◀

Remark: Mathematical arguments often include steps where both a rule of inference for propositions and a rule of inference for quantifiers are used. For example, universal instantiation and modus ponens are often used together. When these rules of inference are combined, the hypothesis $\forall x(P(x) \rightarrow Q(x))$ and $P(c)$, where c is a member of the universe of discourse, show that the conclusion $Q(c)$ is true.

Remark: Many theorems in mathematics state that a property holds for all elements in a particular set, such as the set of integers or the set of real numbers. Although the precise statement of such theorems needs to include a universal quantifier, the standard convention in mathematics is to omit it. For example, the statement "If $x > y$, where x and y are positive real numbers, then $x^2 > y^2$" really means "For all positive real numbers x and y, if $x > y$, then $x^2 > y^2$." Furthermore, when theorems of this type are proved, the law of universal generalization is often used without explicit mention. The first step of the proof usually involves selecting a general element of the universe of discourse. Subsequent steps show that this element has the property in question. Universal generalization implies that the theorem holds for all members of the universe of discourse.

In our subsequent discussions, we will follow the usual conventions and not explicitly mention the use of universal quantification and universal generalization. However, you should always understand when this rule of inference is being implicitly applied.

METHODS OF PROVING THEOREMS

Proving theorems can be difficult. We need all the ammunition that is available to help us prove different results. We now introduce a battery of different proof methods. These methods should become part of your repertoire for proving theorems. Because many theorems are implications, the techniques for proving implications are important. Recall that $p \rightarrow q$ is true unless p is true but q is false. Note that when the statement $p \rightarrow q$ is proved, it need only be shown that q is true if p is true; it is *not* usually the case that q is proved to be true. The following discussion will give the most common techniques for proving implications.

DIRECT PROOFS The implication $p \rightarrow q$ can be proved by showing that if p is true, then q must also be true. This shows that the combination p true and q false never occurs. A proof of this kind is called a **direct proof.** To carry out such a proof, assume that p is true and use rules of inference and theorems already proved to show that q must also be true.

Before we give an example of a direct proof, we need a definition.

DEFINITION 1

The integer n is *even* if there exists an integer k such that $n = 2k$ and it is *odd* if there exists an integer k such that $n = 2k + 1$. (Note that an integer is either even or odd.)

EXAMPLE 14   Give a direct proof of the theorem "If n is an odd integer, then n^2 is an odd integer."

Solution: Assume that the hypothesis of this implication is true, namely, suppose that n is odd. Then $n = 2k + 1$, where k is an integer. It follows that $n^2 = (2k + 1)^2 = 4k^2 + 4k + 1 = 2(2k^2 + 2k) + 1$. Therefore, n^2 is an odd integer (it is one more than twice an integer).   ◀

INDIRECT PROOFS   Since the implication $p \rightarrow q$ is equivalent to its contrapositive, $\neg q \rightarrow \neg p$, the implication $p \rightarrow q$ can be proved by showing that its contrapositive, $\neg q \rightarrow \neg p$, is true. This related implication is usually proved directly, but any proof technique can be used. An argument of this type is called an **indirect proof.**

Extra Examples

EXAMPLE 15   Give an indirect proof of the theorem "If $3n + 2$ is odd, then n is odd."

Solution: Assume that the conclusion of this implication is false; namely, assume that n is even. Then $n = 2k$ for some integer k. It follows that $3n + 2 = 3(2k) + 2 = 6k + 2 = 2(3k + 1)$, so $3n + 2$ is even (since it is a multiple of 2) and therefore not odd. Because the negation of the conclusion of the implication implies that the hypothesis is false, the original implication is true.   ◀

VACUOUS AND TRIVIAL PROOFS   Suppose that the hypothesis p of an implication $p \rightarrow q$ is false. Then the implication $p \rightarrow q$ is true, because the statement has the form $\mathbf{F} \rightarrow \mathbf{T}$ or $\mathbf{F} \rightarrow \mathbf{F}$, and hence is true. Consequently, if it can be shown that p is false, then a proof, called a **vacuous proof,** of the implication $p \rightarrow q$ can be given. Vacuous proofs are often used to establish special cases of theorems that state that an implication is true for all positive integers [i.e., a theorem of the kind $\forall n \, P(n)$ where $P(n)$ is a propositional function]. Proof techniques for theorems of this kind will be discussed in Section 3.3.

EXAMPLE 16   Show that the proposition $P(0)$ is true where $P(n)$ is the propositional function "If $n > 1$, then $n^2 > n$."

Solution: Note that the proposition $P(0)$ is the implication "If $0 > 1$, then $0^2 > 0$." Since the hypothesis $0 > 1$ is false, the implication $P(0)$ is automatically true.   ◀

Remark: The fact that the conclusion of this implication, $0^2 > 0$, is false is irrelevant to the truth value of the implication, because an implication with a false hypothesis is guaranteed to be true.

Suppose that the conclusion q of an implication $p \rightarrow q$ is true. Then $p \rightarrow q$ is true, since the statement has the form $\mathbf{T} \rightarrow \mathbf{T}$ or $\mathbf{F} \rightarrow \mathbf{T}$, which are true. Hence, if it can be shown that q is true, then a proof, called a **trivial proof,** of $p \rightarrow q$ can be given. Trivial proofs are often important when special cases of theorems are proved (see the discussion of proof by cases) and in mathematical induction, which is a proof technique discussed in Section 3.3.

EXAMPLE 17   Let $P(n)$ be "If a and b are positive integers with $a \geq b$, then $a^n \geq b^n$." Show that the proposition $P(0)$ is true.

Solution: The proposition $P(0)$ is "If $a \geq b$, then $a^0 \geq b^0$." Since $a^0 = b^0 = 1$, the conclusion of $P(0)$ is true. Hence, $P(0)$ is true. This is an example of a trivial proof. Note that the hypothesis, which is the statement "$a \geq b$," was not needed in this proof. ◄

A LITTLE PROOF STRATEGY We have described both direct and indirect proofs and we have provided an example of how they are used. However, when confronted with an implication to prove, which method should you use? First, quickly evaluate whether a direct proof looks promising. Begin by expanding the definitions in the hypotheses. Then begin to reason using them, together with axioms and available theorems. If a direct proof does not seem to go anywhere, try the same thing with an indirect proof. Recall that in an indirect proof you assume that the conclusion of the implication is false and use a direct proof to show this implies that the hypothesis must be false. Sometimes when there is no obvious way to approach a direct proof, an indirect proof works nicely. We illustrate this strategy in Examples 18 and 19.

Extra
Examples

Before we present our next example, we need a definition.

DEFINITION 2   The real number r is *rational* if there exist integers p and q with $q \neq 0$ such that $r = p/q$. A real number that is not rational is called *irrational*.

EXAMPLE 18   Prove that the sum of two rational numbers is rational.

Solution: We first attempt a direct proof. To begin, suppose that r and s are rational numbers. From the definition of a rational number, it follows that there are integers p and q, with $q \neq 0$, such that $r = p/q$, and integers t and u, with $u \neq 0$, such that $s = t/u$. Can we use this information to show that $r + s$ is rational? The obvious next step is to add $r = p/q$ and $s = t/u$, to obtain

$$r + s = \frac{p}{q} + \frac{t}{u} = \frac{pu + qt}{qu}.$$

Because $q \neq 0$ and $u \neq 0$, it follows that $qu \neq 0$. Consequently, we have expressed $r + s$ as the ratio of two integers, $pu + qt$ and qu, where $qu \neq 0$. This means that $r + s$ is rational. Our attempt to find a direct proof succeeded. ◄

EXAMPLE 19   Prove that if n is an integer and n^2 is odd, then n is odd.

Solution: We first attempt a direct proof. Suppose that n is an integer and n^2 is odd. Then, there exists an integer k such that $n^2 = 2k + 1$. Can we use this information to show that n is odd? There seems to be no obvious approach to show that n is odd because solving for n produces the equation $n = \pm\sqrt{2k + 1}$, which is not terribly useful.

Because this attempt to use a direct proof did not bear fruit, we next attempt an indirect proof. We take as our hypothesis the statement that n is not odd. Because every integer is odd or even, this means that n is even. This implies that there exists an integer k such that $n = 2k$. To prove the theorem, we need to show that this hypothesis implies the conclusion that n^2 is not odd, that is, that n^2 is even. Can we use the equation $n = 2k$ to achieve this? By squaring both sides of this equation, we obtain $n^2 = 4k^2 = 2(2k^2)$, which implies that n^2 is also even since $n^2 = 2t$, where $t = 2k^2$. Our attempt to find an indirect proof succeeded. ◄

PROOFS BY CONTRADICTION There are other approaches we can use when neither a direct proof nor an indirect proof succeeds. We now introduce several additional proof techniques.

Suppose that a contradiction q can be found so that $\neg p \to q$ is true, that is, $\neg p \to$ **F** is true. Then the proposition $\neg p$ must be false. Consequently, p must be true. This technique can be used when a contradiction, such as $r \wedge \neg r$, can be found so that it is possible to show that the implication $\neg p \to (r \wedge \neg r)$ is true. An argument of this type is called a **proof by contradiction.**

We provide three examples of proof by contradiction. The first is an example of an application of the pigeonhole principle, a combinatorial technique which we will cover in depth in Section 4.2.

EXAMPLE 20   Show that at least four of any 22 days must fall on the same day of the week.

Extra
Examples

Solution: Let p be the proposition "At least four of the 22 chosen days are the same day of the week." Suppose that $\neg p$ is true. Then at most three of the 22 days are the same day of the week. Because there are seven days of the week, this implies that at most 21 days could have been chosen since three is the most days chosen that could be a particular day of the week. This is a contradiction.   ◄

EXAMPLE 21   Prove that $\sqrt{2}$ is irrational by giving a proof by contradiction.

Solution: Let p be the proposition "$\sqrt{2}$ is irrational." Suppose that $\neg p$ is true. Then $\sqrt{2}$ is rational. We will show that this leads to a contradiction. Under the assumption that $\sqrt{2}$ is rational, there exist integers a and b with $\sqrt{2} = a/b$, where a and b have no common factors (so that the fraction a/b is in lowest terms). Since $\sqrt{2} = a/b$, when both sides of this equation are squared, it follows that

$$2 = a^2/b^2.$$

Hence,

$$2b^2 = a^2.$$

This means that a^2 is even, implying that a is even. Furthermore, since a is even, $a = 2c$ for some integer c. Thus

$$2b^2 = 4c^2,$$

so

$$b^2 = 2c^2.$$

This means that b^2 is even. Hence, b must be even as well.

It has been shown that $\neg p$ implies that $\sqrt{2} = a/b$, where a and b have no common factors, and 2 divides a and b. This is a contradiction since we have shown that $\neg p$ implies both r and $\neg r$ where r is the statement that a and b are integers with no common factors. Hence, $\neg p$ is false, so that p: "$\sqrt{2}$ is irrational" is true.   ◄

An indirect proof of an implication can be rewritten as a proof by contradiction. In an indirect proof we show that $p \to q$ is true by using a direct proof to show that $\neg q \to \neg p$ is true. That is, in an indirect proof of $p \to q$ we assume that $\neg q$ is true and show that $\neg p$ must also be true. To rewrite an indirect proof of $p \to q$ as a proof by contradiction, we suppose that both p and $\neg q$ are true. Then we use the steps from the direct proof of $\neg q \rightarrow \neg p$ to show that $\neg p$ must also be true. This leads to the contradiction $p \wedge \neg p$, completing the proof by contradiction. Example 22 illustrates how an indirect proof of an implication can be rewritten as a proof by contradiction.

EXAMPLE 22   Give a proof by contradiction of the theorem "If $3n + 2$ is odd, then n is odd."

Solution: We assume that $3n + 2$ is odd and that n is not odd, so that n is even. Following the same steps as in the solution of Example 15 (an indirect proof of this theorem), we can show that if n is even, then $3n + 2$ is even. This contradicts the assumption that $3n + 2$ is odd, completing the proof.   ◀

PROOF BY CASES To prove an implication of the form

$$(p_1 \vee p_2 \vee \cdots \vee p_n) \rightarrow q$$

the tautology

$$[(p_1 \vee p_2 \vee \cdots \vee p_n) \rightarrow q] \leftrightarrow [(p_1 \rightarrow q) \wedge (p_2 \rightarrow q) \wedge \cdots \wedge (p_n \rightarrow q)]$$

can be used as a rule of inference. This shows that the original implication with a hypothesis made up of a disjunction of the propositions $p_1, p_2, \ldots, p_n$ can be proved by proving each of the n implications $p_i \rightarrow q, i = 1, 2, \ldots, n$, individually. Such an argument is called a **proof by cases.** Sometimes to prove that an implication $p \rightarrow q$ is true, it is convenient to use a disjunction $p_1 \vee p_2 \vee \cdots \vee p_n$ instead of p as the hypothesis of the implication, where p and $p_1 \vee p_2 \vee \cdots \vee p_n$ are equivalent. Consider Example 23.

Extra
Examples

EXAMPLE 23   Use a proof by cases to show that $|xy| = |x||y|$, where x and y are real numbers. (Recall that $|x|$, the absolute value of x, equals x when $x \geq 0$ and equals $-x$ when $x \leq 0$.)

Solution: Let p be "x and y are real numbers" and let q be "$|xy| = |x||y|$." Note that p is equivalent to $p_1 \vee p_2 \vee p_3 \vee p_4$, where p_1 is "$x \geq 0 \wedge y \geq 0$," p_2 is "$x \geq 0 \wedge y < 0$," p_3 is "$x < 0 \wedge y \geq 0$," and p_4 is "$x < 0 \wedge y < 0$." Hence, to show that $p \rightarrow q$, we can show that $p_1 \rightarrow q, p_2 \rightarrow q, p_3 \rightarrow q$, and $p_4 \rightarrow q$. (We have used these four cases because we can remove the absolute value signs by making the appropriate choice of signs within each case.)

     We see that $p_1 \rightarrow q$ because $xy \geq 0$ when $x \geq 0$ and $y \geq 0$, so that $|xy| = xy = |x||y|$.

     To see that $p_2 \rightarrow q$, note that if $x \geq 0$ and $y < 0$, then $xy \leq 0$, so that $|xy| = -xy = x(-y) = |x||y|$. (Here, because $y < 0$, we have $|y| = -y$.)

     To see that $p_3 \rightarrow q$, we follow the same reasoning as the previous case with the roles of x and y reversed.

     To see that $p_4 \rightarrow q$, note that when $x < 0$ and $y < 0$, it follows that $xy > 0$. Hence $|xy| = xy = (-x)(-y) = |x||y|$. This completes the proof.   ◀

PROOFS OF EQUIVALENCE To prove a theorem that is a biconditional, that is, one that is a statement of the form $p \leftrightarrow q$ where p and q are propositions, the tautology

$$(p \leftrightarrow q) \leftrightarrow [(p \rightarrow q) \wedge (q \rightarrow p)]$$

can be used. That is, the proposition "p if and only if q" can be proved if both the implications "if p, then q" and "if q, then p" are proved.

EXAMPLE 24   Prove the theorem "The integer n is odd if and only if n^2 is odd."

Solution: This theorem has the form "p if and only if q," where p is "n is odd" and q is "n^2 is odd." To prove this theorem, we need to show that $p \to q$ and $q \to p$ are true.

We have already shown (in Example 14) that $p \to q$ is true and (in Example 19) that $q \to p$ is true.

Since we have shown that both $p \to q$ and $q \to p$ are true, we have shown that the theorem is true.   ◄

Sometimes a theorem states that several propositions are equivalent. Such a theorem states that propositions $p_1, p_2, p_3, \ldots, p_n$ are equivalent. This can be written as

$$p_1 \leftrightarrow p_2 \leftrightarrow \cdots \leftrightarrow p_n,$$

which states that all n propositions have the same truth values, and consequently, that for all i and j with $1 \leq i \leq n$ and $1 \leq j \leq n$, p_i and p_j are equivalent. One way to prove these mutually equivalent is to use the tautology

$$[p_1 \leftrightarrow p_2 \leftrightarrow \cdots \leftrightarrow p_n] \leftrightarrow [(p_1 \to p_2) \wedge (p_2 \to p_3) \wedge \cdots \wedge (p_n \to p_1)].$$

This shows that if the implications $p_1 \to p_2, p_2 \to p_3, \ldots, p_n \to p_1$ can be shown to be true, then the propositions $p_1, p_2, \ldots, p_n$ are all equivalent.

This is much more efficient than proving that $p_i \to p_j$ for all $i \neq j$ with $1 \leq i \leq n$ and $1 \leq j \leq n$.

When we prove that a group of statements are equivalent, we can establish any chain of implications we choose as long as it is possible to work through the chain to go from any one of these statements to any other statement. For example, we can show that p_1, p_2, and p_3 are equivalent by showing that $p_1 \to p_3, p_3 \to p_2$, and $p_2 \to p_1$.

EXAMPLE 25   Show that these statements are equivalent:

   p_1: n is an even integer.
   p_2: $n - 1$ is an odd integer.
   p_3: n^2 is an even integer.

Solution: We will show that these three statements are equivalent by showing that the implications $p_1 \to p_2, p_2 \to p_3$, and $p_3 \to p_1$ are true.

We use a direct proof to show that $p_1 \to p_2$. Suppose that n is even. Then $n = 2k$ for some integer k. Consequently, $n - 1 = 2k - 1 = 2(k - 1) + 1$. This means that $n - 1$ is odd since it is of the form $2m + 1$, where m is the integer $k - 1$.

We also use a direct proof to show that $p_2 \to p_3$. Now suppose $n - 1$ is odd. Then $n - 1 = 2k + 1$ for some integer k. Hence, $n = 2k + 2$ so that $n^2 = (2k + 2)^2 = 4k^2 + 8k + 4 = 2(2k^2 + 4k + 2)$. This means that n^2 is twice the integer $2k^2 + 4k + 2$, and hence is even.

To prove $p_3 \to p_1$, we use an indirect proof. That is, we prove that if n is not even, then n^2 is not even. This is the same as proving that if n is odd, then n^2 is odd, which we have already done in Example 14. This completes the proof.   ◄

THEOREMS AND QUANTIFIERS

Many theorems are stated as propositions that involve quantifiers. A variety of methods are used to prove theorems that are quantifications. We will describe some of the most important of these here.

EXISTENCE PROOFS Many theorems are assertions that objects of a particular type exist. A theorem of this type is a proposition of the form $\exists x\, P(x)$, where P is a predicate. A proof of a proposition of the form $\exists x\, P(x)$ is called an **existence proof.** There are several ways to prove a theorem of this type. Sometimes an existence proof of $\exists x\, P(x)$ can be given by finding an element a such that $P(a)$ is true. Such an existence proof is called **constructive.** It is also possible to give an existence proof that is **nonconstructive;** that is, we do not find an element a such that $P(a)$ is true, but rather prove that $\exists x\, P(x)$ is true in some other way. One common method of giving a nonconstructive existence proof is to use proof by contradiction and show that the negation of the existential quantification implies a contradiction. The concept of a constructive existence proof is illustrated by Example 26.

Extra Examples

EXAMPLE 26   **A Constructive Existence Proof.** Show that there is a positive integer that can be written as the sum of cubes of positive integers in two different ways.

Solution: After considerable computation (such as a computer search) we find that

$$1729 = 10^3 + 9^3 = 12^3 + 1^3.$$

Because we have displayed a positive integer that can be written as the sum of cubes in two different ways, we are done. ◀

EXAMPLE 27   **A Nonconstructive Existence Proof.** Show that there exist irrational numbers x and y such that x^y is rational.

Solution: By Example 21 we know that $\sqrt{2}$ is irrational. Consider the number $\sqrt{2}^{\sqrt{2}}$. If it is rational, we have two irrational numbers x and y with x^y rational, namely, $x = \sqrt{2}$ and $y = \sqrt{2}$. On the other hand if $\sqrt{2}^{\sqrt{2}}$ is irrational, then we can let $x = \sqrt{2}^{\sqrt{2}}$ and $y = \sqrt{2}$ so that $x^y = (\sqrt{2}^{\sqrt{2}})^{\sqrt{2}} = \sqrt{2}^{(\sqrt{2}\cdot\sqrt{2})} = \sqrt{2}^2 = 2$.

This proof is an example of a nonconstructive existence proof because we have not found irrational numbers x and y such that x^y is rational. Rather, we have shown that either the pair $x = \sqrt{2}, y = \sqrt{2}$ or the pair $x = \sqrt{2}^{\sqrt{2}}, y = \sqrt{2}$ have the desired property, but we do not know which of these two pairs works! ◀

UNIQUENESS PROOFS Some theorems assert the existence of a unique element with a particular property. In other words, these theorems assert that there is exactly one element with this property. To prove a statement of this type we need to show that an element with this property exists and that no other element has this property. The two parts of a uniqueness proof are:

Existence: We show that an element x with the desired property exists.
Uniqueness: We show that if $y \neq x$, then y does not have the desired property.

HISTORICAL NOTE The English mathematician G. H. Hardy, when visiting the ailing Indian prodigy Ramanujan in the hospital, remarked that 1729, the number of the cab he took, was rather dull. Ramanujan replied "No, it is a very interesting number; it is the smallest number expressible as the sum of cubes in two different ways." (See the Supplementary Exercises in Chapter 3 for biographies of Hardy and Ramanujan.)

Remark: Showing that there is a unique element x such that $P(x)$ is the same as proving the statement $\exists x(P(x) \wedge \forall y(y \neq x \rightarrow \neg P(y)))$.

EXAMPLE 28   Show that every integer has a unique additive inverse. That is, show that if p is an integer, then there exists a unique integer q such that $p + q = 0$.

Extra
Examples

Solution: If p is an integer, we find that $p + q = 0$ when $q = -p$ and q is also an integer. Consequently, there exists an integer q such that $p + q = 0$.

To show that given the integer p, the integer q with $p + q = 0$ is unique, suppose that r is an integer with $r \neq q$ such that $p + r = 0$. Then $p + q = p + r$. By subtracting p from both sides of the equation, it follows that $q = r$, which contradicts our assumption that $q \neq r$. Consequently, there is a unique integer q such that $p + q = 0$.   ◄

COUNTEREXAMPLES   In Section 1.3 we mentioned that we can show that a statement of the form $\forall x\, P(x)$ is false if we can find a counterexample, that is, an example x for which $P(x)$ is false. When we are presented with a statement of the form $\forall x\, P(x)$, either which we believe to be false or which has resisted all attempts to find a proof, we look for a counterexample. We illustrate the hunt for a counterexample in Example 29.

Extra
Examples

EXAMPLE 29   Show that the statement "Every positive integer is the sum of the squares of three integers" is false.

Solution: We can show that this statement is false if we can find a counterexample. That is, the statement is false if we can show that there is a particular integer that is not the sum of the squares of three integers. To look for a counterexample, we try to write successive positive integers as a sum of three squares. We find that $1 = 0^2 + 0^2 + 1^2$, $2 = 0^2 + 1^2 + 1^2$, $3 = 1^2 + 1^2 + 1^2$, $4 = 0^2 + 0^2 + 2^2$, $5 = 0^2 + 1^2 + 2^2$, $6 = 1^2 + 1^2 + 2^2$, but we cannot find a way to write 7 as the sum of three squares. To show that there are not three squares that add up to 7, we note that the only possible squares we can use are those not exceeding 7, namely, 0, 1, and 4. Since no three terms where each term is 0, 1, or 4 add up to 7, it follows that 7 is a counterexample. We conclude that the statement "Every positive integer is the sum of the squares of three integers" is false.   ◄

Links

A common error is to assume that one or more examples establish the truth of a statement. No matter how many examples there are where $P(x)$ is true, the universal quantification $\forall x\, P(x)$ may still be false. Consider Example 30.

EXAMPLE 30   Is it true that every positive integer is the sum of 18 fourth powers of integers? That is, is the statement $\forall n\, P(n)$ a theorem where $P(n)$ is the statement "n can be written as the sum of 18 fourth powers of integers" and the universe of discourse consists of all positive integers?

Solution: To determine whether n can be written as the sum of 18 fourth powers of integers, we might begin by examining whether n is the sum of 18 fourth powers of integers for the smallest positive integers. Because the fourth powers of integers are 0, 1, 16, 81, ..., if we can select 18 terms from these numbers that add up to n, then n is the sum of 18 fourth powers. We can show that all positive integers up to 78 can be written as the sum of 18 fourth powers. (The details are left to the reader.) However, if we decided this was enough checking, we would come to the wrong conclusion. It is not true that every positive integer is the sum of 18 fourth powers because 79 is not the sum of 18 fourth powers (as the reader can verify). ◄

MISTAKES IN PROOFS

There are many common errors made in constructing mathematical proofs. We will briefly describe some of these here. Among the most common errors are mistakes in arithmetic and basic algebra. Even professional mathematicians make such errors, especially when working with complicated formulas. Whenever you use such computations you should check them as carefully as possible. (You should also review any troublesome aspects of basic algebra, especially before you study Section 3.3.)

Each step of a mathematical proof needs to be correct and the conclusion needs to logically follow from the steps that precede it. Many mistakes result from the introduction of steps that do not logically follow from those that precede it. This is illustrated in Examples 31–33.

EXAMPLE 31　　What is wrong with this famous supposed "proof" that $1 = 2$?

"Proof:" We use these steps, where a and b are two equal positive integers.

Step	Reason
1. $a = b$	Given
2. $a^2 = ab$	Multiply both sides of (1) by a
3. $a^2 - b^2 = ab - b^2$	Subtract b^2 from both sides of (2)
4. $(a - b)(a + b) = b(a - b)$	Factor both sides of (3)
5. $a + b = b$	Divide both sides of (4) by $a - b$
6. $2b = b$	Replace a by b in (5) because $a = b$ and simplify
7. $2 = 1$	Divide both sides of (6) by b

Solution: Every step is valid except for one, step 5 where we divided both sides by $a - b$. The error is that $a - b$ equals zero; division of both sides of an equation by the same quantity is valid as long as this quantity is not zero. ◄

EXAMPLE 32　　What is wrong with this "proof"?

"Theorem:" If n^2 is positive, then n is positive.

"Proof:" Suppose that n^2 is positive. Because the implication "If n is positive, then n^2 is positive" is true, we can conclude that n is positive.

Solution: Let $P(n)$ be "n is positive" and $Q(n)$ be "n^2 is positive." Then our hypothesis is $Q(n)$. The statement "If n is positive, then n^2 is positive" is the statement $\forall n(P(n) \rightarrow Q(n))$. From the hypothesis $Q(n)$ and the statement $\forall n(P(n) \rightarrow Q(n))$ we cannot conclude $P(n)$, because we are not using a valid rule of inference. Instead, this is an example of the fallacy of affirming the conclusion. A counterexample is supplied by $n = -1$ for which $n^2 = 1$ is positive, but n is negative. ◄

EXAMPLE 33 What is wrong with this "proof"?

"Theorem:" If n is not positive, then n^2 is not positive. (This is the contrapositive of the "theorem" in Example 32.)

"Proof:" Suppose that n is not positive. Because the implication "If n is positive, then n^2 is positive" is true, we can conclude that n^2 is not positive.

Solution: Let $P(n)$ and $Q(n)$ be as in the solution of Example 32. Then our hypothesis is $\neg P(n)$ and the statement "If n is positive, then n^2 is positive" is the statement $\forall n(P(n) \rightarrow Q(n))$. From the hypothesis $\neg P(n)$ and the statement $\forall n(P(n) \rightarrow Q(n))$ we cannot conclude $\neg Q(n)$, because we are not using a valid rule of inference. Instead, this is an example of the fallacy of denying the hypothesis. A counterexample is supplied by $n = -1$, as in Example 32. ◀

A common error in making unwarranted assumptions occurs in proofs by cases, where not all cases are considered. This is illustrated in Example 34.

EXAMPLE 34 What is wrong with this "proof"?

"Theorem:" If x is a real number, then x^2 is a positive real number.

"Proof:" Let p_1 be "x is positive," let p_2 be "x is negative," and let q be "x^2 is positive." To show that $p_1 \rightarrow q$, note that when x is positive, x^2 is positive since it is the product of two positive numbers, x and x. To show that $p_2 \rightarrow q$, note that when x is negative, x^2 is positive since it is the product of two negative numbers, x and x. This completes the proof.

Solution: The problem with the proof we have given is that we missed the case $x = 0$. When $x = 0$, $x^2 = 0$ is not positive, so the supposed theorem is false. If p is "x is a real number," then we can prove results where p is the hypothesis with three cases, p_1, p_2, and p_3, where p_1 is "x is positive," p_2 is "x is negative," and p_3 is "$x = 0$" because of the equivalence $p \leftrightarrow p_1 \vee p_2 \vee p_3$. ◀

Finally, we briefly discuss a particularly nasty type of error. Many incorrect arguments are based on a fallacy called **begging the question.** This fallacy occurs when one or more steps of a proof are based on the truth of the statement being proved. In other words, this fallacy arises when a statement is proved using itself, or a statement equivalent to it. That is why this fallacy is also called **circular reasoning.**

EXAMPLE 35 Is the following argument correct? It supposedly shows that n is an even integer whenever n^2 is an even integer.

Suppose that n^2 is even. Then $n^2 = 2k$ for some integer k. Let $n = 2l$ for some integer l. This shows that n is even.

Solution: This argument is incorrect. The statement "let $n = 2l$ for some integer l" occurs in the proof. No argument has been given to show that n can be written as $2l$ for some integer l. This is circular reasoning because this statement is equivalent to the statement being proved, namely, "n is even." Of course, the result itself is correct; only the method of proof is wrong. ◀

Making mistakes in proofs is part of the learning process. When you make a mistake that someone else finds, you should carefully analyze where you went wrong and make sure that you do not make the same mistake again. Even professional mathematicians make mistakes in proofs. More than a few incorrect proofs of important results have fooled people for many years before subtle errors in them were found.

JUST A BEGINNING

We have introduced a variety of methods for proving theorems. Observe that no algorithm for proving theorems has been given here or even mentioned. It is a deep result that no such procedure exists.

There are many theorems whose proofs are easy to find by directly working through the hypotheses and definitions of the terms of the theorem. However, it is often difficult to prove a theorem without resorting to a clever use of an indirect proof or a proof by contradiction, or some other proof technique. Constructing proofs is an art that can be learned only through experience, including writing proofs, having your proofs critiqued, reading and analyzing other proofs, and so on.

We will present a variety of proofs in the rest of this chapter and in Chapter 2 before we return to the subject of proofs. In Chapter 3 we will address some of the art and the strategy in proving theorems and in working with conjectures. We will also introduce several important proof techniques in Chapter 3, including mathematical induction, which can be used to prove results that hold for all positive integers. In Chapter 4 we will introduce the notion of combinatorial proofs.

Exercises

1. What rule of inference is used in each of these arguments?

   a) Alice is a mathematics major. Therefore, Alice is either a mathematics major or a computer science major.

   b) Jerry is a mathematics major and a computer science major. Therefore, Jerry is a mathematics major.

   c) If it is rainy, then the pool will be closed. It is rainy. Therefore, the pool is closed.

   d) If it snows today, the university will close. The university is not closed today. Therefore, it did not snow today.

   e) If I go swimming, then I will stay in the sun too long. If I stay in the sun too long, then I will sunburn. Therefore, if I go swimming, then I will sunburn.

2. What rule of inference is used in each of these arguments?

   a) Kangaroos live in Australia and are marsupials. Therefore, kangaroos are marsupials.

   b) It is either hotter than 100 degrees today or the pollution is dangerous. It is less than 100 degrees outside today. Therefore, the pollution is dangerous.

   c) Linda is an excellent swimmer. If Linda is an excellent swimmer, then she can work as a lifeguard. Therefore, Linda can work as a lifeguard.

   d) Steve will work at a computer company this summer. Therefore, this summer Steve will work at a computer company or he will be a beach bum.

   e) If I work all night on this homework, then I can answer all the exercises. If I answer all the exercises, I will understand the material. Therefore, if I work all night on this homework, then I will understand the material.

3. Construct an argument using rules of inference to show that the hypotheses "Randy works hard," "If Randy works hard, then he is a dull boy," and "If Randy is a dull boy, then he will not get the job" imply the conclusion "Randy will not get the job."

4. Construct an argument using rules of inference to show that the hypotheses "If it does not rain or if it is not foggy, then the sailing race will be held and the lifesaving demonstration will go on," "If the sailing race is held, then the trophy will be awarded," and "The trophy was not awarded" imply the conclusion "It rained."

5. What rules of inference are used in this famous argument? "All men are mortal. Socrates is a man. Therefore, Socrates is mortal."

6. What rules of inference are used in this argument? "No man is an island. Manhattan is an island. Therefore, Manhattan is not a man."

7. For each of these sets of premises, what relevant conclusion or conclusions can be drawn? Explain the rules of inference used to obtain each conclusion from the premises.

a) "If I take the day off, it either rains or snows." "I took Tuesday off or I took Thursday off." "It was sunny on Tuesday." "It did not snow on Thursday."

b) "If I eat spicy foods, then I have strange dreams." "I have strange dreams if there is thunder while I sleep." "I did not have strange dreams."

c) "I am either clever or lucky." "I am not lucky." "If I am lucky, then I will win the lottery."

d) "Every computer science major has a personal computer." "Ralph does not have a personal computer." "Ann has a personal computer."

e) "What is good for corporations is good for the United States." "What is good for the United States is good for you." "What is good for corporations is for you to buy lots of stuff."

f) "All rodents gnaw their food." "Mice are rodents." "Rabbits do not gnaw their food." "Bats are not rodents."

8. For each of these sets of premises, what relevant conclusion or conclusions can be drawn? Explain the rules of inference used to obtain each conclusion from the premises.

a) "If I play hockey, then I am sore the next day." "I use the whirlpool if I am sore." "I did not use the whirlpool."

b) "If I work, it is either sunny or partly sunny." "I worked last Monday or I worked last Friday." "It was not sunny on Tuesday." "It was not partly sunny on Friday."

c) "All insects have six legs." "Dragonflies are insects." "Spiders do not have six legs." "Spiders eat dragonflies."

d) "Every student has an Internet account." "Homer does not have an Internet account." "Maggie has an Internet account."

e) "All foods that are healthy to eat do not taste good." "Tofu is healthy to eat." "You only eat what tastes good." "You do not eat tofu." "Cheeseburgers are not healthy to eat."

f) "I am either dreaming or hallucinating." "I am not dreaming." "If I am hallucinating, I see elephants running down the road."

9. For each of these arguments, explain which rules of inference are used for each step.

a) "Doug, a student in this class, knows how to write programs in JAVA. Everyone who knows how to write programs in JAVA can get a high-paying job. Therefore, someone in this class can get a high-paying job."

b) "Somebody in this class enjoys whale watching. Every person who enjoys whale watching cares about ocean pollution. Therefore, there is a person in this class who cares about ocean pollution."

c) "Each of the 93 students in this class owns a personal computer. Everyone who owns a personal computer can use a word processing program. Therefore, Zeke, a student in this class, can use a word processing program."

d) "Everyone in New Jersey lives within 50 miles of the ocean. Someone in New Jersey has never seen the ocean. Therefore, someone who lives within 50 miles of the ocean has never seen the ocean."

10. For each of these arguments, explain which rules of inference are used for each step.

a) "Linda, a student in this class, owns a red convertible. Everyone who owns a red convertible has gotten at least one speeding ticket. Therefore, someone in this class has gotten a speeding ticket."

b) "Each of five roommates, Melissa, Aaron, Ralph, Veneesha, and Keeshawn, has taken a course in discrete mathematics. Every student who has taken a course in discrete mathematics can take a course in algorithms. Therefore, all five roommates can take a course in algorithms next year."

c) "All movies produced by John Sayles are wonderful. John Sayles produced a movie about coal miners. Therefore, there is a wonderful movie about coal miners."

d) "There is someone in this class who has been to France. Everyone who goes to France visits the Louvre. Therefore, someone in this class has visited the Louvre."

11. For each of these arguments determine whether the argument is correct or incorrect and explain why.

a) All students in this class understand logic. Xavier is a student in this class. Therefore, Xavier understands logic.

b) Every computer science major takes discrete mathematics. Natasha is taking discrete mathematics. Therefore, Natasha is a computer science major.

c) All parrots like fruit. My pet bird is not a parrot. Therefore, my pet bird does not like fruit.

d) Everyone who eats granola every day is healthy. Linda is not healthy. Therefore, Linda does not eat granola every day.

12. For each of these arguments determine whether the argument is correct or incorrect and explain why.

a) Everyone enrolled in the university has lived in a dormitory. Mia has never lived in a dormitory. Therefore, Mia is not enrolled in the university.

b) A convertible car is fun to drive. Isaac's car is not a convertible. Therefore, Isaac's car is not fun to drive.

c) Quincy likes all action movies. Quincy likes the movie *Eight Men Out*. Therefore, *Eight Men Out* is an action movie.

d) All lobstermen set at least a dozen traps. Hamilton is a lobsterman. Therefore, Hamilton sets at least a dozen traps.

13. Determine whether each of these arguments is valid. If an argument is correct, what rule of inference is being used? If it is not, what logical error occurs?

   a) If n is a real number such that $n > 1$, then $n^2 > 1$. Suppose that $n^2 > 1$. Then $n > 1$.

   b) The number $\log_2 3$ is irrational if it is not the ratio of two integers. Therefore, since $\log_2 3$ cannot be written in the form a/b where a and b are integers, it is irrational.

   c) If n is a real number with $n > 3$, then $n^2 > 9$. Suppose that $n^2 \le 9$. Then $n \le 3$.

   d) If n is a real number with $n > 2$, then $n^2 > 4$. Suppose that $n \le 2$. Then $n^2 \le 4$.

14. Determine whether these are valid arguments.

   a) "If x^2 is irrational, then x is irrational. Therefore, if x is irrational, it follows that x^2 is irrational."

   b) "If x^2 is irrational, then x is irrational. The number $x = \pi^2$ is irrational. Therefore, the number $x = \pi$ is irrational."

15. What is wrong with this argument? Let $H(x)$ be "x is happy." Given the premise $\exists x H(x)$, we conclude that $H(\text{Lola})$. Therefore, Lola is happy.

16. What is wrong with this argument? Let $S(x, y)$ be "x is shorter than y." Given the premise $\exists s S(s, \text{Max})$, it follows that $S(\text{Max}, \text{Max})$. Then by existential generalization it follows that $\exists x S(x, x)$, so that someone is shorter than himself.

17. Prove the proposition $P(0)$, where $P(n)$ is the proposition "If n is a positive integer greater than 1, then $n^2 > n$." What kind of proof did you use?

18. Prove the proposition $P(1)$, where $P(n)$ is the proposition "If n is a positive integer, then $n^2 \ge n$." What kind of proof did you use?

19. Let $P(n)$ be the proposition "If a and b are positive real numbers, then $(a + b)^n \ge a^n + b^n$." Prove that $P(1)$ is true. What kind of proof did you use?

20. Prove that the square of an even number is an even number using

   a) a direct proof.   **b)** an indirect proof.
   c) a proof by contradiction.

21. Prove that if n is an integer and $n^3 + 5$ is odd, then n is even using

   a) an indirect proof.
   b) a proof by contradiction.

22. Prove that if n is an integer and $3n + 2$ is even, then n is even using

   a) an indirect proof.
   b) a proof by contradiction.

23. Prove that the sum of two odd integers is even.
24. Prove that the product of two odd numbers is odd.

25. Prove that the sum of an irrational number and a rational number is irrational using a proof by contradiction.

26. Prove that the product of two rational numbers is rational.

27. Prove or disprove that the product of two irrational numbers is irrational.

28. Prove or disprove that the product of a nonzero rational number and an irrational number is irrational.

29. Prove that if x is irrational, then $1/x$ is irrational.

30. Prove that if x is rational and $x \ne 0$, then $1/x$ is rational.

31. Show that at least 10 of any 64 days chosen must fall on the same day of the week.

32. Show that at least 3 of any 25 days chosen must fall in the same month of the year.

33. Prove that if x and y are real numbers, then $\max(x, y) + \min(x, y) = x + y$. (*Hint:* Use a proof by cases, with the two cases corresponding to $x \ge y$ and $x < y$, respectively.)

34. Use a proof by cases to show that $\min(a, \min(b, c)) = \min(\min(a, b), c)$ whenever a, b, and c are real numbers.

35. Prove the **triangle inequality,** which states that if x and y are real numbers, then $|x| + |y| \ge |x + y|$ (where $|x|$ represents the absolute value of x, which equals x if $x \ge 0$ and equals $-x$ if $x < 0$).

36. Prove that a square of an integer ends with a 0, 1, 4, 5, 6, or 9. (*Hint:* Let $n = 10k + l$ where $l = 0, 1, \ldots, 9$.)

37. Prove that a fourth power of an integer ends with a 0, 1, 5, or 6.

38. Prove that if n is a positive integer, then n is even if and only if $7n + 4$ is even.

39. Prove that if n is a positive integer, then n is odd if and only if $5n + 6$ is odd.

40. Prove that $m^2 = n^2$ if and only if $m = n$ or $m = -n$.

41. Prove or disprove that if m and n are integers such that $mn = 1$, then either $m = 1$ and $n = 1$, or else $m = -1$ and $n = -1$.

42. Show that these three statements are equivalent where a and b are real numbers: (*i*) a is less than b, (*ii*) the average of a and b is greater than a, and (*iii*) the average of a and b is less than b.

43. Show that these statements are equivalent: (*i*) $3x + 2$ is an even integer, (*ii*) $x + 5$ is an odd integer, (*iii*) x^2 is an even integer.

44. Show that these statements are equivalent: (*i*) x is rational, (*ii*) $x/2$ is rational, and (*iii*) $3x - 1$ is rational.

45. Show that these statements are equivalent: (*i*) x is irrational, (*ii*) $3x + 2$ is irrational, (*iii*) $x/2$ is irrational.

46. Is this reasoning for finding the solutions of the equation $\sqrt{2x^2 - 1} = x$ correct? (*1*) $\sqrt{2x^2 - 1} = x$ is given; (*2*) $2x^2 - 1 = x^2$, obtained by squaring both sides of (1); (*3*) $x^2 - 1 = 0$, obtained by subtracting x^2 from both sides of (2); (*4*) $(x - 1)(x + 1) = 0$, obtained by factoring the left-hand side of $x^2 - 1$; (*5*) $x = 1$

or $x = -1$, which follows since $ab = 0$ implies that $a = 0$ or $b = 0$.

47. Are these steps for finding the solutions of $\sqrt{x + 3} = 3 - x$ correct? (*1*) $\sqrt{x + 3} = 3 - x$ is given; (*2*) $x + 3 = x^2 - 6x + 9$, obtained by squaring both sides of (1); (*3*) $0 = x^2 - 7x + 6$, obtained by subtracting $x + 3$ from both sides of (2); (*4*) $0 = (x - 1)(x - 6)$, obtained by factoring the right-hand side of (3); (*5*) $x = 1$ or $x = 6$, which follows from (4) since $ab = 0$ implies that $a = 0$ or $b = 0$.

48. Prove that there is a positive integer that equals the sum of the positive integers not exceeding it. Is your proof constructive or nonconstructive?

49. Prove that there are 100 consecutive positive integers that are not perfect squares. Is your proof constructive or nonconstructive?

50. Prove that either $2 \cdot 10^{500} + 15$ or $2 \cdot 10^{500} + 16$ is not a perfect square. Is your proof constructive or nonconstructive?

51. Prove that there exists a pair of consecutive integers such that one of these integers is a perfect square and the other is a perfect cube.

52. Show that the product of two of the numbers $65^{1000} - 8^{2001} + 3^{177}$, $79^{1212} - 9^{2399} + 2^{2001}$, and $24^{4493} - 5^{8192} + 7^{1777}$ is nonnegative. Is your proof constructive or nonconstructive? (*Hint:* Do not try to evaluate these numbers!)

53. Show that each of these statements can be used to express the fact that there is a unique element x such that $P(x)$ is true. [Note that by Exercise 48 in Section 1.3, this is the statement $\exists! P(x)$.]
   a) $\exists x \forall y (P(y) \leftrightarrow x = y)$
   b) $\exists x P(x) \land \forall x \forall y (P(x) \land P(y) \rightarrow x = y)$
   c) $\exists x (P(x) \land \forall y (P(y) \rightarrow x = y))$

54. Show that if a, b, and c are real numbers and $a \neq 0$, then there is a unique solution of the equation $ax + b = c$.

55. Suppose that a and b are odd integers with $a \neq b$. Show there is a unique integer c such that $|a - c| = |b - c|$.

56. Show that if r is an irrational number, there is a unique integer n such that the distance between r and n is less than $1/2$.

57. Show that if n is an odd integer, then there is a unique integer k such that n is the sum of $k - 2$ and $k + 3$.

58. Prove that given a real number x there exist unique numbers n and ϵ such that $x = n + \epsilon$, n is an integer, and $0 \leq \epsilon < 1$.

59. Prove that given a real number x there exist unique numbers n and ϵ such that $x = n - \epsilon$, n is an integer, and $0 \leq \epsilon < 1$.

60. Use resolution to show the hypotheses "Allen is a bad boy or Hillary is a good girl" and "Allen is a good boy or David is happy" imply the conclusion "Hillary is a good girl or David is happy."

61. Use resolution to show that the hypotheses "It is not raining or Yvette has her umbrella," "Yvette does not have her umbrella or she does not get wet," and "It is raining or Yvette does not get wet" imply that "Yvette does not get wet."

62. Show that the equivalence $p \land \neg p \equiv \mathbf{F}$ can be derived using resolution together with the fact that an implication with a false hypothesis is true. (*Hint:* Let $q = r = \mathbf{F}$ in resolution.)

63. Use resolution to show that the compound proposition $(p \lor q) \land (\neg p \lor q) \land (p \lor \neg q) \land (\neg p \lor \neg q)$ is not satisfiable.

64. Prove or disprove that if a and b are rational numbers, then a^b is also rational.

65. Prove or disprove that there is a rational number x and an irrational number y such that x^y is irrational.

66. Show that the propositions p_1, p_2, p_3, and p_4 can be shown to be equivalent by showing that $p_1 \leftrightarrow p_4$, $p_2 \leftrightarrow p_3$, and $p_1 \leftrightarrow p_3$.

67. Show that the propositions p_1, p_2, p_3, p_4, and p_5 can be shown to be equivalent by proving that the implications $p_1 \rightarrow p_4$, $p_3 \rightarrow p_1$, $p_4 \rightarrow p_2$, $p_2 \rightarrow p_5$, and $p_5 \rightarrow p_3$ are true.

68. Prove that an 8×8 chessboard can be completely covered using dominos (1×2 pieces).

*69. Prove that it is impossible to cover completely with dominos the 8×8 chessboard with two squares at opposite corners of the board removed.

*70. The Logic Problem, taken from *WFF'N PROOF, The Game of Logic*, has these two assumptions:

   1. "Logic is difficult or not many students like logic."
   2. "If mathematics is easy, then logic is not difficult."

   By translating these assumptions into statements involving propositional variables and logical connectives, determine whether each of the following are valid conclusions of these assumptions:

   a) That mathematics is not easy, if many students like logic.
   b) That not many students like logic, if mathematics is not easy.
   c) That mathematics is not easy or logic is difficult.
   d) That logic is not difficult or mathematics is not easy.
   e) That if not many students like logic, then either mathematics is not easy or logic is not difficult.

71. Prove that at least one of the real numbers a_1, $a_2, \ldots, a_n$ is greater than or equal to the average of these numbers. What kind of proof did you use?

72. Use Exercise 71 to show that if the first 10 positive integers are placed around a circle, in any order, there exist three integers in consecutive locations around the circle that have a sum greater than or equal to 17.

73. Prove that if *n* is an integer, these four statements are equivalent: (*i*) *n* is even, (*ii*) $n + 1$ is odd, (*iii*) $3n + 1$ is odd, (*iv*) $3n$ is even.

74. Prove that these four statements are equivalent: (*i*) n^2 is odd, (*ii*) $1 - n$ is even, (*iii*) n^3 is odd, (*iv*) $n^2 + 1$ is even.

75. Which rules of inference are used to establish the conclusion of Lewis Carroll's argument described in Example 19 of Section 1.3?

76. Which rules of inference are used to establish the conclusion of Lewis Carroll's argument described in Example 20 of Section 1.3?

*77. Determine whether this argument, taken from Backhouse [Ba86], is valid.

> If Superman were able and willing to prevent evil, he would do so. If Superman were unable to prevent evil, he would be impotent; if he were unwilling to prevent evil, he would be malevolent. Superman does not prevent evil. If Superman exists, he is neither impotent nor malevolent. Therefore, Superman does not exist.

1.6 Sets

INTRODUCTION

We will study a wide variety of discrete structures in this book. These include relations, which consist of ordered pairs of elements; combinations, which are unordered collections of elements; and graphs, which are sets of vertices and edges connecting vertices. Moreover, we will illustrate how these and other discrete structures are used in modeling and problem solving. In particular, many examples of the use of discrete structures in the storage, communication, and manipulation of data will be described. In this section we study the fundamental discrete structure upon which all other discrete structures are built, namely, the set.

Sets are used to group objects together. Often, the objects in a set have similar properties. For instance, all the students who are currently enrolled in your school make up a set. Likewise, all the students currently taking a course in discrete mathematics at any school make up a set. In addition, those students enrolled in your school who are taking a course in discrete mathematics form a set that can be obtained by taking the elements common to the first two collections. The language of sets is a means to study such collections in an organized fashion. We now provide a definition of a set.

DEFINITION 1   A *set* is an unordered collection of objects.

Note that the term *object* has been used without specifying what an object is. This description of a set as a collection of objects, based on the intuitive notion of an object, was first stated by the German mathematician Georg Cantor in 1895. The theory that results from this intuitive definition of a set leads to **paradoxes,** or logical inconsistencies, as the English philosopher Bertrand Russell showed in 1902 (see Exercise 30 for a description of one of these paradoxes). These logical inconsistencies can be avoided by building set theory starting with basic assumptions, called **axioms.** We will use Cantor's original version of set theory, known as **naive set theory,** without developing an axiomatic version of set theory, since all sets considered in this book can be treated consistently using Cantor's original theory.

We now proceed with our discussion of sets.

DEFINITION 2   The objects in a set are also called the *elements*, or *members*, of the set. A set is said to *contain* its elements.

There are several ways to describe a set. One way is to list all the members of a set, when this is possible. We use a notation where all members of the set are listed between braces. For example, the notation $\{a, b, c, d\}$ represents the set with the four elements a, b, c, and d.

EXAMPLE 1   The set V of all vowels in the English alphabet can be written as $V = \{a, e, i, o, u\}$. ◀

EXAMPLE 2   The set O of odd positive integers less than 10 can be expressed by $O = \{1, 3, 5, 7, 9\}$. ◀

EXAMPLE 3   Although sets are usually used to group together elements with common properties, there is nothing that prevents a set from having seemingly unrelated elements. For instance, $\{a, 2, \text{Fred}, \text{New Jersey}\}$ is the set containing the four elements $a, 2, \text{Fred}, \text{and New Jersey}$. ◀

Sometimes the brace notation is used to describe a set without listing all its members. Some members of the set are listed, and then *ellipses* (...) are used when the general pattern of the elements is obvious.

EXAMPLE 4   The set of positive integers less than 100 can be denoted by $\{1, 2, 3, \ldots, 99\}$. ◀

These sets, each denoted using a boldface letter, play an important role in discrete mathematics:

$\mathbf{N} = \{0, 1, 2, 3, \ldots\}$, the set of **natural numbers**
$\mathbf{Z} = \{\ldots, -2, -1, 0, 1, 2, \ldots\}$, the set of **integers**
$\mathbf{Z}^+ = \{1, 2, 3, \ldots\}$, the set of **positive integers**
$\mathbf{Q} = \{p/q \mid p \in \mathbf{Z}, q \in \mathbf{Z}, q \neq 0\}$, the set of **rational numbers**
$\mathbf{R}$, the set of **real numbers**

GEORG CANTOR (1845–1918)   Georg Cantor was born in St. Petersburg, Russia, where his father was a successful merchant. Cantor developed his interest in mathematics in his teens. He began his university studies in Zurich in 1862, but when his father died he left Zurich. He continued his university studies at the University of Berlin in 1863, where he studied under the eminent mathematicians Weierstrass, Kummer, and Kronecker. He received his doctor's degree in 1867 after having written a dissertation on number theory. Cantor assumed a position at the University of Halle in 1869, where he continued working until his death.

Cantor is considered the founder of set theory. His contributions in this area include the discovery that the set of real numbers is uncountable. He is also noted for his many important contributions to analysis. Cantor also was interested in philosophy and wrote papers relating his theory of sets with metaphysics.

Cantor married in 1874 and had five children. His melancholy temperament was balanced by his wife's happy disposition. Although he received a large inheritance from his father, he was poorly paid as a professor. To mitigate this, he tried to obtain a better-paying position at the University of Berlin. His appointment there was blocked by Kronecker, who did not agree with Cantor's views on set theory. Cantor suffered from mental illness throughout the later years of his life. He died in 1918 in a psychiatric clinic.

(Note that some people do not consider 0 a natural number, so be careful to check how the term *natural numbers* is used when you read other books.)

Since many mathematical statements assert that two differently specified collections of objects are really the same set, we need to understand what it means for two sets to be equal.

DEFINITION 3 Two sets are *equal* if and only if they have the same elements.

EXAMPLE 5 The sets $\{1, 3, 5\}$ and $\{3, 5, 1\}$ are equal, since they have the same elements. Note that the order in which the elements of a set are listed does not matter. Note also that it does not matter if an element of a set is listed more than once, so that $\{1, 3, 3, 3, 5, 5, 5, 5\}$ is the same as the set $\{1, 3, 5\}$ since they have the same elements. ◄

Extra Examples

Another way to describe a set is to use **set builder** notation. We characterize all those elements in the set by stating the property or properties they must have to be members. For instance, the set O of all odd positive integers less than 10 can be written as

$O = \{x \mid x$ is an odd positive integer less than $10\}$.

We often use this type of notation to describe sets when it is impossible to list all the elements of the set. For instance, the set of all real numbers can be written as

$\mathbf{R} = \{x \mid x$ is a real number$\}$.

Sets can also be represented graphically using Venn diagrams, named after the English mathematician John Venn, who introduced their use in 1881. In Venn diagrams the **universal set** U, which contains all the objects under consideration, is represented by a rectangle. Inside this rectangle, circles or other geometrical figures are used to represent sets. Sometimes points are used to represent the particular elements of the set. Venn diagrams are often used to indicate the relationships between sets. We show how a Venn diagram can be used in the following example.

EXAMPLE 6 Draw a Venn diagram that represents V, the set of vowels in the English alphabet.

Solution: We draw a rectangle to indicate the universal set U, which is the set of the 26 letters of the English alphabet. Inside this rectangle we draw a circle to represent V. Inside this circle we indicate the elements of V with points (see Figure 1). ◄

Links

BERTRAND RUSSELL (1872–1970) Bertrand Russell was born into a prominent English family active in the progressive movement and having a strong commitment to liberty. He became an orphan at an early age and was placed in the care of his father's parents, who had him educated at home. He entered Trinity College, Cambridge, in 1890, where he excelled in mathematics and in moral science. He won a fellowship on the basis of his work on the foundations of geometry. In 1910 Trinity College appointed him to a lectureship in logic and the philosophy of mathematics.

Russell fought for progressive causes throughout his life. He held strong pacifist views, and his protests against World War I led to dismissal from his position at Trinity College. He was imprisoned for 6 months in 1918 because of an article he wrote that was branded as seditious. Russell fought for women's suffrage in Great Britain. In 1961, at the age of 89, he was imprisoned for the second time for his protests advocating nuclear disarmament.

Russell's greatest work was in his development of principles that could be used as a foundation for all of mathematics. His most famous work is *Principia Mathematica*, written with Alfred North Whitehead, which attempts to deduce all of mathematics using a set of primitive axioms. He wrote many books on philosophy, physics, and his political ideas. Russell won the Nobel Prize for literature in 1950.

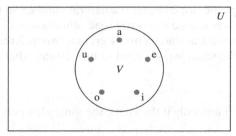

FIGURE 1   Venn Diagram for the Set of Vowels.

We will now introduce notation used to describe membership in sets. We write $a \in A$ to denote that a is an element of the set A. The notation $a \notin A$ denotes that a is not a member of the set A. Note that lowercase letters are usually used to denote elements of sets.

There is a special set that has no elements. This set is called the **empty set,** or **null set,** and is denoted by $\emptyset$. The empty set can also be denoted by { } (that is, we represent the empty set with a pair of braces that encloses all the elements in this set). Often, a set of elements with certain properties turns out to be the null set. For instance, the set of all positive integers that are greater than their squares is the null set.

A common error is to mistake the empty set $\emptyset$ with the set $\{\emptyset\}$, which is a **singleton set**, that is, a set with one element. The single element of the set $\{\emptyset\}$ is the empty set itself!

DEFINITION 4

The set A is said to be a *subset* of B if and only if every element of A is also an element of B. We use the notation $A \subseteq B$ to indicate that A is a subset of the set B.

We see that $A \subseteq B$ if and only if the quantification

$$\forall x (x \in A \rightarrow x \in B)$$

is true. For instance, the set of all odd positive integers less than 10 is a subset of the set of all positive integers less than 10. The set of all computer science majors at your school is a subset of the set of all students at your school.

Theorem 1 shows that every nonempty set S is guaranteed to have at least two subsets, the empty set and the set S itself, that is, $\emptyset \subseteq S$ and $S \subseteq S$.

JOHN VENN (1834–1923)   John Venn was born into a London suburban family noted for its philanthropy. He attended London schools and got his mathematics degree from Caius College, Cambridge, in 1857. He was elected a fellow of this college and held his fellowship there until his death. He took holy orders in 1859 and, after a brief stint of religious work, returned to Cambridge, where he developed programs in the moral sciences. Besides his mathematical work, Venn had an interest in history and wrote extensively about his college and family.

Venn's book *Symbolic Logic* clarifies ideas originally presented by Boole. In this book, Venn presents a systematic development of a method that uses geometric figures, known now as *Venn diagrams*. Today these diagrams are primarily used to analyze logical arguments and to illustrate relationships between sets. In addition to his work on symbolic logic, Venn made contributions to probability theory described in his widely used textbook on that subject.

Links

THEOREM 1

For any set S,

(i) $\emptyset \subseteq S$ and (ii) $S \subseteq S$.

Proof: We will prove (i) and leave the proof of (ii) as an exercise.

Let S be a set. To show that $\emptyset \subseteq S$, we must show that $\forall x (x \in \emptyset \rightarrow x \in S)$ is true. Since the empty set contains no elements, it follows that $x \in \emptyset$ is always false. It follows that the implication $x \in \emptyset \rightarrow x \in S$ is always true, since its hypothesis is always false and an implication with a false hypothesis is true. That is, $\forall x (x \in \emptyset \rightarrow x \in S)$ is true. This completes the proof of (i). Note that this is an example of a vacuous proof. ◁

When we wish to emphasize that a set A is a subset of the set B but that $A \neq B$, we write $A \subset B$ and say that A is a **proper subset** of B. Venn diagrams can be used to show that a set A is a subset of a set B. We draw the universal set U as a rectangle. Within this rectangle we draw a circle for B. Since A is a subset of B, we draw the circle for A within the circle for B. This relationship is shown in Figure 2.

One way to show that two sets have the same elements is to show that each set is a subset of the other. In other words, we can show that if A and B are sets with $A \subseteq B$ and $B \subseteq A$, then $A = B$. This turns out to be a useful way to show that two sets are equal. That is, $A = B$, where A and B are sets, if and only if $\forall x (x \in A \rightarrow x \in B)$ and $\forall x (x \in B \rightarrow x \in A)$, or equivalently if and only if $\forall x (x \in A \leftrightarrow x \in B)$.

Sets may have other sets as members. For instance, we have the sets

$$\{\emptyset, \{a\}, \{b\}, \{a, b\}\} \qquad \text{and} \qquad \{x \mid x \text{ is a subset of the set } \{a, b\}\}.$$

Note that these two sets are equal.

Sets are used extensively in counting problems, and for such applications we need to discuss the size of sets.

DEFINITION 5

Let S be a set. If there are exactly n distinct elements in S where n is a nonnegative integer, we say that S is a *finite set* and that n is the *cardinality* of S. The cardinality of S is denoted by $|S|$.

EXAMPLE 7

Let A be the set of odd positive integers less than 10. Then $|A| = 5$. ◀

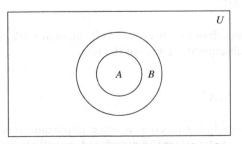

FIGURE 2   Venn Diagram Showing that A Is a Subset of B.

EXAMPLE 8   Let S be the set of letters in the English alphabet. Then $|S| = 26$. ◀

EXAMPLE 9   Since the null set has no elements, it follows that $|\emptyset| = 0$. ◀

We will also be interested in sets that are not finite.

DEFINITION 6   A set is said to be *infinite* if it is not finite.

EXAMPLE 10   The set of positive integers is infinite. ◀

Extra Examples

The cardinality of infinite sets will be discussed in Section 3.2. In that section, we will discuss what it means for a set to be countable and show that certain sets are countable while others are not.

THE POWER SET

Many problems involve testing all combinations of elements of a set to see if they satisfy some property. To consider all such combinations of elements of a set S, we build a new set that has as its members all the subsets of S.

DEFINITION 7   Given a set S, the *power set* of S is the set of all subsets of the set S. The power set of S is denoted by $P(S)$.

EXAMPLE 11   What is the power set of the set $\{0, 1, 2\}$?

Solution: The power set $P(\{0, 1, 2\})$ is the set of all subsets of $\{0, 1, 2\}$. Hence,

$$P(\{0, 1, 2\}) = \{\emptyset, \{0\}, \{1\}, \{2\}, \{0, 1\}, \{0, 2\}, \{1, 2\}, \{0, 1, 2\}\}.$$

Note that the empty set and the set itself are members of this set of subsets. ◀

EXAMPLE 12   What is the power set of the empty set? What is the power set of the set $\{\emptyset\}$?

Solution: The empty set has exactly one subset, namely, itself. Consequently,

$$P(\emptyset) = \{\emptyset\}.$$

The set $\{\emptyset\}$ has exactly two subsets, namely, $\emptyset$ and the set $\{\emptyset\}$ itself. Therefore,

$$P(\{\emptyset\}) = \{\emptyset, \{\emptyset\}\}.$$ ◀

If a set has n elements, then its power set has 2^n elements. We will demonstrate this fact in several ways in subsequent sections of the text.

CARTESIAN PRODUCTS

The order of elements in a collection is often important. Since sets are unordered, a different structure is needed to represent ordered collections. This is provided by **ordered n-tuples.**

DEFINITION 8

The *ordered n-tuple* $(a_1, a_2, \ldots, a_n)$ is the ordered collection that has a_1 as its first element, a_2 as its second element, $\ldots$, and a_n as its nth element.

We say that two ordered n-tuples are equal if and only if each corresponding pair of their elements is equal. In other words, $(a_1, a_2, \ldots, a_n) = (b_1, b_2, \ldots, b_n)$ if and only if $a_i = b_i$, for $i = 1, 2, \ldots, n$. In particular, 2-tuples are called **ordered pairs.** The ordered pairs (a, b) and (c, d) are equal if and only if $a = c$ and $b = d$. Note that (a, b) and (b, a) are not equal unless $a = b$.

Many of the discrete structures we will study in later chapters are based on the notion of the *Cartesian product* of sets (named after René Descartes). We first define the Cartesian product of two sets.

DEFINITION 9

Let A and B be sets. The *Cartesian product* of A and B, denoted by $A \times B$, is the set of all ordered pairs (a, b) where $a \in A$ and $b \in B$. Hence,

$$A \times B = \{(a, b) \mid a \in A \land b \in B\}.$$

EXAMPLE 13

Let A represent the set of all students at a university, and let B represent the set of all courses offered at the university. What is the Cartesian product $A \times B$?

Solution: The Cartesian product $A \times B$ consists of all the ordered pairs of the form (a, b), where a is a student at the university and b is a course offered at the university. The set $A \times B$ can be used to represent all possible enrollments of students in courses at the university. ◄

Links

RENÉ DESCARTES (1596–1650) René Descartes was born into a noble family near Tours, France, about 200 miles southwest of Paris. He was the third child of his father's first wife; she died several days after his birth. Because of René's poor health, his father, a provincial judge, let his son's formal lessons slide until, at the age of 8, René entered the Jesuit college at La Flèche. The rector of the school took a liking to him and permitted him to stay in bed until late in the morning because of his frail health. From then on, Descartes spent his mornings in bed; he considered these times his most productive hours for thinking.

Descartes left school in 1612, moving to Paris, where he spent 2 years studying mathematics. He earned a law degree in 1616 from the University of Poitiers. At 18 Descartes became disgusted with studying and decided to see the world. He moved to Paris and became a successful gambler. However, he grew tired of bawdy living and moved to the suburb of Saint-Germain, where he devoted himself to mathematical study. When his gambling friends found him, he decided to leave France and undertake a military career. However, he never did any fighting. One day, while escaping the cold in an overheated room at a military encampment, he had several feverish dreams, which revealed his future career as a mathematician and philosopher.

After ending his military career, he traveled throughout Europe. He then spent several years in Paris, where he studied mathematics and philosophy and constructed optical instruments. Descartes decided to move to Holland, where he spent 20 years wandering around the country, accomplishing his most important work. During this time he wrote several books, including the *Discours*, which contains his contributions to analytic geometry, for which he is best known. He also made fundamental contributions to philosophy.

In 1649 Descartes was invited by Queen Christina to visit her court in Sweden to tutor her in philosophy. Although he was reluctant to live in what he called "the land of bears amongst rocks and ice," he finally accepted the invitation and moved to Sweden. Unfortunately, the winter of 1649–1650 was extremely bitter. Descartes caught pneumonia and died in mid-February.

EXAMPLE 14 What is the Cartesian product of $A = \{1, 2\}$ and $B = \{a, b, c\}$?

Solution: The Cartesian product $A \times B$ is

$$A \times B = \{(1, a), (1, b), (1, c), (2, a), (2, b), (2, c)\}. \qquad \blacktriangleleft$$

A subset R of the Cartesian product $A \times B$ is called a **relation** from the set A to the set B. The elements of R are ordered pairs, where the first element belongs to A and the second to B. For example, $R = \{(a, 0), (a, 1), (a, 3), (b, 1), (b, 2), (c, 0), (c, 3)\}$ is a relation from the set $\{a, b, c\}$ to the set $\{0, 1, 2, 3\}$. We will study relations at length in Chapter 7.

The Cartesian products $A \times B$ and $B \times A$ are not equal, unless $A = \emptyset$ or $B = \emptyset$ (so that $A \times B = \emptyset$) or unless $A = B$ (see Exercise 26, at the end of this section). This is illustrated in Example 15.

EXAMPLE 15 Show that the Cartesian product $B \times A$ is not equal to the Cartesian product $A \times B$, where A and B are as in Example 14.

Solution: The Cartesian product $B \times A$ is

$$B \times A = \{(a, 1), (a, 2), (b, 1), (b, 2), (c, 1), (c, 2)\}.$$

This is not equal to $A \times B$, which was found in Example 14. $\qquad \blacktriangleleft$

The Cartesian product of more than two sets can also be defined.

DEFINITION 10

The *Cartesian product* of the sets $A_1, A_2, \ldots, A_n$, denoted by $A_1 \times A_2 \times \cdots \times A_n$, is the set of ordered n-tuples $(a_1, a_2, \ldots, a_n)$, where a_i belongs to A_i for $i = 1, 2, \ldots, n$. In other words

$$A_1 \times A_2 \times \cdots \times A_n = \{(a_1, a_2, \ldots, a_n) \mid a_i \in A_i \text{ for } i = 1, 2, \ldots, n\}.$$

EXAMPLE 16 What is the Cartesian product $A \times B \times C$, where $A = \{0, 1\}$, $B = \{1, 2\}$, and $C = \{0, 1, 2\}$?

Solution: The Cartesian product $A \times B \times C$ consists of all ordered triples (a, b, c), where $a \in A, b \in B$, and $c \in C$. Hence,

$$A \times B \times C = \{(0,1,0), (0,1,1), (0,1,2), (0,2,0), (0,2,1), (0,2,2), (1,1,0), (1,1,1),$$
$$(1,1,2), (1,2,0), (1,2,1), (1,2,2)\}. \qquad \blacktriangleleft$$

USING SET NOTATION WITH QUANTIFIERS

Sometimes we specify the universe of discourse of a statement explicitly in the notation. In particular, $\forall x \in S\, P(x)$ denotes the universal quantification of $P(x)$, where the universe of discourse is the set S. Similarly, $\exists x \in S\, P(x)$ denotes the existential quantification of $P(x)$, where the universe of discourse is S.

EXAMPLE 17 What do the statements $\forall x \in \mathbf{R}\ (x^2 \geq 0)$ and $\exists x \in \mathbf{Z}\ (x^2 = 1)$ mean?

Solution: The statement $\forall x \in \mathbf{R}(x^2 \geq 0)$ states that for every real number x, $x^2 \geq 0$. This statement can be expressed as "The square of every real number is nonnegative." This is a true statement.

The statement $\exists x \in \mathbf{Z}(x^2 = 1)$ states that there exists an integer x such that $x^2 = 1$. This statement can be expressed as "There is an integer whose square is 1." This is also a true statement since $x = 1$ is such an integer (as is -1). ◀

Exercises

1. List the members of these sets.

  a) $\{x \mid x$ is a real number such that $x^2 = 1\}$

  b) $\{x \mid x$ is a positive integer less than 12$\}$

  c) $\{x \mid x$ is the square of an integer and $x < 100\}$

  d) $\{x \mid x$ is an integer such that $x^2 = 2\}$

2. Use set builder notation to give a description of each of these sets.

  a) $\{0, 3, 6, 9, 12\}$

  b) $\{-3, -2, -1, 0, 1, 2, 3\}$

  c) $\{m, n, o, p\}$

3. Determine whether each of these pairs of sets are equal.

  a) $\{1, 3, 3, 3, 5, 5, 5, 5, 5\}, \{5, 3, 1\}$

  b) $\{\{1\}\}, \{1, \{1\}\}$

  c) $\emptyset, \{\emptyset\}$

4. Suppose that $A = \{2, 4, 6\}$, $B = \{2, 6\}$, $C = \{4, 6\}$, and $D = \{4, 6, 8\}$. Determine which of these sets are subsets of which other of these sets.

5. For each of the following sets, determine whether 2 is an element of that set.

  a) $\{x \in \mathbf{R} \mid x$ is an integer greater than 1$\}$

  b) $\{x \in \mathbf{R} \mid x$ is the square of an integer$\}$

  c) $\{2, \{2\}\}$

  d) $\{\{2\}, \{\{2\}\}\}$

  e) $\{\{2\}, \{2, \{2\}\}\}$

  f) $\{\{\{2\}\}\}$

6. For each of the sets in Exercise 5, determine whether $\{2\}$ is an element of that set.

7. Determine whether each of these statements is true or false.

  a) $0 \in \emptyset$ **b)** $\emptyset \in \{0\}$

  c) $\{0\} \subset \emptyset$ **d)** $\emptyset \subset \{0\}$

  e) $\{0\} \in \{0\}$ **f)** $\{0\} \subset \{0\}$

  g) $\{\emptyset\} \subseteq \{\emptyset\}$

8. Determine whether these statements are true or false.

  a) $\emptyset \in \{\emptyset\}$ **b)** $\emptyset \in \{0, \{\emptyset\}\}$

  c) $\{\emptyset\} \in \{\emptyset\}$ **d)** $\{\emptyset\} \in \{\{\emptyset\}\}$

  e) $\{\emptyset\} \subset \{\emptyset, \{\emptyset\}\}$ **f)** $\{\{\emptyset\}\} \subset \{\emptyset, \{\emptyset\}\}$

  g) $\{\{\emptyset\}\} \subset \{\{\emptyset\}, \{\emptyset\}\}$

9. Determine whether each of these statements is true or false.

  a) $x \in \{x\}$ **b)** $\{x\} \subseteq \{x\}$ **c)** $\{x\} \in \{x\}$

  d) $\{x\} \in \{\{x\}\}$ **e)** $\emptyset \subseteq \{x\}$ **f)** $\emptyset \in \{x\}$

10. Use a Venn diagram to illustrate the relationship $A \subseteq B$ and $B \subseteq C$.

11. Suppose that A, B, and C are sets such that $A \subseteq B$ and $B \subseteq C$. Show that $A \subseteq C$.

12. Find two sets A and B such that $A \in B$ and $A \subseteq B$.

13. What is the cardinality of each of these sets?

  a) $\{a\}$ **b)** $\{\{a\}\}$

  c) $\{a, \{a\}\}$ **d)** $\{a, \{a\}, \{a, \{a\}\}\}$

14. What is the cardinality of each of these sets?

  a) $\emptyset$ **b)** $\{\emptyset\}$

  c) $\{\emptyset, \{\emptyset\}\}$ **d)** $\{\emptyset, \{\emptyset\}, \{\emptyset, \{\emptyset\}\}\}$

15. Find the power set of each of these sets.

  a) $\{a\}$ **b)** $\{a, b\}$ **c)** $\{\emptyset, \{\emptyset\}\}$

16. Can you conclude that $A = B$ if A and B are two sets with the same power set?

17. How many elements does each of these sets have?

  a) $P(\{a, b, \{a, b\}\})$

  b) $P(\{\emptyset, a, \{a\}, \{\{a\}\}\})$

  c) $P(P(\emptyset))$

18. Determine whether each of these sets is the power set of a set.

  a) $\emptyset$ **b)** $\{\emptyset, \{a\}\}$

  c) $\{\emptyset, \{a\}, \{\emptyset, a\}\}$ **d)** $\{\emptyset, \{a\}, \{b\}, \{a, b\}\}$

19. Let $A = \{a, b, c, d\}$ and $B = \{y, z\}$. Find

  a) $A \times B$ **b)** $B \times A$

20. What is the Cartesian product $A \times B$, where A is the set of courses offered by the mathematics department at a university and B is the set of mathematics professors at this university?

21. What is the Cartesian product $A \times B \times C$, where A is the set of all airlines and B and C are both the set of all cities in the United States?

22. Suppose that $A \times B = \emptyset$, where A and B are sets. What can you conclude?

23. Let A be a set. Show that $\emptyset \times A = A \times \emptyset = \emptyset$.

24. Let $A = \{a, b, c\}$, $B = \{x, y\}$, and $C = \{0, 1\}$. Find

  a) $A \times B \times C$ **b)** $C \times B \times A$

  c) $C \times A \times B$ **d)** $B \times B \times B$

25. How many different elements does $A \times B$ have if A has m elements and B has n elements?

26. Show that $A \times B \neq B \times A$, when A and B are nonempty, unless $A = B$.

27. Translate each of these quantifications into English and determine its truth value.

a) $\forall x \in \mathbf{R}\ (x^2 \neq -1)$ **b)** $\exists x \in \mathbf{Z}\ (x^2 = 2)$
c) $\forall x \in \mathbf{Z}\ (x^2 > 0)$ **d)** $\exists x \in \mathbf{R}\ (x^2 = x)$

28. Translate each of these quantifications into English and determine its truth value.

a) $\exists x \in \mathbf{R}\ (x^3 = -1)$
b) $\exists x \in \mathbf{Z}\ (x + 1 > x)$
c) $\forall x \in \mathbf{Z}\ (x - 1 \in \mathbf{Z})$
d) $\forall x \in \mathbf{Z}\ (x^2 \in \mathbf{Z})$

*29. Show that the ordered pair (a, b) can be defined in terms of sets as $\{\{a\}, \{a, b\}\}$. (*Hint:* First show that $\{\{a\}, \{a, b\}\} = \{\{c\}, \{c, d\}\}$ if and only if $a = c$ and $b = d$.)

*30. In this exercise **Russell's paradox** is presented. Let S be the set that contains a set x if the set x does not belong to itself, so that $S = \{x \mid x \notin x\}$.

a) Show that the assumption that S is a member of S leads to a contradiction.

b) Show that the assumption that S is not a member of S leads to a contradiction.

From parts (a) and (b) it follows that the set S cannot be defined as it was. This paradox can be avoided by restricting the types of elements that sets can have.

*31. Describe a procedure for listing all the subsets of a finite set.

1.7   Set Operations

INTRODUCTION

Two sets can be combined in many different ways. For instance, starting with the set of mathematics majors and the set of computer science majors at your school, we can form the set of students who are mathematics majors or computer science majors, the set of students who are joint majors in mathematics and computer science, the set of all students not majoring in mathematics, and so on.

DEFINITION 1

Let A and B be sets. The *union* of the sets A and B, denoted by $A \cup B$, is the set that contains those elements that are either in A or in B, or in both.

An element x belongs to the union of the sets A and B if and only if x belongs to A or x belongs to B. This tells us that

$$A \cup B = \{x \mid x \in A \vee x \in B\}.$$

The Venn diagram shown in Figure 1 represents the union of two sets A and B. The shaded area within the circle representing A or the circle representing B is the area that represents the union of A and B.

We will give some examples of the union of sets.

EXAMPLE 1
The union of the sets $\{1, 3, 5\}$ and $\{1, 2, 3\}$ is the set $\{1, 2, 3, 5\}$; that is, $\{1, 3, 5\} \cup \{1, 2, 3\} = \{1, 2, 3, 5\}$.   ◀

EXAMPLE 2
The union of the set of all computer science majors at your school and the set of all mathematics majors at your school is the set of students at your school who are majoring either in mathematics or in computer science (or in both).   ◀

DEFINITION 2

Let A and B be sets. The *intersection* of the sets A and B, denoted by $A \cap B$, is the set containing those elements in both A and B.

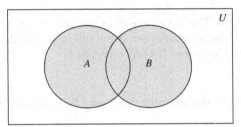

$A \cup B$ is shaded.

FIGURE 1   Venn Diagram Representing the Union of A and B.

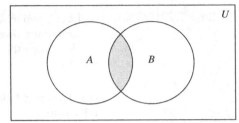

$A \cap B$ is shaded.

FIGURE 2   Venn Diagram Representing the Intersection of A and B.

An element x belongs to the intersection of the sets A and B if and only if x belongs to A and x belongs to B. This tells us that

$$A \cap B = \{x \mid x \in A \land x \in B\}.$$

The Venn diagram shown in Figure 2 represents the intersection of two sets A and B. The shaded area that is within both the circles representing the sets A and B is the area that represents the intersection of A and B.

We give some examples of the intersection of sets.

EXAMPLE 3   The intersection of the sets $\{1, 3, 5\}$ and $\{1, 2, 3\}$ is the set $\{1, 3\}$; that is, $\{1, 3, 5\} \cap \{1, 2, 3\} = \{1, 3\}$.   ◀

EXAMPLE 4   The intersection of the set of all computer science majors at your school and the set of all mathematics majors is the set of all students who are joint majors in mathematics and computer science.   ◀

DEFINITION 3   Two sets are called *disjoint* if their intersection is the empty set.

EXAMPLE 5   Let $A = \{1, 3, 5, 7, 9\}$ and $B = \{2, 4, 6, 8, 10\}$. Since $A \cap B = \emptyset$, A and B are disjoint.   ◀

We often are interested in finding the cardinality of the union of sets. To find the number of elements in the union of two finite sets A and B, note that $|A| + |B|$ counts each element that is in A but not in B or in B but not in A exactly once, and each element that is in both A and B exactly twice. Thus, if the number of elements that are in both A and B is subtracted from $|A| + |B|$, elements in $A \cap B$ will be counted only once. Hence,

$$|A \cup B| = |A| + |B| - |A \cap B|.$$

The generalization of this result to unions of an arbitrary number of sets is called the **principle of inclusion–exclusion.** The principle of inclusion–exclusion is an important technique used in the art of enumeration. We will discuss this principle and other counting techniques in detail in Chapters 4 and 6.

There are other important ways to combine sets.

DEFINITION 4	Let A and B be sets. The *difference* of A and B, denoted by $A - B$, is the set containing those elements that are in A but not in B. The difference of A and B is also called the *complement of B with respect to A.*

An element x belongs to the difference of A and B if and only if $x \in A$ and $x \notin B$. This tells us that

$$A - B = \{x \mid x \in A \wedge x \notin B\}.$$

The Venn diagram shown in Figure 3 represents the difference of the sets A and B. The shaded area inside the circle that represents A and outside the circle that represents B is the area that represents $A - B$.

We give some examples of differences of sets.

EXAMPLE 6   The difference of $\{1, 3, 5\}$ and $\{1, 2, 3\}$ is the set $\{5\}$; that is, $\{1, 3, 5\} - \{1, 2, 3\} = \{5\}$. This is different from the difference of $\{1, 2, 3\}$ and $\{1, 3, 5\}$, which is the set $\{2\}$.   ◄

EXAMPLE 7   The difference of the set of computer science majors at your school and the set of mathematics majors at your school is the set of all computer science majors at your school who are not also mathematics majors.   ◄

Once the universal set U has been specified, the **complement** of a set can be defined.

DEFINITION 5	Let U be the universal set. The *complement* of the set A, denoted by $\overline{A}$, is the complement of A with respect to U. In other words, the complement of the set A is $U - A$.

An element belongs to $\overline{A}$ if and only if $x \notin A$. This tells us that

$$\overline{A} = \{x \mid x \notin A\}.$$

In Figure 4 the shaded area outside the circle representing A is the area representing $\overline{A}$.

We give some examples of the complement of a set.

EXAMPLE 8   Let $A = \{a, e, i, o, u\}$ (where the universal set is the set of letters of the English alphabet). Then $\overline{A} = \{b, c, d, f, g, h, j, k, l, m, n, p, q, r, s, t, v, w, x, y, z\}$.   ◄

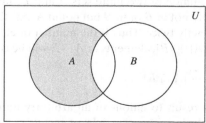

$A - B$ is shaded.

FIGURE 3   **Venn Diagram for the Difference of A and B.**

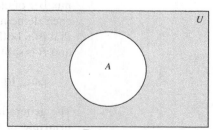

$\overline{A}$ is shaded.

FIGURE 4   **Venn Diagram for the Complement of the Set A.**

TABLE 1 Set Identities.

Identity	Name
$A \cup \emptyset = A$ $A \cap U = A$	Identity laws
$A \cup U = U$ $A \cap \emptyset = \emptyset$	Domination laws
$A \cup A = A$ $A \cap A = A$	Idempotent laws
$\overline{(\overline{A})} = A$	Complementation law
$A \cup B = B \cup A$ $A \cap B = B \cap A$	Commutative laws
$A \cup (B \cup C) = (A \cup B) \cup C$ $A \cap (B \cap C) = (A \cap B) \cap C$	Associative laws
$A \cap (B \cup C) = (A \cap B) \cup (A \cap C)$ $A \cup (B \cap C) = (A \cup B) \cap (A \cup C)$	Distributive laws
$\overline{A \cup B} = \overline{A} \cap \overline{B}$ $\overline{A \cap B} = \overline{A} \cup \overline{B}$	De Morgan's laws
$A \cup (A \cap B) = A$ $A \cap (A \cup B) = A$	Absorption laws
$A \cup \overline{A} = U$ $A \cap \overline{A} = \emptyset$	Complement laws

EXAMPLE 9   Let A be the set of positive integers greater than 10 (with universal set the set of all positive integers). Then $\overline{A} = \{1, 2, 3, 4, 5, 6, 7, 8, 9, 10\}$. ◀

SET IDENTITIES

Table 1 lists the most important set identities. We will prove several of these identities here, using three different methods. These methods are presented to illustrate that there are often many different approaches to the solution of a problem. The proofs of the remaining identities will be left as exercises. The reader should note the similarity between these set identities and the logical equivalences discussed in Section 1.2. In fact, the set identities given can be proved directly from the corresponding logical equivalences. Furthermore, both are special cases of identities that hold for Boolean algebra (discussed in Chapter 10).

Extra
Examples

One way to prove that two sets are equal is to show that one of the sets is a subset of the other and vice versa. We illustrate this type of proof by establishing the second of De Morgan's laws.

EXAMPLE 10   Prove that $\overline{A \cap B} = \overline{A} \cup \overline{B}$.

Solution: We will prove that these two sets are equal by showing that each is a subset of the other.

First, suppose that $x \in \overline{A \cap B}$. By the definition of complement, $x \notin A \cap B$. By the definition of the intersection, $\neg((x \in A) \wedge (x \in B))$ is true. Applying De Morgan's law (from logic), we see that $\neg(x \in A)$ or $\neg(x \in B)$. Hence, by the definition of negation, $x \notin A$ or $x \notin B$. By the definition of complement, $x \in \overline{A}$ or $x \in \overline{B}$. It follows by the definition of union that $x \in \overline{A} \cup \overline{B}$. This shows that $\overline{A \cap B} \subseteq \overline{A} \cup \overline{B}$.

Now suppose that $x \in \overline{A} \cup \overline{B}$. By the definition of union, $x \in \overline{A}$ or $x \in \overline{B}$. Using the definition of complement, we see that $x \notin A$ or $x \notin B$. Consequently, $\neg(x \in A) \vee \neg(x \in B)$ is true. By De Morgan's law (from logic), we conclude that $\neg((x \in A) \wedge (x \in B))$ is true. By the definition of intersection, it follows that $\neg(x \in A \cap B)$ holds. We use the definition of complement to conclude that $x \in \overline{A \cap B}$. This shows that $\overline{A} \cup \overline{B} \subseteq \overline{A \cap B}$. Since we have shown that each set is a subset of the other, the two sets are equal, and the identity is proved. ◀

We can more succinctly express the reasoning used in Example 10 using set builder notation, as Example 11 illustrates.

EXAMPLE 11   Use set builder notation and logical equivalences to show that $\overline{A \cap B} = \overline{A} \cup \overline{B}$.

Solution: The following chain of equalities provides a demonstration of this identity:

$$
\begin{aligned}
\overline{A \cap B} &= \{x \mid x \notin A \cap B\} \\
&= \{x \mid \neg(x \in (A \cap B))\} \\
&= \{x \mid \neg(x \in A \wedge x \in B)\} \\
&= \{x \mid x \notin A \vee x \notin B\} \\
&= \{x \mid x \in \overline{A} \vee x \in \overline{B}\} \\
&= \{x \mid x \in \overline{A} \cup \overline{B}\}. \\
&= \overline{A} \cup \overline{B}
\end{aligned}
$$

Note that the second De Morgan's law for logical equivalences was used in the fourth equality of this chain. ◀

Proving a set identity involving more than two sets by showing each side of the identity is a subset of the other often requires that we keep track of different cases, as illustrated by the proof in Example 12 of one of the distributive laws for sets.

EXAMPLE 12   Prove that $A \cap (B \cup C) = (A \cap B) \cup (A \cap C)$ for all sets A, B, and C.

Solution: We will prove this identity by showing that each side is a subset of the other side.

Suppose that $x \in A \cap (B \cup C)$. Then $x \in A$ and $x \in B \cup C$. By the definition of union, it follows that $x \in A$, and $x \in B$ or $x \in C$ (or both). Consequently, we know that $x \in A$ and $x \in B$ or that $x \in A$ and $x \in C$. By the definition of intersection, it follows that $x \in A \cap B$ or $x \in A \cap C$. Using the definition of union, we conclude that $x \in (A \cap B) \cup (A \cap C)$. We conclude that $A \cap (B \cup C) \subseteq (A \cap B) \cup (A \cap C)$.

Now suppose that $x \in (A \cap B) \cup (A \cap C)$. Then, by the definition of union, $x \in A \cap B$ or $x \in A \cap C$. By the definition of intersection, it follows that $x \in A$ and $x \in B$ or that $x \in A$ and $x \in C$. From this we see that $x \in A$, and $x \in B$ or $x \in C$. Consequently, by the definition of union we see that $x \in A$ and $x \in B \cup C$.

TABLE 2 A Membership Table for the Distributive Property.							
A	*B*	*C*	$B \cup C$	$A \cap (B \cup C)$	$A \cap B$	$A \cap C$	$(A \cap B) \cup (A \cap C)$
1	1	1	1	1	1	1	1
1	1	0	1	1	1	0	1
1	0	1	1	1	0	1	1
1	0	0	0	0	0	0	0
0	1	1	1	0	0	0	0
0	1	0	1	0	0	0	0
0	0	1	1	0	0	0	0
0	0	0	0	0	0	0	0

Furthermore, by the definition of intersection, it follows that $x \in A \cap (B \cup C)$. We conclude that $(A \cap B) \cup (A \cap C) \subseteq A \cap (B \cup C)$. This completes the proof of the identity. ◄

Set identities can also be proved using **membership tables.** We consider each combination of sets that an element can belong to and verify that elements in the same combinations of sets belong to both the sets in the identity. To indicate that an element is in a set, a 1 is used; to indicate that an element is not in a set, a 0 is used. (The reader should note the similarity between membership tables and truth tables.)

EXAMPLE 13   Use a membership table to show that $A \cap (B \cup C) = (A \cap B) \cup (A \cap C)$.

Solution: The membership table for these combinations of sets is shown in Table 2. This table has eight rows. Since the columns for $A \cap (B \cup C)$ and $(A \cap B) \cup (A \cap C)$ are the same, the identity is valid. ◄

Additional set identities can be established using those that we have already proved. Consider Example 14.

EXAMPLE 14   Let A, B, and C be sets. Show that

$$\overline{A \cup (B \cap C)} = (\overline{C} \cup \overline{B}) \cap \overline{A}.$$

Solution: We have

$$\begin{aligned}
\overline{A \cup (B \cap C)} &= \overline{A} \cap \overline{(B \cap C)} & &\text{by the first De Morgan's law} \\
&= \overline{A} \cap (\overline{B} \cup \overline{C}) & &\text{by the second De Morgan's law} \\
&= (\overline{B} \cup \overline{C}) \cap \overline{A} & &\text{by the commutative law for intersections} \\
&= (\overline{C} \cup \overline{B}) \cap \overline{A} & &\text{by the commutative law for unions.} \quad◄
\end{aligned}$$

GENERALIZED UNIONS AND INTERSECTIONS

Since unions and intersections of sets satisfy associative laws, the sets $A \cup B \cup C$ and $A \cap B \cap C$ are well defined when A, B, and C are sets. Note that $A \cup B \cup C$ contains those elements that are in at least one of the sets A, B, and C, and that $A \cap B \cap C$

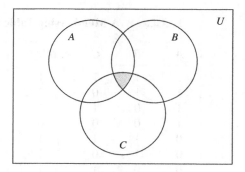

(a) $A \cup B \cup C$ is shaded. (b) $A \cap B \cap C$ is shaded.

FIGURE 5 **The Union and Intersection of A, B, and C.**

contains those elements that are in all of A, B, and C. These combinations of the three sets, A, B, and C, are shown in Figure 5.

EXAMPLE 15 Let $A = \{0, 2, 4, 6, 8\}$, $B = \{0, 1, 2, 3, 4\}$, and $C = \{0, 3, 6, 9\}$. What are $A \cup B \cup C$ and $A \cap B \cap C$?

Solution: The set $A \cup B \cup C$ contains those elements in at least one of A, B, and C. Hence,

$$A \cup B \cup C = \{0, 1, 2, 3, 4, 6, 8, 9\}.$$

The set $A \cap B \cap C$ contains those elements in all three of A, B, and C. Thus,

$$A \cap B \cap C = \{0\}. \qquad \blacktriangleleft$$

We can also consider unions and intersections of an arbitrary number of sets. We use these definitions.

DEFINITION 6 The *union* of a collection of sets is the set that contains those elements that are members of at least one set in the collection.

We use the notation

$$A_1 \cup A_2 \cup \cdots \cup A_n = \bigcup_{i=1}^{n} A_i$$

to denote the union of the sets $A_1, A_2, \ldots, A_n$.

DEFINITION 7 The *intersection* of a collection of sets is the set that contains those elements that are members of all the sets in the collection.

We use the notation

$$A_1 \cap A_2 \cap \cdots \cap A_n = \bigcap_{i=1}^{n} A_i$$

to denote the intersection of the sets $A_1, A_2, \ldots, A_n$. We illustrate generalized unions and intersections with Example 16.

EXAMPLE 16 Let $A_i = \{i, i + 1, i + 2, \ldots\}$. Then

$$\bigcup_{i=1}^{n} A_i = \bigcup_{i=1}^{n} \{i, i + 1, i + 2, \ldots\} = \{1, 2, 3, \ldots\},$$

and

$$\bigcap_{i=1}^{n} A_i = \bigcap_{i=1}^{n} \{i, i + 1, i + 2, \ldots\} = \{n, n + 1, n + 2, \ldots\}. \qquad \blacktriangleleft$$

COMPUTER REPRESENTATION OF SETS

There are various ways to represent sets using a computer. One method is to store the elements of the set in an unordered fashion. However, if this is done, the operations of computing the union, intersection, or difference of two sets would be time-consuming, since each of these operations would require a large amount of searching for elements. We will present a method for storing elements using an arbitrary ordering of the elements of the universal set. This method of representing sets makes computing combinations of sets easy.

Assume that the universal set U is finite (and of reasonable size so that the number of elements of U is not larger than the memory size of the computer being used). First, specify an arbitrary ordering of the elements of U, for instance $a_1, a_2, \ldots, a_n$. Represent a subset A of U with the bit string of length n, where the ith bit in this string is 1 if a_i belongs to A and is 0 if a_i does not belong to A. Example 17 illustrates this technique.

EXAMPLE 17 Let $U = \{1, 2, 3, 4, 5, 6, 7, 8, 9, 10\}$, and the ordering of elements of U has the elements in increasing order; i.e., $a_i = i$. What bit strings represent the subset of all odd integers in U, the subset of all even integers in U, and the subset of integers not exceeding 5 in U?

Solution: The bit string that represents the set of odd integers in U, namely, $\{1, 3, 5, 7, 9\}$, has a one bit in the first, third, fifth, seventh, and ninth positions, and a zero elsewhere. It is

10 1010 1010.

(We have split this bit string of length ten into blocks of length four for easy reading since long bit strings are difficult to read.) Similarly, we represent the subset of all even integers in U, namely, $\{2, 4, 6, 8, 10\}$, by the string

01 0101 0101.

The set of all integers in U that do not exceed 5, namely, $\{1, 2, 3, 4, 5\}$, is represented by the string

11 1110 0000. $\qquad \blacktriangleleft$

Using bit strings to represent sets, it is easy to find complements of sets and unions, intersections, and differences of sets. To find the bit string for the complement of a set from the bit string for that set, we simply change each 1 to a 0 and each 0 to 1, since $x \in A$ if and only if $x \notin \overline{A}$. Note that this operation corresponds to taking the negation of each bit when we associate a bit with a truth value—with 1 representing true and 0, false.

EXAMPLE 18 We have seen that the bit string for the set $\{1, 3, 5, 7, 9\}$ (with universal set $\{1, 2, 3, 4, 5, 6, 7, 8, 9, 10\}$) is

10 1010 1010.

What is the bit string for the complement of this set?

Solution: The bit string for the complement of this set is obtained by replacing 0s with 1s and vice versa. This yields the string

01 0101 0101,

which corresponds to the set $\{2, 4, 6, 8, 10\}$. ◄

To obtain the bit string for the union and intersection of two sets we perform bitwise Boolean operations on the bit strings representing the two sets. The bit in the ith position of the bit string of the union is 1 if either of the bits in the ith position in the two strings is 1 (or both are 1), and is 0 when both bits are 0. Hence, the bit string for the union is the bitwise *OR* of the bit strings for the two sets. The bit in the ith position of the bit string of the intersection is 1 when the bits in the corresponding position in the two strings are both 1, and is 0 when either of the two bits is 0 (or both are). Hence, the bit string for the intersection is the bitwise *AND* of the bit strings for the two sets.

EXAMPLE 19 The bit strings for the sets $\{1, 2, 3, 4, 5\}$ and $\{1, 3, 5, 7, 9\}$ are 11 1110 0000 and 10 1010 1010, respectively. Use bit strings to find the union and intersection of these sets.

Solution: The bit string for the union of these sets is

11 1110 0000 $\vee$ 10 1010 1010 $=$ 11 1110 1010,

which corresponds to the set $\{1, 2, 3, 4, 5, 7, 9\}$. The bit string for the intersection of these sets is

11 1110 0000 $\wedge$ 10 1010 1010 $=$ 10 1010 0000,

which corresponds to the set $\{1, 3, 5\}$. ◄

Exercises

1. Let A be the set of students who live within one mile of school and let B be the set of students who walk to classes. Describe the students in each of these sets.

   a) $A \cap B$ **b)** $A \cup B$
   c) $A - B$ **d)** $B - A$

2. Suppose that A is the set of sophomores at your school and B is the set of students in discrete mathematics

at your school. Express each of these sets in terms of A and B.

   a) the set of sophomores taking discrete mathematics in your school

   b) the set of sophomores at your school who are not taking discrete mathematics

   c) the set of students at your school who either are sophomores or are taking discrete mathematics

d) the set of students at your school who either are not sophomores or are not taking discrete mathematics

3. Let $A = \{1, 2, 3, 4, 5\}$ and $B = \{0, 3, 6\}$. Find

a) $A \cup B$.
b) $A \cap B$.
c) $A - B$.
d) $B - A$.

4. Let $A = \{a, b, c, d, e\}$ and $B = \{a, b, c, d, e, f, g, h\}$. Find

a) $A \cup B$.
b) $A \cap B$.
c) $A - B$.
d) $B - A$.

5. Let A be a set. Show that $\overline{\overline{A}} = A$.

6. Let A be a set. Show that

a) $A \cup \emptyset = A$.
b) $A \cap \emptyset = \emptyset$.
c) $A \cup A = A$.
d) $A \cap A = A$.
e) $A - \emptyset = A$.
f) $A \cup U = U$.
g) $A \cap U = A$.
h) $\emptyset - A = \emptyset$.

7. Let A and B be sets. Show that

a) $A \cup B = B \cup A$.
b) $A \cap B = B \cap A$.

8. Let A and B be sets. Show that $A \cup (A \cap B) = A$.

9. Let A and B be sets. Show that $A \cap (A \cup B) = A$.

10. Find the sets A and B if $A - B = \{1, 5, 7, 8\}$, $B - A = \{2, 10\}$, and $A \cap B = \{3, 6, 9\}$.

11. Show that if A and B are sets, then $\overline{A \cup B} = \overline{A} \cap \overline{B}$

a) by showing each side is a subset of the other side.
b) using a membership table.

12. Let A and B be sets. Show that

a) $(A \cap B) \subseteq A$.
b) $A \subseteq (A \cup B)$.
c) $A - B \subseteq A$.
d) $A \cap (B - A) = \emptyset$.
e) $A \cup (B - A) = A \cup B$.

13. Show that if A, B, and C are sets, then $\overline{A \cap B \cap C} = \overline{A} \cup \overline{B} \cup \overline{C}$

a) by showing each side is a subset of the other side.
b) using a membership table.

14. Let A, B, and C be sets. Show that

a) $(A \cup B) \subseteq (A \cup B \cup C)$.
b) $(A \cap B \cap C) \subseteq (A \cap B)$.
c) $(A - B) - C \subseteq A - C$.
d) $(A - C) \cap (C - B) = \emptyset$.
e) $(B - A) \cup (C - A) = (B \cup C) - A$.

15. Show that if A and B are sets, then $A - B = A \cap \overline{B}$.

16. Show that if A and B are sets, then $(A \cap B) \cup (A \cap \overline{B}) = A$.

17. Let A, B, and C be sets. Show that

a) $A \cup (B \cup C) = (A \cup B) \cup C$.
b) $A \cap (B \cap C) = (A \cap B) \cap C$.
c) $A \cup (B \cap C) = (A \cup B) \cap (A \cup C)$.

18. Let A, B, and C be sets. Show that $(A - B) - C = (A - C) - (B - C)$.

19. Let $A = \{0, 2, 4, 6, 8, 10\}$, $B = \{0, 1, 2, 3, 4, 5, 6\}$, and $C = \{4, 5, 6, 7, 8, 9, 10\}$. Find

a) $A \cap B \cap C$.
b) $A \cup B \cup C$.
c) $(A \cup B) \cap C$.
d) $(A \cap B) \cup C$.

20. Draw the Venn diagrams for each of these combinations of the sets A, B, and C.

a) $A \cap (B \cup C)$
b) $\overline{A} \cap \overline{B} \cap \overline{C}$
c) $(A - B) \cup (A - C) \cup (B - C)$

21. What can you say about the sets A and B if we know that

a) $A \cup B = A$?
b) $A \cap B = A$?
c) $A - B = A$?
d) $A \cap B = B \cap A$?
e) $A - B = B - A$?

22. Can you conclude that $A = B$ if A, B, and C are sets such that

a) $A \cup C = B \cup C$?
b) $A \cap C = B \cap C$?

23. Let A and B be subsets of a universal set U. Show that $A \subseteq B$ if and only if $\overline{B} \subseteq \overline{A}$.

The **symmetric difference** of A and B, denoted by $A \oplus B$, is the set containing those elements in either A or B, but not in both A and B.

24. Find the symmetric difference of $\{1, 3, 5\}$ and $\{1, 2, 3\}$.

25. Find the symmetric difference of the set of computer science majors at a school and the set of mathematics majors at this school.

26. Draw a Venn diagram for the symmetric difference of the sets A and B.

27. Show that $A \oplus B = (A \cup B) - (A \cap B)$.

28. Show that $A \oplus B = (A - B) \cup (B - A)$.

29. Show that if A is a subset of a universal set U, then

a) $A \oplus A = \emptyset$.
b) $A \oplus \emptyset = A$.
c) $A \oplus U = \overline{A}$.
d) $A \oplus \overline{A} = U$.

30. Show that if A and B are sets, then

a) $A \oplus B = B \oplus A$.
b) $(A \oplus B) \oplus B = A$.

31. What can you say about the sets A and B if $A \oplus B = A$?

*32. Determine whether the symmetric difference is associative; that is, if A, B, and C are sets, does it follow that $A \oplus (B \oplus C) = (A \oplus B) \oplus C$?

*33. Suppose that A, B, and C are sets such that $A \oplus C = B \oplus C$. Must it be the case that $A = B$?

34. If A, B, C, and D are sets, does it follow that $(A \oplus B) \oplus (C \oplus D) = (A \oplus C) \oplus (B \oplus D)$?

35. If A, B, C, and D are sets, does it follow that $(A \oplus B) \oplus (C \oplus D) = (A \oplus D) \oplus (B \oplus C)$?

*36. Show that if A, B, and C are sets, then

$$|A \cup B \cup C| = |A| + |B| + |C| - |A \cap B|$$
$$- |A \cap C| - |B \cap C| + |A \cap B \cap C|.$$

(This is a special case of the inclusion–exclusion principle, which will be studied in Chapter 6.)

*37. Let $A_i = \{1, 2, 3, \ldots, i\}$ for $i = 1, 2, 3, \ldots$. Find

a) $\displaystyle\bigcup_{i=1}^{n} A_i$.
b) $\displaystyle\bigcap_{i=1}^{n} A_i$.

*38. Let $A_i = \{\ldots, -2, -1, 0, 1, \ldots, i\}$. Find

a) $\displaystyle\bigcup_{i=1}^{n} A_i$.
b) $\displaystyle\bigcap_{i=1}^{n} A_i$.

39. Let A_i be the set of all nonempty bit strings (that is, bit strings of length at least one) of length not exceeding i. Find

a) $\bigcup_{i=1}^{n} A_i$.
b) $\bigcap_{i=1}^{n} A_i$.

40. Suppose that the universal set is $U = \{1, 2, 3, 4, 5, 6, 7, 8, 9, 10\}$. Express each of these sets with bit strings where the ith bit in the string is 1 if i is in the set and 0 otherwise.

a) $\{3, 4, 5\}$ **b)** $\{1, 3, 6, 10\}$ **c)** $\{2, 3, 4, 7, 8, 9\}$

41. Using the same universal set as in the last problem, find the set specified by each of these bit strings.

a) 11 1100 1111   **b)** 01 0111 1000
c) 10 0000 0001

42. What subsets of a finite universal set do these bit strings represent?

a) the string with all zeros
b) the string with all ones

43. What is the bit string corresponding to the difference of two sets?

44. What is the bit string corresponding to the symmetric difference of two sets?

45. Show how bitwise operations on bit strings can be used to find these combinations of $A = \{a, b, c, d, e\}$, $B = \{b, c, d, g, p, t, v\}$, $C = \{c, e, i, o, u, x, y, z\}$, and $D = \{d, e, h, i, n, o, t, u, x, y\}$.

a) $A \cup B$ **b)** $A \cap B$
c) $(A \cup D) \cap (B \cup C)$
d) $A \cup B \cup C \cup D$

46. How can the union and intersection of n sets that all are subsets of the universal set U be found using bit strings?

47. The **successor** of the set A is the set $A \cup \{A\}$. Find the successors of the following sets.

a) $\{1, 2, 3\}$ **b)** $\emptyset$
c) $\{\emptyset\}$ **d)** $\{\emptyset, \{\emptyset\}\}$

48. How many elements does the successor of a set with n elements have?

Sometimes the number of times that an element occurs in an unordered collection matters. **Multisets** are unordered collections of elements where an element can occur as a member more than once. The notation $\{m_1 \cdot a_1, m_2 \cdot a_2, \ldots, m_r \cdot a_r\}$ denotes the multiset with element a_1 occurring m_1 times, element a_2 occurring m_2 times, and so on. The numbers $m_i, i = 1, 2, \ldots, r$ are called the **multiplicities** of the elements $a_i, i = 1, 2, \ldots, r$.

Let P and Q be multisets. The **union** of the multisets P and Q is the multiset where the multiplicity of an element is the maximum of its multiplicities in P and Q. The **intersection** of P and Q is the multiset where the multiplicity of an element is the minimum of its multi-

plicities in P and Q. The **difference** of P and Q is the multiset where the multiplicity of an element is the multiplicity of the element in P less its multiplicity in Q unless this difference is negative, in which case the multiplicity is 0. The **sum** of P and Q is the multiset where the multiplicity of an element is the sum of multiplicities in P and Q. The union, intersection, and difference of P and Q are denoted by $P \cup Q, P \cap Q$, and $P - Q$, respectively (where these operations should not be confused with the analogous operations for sets). The sum of P and Q is denoted by $P + Q$.

49. Let A and B be the multisets $\{3 \cdot a, 2 \cdot b, 1 \cdot c\}$ and $\{2 \cdot a, 3 \cdot b, 4 \cdot d\}$, respectively. Find

a) $A \cup B$.   **b)** $A \cap B$.   **c)** $A - B$.
d) $B - A$.   **e)** $A + B$.

50. Suppose that A is the multiset that has as its elements the types of computer equipment needed by one department of a university where the multiplicities are the number of pieces of each type needed, and B is the analogous multiset for a second department of the university. For instance, A could be the multiset $\{107 \cdot$ personal computers, $44 \cdot$ routers, $6 \cdot$ servers$\}$ and B could be the multiset $\{14 \cdot$ personal computers, $6 \cdot$ routers, $2 \cdot$ mainframes$\}$.

a) What combination of A and B represents the equipment the university should buy assuming both departments use the same equipment?
b) What combination of A and B represents the equipment that will be used by both departments if both departments use the same equipment?
c) What combination of A and B represents the equipment that the second department uses, but the first department does not, if both departments use the same equipment?
d) What combination of A and B represents the equipment that the university should purchase if the departments do not share equipment?

Fuzzy sets are used in artificial intelligence. Each element in the universal set U has a **degree of membership,** which is a real number between 0 and 1 (including 0 and 1), in a fuzzy set S. The fuzzy set S is denoted by listing the elements with their degrees of membership (elements with 0 degree of membership are not listed). For instance, we write $\{0.6$ Alice, 0.9 Brian, 0.4 Fred, 0.1 Oscar, 0.5 Rita$\}$ for the set F (of famous people) to indicate that Alice has a 0.6 degree of membership in F, Brian has a 0.9 degree of membership in F, Fred has a 0.4 degree of membership in F, Oscar has a 0.1 degree of membership in F, and Rita has a 0.5 degree of membership in F (so that Brian is the most famous and Oscar is the least famous of these people). Also suppose that R is the set of rich people with $R = \{0.4$ Alice, 0.8 Brian, 0.2 Fred, 0.9 Oscar, 0.7 Rita$\}$.

51. The **complement** of a fuzzy set S is the set $\overline{S}$, with the degree of the membership of an element in $\overline{S}$ equal to 1 minus the degree of membership of this element in *S*. Find $\overline{F}$ (the fuzzy set of people who are not famous) and $\overline{R}$ (the fuzzy set of people who are not rich).

52. The **union** of two fuzzy sets *S* and *T* is the fuzzy set $S \cup T$, where the degree of membership of an element in $S \cup T$ is the maximum of the degrees of member-

ship of this element in *S* and in *T*. Find the fuzzy set $F \cup R$ of rich or famous people.

53. The **intersection** of two fuzzy sets *S* and *T* is the fuzzy set $S \cap T$, where the degree of membership of an element in $S \cap T$ is the minimum of the degrees of membership of this element in *S* and in *T*. Find the fuzzy set $F \cap R$ of rich and famous people.

1.8 Functions

INTRODUCTION

In many instances we assign to each element of a set a particular element of a second set (which may be the same as the first). For example, suppose that each student in a discrete mathematics class is assigned a letter grade from the set $\{A, B, C, D, F\}$. And suppose that the grades are *A* for Adams, *C* for Chou, *B* for Goodfriend, *A* for Rodriguez, and *F* for Stevens. This assignment of grades is illustrated in Figure 1.

This assignment is an example of a function. The concept of a function is extremely important in discrete mathematics. Functions are used in the definition of such discrete structures as sequences and strings. Functions are also used to represent how long it takes a computer to solve problems of a given size. Recursive functions, which are functions defined in terms of themselves, are used throughout computer science; they will be studied in Chapter 3. This section reviews the basic concepts involving functions needed in discrete mathematics.

DEFINITION 1

> Let *A* and *B* be sets. A *function f* from *A* to *B* is an assignment of exactly one element of *B* to each element of *A*. We write $f(a) = b$ if *b* is the unique element of *B* assigned by the function *f* to the element *a* of *A*. If *f* is a function from *A* to *B*, we write $f : A \to B$.

Functions are specified in many different ways. Sometimes we explicitly state the assignments, as in Figure 1. Often we give a formula, such as $f(x) = x + 1$, to define a function. Other times we use a computer program to specify a function.

Remark: A function $f : A \to B$ is sometimes defined in terms of a relation from *A* to *B*, defined in Section 1.6. We will discuss this approach in Chapter 7.

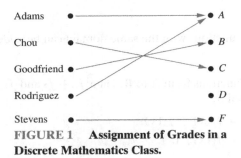

FIGURE 1   Assignment of Grades in a Discrete Mathematics Class.

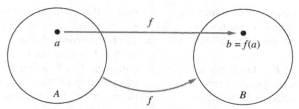

FIGURE 2   **The Function f Maps A to B.**

DEFINITION 2

> If f is a function from A to B, we say that A is the *domain* of f and B is the *codomain* of f. If $f(a) = b$, we say that b is the *image* of a and a is a *pre-image* of b. The *range* of f is the set of all images of elements of A. Also, if f is a function from A to B, we say that f *maps* A to B.

Figure 2 represents a function f from A to B.

Consider the example that began this section. Let G be the function that assigns a grade to a student in our discrete mathematics class. Note that $G(\text{Adams}) = A$, for instance. The domain of G is the set {Adams, Chou, Goodfriend, Rodriguez, Stevens}, and the codomain is the set $\{A, B, C, D, F\}$. The range of G is the set $\{A, B, C, F\}$, because each grade except D is assigned to some student. Also consider Examples 1 and 2.

EXAMPLE 1

Extra Examples

Let f be the function that assigns the last two bits of a bit string of length 2 or greater to that string. Then, the domain of f is the set of all bit strings of length 2 or greater, and both the codomain and range are the set $\{00, 01, 10, 11\}$.   ◀

EXAMPLE 2

Let $f: \mathbf{Z} \to \mathbf{Z}$ assign the square of an integer to this integer. Then, $f(x) = x^2$, where the domain of f is the set of all integers, the codomain of f can be chosen to be the set of all integers, and the range of f is the set of all nonnegative integers that are perfect squares, namely, $\{0, 1, 4, 9, \dots\}$.   ◀

EXAMPLE 3

The domain and codomain of functions are often specified in programming languages. For instance, the Java statement

    int **floor**(float real){...}

and the Pascal statement

    function *floor*(x: **real**): **integer**

both state that the domain of the floor function is the set of real numbers and its codomain is the set of integers.   ◀

Two real-valued functions with the same domain can be added and multiplied.

DEFINITION 3

> Let f_1 and f_2 be functions from A to $\mathbf{R}$. Then $f_1 + f_2$ and $f_1 f_2$ are also functions from A to $\mathbf{R}$ defined by
> $$(f_1 + f_2)(x) = f_1(x) + f_2(x),$$
> $$(f_1 f_2)(x) = f_1(x) f_2(x).$$

Note that the functions $f_1 + f_2$ and $f_1 f_2$ have been defined by specifying their values at x in terms of the values of f_1 and f_2 at x.

EXAMPLE 4 Let f_1 and f_2 be functions from **R** to **R** such that $f_1(x) = x^2$ and $f_2(x) = x - x^2$. What are the functions $f_1 + f_2$ and $f_1 f_2$?

Solution: From the definition of the sum and product of functions, it follows that

$$(f_1 + f_2)(x) = f_1(x) + f_2(x) = x^2 + (x - x^2) = x$$

and

$$(f_1 f_2)(x) = x^2(x - x^2) = x^3 - x^4. \qquad \blacktriangleleft$$

When f is a function from a set A to a set B, the image of a subset of A can also be defined.

DEFINITION 4   Let f be a function from the set A to the set B and let S be a subset of A. The *image* of S is the subset of B that consists of the images of the elements of S. We denote the image of S by $f(S)$, so that

$$f(S) = \{f(s) \mid s \in S\}.$$

EXAMPLE 5 Let $A = \{a, b, c, d, e\}$ and $B = \{1, 2, 3, 4\}$ with $f(a) = 2$, $f(b) = 1$, $f(c) = 4$, $f(d) = 1$, and $f(e) = 1$. The image of the subset $S = \{b, c, d\}$ is the set $f(S) = \{1, 4\}$. $\blacktriangleleft$

ONE-TO-ONE AND ONTO FUNCTIONS

Assessment

Some functions have distinct images at distinct members of their domain. These functions are said to be **one-to-one.**

DEFINITION 5   A function f is said to be *one-to-one*, or *injective*, if and only if $f(x) = f(y)$ implies that $x = y$ for all x and y in the domain of f. A function is said to be an *injection* if it is one-to-one.

Remark: A function f is one-to-one if and only if $f(x) \neq f(y)$ whenever $x \neq y$. This way of expressing that f is one-to-one is obtained by taking the contrapositive of the implication in the definition. Note that we can express that f is one-to-one using quantifiers as $\forall x \forall y(f(x) = f(y) \rightarrow x = y)$ or equivalently $\forall x \forall y(x \neq y \rightarrow f(x) \neq f(y))$, where the universe of discourse is the domain of the function.

Extra Examples

We illustrate this concept by giving examples of functions that are one-to-one and other functions that are not one-to-one.

EXAMPLE 6 Determine whether the function f from $\{a, b, c, d\}$ to $\{1, 2, 3, 4, 5\}$ with $f(a) = 4$, $f(b) = 5$, $f(c) = 1$, and $f(d) = 3$ is one-to-one.

Solution: The function f is one-to-one since f takes on different values at the four elements of its domain. This is illustrated in Figure 3.   ◀

EXAMPLE 7   Determine whether the function $f(x) = x^2$ from the set of integers to the set of integers is one-to-one.

Solution: The function $f(x) = x^2$ is not one-to-one because, for instance, $f(1) = f(-1) = 1$, but $1 \neq -1$. Note that the function f is one-to-one if its domain is restricted to $\mathbf{Z}^+$.   ◀

EXAMPLE 8   Determine whether the function $f(x) = x + 1$ is one-to-one.

Solution: The function $f(x) = x + 1$ is a one-to-one function. To demonstrate this, note that $x + 1 \neq y + 1$ when $x \neq y$.   ◀

We now give some conditions that guarantee that a function is one-to-one.

DEFINITION 6   A function f whose domain and codomain are subsets of the set of real numbers is called *strictly increasing* if $f(x) < f(y)$ whenever $x < y$ and x and y are in the domain of f. Similarly, f is called *strictly decreasing* if $f(x) > f(y)$ whenever $x < y$ and x and y are in the domain of f.

Remark: A function f is strictly increasing if $\forall x \forall y((x < y) \rightarrow (f(x) < f(y)))$ and is strictly decreasing if $\forall x \forall y((x < y) \rightarrow (f(x) > f(y)))$, where the universe of discourse is the domain of f.

From these definitions, we see that a function that is either strictly increasing or strictly decreasing must be one-to-one.

For some functions the range and the codomain are equal. That is, every member of the codomain is the image of some element of the domain. Functions with this property are called **onto** functions.

DEFINITION 7   A function f from A to B is called *onto*, or *surjective*, if and only if for every element $b \in B$ there is an element $a \in A$ with $f(a) = b$. A function f is called a *surjection* if it is onto.

Remark: A function f is onto if $\forall y \exists x(f(x) = y)$, where the universe of discourse for x is the domain of the function and the universe of discourse for y is the codomain of the function.

Extra
Examples

We now give examples of onto functions and functions that are not onto.

EXAMPLE 9   Let f be the function from $\{a, b, c, d\}$ to $\{1, 2, 3\}$ defined by $f(a) = 3$, $f(b) = 2$, $f(c) = 1$, and $f(d) = 3$. Is f an onto function?

Solution: Since all three elements of the codomain are images of elements in the domain, we see that f is onto. This is illustrated in Figure 4. Note that if the codomain were $\{1, 2, 3, 4\}$ then f would not be onto.   ◀

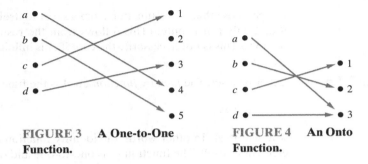

FIGURE 3   **A One-to-One Function.**   FIGURE 4   **An Onto Function.**

EXAMPLE 10   Is the function $f(x) = x^2$ from the set of integers to the set of integers onto?

Solution: The function f is not onto since there is no integer x with $x^2 = -1$, for instance.   ◄

EXAMPLE 11   Is the function $f(x) = x + 1$ from the set of integers to the set of integers onto?

Solution: This function is onto, since for every integer y there is an integer x such that $f(x) = y$. To see this, note that $f(x) = y$ if and only if $x + 1 = y$, which holds if and only if $x = y - 1$.   ◄

DEFINITION 8   The function f is a *one-to-one correspondence*, or a *bijection*, if it is both one-to-one and onto.

Examples 12 and 13 illustrate the concept of a bijection.

EXAMPLE 12   Let f be the function from $\{a, b, c, d\}$ to $\{1, 2, 3, 4\}$ with $f(a) = 4, f(b) = 2, f(c) = 1$, and $f(d) = 3$. Is f a bijection?

Solution: The function f is one-to-one and onto. It is one-to-one since the function takes on distinct values. It is onto since all four elements of the codomain are images of elements in the domain. Hence, f is a bijection.   ◄

Figure 5 displays four functions where the first is one-to-one but not onto, the second is onto but not one-to-one, the third is both one-to-one and onto, and the fourth is neither one-to-one nor onto. The fifth correspondence in Figure 5 is not a function, since it sends an element to two different elements.

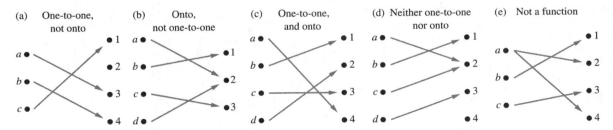

FIGURE 5   **Examples of Different Types of Correspondences.**

Suppose that f is a function from a set A to itself. If A is finite, then f is one-to-one if and only if it is onto. (This follows from the result in Exercise 64 at the end of this section.) This is not necessarily the case if A is infinite (as will be shown in Section 3.2).

EXAMPLE 13   Let A be a set. The *identity function* on A is the function $\iota_A : A \rightarrow A$ where

$$\iota_A(x) = x$$

where $x \in A$. In other words, the identity function ι_A is the function that assigns each element to itself. The function ι_A is one-to-one and onto, so that it is a bijection.   ◄

INVERSE FUNCTIONS AND COMPOSITIONS OF FUNCTIONS

Now consider a one-to-one correspondence f from the set A to the set B. Since f is an onto function, every element of B is the image of some element in A. Furthermore, because f is also a one-to-one function, every element of B is the image of a *unique* element of A. Consequently, we can define a new function from B to A that reverses the correspondence given by f. This leads to Definition 9.

DEFINITION 9

> Let f be a one-to-one correspondence from the set A to the set B. The *inverse function* of f is the function that assigns to an element b belonging to B the unique element a in A such that $f(a) = b$. The inverse function of f is denoted by f^{-1}. Hence, $f^{-1}(b) = a$ when $f(a) = b$.

Figure 6 illustrates the concept of an inverse function.

If a function f is not a one-to-one correspondence, we cannot define an inverse function of f. When f is not a one-to-one correspondence, either it is not one-to-one or it is not onto. If f is not one-to-one, some element b in the codomain is the image of more than one element in the domain. If f is not onto, for some element b in the codomain, no element a in the domain exists for which $f(a) = b$. Consequently, if f is not a one-to-one correspondence, we cannot assign to each element b in the codomain a unique element a in the domain such that $f(a) = b$ (because for some b there is either more than one such a or no such a).

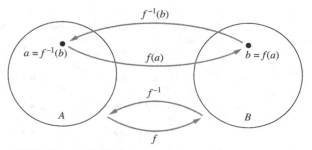

FIGURE 6   **The Function f^{-1} Is the Inverse of Function f.**

A one-to-one correspondence is called **invertible** since we can define an inverse of this function. A function is **not invertible** if it is not a one-to-one correspondence, since the inverse of such a function does not exist.

EXAMPLE 14 Let f be the function from $\{a, b, c\}$ to $\{1, 2, 3\}$ such that $f(a) = 2$, $f(b) = 3$, and $f(c) = 1$. Is f invertible, and if it is, what is its inverse?

Solution: The function f is invertible since it is a one-to-one correspondence. The inverse function f^{-1} reverses the correspondence given by f, so that $f^{-1}(1) = c, f^{-1}(2) = a$, and $f^{-1}(3) = b$. ◄

EXAMPLE 15 Let f be the function from the set of integers to the set of integers such that $f(x) = x+1$. Is f invertible, and if it is, what is its inverse?

Solution: The function f has an inverse since it is a one-to-one correspondence, as we have shown. To reverse the correspondence, suppose that y is the image of x, so that $y = x + 1$. Then $x = y - 1$. This means that $y - 1$ is the unique element of $\mathbf{Z}$ that is sent to y by f. Consequently, $f^{-1}(y) = y - 1$. ◄

EXAMPLE 16 Let f be the function from $\mathbf{Z}$ to $\mathbf{Z}$ with $f(x) = x^2$. Is f invertible?

Solution: Since $f(-1) = f(1) = 1$, f is not one-to-one. If an inverse function were defined, it would have to assign two elements to 1. Hence, f is not invertible. ◄

DEFINITION 10 Let g be a function from the set A to the set B and let f be a function from the set B to the set C. The *composition* of the functions f and g, denoted by $f \circ g$, is defined by

$$(f \circ g)(a) = f(g(a)).$$

In other words, $f \circ g$ is the function that assigns to the element a of A the element assigned by f to $g(a)$. Note that the composition $f \circ g$ cannot be defined unless the range of g is a subset of the domain of f. In Figure 7 the composition of functions is shown.

EXAMPLE 17 Let g be the function from the set $\{a, b, c\}$ to itself such that $g(a) = b, g(b) = c$, and $g(c) = a$. Let f be the function from the set $\{a, b, c\}$ to the set $\{1, 2, 3\}$ such that $f(a) = 3, f(b) = 2$, and $f(c) = 1$. What is the composition of f and g, and what is the composition of g and f?

Solution: The composition $f \circ g$ is defined by $(f \circ g)(a) = f(g(a)) = f(b) = 2$, $(f \circ g)(b) = f(g(b)) = f(c) = 1$, and $(f \circ g)(c) = f(g(c)) = f(a) = 3$.
   Note that $g \circ f$ is not defined, because the range of f is not a subset of the domain of g. ◄

EXAMPLE 18 Let f and g be the functions from the set of integers to the set of integers defined by $f(x) = 2x + 3$ and $g(x) = 3x + 2$. What is the composition of f and g? What is the composition of g and f?

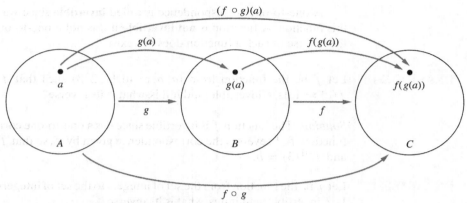

FIGURE 7 **The Composition of the Functions f and g.**

Solution: Both the compositions $f \circ g$ and $g \circ f$ are defined. Moreover,

$$(f \circ g)(x) = f(g(x)) = f(3x + 2) = 2(3x + 2) + 3 = 6x + 7$$

and

$$(g \circ f)(x) = g(f(x)) = g(2x + 3) = 3(2x + 3) + 2 = 6x + 11.$$

◀

Remark: Note that even though $f \circ g$ and $g \circ f$ are defined for the functions f and g in Example 18, $f \circ g$ and $g \circ f$ are not equal. In other words, the commutative law does not hold for the composition of functions.

When the composition of a function and its inverse is formed, in either order, an identity function is obtained. To see this, suppose that f is a one-to-one correspondence from the set A to the set B. Then the inverse function f^{-1} exists and is a one-to-one correspondence from B to A. The inverse function reverses the correspondence of the original function, so that $f^{-1}(b) = a$ when $f(a) = b$, and $f(a) = b$ when $f^{-1}(b) = a$. Hence,

$$(f^{-1} \circ f)(a) = f^{-1}(f(a)) = f^{-1}(b) = a,$$

and

$$(f \circ f^{-1})(b) = f(f^{-1}(b)) = f(a) = b.$$

Consequently $f^{-1} \circ f = \iota_A$ and $f \circ f^{-1} = \iota_B$, where ι_A and ι_B are the identity functions on the sets A and B, respectively. That is, $(f^{-1})^{-1} = f$.

THE GRAPHS OF FUNCTIONS

We can associate a set of pairs in $A \times B$ to each function from A to B. This set of pairs is called the **graph** of the function and is often displayed pictorially to aid in understanding the behavior of the function.

DEFINITION 11 Let f be a function from the set A to the set B. The *graph* of the function f is the set of ordered pairs $\{(a, b) \mid a \in A \text{ and } f(a) = b\}$.

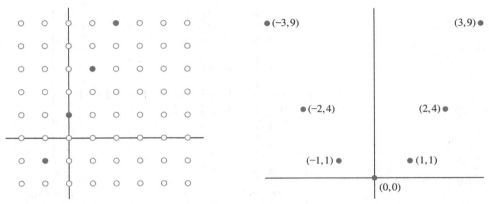

FIGURE 8   The Graph of the Function $f(n) = 2n + 1$ from Z to Z.

FIGURE 9   The Graph of $f(x) = x^2$ from Z to Z.

From the definition, the graph of a function f from A to B is the subset of $A \times B$ containing the ordered pairs with the second entry equal to the element of B assigned by f to the first entry.

EXAMPLE 19   Display the graph of the function $f(n) = 2n + 1$ from the set of integers to the set of integers.

Solution: The graph of f is the set of ordered pairs of the form $(n, 2n + 1)$ where n is an integer. This graph is displayed in Figure 8.   ◀

EXAMPLE 20   Display the graph of the function $f(x) = x^2$ from the set of integers to the set of integers.

Solution: The graph of f is the set of ordered pairs of the form $(x, f(x)) = (x, x^2)$ where x is an integer. This graph is displayed in Figure 9.   ◀

SOME IMPORTANT FUNCTIONS

Next, we introduce two important functions in discrete mathematics, namely, the floor and ceiling functions. Let x be a real number. The floor function rounds x down to the closest integer less than or equal to x, and the ceiling function rounds x up to the closest integer greater than or equal to x. These functions are often used when objects are counted. They play an important role in the analysis of the number of steps used by procedures to solve problems of a particular size.

DEFINITION 12   The *floor function* assigns to the real number x the largest integer that is less than or equal to x. The value of the floor function at x is denoted by $\lfloor x \rfloor$. The *ceiling function* assigns to the real number x the smallest integer that is greater than or equal to x. The value of the ceiling function at x is denoted by $\lceil x \rceil$.

Remark: The floor function is often also called the *greatest integer function*. It is often denoted by $[x]$.

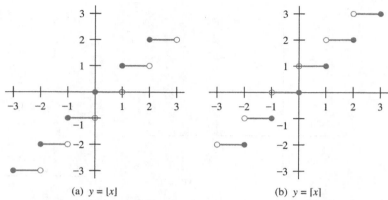

(a) $y = \lfloor x \rfloor$ (b) $y = \lceil x \rceil$

FIGURE 10   **Graphs of the (a) Floor and (b) Ceiling Functions.**

EXAMPLE 21   These are some values of the floor and ceiling functions:

$$\lfloor \tfrac{1}{2} \rfloor = 0, \qquad \lceil \tfrac{1}{2} \rceil = 1, \qquad \lfloor -\tfrac{1}{2} \rfloor = -1, \qquad \lceil -\tfrac{1}{2} \rceil = 0,$$

$$\lfloor 3.1 \rfloor = 3, \qquad \lceil 3.1 \rceil = 4, \qquad \lfloor 7 \rfloor = 7, \qquad \lceil 7 \rceil = 7.$$ ◄

Links

We display the graphs of the floor and ceiling functions in Figure 10. In Figure 10(a) we display the graph of the floor function $\lfloor x \rfloor$. Note that this function has the same value throughout the interval $[n, n + 1)$, namely n, and then it jumps up to $n + 1$ when $x = n + 1$. In Figure 10(b) we display the graph of the ceiling function $\lceil x \rceil$. Note that this function has the same value throughout the interval $(n, n + 1]$, namely $n + 1$, and then jumps to $n + 2$ when x is a little larger than $n + 1$.

Extra Examples

The floor and ceiling functions are useful in a wide variety of applications, including those involving data storage and data transmission. Consider Examples 22 and 23, typical of basic calculations done when database and data communications problems are studied.

EXAMPLE 22   Data stored on a computer disk or transmitted over a data network are usually represented as a string of bytes. Each byte is made up of 8 bits. How many bytes are required to encode 100 bits of data?

Solution: To determine the number of bytes needed, we determine the smallest integer that is at least as large as the quotient when 100 is divided by 8, the number of bits in a byte. Consequently, $\lceil 100/8 \rceil = \lceil 12.5 \rceil = 13$ bytes are required.   ◄

EXAMPLE 23   In asynchronous transfer mode (ATM) (a communications protocol used on backbone networks), data are organized into cells of 53 bytes. How many ATM cells can be transmitted in 1 minute over a connection that transmits data at the rate of 500 kilobits per second?

Solution: In 1 minute, this connection can transmit $500,000 \cdot 60 = 30,000,000$ bits. Each ATM cell is 53 bytes long, which means that it is $53 \cdot 8 = 424$ bits long. To determine the number of cells that can be transmitted in 1 minute, we determine the largest integer not exceeding the quotient when 30,000,000 is divided by 424. Consequently, $\lfloor 30,000,000/424 \rfloor = 70,754$ ATM cells can be transmitted in 1 minute over a 500 kilobit per second connection.   ◄

TABLE 1 **Useful Properties of the Floor and Ceiling Functions.** (n is an integer)
(1a) $\lfloor x \rfloor = n$ if and only if $n \le x < n + 1$ (1b) $\lceil x \rceil = n$ if and only if $n - 1 < x \le n$ (1c) $\lfloor x \rfloor = n$ if and only if $x - 1 < n \le x$ (1d) $\lceil x \rceil = n$ if and only if $x \le n < x + 1$
(2) $x - 1 < \lfloor x \rfloor \le x \le \lceil x \rceil < x + 1$
(3a) $\lfloor -x \rfloor = -\lceil x \rceil$ (3b) $\lceil -x \rceil = -\lfloor x \rfloor$
(4a) $\lfloor x + n \rfloor = \lfloor x \rfloor + n$ (4b) $\lceil x + n \rceil = \lceil x \rceil + n$

Table 1, with x denoting a real number, displays some simple but important properties of the floor and ceiling functions. Since these functions appear so frequently in discrete mathematics, it is useful to look over these identities. Each property in this table can be established using the definitions of the floor and ceiling functions. Properties (1a), (1b), (1c), and (1d) follow directly from these definitions. For example, (1a) states that $\lfloor x \rfloor = n$ if and only if the integer n is less than or equal to x and $n + 1$ is larger than x. This is precisely what it means for n to be the greatest integer not exceeding x, which is the definition of $\lfloor x \rfloor = n$. Properties (1b), (1c), and (1d) can be established similarly. We will prove property (4a) using a direct proof.

Proof: Suppose that $\lfloor x \rfloor = m$, where m is a positive integer. By property (1a), it follows that $m \le x < m + 1$. Adding n to both sides of this inequality shows that $m + n \le x + n < m + n + 1$. Using property (1a) again, we see that $\lfloor x + n \rfloor = m + n = \lfloor x \rfloor + n$. This completes the proof. We defer establishing the other properties to the exercises.   ◁

The floor and ceiling functions enjoy many other useful properties besides those displayed in Table 1. There are also many statements about these functions that may appear to be correct, but actually are not. We will consider statements about the floor and ceiling functions in Examples 24 and 25.

A useful approach for considering statements about the floor function is to let $x = n + \epsilon$, where $n = \lfloor x \rfloor$ is an integer and ϵ, the fractional part of x, satisfies the inequality $0 \le \epsilon < 1$. Similarly, when considering statements about the ceiling function, it is useful to write $x = n - \epsilon$, where $n = \lceil x \rceil$ is an integer and $0 \le \epsilon < 1$.

EXAMPLE 24 Prove that if x is a real number, then $\lfloor 2x \rfloor = \lfloor x \rfloor + \lfloor x + \frac{1}{2} \rfloor$.

Solution: To prove this statement we let $x = n + \epsilon$, where n is a positive integer and $0 \le \epsilon < 1$. There are two cases to consider depending whether ϵ is less than $\frac{1}{2}$. (The reason we choose these two cases will be made clear in the proof.)

We first consider the case when $0 \le \epsilon < \frac{1}{2}$. In this case, $2x = 2n + 2\epsilon$ and $\lfloor 2x \rfloor = 2n$ because $0 \le 2\epsilon < 1$. Similarly, $x + \frac{1}{2} = n + (\frac{1}{2} + \epsilon)$, so that $\lfloor x + \frac{1}{2} \rfloor = n$, because $0 < \frac{1}{2} + \epsilon < 1$. Consequently, $\lfloor 2x \rfloor = 2n$ and $\lfloor x \rfloor + \lfloor x + \frac{1}{2} \rfloor = n + n = 2n$.

Next, we consider the case when $\frac{1}{2} \le \epsilon < 1$. In this case, $2x = 2n + 2\epsilon = (2n + 1) + (2\epsilon - 1)$. Since $0 \le 2\epsilon - 1 < 1$, it follows that $\lfloor 2x \rfloor = 2n + 1$. Because

$\lfloor x + \frac{1}{2} \rfloor = \lfloor n + (\frac{1}{2} + \epsilon) \rfloor = \lfloor n + 1 + (\epsilon - \frac{1}{2}) \rfloor$ and $0 \leq \epsilon - \frac{1}{2} < 1$, it follows that $\lfloor x + \frac{1}{2} \rfloor = n + 1$. Consequently, $\lfloor 2x \rfloor = 2n + 1$ and $\lfloor x \rfloor + \lfloor x + \frac{1}{2} \rfloor = n + (n + 1) = 2n + 1$. This concludes the proof.   ◀

EXAMPLE 25   Prove or disprove that $\lceil x + y \rceil = \lceil x \rceil + \lceil y \rceil$ for all real numbers x and y.

Solution: Although this statement may appear reasonable, it is false. A counterexample is supplied by $x = \frac{1}{2}$ and $y = \frac{1}{2}$. With these values we find that $\lceil x + y \rceil = \lceil \frac{1}{2} + \frac{1}{2} \rceil = \lceil 1 \rceil = 1$, but $\lceil x \rceil + \lceil y \rceil = \lceil \frac{1}{2} \rceil + \lceil \frac{1}{2} \rceil = 1 + 1 = 2$.   ◀

There are certain types of functions that will be used throughout the text. These include polynomial, logarithmic, and exponential functions. A brief review of the properties of these functions needed in this text is given in Appendix 1. In this book the notation $\log x$ will be used to denote the logarithm to the base 2 of x, since 2 is the base that we will usually use for logarithms. We will denote logarithms to the base b, where b is any real number greater than 1, by $\log_b x$, and the natural logarithm by $\ln x$.

Another function we will use throughout this text is the **factorial function** $f : \mathbf{N} \to \mathbf{Z}^+$, denoted by $f(n) = n!$. The value of $f(n) = n!$ is the product of the first n positive integers, so that $f(n) = 1 \cdot 2 \cdots (n - 1) \cdot n$ [and $f(0) = 0! = 1$].

EXAMPLE 26   We have $f(6) = 6! = 1 \cdot 2 \cdot 3 \cdot 4 \cdot 5 \cdot 6 = 720$.   ◀

Exercises

1. Why is f not a function from $\mathbf{R}$ to $\mathbf{R}$ if
   a) $f(x) = 1/x$?
   b) $f(x) = \sqrt{x}$?
   c) $f(x) = \pm\sqrt{(x^2 + 1)}$?

2. Determine whether f is a function from $\mathbf{Z}$ to $\mathbf{R}$ if
   a) $f(n) = \pm n$.
   b) $f(n) = \sqrt{n^2 + 1}$.
   c) $f(n) = 1/(n^2 - 4)$.

3. Determine whether f is a function from the set of all bit strings to the set of integers if
   a) $f(S)$ is the position of a 0 bit in S.
   b) $f(S)$ is the number of 1 bits in S.
   c) $f(S)$ is the smallest integer i such that the ith bit of S is 1 and $f(S) = 0$ when S is the empty string, the string with no bits.

4. Find the domain and range of these functions.
   a) the function that assigns to each nonnegative integer its last digit
   b) the function that assigns the next largest integer to a positive integer
   c) the function that assigns to a bit string the number of one bits in the string
   d) the function that assigns to a bit string the number of bits in the string

5. Find the domain and range of these functions.
   a) the function that assigns to each bit string the difference between the number of ones and the number of zeros
   b) the function that assigns to each bit string twice the number of zeros in that string
   c) the function that assigns the number of bits left over when a bit string is split into bytes (which are blocks of 8 bits)
   d) the function that assigns to each positive integer the largest perfect square not exceeding this integer

6. Find the domain and range of these functions.
   a) the function that assigns to each pair of positive integers the first integer of the pair
   b) the function that assigns to each positive integer its largest decimal digit
   c) the function that assigns to a bit string the difference between the number of ones and the number of zeros in the string
   d) the function that assigns to each positive integer the largest integer not exceeding the square root of the integer
   e) the function that assigns to a bit string the longest string of ones in the string

7. Find the domain and range of these functions.

a) the function that assigns to each pair of positive integers the maximum of these two integers

b) the function that assigns to each positive integer the number of the digits $0, 1, 2, 3, 4, 5, 6, 7, 8, 9$ that do not appear as decimal digits of the integer

c) the function that assigns to a bit string the number of times the block 11 appears

d) the function that assigns to a bit string the numerical position of the first 1 in the string and that assigns the value 0 to a bit string consisting of all 0s

8. Find these values.

a) $\lfloor 1.1 \rfloor$ **b)** $\lceil 1.1 \rceil$ **c)** $\lfloor -0.1 \rfloor$

d) $\lceil -0.1 \rceil$ **e)** $\lceil 2.99 \rceil$ **f)** $\lceil -2.99 \rceil$

g) $\lfloor \frac{1}{2} + \lceil \frac{1}{2} \rceil \rfloor$ **h)** $\lceil \lfloor \frac{1}{2} \rfloor + \lceil \frac{1}{2} \rceil + \frac{1}{2} \rceil$

9. Find these values.

a) $\lceil \frac{3}{4} \rceil$ **b)** $\lfloor \frac{7}{8} \rfloor$ **c)** $\lceil -\frac{3}{4} \rceil$ **d)** $\lfloor -\frac{7}{8} \rfloor$

e) $\lceil 3 \rceil$ **f)** $\lfloor -1 \rfloor$ **g)** $\lfloor \frac{1}{2} + \lceil \frac{3}{2} \rceil \rfloor$ **h)** $\lfloor \frac{1}{2} \cdot \lfloor \frac{5}{2} \rfloor \rfloor$

10. Determine whether each of these functions from $\{a, b, c, d\}$ to itself is one-to-one.

a) $f(a) = b, f(b) = a, f(c) = c, f(d) = d$

b) $f(a) = b, f(b) = b, f(c) = d, f(d) = c$

c) $f(a) = d, f(b) = b, f(c) = c, f(d) = d$

11. Which functions in Exercise 10 are onto?

12. Determine whether each of these functions from $\mathbf{Z}$ to $\mathbf{Z}$ is one-to-one.

a) $f(n) = n - 1$ **b)** $f(n) = n^2 + 1$

c) $f(n) = n^3$ **d)** $f(n) = \lceil n/2 \rceil$

13. Which functions in Exercise 12 are onto?

14. Determine whether $f : \mathbf{Z} \times \mathbf{Z} \to \mathbf{Z}$ is onto if

a) $f(m, n) = 2m - n.$

b) $f(m, n) = m^2 - n^2.$

c) $f(m, n) = m + n + 1.$

d) $f(m, n) = |m| - |n|.$

e) $f(m, n) = m^2 - 4.$

15. Determine whether the function $f : \mathbf{Z} \times \mathbf{Z} \to \mathbf{Z}$ is onto if

a) $f(m, n) = m + n.$

b) $f(m, n) = m^2 + n^2.$

c) $f(m, n) = m.$

d) $f(m, n) = |n|.$

e) $f(m, n) = m - n.$

16. Give an example of a function from $\mathbf{N}$ to $\mathbf{N}$ that is

a) one-to-one but not onto.

b) onto but not one-to-one.

c) both onto and one-to-one (but different from the identity function).

d) neither one-to-one nor onto.

17. Give an explicit formula for a function from the set of integers to the set of positive integers that is

a) one-to-one, but not onto.

b) onto, but not one-to-one.

c) one-to-one and onto.

d) neither one-to-one nor onto.

18. Determine whether each of these functions is a bijection from $\mathbf{R}$ to $\mathbf{R}$.

a) $f(x) = -3x + 4$

b) $f(x) = -3x^2 + 7$

c) $f(x) = (x + 1)/(x + 2)$

d) $f(x) = x^5 + 1$

19. Determine whether each of these functions is a bijection from $\mathbf{R}$ to $\mathbf{R}$.

a) $f(x) = 2x + 1$

b) $f(x) = x^2 + 1$

c) $f(x) = x^3$

d) $f(x) = (x^2 + 1)/(x^2 + 2)$

20. Let $f : \mathbf{R} \to \mathbf{R}$ and let $f(x) > 0$ for all $x \in \mathbf{R}$. Show that $f(x)$ is strictly increasing if and only if the function $g(x) = 1/f(x)$ is strictly decreasing.

21. Let $f : \mathbf{R} \to \mathbf{R}$ and let $f(x) > 0$. Show that $f(x)$ is strictly decreasing if and only if the function $g(x) = 1/f(x)$ is strictly increasing.

22. Let $S = \{-1, 0, 2, 4, 7\}$. Find $f(S)$ if

a) $f(x) = 1.$ **b)** $f(x) = 2x + 1.$

c) $f(x) = \lceil x/5 \rceil.$ **d)** $f(x) = \lfloor (x^2 + 1)/3 \rfloor.$

23. Let $f(x) = \lfloor x^2/3 \rfloor$. Find $f(S)$ if

a) $S = \{-2, -1, 0, 1, 2, 3\}.$

b) $S = \{0, 1, 2, 3, 4, 5\}.$

c) $S = \{1, 5, 7, 11\}.$

d) $S = \{2, 6, 10, 14\}.$

24. Let $f(x) = 2x$. What is

a) $f(\mathbf{Z})?$ **b)** $f(\mathbf{N})?$ **c)** $f(\mathbf{R})?$

25. Suppose that g is a function from A to B and f is a function from B to C.

a) Show that if both f and g are one-to-one functions, then $f \circ g$ is also one-to-one.

b) Show that if both f and g are onto functions, then $f \circ g$ is also onto.

*26. If f and $f \circ g$ are one-to-one, does it follow that g is one-to-one? Justify your answer.

*27. If f and $f \circ g$ are onto, does it follow that g is onto? Justify your answer.

28. Find $f \circ g$ and $g \circ f$ where $f(x) = x^2 + 1$ and $g(x) = x + 2$ are functions from $\mathbf{R}$ to $\mathbf{R}$.

29. Find $f + g$ and fg for the functions f and g given in Exercise 28.

30. Let $f(x) = ax + b$ and $g(x) = cx + d$ where $a, b, c,$ and d are constants. Determine for which constants $a, b, c,$ and d it is true that $f \circ g = g \circ f$.

31. Show that the function $f(x) = ax + b$ from $\mathbf{R}$ to $\mathbf{R}$ is invertible, where a and b are constants, with $a \neq 0$, and find the inverse of f.

32. Let f be a function from the set A to the set B. Let S and T be subsets of A. Show that

a) $f(S \cup T) = f(S) \cup f(T).$

b) $f(S \cap T) \subseteq f(S) \cap f(T).$

33. Give an example to show that the inclusion in part (b) in Exercise 32 may be proper.

Let f be a function from the set A to the set B. Let S be a subset of B. We define the **inverse image** of S to be the subset of A containing all pre-images of all elements of S. We denote the inverse image of S by $f^{-1}(S)$, so that $f^{-1}(S) = \{a \in A \mid f(a) \in S\}$.

34. Let f be the function from $\mathbf{R}$ to $\mathbf{R}$ defined by $f(x) = x^2$. Find

    a) $f^{-1}(\{1\})$.   **b)** $f^{-1}(\{x \mid 0 < x < 1\})$.

    c) $f^{-1}(\{x \mid x > 4\})$.

35. Let $g(x) = \lfloor x \rfloor$. Find

    a) $g^{-1}(\{0\})$.

    b) $g^{-1}(\{-1, 0, 1\})$.

    c) $g^{-1}(\{x \mid 0 < x < 1\})$.

36. Let f be a function from A to B. Let S and T be subsets of B. Show that

    a) $f^{-1}(S \cup T) = f^{-1}(S) \cup f^{-1}(T)$.

    b) $f^{-1}(S \cap T) = f^{-1}(S) \cap f^{-1}(T)$.

37. Let f be a function from A to B. Let S be a subset of B. Show that $f^{-1}(\overline{S}) = \overline{f^{-1}(S)}$.

38. Show that $\lfloor x + \frac{1}{2} \rfloor$ is the closest integer to the number x, except when x is midway between two integers, when it is the larger of these two integers.

39. Show that $\lceil x - \frac{1}{2} \rceil$ is the closest integer to the number x, except when x is midway between two integers, when it is the smaller of these two integers.

40. Show that if x is a real number, then $\lceil x \rceil - \lfloor x \rfloor = 1$ if x is not an integer and $\lceil x \rceil - \lfloor x \rfloor = 0$ if x is an integer.

41. Show that if x is a real number, then $x - 1 < \lfloor x \rfloor \le x \le \lceil x \rceil < x + 1$.

42. Show that if x is a real number and m is an integer, then $\lceil x + m \rceil = \lceil x \rceil + m$.

43. Show that if x is a real number and n is an integer, then

    a) $x < n$ if and only if $\lfloor x \rfloor < n$.

    b) $n < x$ if and only if $n < \lceil x \rceil$.

44. Show that if x is a real number and n is an integer, then

    a) $x \le n$ if and only if $\lceil x \rceil \le n$.

    b) $n \le x$ if and only if $n \le \lfloor x \rfloor$.

45. Prove that if n is an integer, then $\lfloor n/2 \rfloor = n/2$ if n is even and $(n-1)/2$ if n is odd.

46. Prove that if x is a real number, then $\lfloor -x \rfloor = -\lceil x \rceil$ and $\lceil -x \rceil = -\lfloor x \rfloor$.

47. The function INT is found on some calculators, where $\text{INT}(x) = \lfloor x \rfloor$ when x is a nonnegative real number and $\text{INT}(x) = \lceil x \rceil$ when x is a negative real number. Show that this INT function satisfies the identity $\text{INT}(-x) = -\text{INT}(x)$.

48. Let a and b be real numbers with $a < b$. Use the floor and/or ceiling functions to express the number of integers n that satisfy the inequality $a \le n \le b$.

49. Let a and b be real numbers with $a < b$. Use the floor and/or ceiling functions to express the number of integers n that satisfy the inequality $a < n < b$.

50. How many bytes are required to encode n bits of data where n equals

    a) 4?   **b)** 10?   **c)** 500?   **d)** 3000?

51. How many bytes are required to encode n bits of data where n equals

    a) 7?   **b)** 17?   **c)** 1001?   **d)** 28,800?

52. How many ATM cells (described in Example 23) can be transmitted in 10 seconds over a link operating at the following rates?

    a) 128 kilobits per second (1 kilobit = 1000 bits)

    b) 300 kilobits per second

    c) 1 megabit per second (1 megabit = 1,000,000 bits)

53. Data are transmitted over a particular Ethernet network in blocks of 1500 octets (blocks of 8 bits). How many blocks are required to transmit the following amounts of data over this Ethernet network? (Note that a byte is a synonym for an octet, a kilobyte is 1000 bytes, and a megabyte is 1,000,000 bytes.)

    a) 150 kilobytes of data

    b) 384 kilobytes of data

    c) 1.544 megabytes of data

    d) 45.3 megabytes of data

54. Draw the graph of the function $f(n) = 1 - n^2$ from $\mathbf{Z}$ to $\mathbf{Z}$.

55. Draw the graph of the function $f(x) = \lfloor 2x \rfloor$ from $\mathbf{R}$ to $\mathbf{R}$.

56. Draw the graph of the function $f(x) = \lfloor x/2 \rfloor$ from $\mathbf{R}$ to $\mathbf{R}$.

57. Draw the graph of the function $f(x) = \lfloor x \rfloor + \lfloor x/2 \rfloor$ from $\mathbf{R}$ to $\mathbf{R}$.

58. Draw the graph of the function $f(x) = \lceil x \rceil + \lfloor x/2 \rfloor$ from $\mathbf{R}$ to $\mathbf{R}$.

59. Draw graphs of each of these functions.

    a) $f(x) = \lfloor x + \frac{1}{2} \rfloor$ **b)** $f(x) = \lfloor 2x + 1 \rfloor$

    c) $f(x) = \lceil x/3 \rceil$ **d)** $f(x) = \lceil 1/x \rceil$

    e) $f(x) = \lceil x - 2 \rceil + \lfloor x + 2 \rfloor$

    f) $f(x) = \lfloor 2x \rfloor \lceil x/2 \rceil$

    g) $f(x) = \lceil \lfloor x - \frac{1}{2} \rfloor + \frac{1}{2} \rceil$

60. Draw graphs of each of these functions.

    a) $f(x) = \lceil 3x - 2 \rceil$ **b)** $f(x) = \lceil 0.2x \rceil$

    c) $f(x) = \lfloor -1/x \rfloor$ **d)** $f(x) = \lfloor x^2 \rfloor$

    e) $f(x) = \lceil x/2 \rceil \lfloor x/2 \rfloor$

    f) $f(x) = \lfloor x/2 \rfloor + \lceil x/2 \rceil$

    g) $f(x) = \lfloor 2 \lceil x/2 \rceil + \frac{1}{2} \rfloor$

61. Find the inverse function of $f(x) = x^3 + 1$.

62. Suppose that f is an invertible function from Y to Z and g is an invertible function from X to Y. Show that the inverse of the composition $f \circ g$ is given by $(f \circ g)^{-1} = g^{-1} \circ f^{-1}$.

63. Let S be a subset of a universal set U. The **characteristic function** f_S of S is the function from U to the set $\{0, 1\}$ such that $f_S(x) = 1$ if x belongs to S and $f_S(x) = 0$ if x does not belong to S. Let A and B be sets. Show that for all x

a) $f_{A \cap B}(x) = f_A(x) \cdot f_B(x)$
b) $f_{A \cup B}(x) = f_A(x) + f_B(x) - f_A(x) \cdot f_B(x)$
c) $f_{\overline{A}}(x) = 1 - f_A(x)$
d) $f_{A \oplus B}(x) = f_A(x) + f_B(x) - 2f_A(x)f_B(x)$

64. Suppose that f is a function from A to B, where A and B are finite sets with $|A| = |B|$. Show that f is one-to-one if and only if it is onto.

65. Prove or disprove each of these statements about the floor and ceiling functions.

a) $\lceil \lfloor x \rfloor \rceil = \lfloor x \rfloor$ for all real numbers x.
b) $\lfloor 2x \rfloor = 2\lfloor x \rfloor$ whenever x is a real number.
c) $\lceil x \rceil + \lceil y \rceil - \lceil x + y \rceil = 0$ or 1 whenever x and y are real numbers.
d) $\lceil xy \rceil = \lceil x \rceil \lceil y \rceil$ for all real numbers x and y.
e) $\left\lceil \dfrac{x}{2} \right\rceil = \left\lfloor \dfrac{x+1}{2} \right\rfloor$ for all real numbers x.

66. Prove or disprove each of these statements about the floor and ceiling functions.

a) $\lfloor \lceil x \rceil \rfloor = \lceil x \rceil$ for all real numbers x.
b) $\lfloor x + y \rfloor = \lfloor x \rfloor + \lfloor y \rfloor$ for all real numbers x and y.
c) $\lceil \lceil x/2 \rceil / 2 \rceil = \lceil x/4 \rceil$ for all real numbers x.
d) $\lfloor \sqrt{\lceil x \rceil} \rfloor = \lfloor \sqrt{x} \rfloor$ for all real numbers x.
e) $\lfloor x \rfloor + \lfloor y \rfloor + \lfloor x + y \rfloor \leq \lfloor 2x \rfloor + \lfloor 2y \rfloor$ for all real numbers x and y.

67. Prove that if x is a positive real number, then

a) $\lfloor \sqrt{\lfloor x \rfloor} \rfloor = \lfloor \sqrt{x} \rfloor$.
b) $\lceil \sqrt{\lceil x \rceil} \rceil = \lceil \sqrt{x} \rceil$.

68. Let x be a real number. Show that $\lfloor 3x \rfloor = \lfloor x \rfloor + \lfloor x + \frac{1}{3} \rfloor + \lfloor x + \frac{2}{3} \rfloor$.

A program designed to evaluate a function may not produce the correct value of the function for all elements in the domain of this function. For example, a program

may not produce a correct value because evaluating the function may lead to an infinite loop or an overflow.

To study such situations, we use the concept of a partial function. A **partial function** f from a set A to a set B is an assignment to each element a in a subset of A, called the **domain of definition** of f, of a unique element b in B. The sets A and B are called the **domain** and **codomain** of f, respectively. We say that f is **undefined** for elements in A that are not in the domain of definition of f. We write $f : A \to B$ to denote that f is a partial function from A to B. (This is the same notation as is used for functions. The context in which the notation is used determines whether f is a partial function or a total function.) When the domain of definition of f equals A, we say that f is a **total function.**

69. For each of these partial functions, determine its domain, codomain, domain of definition, and the set of values for which it is undefined. Also, determine whether it is a total function.

a) $f : \mathbf{Z} \to \mathbf{R}, f(n) = 1/n$
b) $f : \mathbf{Z} \to \mathbf{Z}, f(n) = \lceil n/2 \rceil$
c) $f : \mathbf{Z} \times \mathbf{Z} \to \mathbf{Q}, f(m, n) = m/n$
d) $f : \mathbf{Z} \times \mathbf{Z} \to \mathbf{Z}, f(m, n) = mn$
e) $f : \mathbf{Z} \times \mathbf{Z} \to \mathbf{Z}, f(m, n) = m - n$ if $m > n$

70. a) Show that a partial function from A to B can be viewed as a function f^* from A to $B \cup \{u\}$ where u is not an element of B and

$$f^*(a) = \begin{cases} f(a) & \text{if } a \text{ belongs to the domain} \\ & \text{of definition of } f \\ u & \text{if } f \text{ is undefined at } a. \end{cases}$$

b) Using the construction in (a), find the function f^* corresponding to each partial function in Exercise 69.

*71. Show that the function $f : \mathbf{Z}^+ \times \mathbf{Z}^+ \to \mathbf{Z}^+$ with $f(m, n) = (m + n - 2)(m + n - 1)/2 + m$ is one-to-one and onto.

Key Terms and Results

LOGIC (SECTIONS 1–4):

TERMS

proposition: a statement that is true or false

truth value: true or false

¬ p (negation of p): the proposition with truth value opposite to the truth value of p

logical operators: operators used to combine propositions

compound proposition: a proposition constructed by combining propositions using logical operators

truth table: a table displaying the truth values of propositions

$p \vee q$ (disjunction of p and q): the proposition that is true unless both p and q are false

$p \wedge q$ (conjunction of p and q): the proposition that is true only when both p and q are true

$p \oplus q$ (exclusive or of p and q): the proposition that is true when exactly one of p and q is true

$p \rightarrow q$ (**p implies q**): the proposition that is false only when p is true and q is false

converse of $p \rightarrow q$: the implication $q \rightarrow p$

contrapositive of $p \rightarrow q$: the implication $\neg q \rightarrow \neg p$

inverse of $p \rightarrow q$: the implication $\neg p \rightarrow \neg q$

$p \leftrightarrow q$ (**biconditional**): the proposition that is true only when p and q have the same truth value

bit: either a 0 or a 1

Boolean variable: a variable that has a value of 0 or 1

bit operation: an operation on a bit or bits

bit string: a list of bits

bitwise operations: operations on bit strings that operate on each bit in one string and the corresponding bit in the other string

tautology: a compound proposition that is always true

contradiction: a compound proposition that is always false

contingency: a compound proposition that is sometimes true and sometimes false

consistent compound propositions: compound propositions for which there is an assignment of truth values to the variables that makes all these propositions true

logical equivalence: compound propositions are logically equivalent if they always have the same truth values

propositional function: the combination of a variable and a predicate

universe of discourse: the domain of the variable in a propositional function

∃ $x\,P(x)$ (existential quantification of $P(x)$): the proposition that is true if and only if there exists an x in the universe of discourse such that $P(x)$ is true

∀ $x\,P(x)$ (universal quantification of $P(x)$): the proposition that is true if and only if $P(x)$ is true for all x in the universe of discourse

free variable: a variable not bound in a propositional function

RESULTS

The logical equivalences given in Tables 5, 6, and 7 in Section 1.2.

METHODS OF PROOF (SECTION 5):

TERMS

theorem: a mathematical assertion that can be shown to be true

conjecture: a mathematical assertion whose truth value is unknown

proof: a demonstration that a theorem is true

lemma: a simple theorem used to prove other theorems

corollary: a proposition that can be proved as a consequence of a theorem that has just been proved

rule of inference: an implication that is a tautology that is then used to draw conclusions from known assertions

fallacy: an implication that is a contingency that is often incorrectly used to draw conclusions

circular reasoning or **begging the question:** reasoning where one or more steps are based on the truth of the statement being proved

vacuous proof: a proof that the implication $p \rightarrow q$ is true based on the fact that p is false

trivial proof: a proof that the implication $p \rightarrow q$ is true based on the fact that q is true

direct proof: a proof that the implication $p \rightarrow q$ is true

that proceeds by showing that q must be true when p is true

indirect proof: a proof that the implication $p \rightarrow q$ is true that proceeds by showing that p must be false when q is false

proof by contradiction: a proof that a proposition p is true based on the truth of the implication $\neg p \rightarrow q$ where q is a contradiction

proof by cases: a proof of an implication where the hypothesis is a disjunction of propositions that shows that each hypothesis separately implies the conclusion

counterexample: an element x such that $P(x)$ is false

constructive existence proof: a proof that an element with a specified property exists that explicitly finds such an element

nonconstructive existence proof: a proof that an element with a specified property exists that does not explicitly find such an element

rational number: a number that can be expressed as the ratio of two integers p and q such that $q \neq 0$

uniqueness proof: a proof that there is exactly one element satisfying a specified property

SETS (SECTIONS 6–7):

TERMS

set: a collection of distinct objects

axiom: a basic assumption of a theory

paradox: a logical inconsistency

element, member of a set: an object in a set

∅ (empty set, null set): the set with no members

universal set: the set containing all objects under consideration

Venn diagram: a graphical representation of a set or sets

$S = T$ (**set equality**): S and T have the same elements

$S \subseteq T$ (**S is a subset of T**): every element of S is also an element of T

$S \subset T$ (**S is a proper subset of T**): S is a subset of T and $S \neq T$

finite set: a set with n elements where n is a nonnegative integer

infinite set: a set that is not finite

$|S|$ (**the cardinality of S**): the number of elements in S

$P(S)$ (**the power set of S**): the set of all subsets of S

$A \cup B$ (**the union of A and B**): the set containing those elements that are in at least one of A and B

$A \cap B$ (**the intersection of A and B**): the set containing those elements that are in both A and B.

$A - B$ (**the difference of A and B**): the set containing those elements that are in A but not in B

$\overline{A}$ (**the complement of A**): the set of elements in the universal set that are not in A

$A \oplus B$ (**the symmetric difference of A and B**): the set containing those elements in exactly one of A and B

membership table: a table displaying the membership of elements in sets

RESULTS

The set identities given in Table 1 in Section 1.7

FUNCTIONS (SECTION 8):

TERMS

function from A to B: an assignment of exactly one element of B to each element of A

domain of f: the set A where f is a function from A to B

codomain of f: the set B where f is a function from A to B

b is the image of a under f: $b = f(a)$

a is a pre-image of b under f: $f(a) = b$

range of f: the set of images of f

onto function, surjection: a function from A to B such that every element of B is the image of some element in A

one-to-one function, injection: a function such that the images of elements in its domain are all different

one-to-one correspondence, bijection: a function that is both one-to-one and onto

inverse of f: the function that reverses the correspondence given by f (when f is a bijection)

$f \circ g$ (composition of f and g): the function that assigns $f(g(x))$ to x

$\lfloor x \rfloor$ (**floor function**): the largest integer not exceeding x

$\lceil x \rceil$ (**ceiling function**): the smallest integer greater than or equal to x

Review Questions

1. a) Define the negation of a proposition.
   b) What is the negation of "This is a boring course"?
2. a) Define (using truth tables) the disjunction, conjunction, exclusive or, conditional, and biconditional of the propositions p and q.
   b) What are the disjunction, conjunction, exclusive or, implication, and biconditional of the propositions "I'll go to the movies tonight" and "I'll finish my discrete mathematics homework"?
3. a) Describe at least five different ways to write the implication $p \rightarrow q$ in English.
   b) Define the converse and contrapositive of an implication.
   c) State the converse and the contrapositive of the implication "If it is sunny tomorrow, then I will go for a walk in the woods."
4. a) What does it mean for two propositions to be logically equivalent?
   b) Describe the different ways to show that two compound propositions are logically equivalent.

   c) Show in at least two different ways that the compound propositions $\neg p \vee (r \rightarrow \neg q)$ and $\neg p \vee \neg q \vee \neg r$ are equivalent.

5. (*Depends on the Exercise Set in Section 1.2*)

   a) Given a truth table, explain how to use disjunctive normal form to construct a compound proposition with this truth table.
   b) Explain why part (a) shows that the operators $\wedge$, $\vee$, and $\neg$ are functionally complete.
   c) Is there an operator such that the set containing just this operator is functionally complete?

6. What are the universal and existential quantifications of a predicate $P(x)$? What are their negations?
7. a) What is the difference between the quantification $\exists x \forall y\, P(x, y)$ and $\forall y \exists x\, P(x, y)$, where $P(x, y)$ is a predicate?
   b) Give an example of a predicate $P(x, y)$ such that $\exists x \forall y\, P(x, y)$ and $\forall y \exists x\, P(x, y)$ have different truth values.

8. a) Describe what is meant by a direct proof, an indirect proof, and a proof by contradiction of an implication $p \rightarrow q$.

b) Give a direct proof, an indirect proof, and a proof by contradiction of the statement: "If n is even, then $n + 4$ is even."

9. a) Describe one way to prove the biconditional $p \leftrightarrow q$.

b) Prove the statement: "The integer $3n + 2$ is odd if and only if the integer $9n + 5$ is even, where n is an integer."

10. To prove that the statements p_1, p_2, p_3, and p_4 are equivalent, is it sufficient to show that the implications $p_4 \rightarrow p_2$, $p_3 \rightarrow p_1$, and $p_1 \rightarrow p_2$ are valid? If not, provide another set of implications that can be used to show that the four statements are equivalent.

11. a) Suppose that a statement of the form $\forall x\, P(x)$ is false. How can this be proved?

b) Show that the statement "For every positive integer n, $n^2 \geq 2n$" is false.

12. What is the difference between a constructive and nonconstructive existence proof? Give an example of each.

13. What are the elements of a proof that there is a unique element x such that $P(x)$, where $P(x)$ is a propositional function?

14. a) Define the union, intersection, difference, and symmetric difference of two sets.

b) What are the union, intersection, difference, and symmetric difference of the set of positive integers and the set of odd integers?

15. a) Define what it means for two sets to be equal.

b) Describe the ways to show that two sets are equal.

c) Show in at least two different ways that the sets $A - (B \cap C)$ and $(A - B) \cup (A - C)$ are equal.

16. Explain the relationship between logical equivalences and set identities.

17. a) Define $|S|$, the cardinality of the set S.

b) Give a formula for $|A \cup B|$ where A and B are sets.

18. a) Define the power set of a set S.

b) When is the empty set in the power set of a set S?

c) How many elements does the power set of a set S with n elements have?

19. a) Define the domain, codomain, and the range of a function.

b) Let $f(n)$ be the function from the set of integers to the set of integers such that $f(n) = n^2 + 1$. What are the domain, codomain, and range of this function?

20. a) Define what it means for a function from the set of positive integers to the set of positive integers to be one-to-one.

b) Define what it means for a function from the set of positive integers to the set of positive integers to be onto.

c) Give an example of a function from the set of positive integers to the set of positive integers that is both one-to-one and onto.

d) Give an example of a function from the set of positive integers to the set of positive integers that is one-to-one but not onto.

e) Give an example of a function from the set of positive integers to the set of positive integers that is not one-to-one but is onto.

f) Give an example of a function from the set of positive integers to the set of positive integers that is neither one-to-one nor onto.

21. a) Define the inverse of a function.

b) When does a function have an inverse?

c) Does the function $f(n) = 10 - n$ from the set of integers to the set of integers have an inverse? If so, what is it?

22. a) Define the floor and ceiling functions from the set of real numbers to the set of integers.

b) For which real numbers x is it true that $\lfloor x \rfloor = \lceil x \rceil$?

Supplementary Exercises

1. Let p be the proposition "I will do every exercise in this book" and q be the proposition "I will get an 'A' in this course." Express each of these as a combination of p and q.

a) I will get an 'A' in this course only if I do every exercise in this book.

b) I will get an 'A' in this course and I will do every exercise in this book.

c) Either I will not get an 'A' in this course or I will not do every exercise in this book.

d) For me to get an 'A' in this course it is necessary and sufficient that I do every exercise in this book.

2. Find the truth table of the compound proposition $(p \vee q) \rightarrow (p \wedge \neg r)$.

3. Show that these propositions are tautologies.

a) $(\neg q \wedge (p \rightarrow q)) \rightarrow \neg p$

b) $((p \vee q) \wedge \neg p) \rightarrow q$

4. Give the converse, the contrapositive, and the inverse of these implications.

a) If it rains today, then I will drive to work.

b) If $|x| = x$, then $x \geq 0$.

c) If n is greater than 3, then n^2 is greater than 9.

5. Find a compound proposition involving the propositional variables $p, q, r,$ and s that is true when exactly three of these propositional variables are true and is false otherwise.

6. Show that these statements are inconsistent: "If Sergei takes the job offer then he will get a signing bonus." "If Sergei takes the job offer, then he will receive a higher salary." "If Sergei gets a signing bonus, then he will not receive a higher salary." "Sergei takes the job offer."

7. Show that these statements are inconsistent: "If Miranda does not take a course in discrete mathematics, then she will not graduate." "If Miranda does not graduate, then she is not qualified for the job." "If Miranda reads this book, then she is qualified for the job." "Miranda does not take a course in discrete mathematics but she reads this book."

8. Suppose that you meet three people, $A, B,$ and $C,$ on the island of knights and knaves described in Example 15 in Section 1.1. What are $A, B,$ and C if A says "I am a knave and B is a knight" and B says "Exactly one of the three of us is a knight."

9. (Adapted from [Sm78]) Suppose that on an island there are three types of people, knights, knaves, and normals. Knights always tell the truth, knaves always lie, and normals sometimes lie and sometimes tell the truth. Detectives questioned three inhabitants of the island—Amy, Brenda, and Claire—as part of the investigation of a crime. The detectives knew that one of the three committed the crime, but not which one. They also knew that the criminal was a knight, and that the other two were not. Additionally, the detectives recorded these statements: Amy: "I am innocent." Brenda: "What Amy says is true." Claire: "Brenda is not a normal." After analyzing their information, the detectives positively identified the guilty party. Who was it?

10. Let $P(x)$ be the statement "student x knows calculus" and let $Q(y)$ be the statement "class y contains a student who knows calculus." Express each of these as quantifications of $P(x)$ and $Q(y)$.

   a) Some students know calculus.
   b) Not every student knows calculus.
   c) Every class has a student in it who knows calculus.
   d) Every student in every class knows calculus.
   e) There is at least one class with no students who know calculus.

11. Let $P(m, n)$ be the statement "m divides n," where the universe of discourse for both variables is the set of positive integers. Determine the truth values of each of these propositions.

   a) $P(4, 5)$ **b)** $P(2, 4)$
   c) $\forall m\, \forall n\, P(m, n)$ **d)** $\exists m\, \forall n\, P(m, n)$
   e) $\exists n\, \forall m\, P(m, n)$ **f)** $\forall n\, P(1, n)$

12. Use quantifiers to express the statement "No one has more than three grandmothers" using the propositional function $G(x, y)$, which represents "x is the grandmother of y."

13. Use quantifiers to express the statement "Everyone has exactly two biological parents" using the propositional function $P(x, y)$, which represents "x is the biological parent of y."

14. Let $P(x, y)$ be a propositional function. Show that the implication $\exists x\, \forall y\, P(x, y) \rightarrow \forall y\, \exists x\, P(x, y)$ is a tautology.

15. Let $P(x)$ and $Q(x)$ be propositional functions. Show that $\exists x\, (P(x) \rightarrow Q(x))$ and $\forall x\, P(x) \rightarrow \exists x\, Q(x)$ always have the same truth value.

16. If $\forall y\, \exists x\, P(x, y)$ is true, does it necessarily follow that $\exists x\, \forall y\, P(x, y)$ is true?

17. If $\forall x\, \exists y\, P(x, y)$ is true, does it necessarily follow that $\exists x\, \forall y\, P(x, y)$ is true?

18. Find the negations of these statements.

   a) If it snows today, then I will go skiing tomorrow.
   b) Every person in this class understands mathematical induction.
   c) Some students in this class do not like discrete mathematics.
   d) In every mathematics class there is some student who falls asleep during lectures.

19. Express this statement using quantifiers: "Every student in this class has taken some course in every department in the school of mathematical sciences."

20. Express this statement using quantifiers: "There is a building on the campus of some college in the United States in which every room is painted white."

21. Let A be the set of English words that contain the letter $x,$ and let B be the set of English words that contain the letter $q.$ Express each of these sets as a combination of A and $B.$

   a) The set of English words that do not contain the letter $x.$
   b) The set of English words that contain both an x and a $q.$
   c) The set of English words that contain an x but not a $q.$
   d) The set of English words that do not contain either an x or a $q.$
   e) The set of English words that contain an x or a $q,$ but not both.

22. Describe a rule of inference that can be used to prove that there are exactly two elements x and y in a universe of discourse such that $P(x)$ and $P(y)$ are true. Express this rule of inference as a statement in English.

23. What is wrong with this argument? Given the premise $\exists x\, P(x) \land \exists x\, Q(x),$ use simplification to obtain $\exists x\, P(x);$ use existential instantiation to obtain $P(c)$ for some element $c;$ use simplification again to obtain $\exists x\, Q(x)$; use existential instantiation to obtain $Q(c)$ for some element c; use conjunction to conclude that $P(c) \land Q(c)$; and finally, use existential generalization to conclude that $\exists x (P(x) \land Q(x))$.

24. Use rules of inference to show that the premises $\forall x(P(x) \to Q(x))$, $\forall x(Q(x) \to R(x))$ and $\neg R(a)$, where a is in the universe of discourse, imply the conclusion $\neg P(a)$.

25. Use rules of inference to show that the premises $\forall x(P(x) \land Q(x))$ and $\forall x(\neg P(x) \land Q(x) \to R(x))$ imply the conclusion $\forall x(\neg R(x) \to P(x))$.

26. Prove that if x^3 is irrational, then x is irrational.

27. Prove that if x is irrational and $x \geq 0$, then $\sqrt{x}$ is irrational.

28. Prove that given a nonnegative integer n, there is a unique nonnegative integer m such that $m^2 \leq n < (m+1)^2$.

29. Prove that there exists an integer m such that $m^2 > 10^{1000}$. Is your proof constructive or nonconstructive?

30. Prove that there is a positive integer that can be written as the sum of squares of positive integers in two different ways. (Use a computer or calculator to speed up your work.)

31. Disprove the statement that every positive integer is the sum of the cubes of eight nonnegative integers.

32. Disprove the statement that every positive integer is the sum of at most two squares and a cube of nonnegative integers.

33. Disprove the statement that every positive integer is the sum of 36 fifth powers of nonnegative integers.

34. Show that if A is a subset of B, then the power set of A is a subset of the power set of B.

35. Suppose that A and B are sets such that the power set of A is a subset of the power set of B. Does it follow that A is a subset of B?

36. Let **E** denote the set of even integers and **O** denote the set of odd integers. As usual, let **Z** denote the set of all integers. Determine each of these sets.
   a) $\mathbf{E} \cup \mathbf{O}$ b) $\mathbf{E} \cap \mathbf{O}$ c) $\mathbf{Z} - \mathbf{E}$ d) $\mathbf{Z} - \mathbf{O}$

37. Show that if A is a set and U is the universal set, then
   a) $A \cap \overline{A} = \emptyset$.   b) $A \cup \overline{A} = U$.

38. Show that if A and B are sets, then
   a) $A = A \cap (A \cup B)$.
   b) $A = A \cup (A \cap B)$.

39. Show that if A and B are sets, then $A - (A - B) = A \cap B$.

40. Let A and B be sets. Show that $A \subseteq B$ if and only if $A \cap B = A$.

41. Let A, B, and C be sets. Show that $(A - B) - C$ is not necessarily equal to $A - (B - C)$.

42. Suppose that A, B, and C are sets. Prove or disprove that $(A - B) - C = (A - C) - B$.

43. Suppose that A, B, C, and D are sets. Prove or disprove that $(A - B) - (C - D) = (A - C) - (B - D)$.

44. Show that if A and B are finite sets, then $|A \cap B| \leq |A \cup B|$. Determine when this relationship is an equality.

45. Let A and B be sets in a finite universal set U. List the following in order of increasing size.
   a) $|A|, |A \cup B|, |A \cap B|, |U|, |\emptyset|$
   b) $|A - B|, |A \oplus B|, |A| + |B|, |A \cup B|, |\emptyset|$

46. Let A and B be subsets of the finite universal set U. Show that $|\overline{A} \cap \overline{B}| = |U| - |A| - |B| + |A \cap B|$.

47. Let f and g be functions from $\{1, 2, 3, 4\}$ to $\{a, b, c, d\}$ and from $\{a, b, c, d\}$ to $\{1, 2, 3, 4\}$, respectively, such that $f(1) = d$, $f(2) = c$, $f(3) = a$, $f(4) = b$, and $g(a) = 2, g(b) = 1, g(c) = 3, g(d) = 2$.
   a) Is f one-to-one? Is g one-to-one?
   b) Is f onto? Is g onto?
   c) Does either f or g have an inverse? If so, find this inverse.

48. Let f be a one-to-one function from the set A to the set B. Let S and T be subsets of A. Show that $f(S \cap T) = f(S) \cap f(T)$.

49. Give an example to show that the equality in Exercise 48 may not hold if f is not one-to-one.

50. Show that if n is an integer, then $n = \lceil n/2 \rceil + \lfloor n/2 \rfloor$.

51. For which real numbers x and y is it true that $\lfloor x + y \rfloor = \lfloor x \rfloor + \lfloor y \rfloor$?

52. For which real numbers x and y is it true that $\lceil x + y \rceil = \lceil x \rceil + \lceil y \rceil$?

Computer Projects

WRITE PROGRAMS WITH THE SPECIFIED INPUT AND OUTPUT.

1. Given the truth values of the propositions p and q, find the truth values of the conjunction, disjunction, exclusive or, implication, and biconditional of these propositions.

2. Given two bit strings of length n, find the bitwise *AND*, bitwise *OR*, and bitwise *XOR* of these strings.

3. Given the truth values of the propositions p and q in fuzzy logic, find the truth value of the disjunction and the conjunction of p and q (see Exercises 35–37 of Section 1.1).

4. Given subsets A and B of a set with n elements, use bit strings to find $\overline{A}$, $A \cup B$, $A \cap B$, $A - B$, and $A \oplus B$.

5. Given multisets A and B from the same universal set, find $A \cup B, A \cap B, A - B,$ and $A + B$ (see preamble to Exercise 49 of Section 1.7).

6. Given fuzzy sets A and B, find $\overline{A}, A \cup B,$ and $A \cap B$ (see preamble to Exercise 51 of Section 1.7).

7. Given a function f from $\{1, 2, \ldots, n\}$ to the set of integers, determine whether f is one-to-one.

8. Given a function f from $\{1, 2, \ldots, n\}$ to itself, determine whether f is onto.

9. Given a bijection f from the set $\{1, 2, \ldots, n\}$ to itself, find f^{-1}.

Computations and Explorations

USE A COMPUTATIONAL PROGRAM OR PROGRAMS YOU HAVE WRITTEN TO DO THESE EXERCISES.

1. Look for positive integers that are not the sum of the cubes of nine different positive integers.

2. Look for positive integers greater than 79 that are not the sum of the fourth powers of 18 positive integers.

3. Find as many positive integers as you can that can be written as the sum of cubes of positive integers in two different ways, sharing this property with 1729.

4. Calculate the number of one-to-one functions from a set S to a set T, where S and T are finite sets of various sizes. Can you determine a formula for the number of such functions? (We will find such a formula in Chapter 4.)

5. Calculate the number of onto functions from a set S to a set T where S and T are finite sets of various sizes. Can you determine a formula for the number of such functions? (We will find such a formula in Chapter 6.)

Writing Projects

RESPOND TO THESE WITH ESSAYS USING OUTSIDE SOURCES.

1. Discuss logical paradoxes including the paradox of Epimenides the Cretan, Jourdain's card paradox, and the barber paradox and how they are resolved.

2. Describe how fuzzy logic is being applied to practical applications. Consult one or more of the recent books on fuzzy logic written for general audiences.

3. Describe the basic rules of *WFF'N PROOF, The Game of Modern Logic*, developed by Layman Allen. Give examples of some of the games included in *WFF'N PROOF*.

4. Read some of the writings of Lewis Carroll on symbolic logic. Describe in detail some of the models he used to represent logical arguments and the rules of inference he used in these arguments.

5. Extend the discussion of Prolog given in Section 1.3, explaining in more depth how Prolog employs resolution.

6. Discuss some of the techniques used in computational logic, including Skolem's rule.

7. "Automated theorem proving" is the task of using computers to mechanically prove theorems. Discuss the goals and applications of automated theorem proving and the progress made in developing automated theorem provers.

8. Discuss how an axiomatic set theory can be developed to avoid Russell's paradox. (See Exercise 30 of Section 1.6.)

9. Research where the concept of a function first arose, and describe how this concept was first used.

10. Describe how DNA computing has been used to solve instances of the satisfiability problem.

Answers to Odd-Numbered Exercises

CHAPTER 1

SECTION 1.1

1. a) Yes, T **b)** Yes, F **c)** Yes, T **d)** Yes, F **e)** No **f)** No **g)** Yes, T **3. a)** Today is not Thursday. **b)** There is pollution in New Jersey. **c)** $2 + 1 \neq 3$. **d)** The summer in Maine is not hot or it is not sunny. **5. a)** Sharks have not been spotted near the shore. **b)** Swimming at the New Jersey shore is allowed, and sharks have been spotted near the shore. **c)** Swimming at the New Jersey shore is not allowed, or sharks have been spotted near the shore. **d)** If swimming at the New Jersey shore is allowed, then sharks have not been spotted near the shore. **e)** If sharks have not been spotted near the shore, then swimming at the New Jersey shore is allowed. **f)** If swimming at the New Jersey shore is not allowed, then sharks have not been spotted near the shore. **g)** Swimming at the New Jersey shore is allowed if and only if sharks have not been spotted near the shore. **h)** Swimming at the New Jersey shore is not allowed, and either swimming at the New Jersey shore is allowed or sharks have not been spotted near the shore. (Note that we were able to incorporate the parentheses by using the word "either" in the second half of the sentence.) **7. a)** $p \wedge q$ **b)** $p \wedge \neg q$ **c)** $\neg p \wedge \neg q$ **d)** $p \vee q$ **e)** $p \to q$ **f)** $(p \vee q) \wedge (p \to \neg q)$ **g)** $q \leftrightarrow p$ **9. a)** $\neg p$ **b)** $p \wedge \neg q$ **c)** $p \to q$ **d)** $\neg p \to \neg q$ **e)** $p \to q$ **f)** $q \wedge \neg p$ **g)** $q \to p$ **11. a)** $r \wedge \neg p$ **b)** $\neg p \wedge q \wedge r$ **c)** $r \to (q \leftrightarrow \neg p)$ **d)** $\neg q \wedge \neg p \wedge r$ **e)** $(q \to (\neg r \wedge \neg p)) \wedge \neg((\neg r \wedge \neg p) \to q)$ **f)** $(p \wedge r) \to \neg q$ **13. a)** False **b)** True **c)** True **d)** True **e)** True **f)** True **g)** False **h)** True **15. a)** Inclusive *or:* It is allowable to take discrete mathematics if you have had calculus or computer science, or both. Exclusive *or:* It is allowable to take discrete mathematics if you have had calculus or computer science, but not if you have had both. Most likely the inclusive *or* is intended. **b)** Inclusive *or:* You can take the rebate, or you can get a low-interest loan, or you can get both the rebate and a low-interest loan. Exclusive *or:* You can take the rebate, or you can get a low-interest loan, but you cannot get both the rebate and a low-interest loan. Most likely the exclusive *or* is intended. **c)** Inclusive *or:* You can order two items from column A and none from column B, or three items from column B and none from column A, or five items including two from column A and three from column B. Exclusive *or:* You can order two items from column A or three items from column B, but not both. Almost certainly the exclusive *or* is intended. **d)** Inclusive *or:* More than 2 feet of snow or windchill below -100, or both, will close school. Exclusive *or:* More than 2 feet of snow or windchill below -100, but not both, will close school. Certainly the inclusive *or* is intended. **17. a)** If the wind blows from the northeast, then it snows. **b)** If it stays warm for a week, then the apple trees will bloom. **c)** If the Pistons win the championship, then they beat the Lakers. **d)** If you get to the top of Long's Peak, then you must have walked 8 miles. **e)** If you are world-famous, then you will get tenure as a professor. **f)** If you drive more than 400 miles, then you will need to buy gasoline. **g)** If your guarantee is good, then you must have bought your CD player less than 90 days ago. **19. a)** You buy an ice cream cone if and only if it is hot outside. **b)** You win the contest if and only if you hold the only winning ticket. **c)** You get promoted if and only if you have connections. **d)** Your mind will decay if and only if you watch television. **e)** The train runs late if and only if it is a day I take the train. **21. a)** Converse: "I will ski tomorrow only if it snows today." Contrapositive: "If I do not ski tomorrow, then it will not have snowed today." Inverse: "If it does not snow today, then I will not ski tomorrow." **b)** Converse: "If I come to class, then there will be a quiz." Contrapositive: "If I do not come to class, then there will not be a quiz." Inverse: "If there is not going to be a quiz, then I don't come to class." **c)** Converse: "A positive integer is a prime if it has no divisors other than 1 and itself." Contrapositive: "If a positive integer has a divisor other than 1 and itself, then it is not prime." Inverse: "If a positive integer is not prime, then it has a divisor other than 1 and itself."

23. a)

p	$\neg p$	$p \wedge \neg p$
T	F	F
F	T	F

b)

p	$\neg p$	$p \vee \neg p$
T	F	T
F	T	T

c)

p	q	$\neg q$	$p \vee \neg q$	$(p \vee \neg q) \to q$
T	T	F	T	T
T	F	T	T	F
F	T	F	F	T
F	F	T	T	F

d)

p	q	p ∨ q	p ∧ q	(p ∨ q) → (p ∧ q)
T	T	T	T	T
T	F	T	F	F
F	T	T	F	F
F	F	F	F	T

e)

p	q	p → q	¬q	¬p	¬q → ¬p	(p → q) ↔ (¬q → ¬p)
T	T	T	F	F	T	T
T	F	F	T	F	F	T
F	T	T	F	T	T	T
F	F	T	T	T	T	T

f)

p	q	p → q	q → p	(p → q) → (q → p)
T	T	T	T	T
T	F	F	T	T
F	T	T	F	F
F	F	T	T	T

25. For parts **(a)**, **(b)**, **(c)**, **(d)**, and **(f)** we have this table.

p	q	(p ∨ q) → (p ⊕ q)	(p ⊕ q) → (p ∧ q)	(p ∨ q) ⊕ (p ∧ q)	(p ↔ q) ⊕ (¬p ↔ q)	(p ⊕ q) → (p ⊕ ¬q)
T	T	F	T	F	T	T
T	F	T	F	T	T	F
F	T	T	F	T	T	F
F	F	T	T	F	T	T

For part **(e)** we have this table.

p	q	r	¬p	¬r	p ↔ q	¬p ↔ ¬r	(p ↔ q) ⊕ (¬p ↔ ¬r)
T	T	T	F	F	T	T	F
T	T	F	F	T	T	F	T
T	F	T	F	F	F	T	T
T	F	F	F	T	F	F	F
F	T	T	T	F	F	F	F
F	T	F	T	T	F	T	T
F	F	T	T	F	T	F	T
F	F	F	T	T	T	T	F

27.

p	q	p → ¬q	¬p ↔ q	(p → q)∨(¬p → q)	(p → q)∧(¬p → q)	(p ↔ q)∨(¬p ↔ q)	(¬p ↔ ¬q) ↔ (p ↔ q)
T	T	F	F	T	T	T	T
T	F	T	T	T	F	T	T
F	T	T	T	T	T	F	T
F	F	T	F	T	F	T	T

29.

p	q	r	p → (¬q ∨ r)	¬p → (q → r)	(p → q)∨(¬p → r)	(p → q)∧(¬p → r)	(p ↔ q)∨(¬q ↔ r)	(¬p ↔ ¬q) ↔ (q ↔ r)
T	T	T	T	T	T	T	T	T
T	T	F	F	T	T	T	T	F
T	F	T	T	T	T	F	T	T
T	F	F	T	T	T	F	F	F
F	T	T	T	T	T	T	T	F
F	T	F	T	F	F	F	T	T
F	F	T	T	T	T	T	T	F
F	F	F	T	T	T	F	T	T

31.

p	q	r	s	$p \leftrightarrow q$	$r \leftrightarrow s$	$(p \leftrightarrow q) \leftrightarrow (r \leftrightarrow s)$
T	T	T	T	T	T	T
T	T	T	F	T	F	F
T	T	F	T	T	F	F
T	T	F	F	T	T	T
T	F	T	T	F	T	F
T	F	T	F	F	F	T
T	F	F	T	F	F	T
T	F	F	F	F	T	F
F	T	T	T	F	T	F
F	T	T	F	F	F	T
F	T	F	T	F	F	T
F	T	F	F	F	T	F
F	F	T	T	T	T	T
F	F	T	F	T	F	F
F	F	F	T	T	F	F
F	F	F	F	T	T	T

33. **a)** Bitwise *OR* is 111 1111; bitwise *AND* is 000 0000; bitwise *XOR* is 111 1111. **b)** Bitwise *OR* is 1111 1010; bitwise *AND* is 1010 0000; bitwise *XOR* is 0101 1010. **c)** Bitwise *OR* is 10 0111 1001; bitwise *AND* is 00 0100 0000; bitwise *XOR* is 10 0011 1001. **d)** Bitwise *OR* is 11 1111 1111; bitwise *AND* is 00 0000 0000; bitwise *XOR* is 11 1111 1111. **35.** 0.2, 0.6 **37.** 0.8, 0.6 **39. a)** The 99th statement is true and the rest are false. **b)** Statements 1 through 50 are all true and statements 51 through 99 are all false. **c)** This cannot happen; it is a paradox, showing that these cannot be statements. **41.** "If I were to ask you whether the right branch leads to the ruins, would you answer yes?" **43. a)** $q \rightarrow p$ **b)** $q \wedge \neg p$ **c)** $q \rightarrow p$ **d)** $\neg q \rightarrow \neg p$ **45.** Not consistent **47.** Consistent **49.** NEW **AND** JERSEY **AND** BEACHES, (JERSEY **AND** BEACHES) **NOT** NEW **51.** *A* is a knight and *B* is a knave. **53.** *A* is a knight and *B* is a knight. **55.** *A* is a knave and *B* is a knight. **57.** In order of decreasing salary: Fred, Maggie, Janice **59.** The detective can determine that the butler and cook are lying but cannot determine whether the gardener is telling the truth or whether the handyman is telling the truth. **61.** The Japanese man owns the zebra, and the Norwegian drinks water.

SECTION 1.2

1. The equivalences follow by showing that the appropriate pairs of columns of this table agree.

p	$p \wedge T$	$p \vee F$	$p \wedge F$	$p \vee T$	$p \vee p$	$p \wedge p$
T	T	T	F	T	T	T
F	F	F	F	T	F	F

3. a)

p	q	$p \vee q$	$q \vee p$
T	T	T	T
T	F	T	T
F	T	T	T
F	F	F	F

b)

p	q	$p \wedge q$	$q \wedge p$
T	T	T	T
T	F	F	F
F	T	F	F
F	F	F	F

5.

p	q	r	$q \vee r$	$p \wedge (q \vee r)$	$p \wedge q$	$p \wedge r$	$(p \wedge q) \vee (p \wedge r)$
T	T	T	T	T	T	T	T
T	T	F	T	T	T	F	T
T	F	T	T	T	F	T	T
T	F	F	F	F	F	F	F
F	T	T	T	F	F	F	F
F	T	F	T	F	F	F	F
F	F	T	T	F	F	F	F
F	F	F	F	F	F	F	F

7. a)

p	q	$p \wedge q$	$(p \wedge q) \rightarrow p$
T	T	T	T
T	F	F	T
F	T	F	T
F	F	F	T

b)

p	q	$p \vee q$	$p \rightarrow (p \vee q)$
T	T	T	T
T	F	T	T
F	T	T	T
F	F	F	T

c)

p	q	$\neg p$	$p \rightarrow q$	$\neg p \rightarrow (p \rightarrow q)$
T	T	F	T	T
T	F	F	F	T
F	T	T	T	T
F	F	T	T	T

d)

p	q	$p \wedge q$	$p \rightarrow q$	$(p \wedge q) \rightarrow (p \rightarrow q)$
T	T	T	T	T
T	F	F	F	T
F	T	F	T	T
F	F	F	T	T

e)

p	q	$p \rightarrow q$	$\neg (p \rightarrow q)$	$\neg (p \rightarrow q) \rightarrow p$
T	T	T	F	T
T	F	F	T	T
F	T	T	F	T
F	F	T	F	T

f)

p	q	$p \to q$	$\neg(p \to q)$	$\neg q$	$\neg(p \to q) \to \neg q$
T	T	T	F	F	T
T	F	F	T	T	T
F	T	T	F	F	T
F	F	T	F	T	T

9. In each case we will show that if the hypothesis is true, then the conclusion is also. **a)** If the hypothesis $p \wedge q$ is true, then by the definition of conjunction, the conclusion p must also be true. **b)** If the hypothesis p is true, by the definition of disjunction, the conclusion $p \vee q$ is also true. **c)** If the hypothesis $\neg p$ is true, that is, if p is false, then the conclusion $p \to q$ is true. **d)** If the hypothesis $p \wedge q$ is true, then both p and q are true so that the conclusion $p \to q$ is also true. **e)** If the hypothesis $\neg(p \to q)$ is true, then $p \to q$ is false, so that the conclusion p is true (and q is false). **f)** If the hypothesis $\neg(p \to q)$ is true, then $p \to q$ is false, so that p is true and q is false. Hence, the conclusion $\neg q$ is true. **11.** That the fourth column of the truth table shown is identical to the first column proves part **(a)**, and that the sixth column is identical to the first column proves part **(b)**.

p	q	$p \wedge q$	$p \vee (p \wedge q)$	$p \vee q$	$p \wedge (p \vee q)$
T	T	T	T	T	T
T	F	F	T	T	T
F	T	F	F	T	F
F	F	F	F	F	F

13. The only way this implication can be false is when $\neg q \wedge (p \to q)$ is true and $\neg p$ is false. For $\neg p$ to be false, p must be true. For $\neg q \wedge (p \to q)$ to be true, $\neg q$ must be true, so q is false. Since p is true, this makes $p \to q$ false, which is impossible. **15.** These are not logically equivalent since when p, q, and r are all false, $(p \to q) \to r$ is false, but $p \to (q \to r)$ is true. **17.** The proposition $\neg p \leftrightarrow q$ is true when $\neg p$ and q have the same truth values, which means that p and q have different truth values. Similarly, $p \leftrightarrow \neg q$ is true in exactly the same cases. Therefore, these two expressions are logically equivalent. **19.** The proposition $\neg(p \leftrightarrow q)$ is true when $p \leftrightarrow q$ is false, which means that p and q have different truth values. Since this is precisely when $\neg p \leftrightarrow q$ is true, the two expressions are logically equivalent. **21.** For $(p \to r) \wedge (q \to r)$ to be false, one of the two implications must be false, which happens exactly when r is false and at least one of p and q is true. But these are precisely the cases in which $p \vee q$ is true and r is false, which is precisely when $(p \vee q) \to r$ is false. Since the two propositions are false in exactly the same situations, they are logically equivalent. **23.** For $(p \to r) \vee (q \to r)$ to be false, both of the two implications must be false, which happens exactly when r is false and both p and q are true. But this is precisely the case in which $p \wedge q$ is true and r is false, which is precisely when $(p \wedge q) \to r$ is false. Since the two propositions are false in exactly the same situations, they are logically equivalent. **25.** This fact was observed in Section 1 when the biconditional was first defined. Each of these is true precisely when p and q have the same truth values. **27.** Each of these is true precisely when p and q have opposite truth values. **29.** The last column is all Ts.

p	q	r	$p \to q$	$q \to r$	$(p \to q) \wedge (q \to r)$	$p \to r$	$(p \to q) \wedge (q \to r) \to (p \to r)$
T	T	T	T	T	T	T	T
T	T	F	T	F	F	F	T
T	F	T	F	T	F	T	T
T	F	F	F	T	F	F	T
F	T	T	T	T	T	T	T
F	T	F	T	F	F	T	T
F	F	T	T	T	T	T	T
F	F	F	T	T	T	T	T

31. If we take duals twice, every $\vee$ changes to an $\wedge$ and then back to an $\vee$, every $\wedge$ changes to an $\vee$ and then back to an $\wedge$, every **T** changes to an **F** and then back to a **T**, every **F** changes to a **T** and then back to an **F**. Hence, $(s^*)^* = s$. **33.** Let p and q be equivalent compound propositions involving only the operators $\wedge$, $\vee$, and $\neg$, and **T** and **F**. Note that $\neg p$ and $\neg q$ are also equivalent. Use De Morgan's laws as many times as necessary to push negations in as far as possible within these compound propositions, changing $\vee$s to $\wedge$s, and vice versa, and changing **T**s to **F**s, and vice versa. This shows that $\neg p$ and $\neg q$ are the same as p^* and q^* except that each atomic proposition p_i within them is replaced by its negation. From this we can conclude that p^* and q^* are equivalent since $\neg p$ and $\neg q$ are. **35.** $(p \wedge q \wedge \neg r) \vee (p \wedge \neg q \wedge r) \vee (\neg p \wedge q \wedge r)$ **37.** Given a compound proposition p, form its truth table and then write down a proposition q in disjunctive normal form that is logically equivalent to p. Since q involves only $\neg$, $\wedge$, and $\vee$, this shows that these three operators form a functionally complete set. **39.** By Exercise 37, given a compound proposition p, we can write down a proposition q that is logically equivalent to p and involves only $\neg$, $\wedge$, and $\vee$. By De Morgan's law we can eliminate all the $\wedge$s by replacing each occurrence of $p_1 \wedge p_2 \wedge \cdots \wedge p_n$ with $\neg(\neg p_1 \vee \neg p_2 \vee \cdots \vee \neg p_n)$. **41.** $\neg(p \wedge q)$ is true when either p or q, or both, are false, and is false when both p and q are true. Since this was the definition of $p \mid q$, the two compound propositions are logically equivalent. **43.** $\neg(p \vee q)$ is true when both p and q are false, and is false otherwise. Since this was the definition of $p \downarrow q$, the two are logically equivalent. **45.** $((p \downarrow p) \downarrow q) \downarrow ((p \downarrow p) \downarrow q)$ **47.** This follows immediately from the truth table or definition of $p \mid q$. **49.** 16 **51.** If the database is open, then either the system is in its initial state or the monitor is put in a closed state. **53.** All nine **55.** To determine whether c is a tautology apply an algorithm for satisfiability to $\neg c$. If the algorithm says that $\neg c$ is satisfiable, then we report that c is not a tautology, and if the algorithm says that $\neg c$ is not satisfiable, then we report that c is a tautology.

SECTION 1.3

1. a) T **b)** T **c)** F **3. a)** T **b)** F **c)** F **d)** F **5. a)** There is a student who spends more than 5 hours every weekday in class. **b)** Every student spends more than 5 hours every weekday in class. **c)** There is a student who does not spend more than 5 hours every weekday in class. **d)** No student spends more than 5 hours every weekday in class. **7. a)** Every comedian is funny. **b)** Every person is a funny comedian. **c)** There exists a person such that if she or he is a comedian, then she or he is funny. **d)** Some comedians are funny. **9. a)** $\exists x(P(x) \wedge Q(x))$ **b)** $\exists x(P(x) \wedge \neg Q(x))$ **c)** $\forall x(P(x) \vee Q(x))$ **d)** $\forall x \neg(P(x) \vee Q(x))$ **11. a)** T **b)** T **c)** F **d)** F **e)** T **f)** F **13. a)** True **b)** True **c)** True **d)** True **15. a)** True **b)** False **c)** True **d)** False **17. a)** $P(0) \vee P(1) \vee P(2) \vee P(3) \vee P(4)$ **b)** $P(0) \wedge P(1) \wedge P(2) \wedge P(3) \wedge P(4)$ **c)** $\neg P(0) \vee \neg P(1) \vee \neg P(2) \vee \neg P(3) \vee \neg P(4)$ **d)** $\neg P(0) \wedge \neg P(1) \wedge \neg P(2) \wedge \neg P(3) \wedge \neg P(4)$ **e)** $\neg(P(0) \vee P(1) \vee P(2) \vee P(3) \vee P(4))$ **f)** $\neg(P(0) \wedge P(1) \wedge P(2) \wedge P(3) \wedge P(4))$ **19. a)** $P(1) \vee P(2) \vee P(3) \vee P(4) \vee P(5)$ **b)** $P(1) \wedge P(2) \wedge P(3) \wedge P(4) \wedge P(5)$ **c)** $\neg(P(1) \vee P(2) \vee P(3) \vee P(4) \vee P(5))$ **d)** $\neg(P(1) \wedge P(2) \wedge P(3) \wedge P(4) \wedge P(5))$ **e)** $(P(1) \wedge P(2) \wedge P(4) \wedge P(5)) \vee (\neg P(1) \vee \neg P(2) \vee \neg P(3) \vee \neg P(4) \vee \neg P(5))$ **21.** Let $C(x)$ be the propositional function "x is in your class." **a)** $\exists x H(x)$ and $\exists x(C(x) \wedge H(x))$, where $H(x)$ is "x can speak Hindi" **b)** $\forall x F(x)$ and $\forall x(C(x) \rightarrow F(x))$, where $F(x)$ is "x is friendly" **c)** $\exists x \neg B(x)$ and $\exists x(C(x) \wedge \neg B(x))$, where $B(x)$ is "x was born in California" **d)** $\exists x M(x)$ and $\exists x(C(x) \wedge M(x))$, where $M(x)$ is "x has been in a movie" **e)** $\forall x \neg L(x)$ and $\forall x(C(x) \rightarrow \neg L(x))$, where $L(x)$ is "x has taken a course in logic programming" **23.** Let $P(x)$ be "x is perfect"; let $F(x)$ be "x is your friend"; and let the universe of discourse be all people. **a)** $\forall x \neg P(x)$ **b)** $\neg \forall x P(x)$ **c)** $\forall x(F(x) \rightarrow P(x))$ **d)** $\exists x(F(x) \wedge P(x))$, assuming that this means "at least one" of your friends is perfect **e)** $\forall x(F(x) \wedge P(x))$ or $(\forall x F(x)) \wedge (\forall x P(x))$ **f)** $(\forall x \neg F(x)) \vee (\exists x \neg P(x))$ **25.** Let $Y(x)$ be the propositional function that x is in your school or class, as appropriate. **a)** If we let $V(x)$ be "x has lived in Vietnam," then we have $\exists x V(x)$ if the universe is just your schoolmates, or $\exists x(Y(x) \wedge V(x))$ if the universe is all people. If we let $D(x, y)$ mean that person x has lived in country y, then we can rewrite this last one as $\exists x(Y(x) \wedge D(x, \text{Vietnam}))$. **b)** If we let $H(x)$ be "x can speak Hindi," then we have $\exists x \neg H(x)$ if the universe is just your schoolmates, or $\exists x(Y(x) \wedge \neg H(x))$ if the universe is all people. If we let $S(x, y)$ mean that person x

can speak language y, then we can rewrite this last one as $\exists x(Y(x) \wedge \neg S(x, \text{Hindi}))$. **c)** If we let $J(x)$, $P(x)$, and $C(x)$ be the propositional functions asserting x's knowledge of Java, Prolog, and C++, respectively, then we have $\exists x(J(x) \wedge P(x) \wedge C(x))$ if the universe is just your schoolmates, or $\exists x(Y(x) \wedge J(x) \wedge P(x) \wedge C(x))$ if the universe is all people. If we let $K(x, y)$ mean that person x knows programming language y, then we can rewrite this last one as $\exists x(Y(x) \wedge K(x, \text{Java}) \wedge K(x, \text{Prolog}) \wedge K(x, \text{C++}))$. **d)** If we let $T(x)$ be "x enjoys Thai food," then we have $\forall x T(x)$ if the universe is just your classmates, or $\forall x(Y(x) \rightarrow T(x))$ if the universe is all people. If we let $E(x, y)$ mean that person x enjoys food of type y, then we can rewrite this last one as $\forall x(Y(x) \rightarrow E(x, \text{Thai}))$. **e)** If we let $H(x)$ be "x plays hockey," then we have $\exists x \neg H(x)$ if the universe is just your classmates, or $\exists x(Y(x) \wedge \neg H(x))$ if the universe is all people. If we let $P(x, y)$ mean that person x plays game y, then we can rewrite this last one as $\exists x(Y(x) \wedge \neg P(x, \text{hockey}))$. **27.** Let $T(x)$ mean that x is a tautology and $C(x)$ mean that x is a contradiction. **a)** $\exists x T(x)$ **b)** $\forall x(C(x) \rightarrow T(\neg x))$ **c)** $\exists x \exists y(\neg T(x) \wedge \neg C(x) \wedge \neg T(y) \wedge \neg C(y) \wedge T(x \vee y))$ **d)** $\forall x \forall y((T(x) \wedge T(y)) \rightarrow T(x \wedge y))$ **29. a)** $Q(0, 0, 0) \wedge Q(0, 1, 0)$ **b)** $Q(0, 1, 1) \vee Q(1, 1, 1) \vee Q(2, 1, 1)$ **c)** $\neg Q(0, 0, 0) \vee \neg Q(0, 0, 1)$ **d)** $\neg Q(0, 0, 1) \vee \neg Q(1, 0, 1) \vee \neg Q(2, 0, 1)$ **31. a)** Let $T(x)$ be the predicate that x can learn new tricks, and let the universe of discourse be old dogs. Original is $\exists x T(x)$. Negation is $\forall x \neg T(x)$: "No old dogs can learn new tricks." **b)** Let $C(x)$ be the predicate that x knows calculus, and let the universe of discourse be rabbits. Original is $\neg \exists x C(x)$. Negation is $\exists x C(x)$: "There is a rabbit that knows calculus." **c)** Let $F(x)$ be the predicate that x can fly, and let the universe of discourse be birds. Original is $\forall x F(x)$. Negation is $\exists x \neg F(x)$: "There is a bird who cannot fly." **d)** Let $T(x)$ be the predicate that x can talk, and let the universe of discourse be dogs. Original is $\neg \exists x T(x)$. Negation is $\exists x T(x)$: "There is a dog that talks." **e)** Let $F(x)$ and $R(x)$ be the predicates that x knows French and knows Russian, respectively, and let the universe of discourse be people in this class. Original is $\neg \exists x(F(x) \wedge R(x))$. Negation is $\exists x(F(x) \wedge R(x))$: "There is someone in this class who knows French and Russian." **33. a)** There is no counterexample. **b)** $x = 0$ **c)** $x = 2$ **35. a)** $\forall x((F(x, 25{,}000) \vee S(x, 25)) \rightarrow E(x))$, where $E(x)$ is "Person x qualifies as an elite flyer in a given year," $F(x, y)$ is "Person x flies more than y miles in a given year," and $S(x, y)$ is "Person x takes more than y flights in a given year" **b)** $\forall x(((M(x) \wedge T(x, 3)) \vee (\neg M(x) \wedge T(x, 3.5))) \rightarrow Q(x))$, where $Q(x)$ is "Person x qualifies for the marathon," $M(x)$ is "Person x is a man," and $T(x, y)$ is "Person x has run the marathon in less than y hours" **c)** $M \rightarrow ((H(60) \vee (H(45) \wedge T)) \wedge \forall y G(\text{B}, y))$, where M is the proposition "The student received a masters degree," $H(x)$ is "The student took at least x course hours," T is the proposition "The student wrote a thesis," and $G(x, y)$ is "The person got grade x or higher in course y"

d) $\exists x\,((T(x, 21) \wedge G(x, 4.0))$, where $T(x, y)$ is "Person x took more than y credit hours" and $G(x, p)$ is "Person x earned grade point average p" (we assume that we are talking about one given semester) **37. a)** If there is a printer that is both out of service and busy, then some job has been lost. **b)** If every printer is busy, then there is a job in the queue. **c)** If there is a job that is both queued and lost, then some printer is out of service. **d)** If every printer is busy and every job is queued, then some job is lost. **39. a)** $(\exists x\,F(x, 10)) \to \exists x\,S(x)$, where $F(x, y)$ is "Disk x has more than y kilobytes of free space," and $S(x)$ is "Mail message x can be saved" **b)** $(\exists x\,A(x)) \to \forall x(Q(x) \to T(x))$, where $A(x)$ is "Alert x is active," $Q(x)$ is "Message x is queued," and $T(x)$ is "Message x is transmitted" **c)** $\forall x((x \neq \text{main console}) \to T(x))$, where $T(x)$ is "The diagnostic monitor tracks the status of system x" **d)** $\forall x(\neg L(x) \to B(x))$, where $L(x)$ is "The host of the conference call put participant x on a special list" and $B(x)$ is "Participant x was billed" **41.** Not always **43.** Both statements are true precisely when at least one of $P(x)$ and $Q(x)$ is true for at least one value of x in the universe of discourse. **45. a)** If A is true, then both sides are logically equivalent to $\forall x\,P(x)$. If A is false, the left-hand side is clearly false. Furthermore, for every x, $P(x) \wedge A$ is false, so the right-hand side is false. Hence, the two sides are logically equivalent. **b)** If A is true, then both sides are logically equivalent to $\exists x\,P(x)$. If A is false, the left-hand side is clearly false. Furthermore, for every x, $P(x) \wedge A$ is false, so $\exists x(P(x) \wedge A)$ is false. Hence, the two sides are logically equivalent. **47.** To show these are not logically equivalent, let $P(x)$ be the statement "x is positive," and let $Q(x)$ be the statement "x is negative" with universe of discourse the set of integers. Then $\exists x\,P(x) \wedge \exists x\,Q(x)$ is true, but $\exists x(P(x) \wedge Q(x))$ is false. **49. a)** True **b)** False, unless the universe of discourse consists of just one element **c)** True **51. a)** Yes **b)** No **c)** juana, kiko **d)** math273, cs301 **e)** juana, kiko **53.** sibling(X, Y) :- mother(M, X), mother(M, Y), father(F, X), father(F, Y) **55. a)** $\forall x(P(x) \to \neg Q(x))$ **b)** $\forall x(Q(x) \to R(x))$ **c)** $\forall x(P(x) \to \neg R(x))$ **d)** The conclusion does not follow. There may be vain professors, since the premises do not rule out the possibility that there are other vain people besides ignorant ones. **57. a)** $\forall x(P(x) \to \neg Q(x))$ **b)** $\forall x(R(x) \to \neg S(x))$ **c)** $\forall x(\neg Q(x) \to S(x))$ **d)** $\forall x(P(x) \to \neg R(x))$ **e)** The conclusion follows. Suppose x is a baby. Then by the first premise, x is illogical, so by the third premise, x is despised. The second premise says that if x could manage a crocodile, then x would not be despised. Therefore, x cannot manage a crocodile.

SECTION 1.4

1. a) For every real number x there exists a real number y such that x is less than y. **b)** For every real number x and real number y, if x and y are both nonnegative, then their product is nonnegative. **c)** For every real number x and real number y, there exists a real number z such that $xy = z$. **3. a)** There is some student in your class who has sent a message to some student in your class. **b)** There is some student in your class who has sent a message to every student in your class. **c)** Every student in your class has sent a message to at least one student in your class. **d)** There is a student in your class who has been sent a message by every student in your class. **e)** Every student in your class has been sent a message from at least one student in your class. **f)** Every student in the class has sent a message to every student in the class. **5. a)** Sarah Smith has visited www.att.com. **b)** At least one person has visited www.imdb.org. **c)** Jose Orez has visited at least one website. **d)** There is a website that both Ashok Puri and Cindy Yoon have visited. **e)** There is a person besides David Belcher who has visited all the websites that David Belcher has visited. **f)** There are two different people who have visited exactly the same websites. **7. a)** Abdallah Hussein does not like Japanese cuisine. **b)** Some student at your school likes Korean cuisine, and everyone at your school likes Mexican cuisine. **c)** There is some cuisine that either Monique Arsenault or Jay Johnson likes. **d)** For every pair of distinct students at your school, there is some cuisine that at least one them does not like. **e)** There are two students at your school who like exactly the same set of cuisines. **f)** For every pair of students at your school, there is some cuisine about which they have the same opinion (either they both like it or they both do not like it). **9. a)** $\forall x\,L(x, \text{Jerry})$ **b)** $\forall x\exists y\,L(x, y)$ **c)** $\exists y\forall x\,L(x, y)$ **d)** $\forall x\exists y\,\neg L(x, y)$ **e)** $\exists x\,\neg L(\text{Lydia}, x)$ **f)** $\exists x\forall y\,\neg L(y, x)$ **g)** $\exists x(\forall y\,L(y, x) \wedge \forall z((\forall w\,L(w, z)) \to z = x))$ **h)** $\exists x\exists y(x \neq y \wedge L(\text{Lynn}, x) \wedge L(\text{Lynn}, y) \wedge \forall z(L(\text{Lynn}, z) \to (z = x \vee z = y)))$ **i)** $\forall x\,L(x, x)$ **j)** $\exists x\forall y(L(x, y) \leftrightarrow x = y)$ **11. a)** $A(\text{Lois}, \text{Professor Michaels})$ **b)** $\forall x(S(x) \to A(x, \text{Professor Gross}))$ **c)** $\forall x(F(x) \to (A(x, \text{Professor Miller}) \vee A(\text{Professor Miller}, x)))$ **d)** $\exists x(S(x) \wedge \forall y(F(y) \to \neg A(x, y)))$ **e)** $\exists x(F(x) \wedge \forall y(S(y) \to \neg A(y, x)))$ **f)** $\forall y(F(y) \to \exists x(S(x) \vee A(x, y)))$ **g)** $\exists x(F(x) \wedge \forall y((F(y) \wedge (y \neq x)) \to A(x, y)))$ **h)** $\exists x(S(x) \wedge \forall y(F(y) \to \neg A(y, x)))$ **13. a)** $\neg M(\text{Chou}, \text{Koko})$ **b)** $\neg M(\text{Arlene}, \text{Sarah}) \wedge \neg T(\text{Arlene}, \text{Sarah})$ **c)** $\neg M(\text{Deborah}, \text{Jose})$ **d)** $\forall x\,M(x, \text{Ken})$ **e)** $\forall x\,\neg T(x, \text{Nina})$ **f)** $\forall x((T, x, \text{Avi}) \vee M(x, \text{Avi}))$ **g)** $\exists x\forall y(y \neq x \to M(x, y))$ **h)** $\exists x\forall y(y \neq x \to (M(x, y) \vee T(x, y)))$ **i)** $\exists x\exists y(x \neq y \wedge M(x, y) \wedge M(y, x))$ **j)** $\exists x\,M(x, x)$ **k)** $\exists x\forall y(x \neq y \to (\neg M(x, y) \wedge \neg T(y, x)))$ **l)** $\forall x(\exists y(x \neq y \wedge (M(y, x) \vee T(y, x))))$ **m)** $\exists x\exists y(x \neq y \wedge M(x, y) \wedge T(y, x))$ **n)** $\exists x\exists y(x \neq y \wedge \forall z((z \neq x \wedge z \neq y) \to (M(x, z) \vee M(y, z) \vee T(x, z) \vee T(y, z))))$ **15. a)** $\forall x\,P(x)$, where $P(x)$ is "x needs a course in discrete mathematics" and the universe of discourse consists of all computer science students **b)** $\exists x\,P(x)$, where $P(x)$ is "x owns a personal computer" and the universe consists of all students in this class **c)** $\forall x\exists y\,P(x, y)$, where $P(x, y)$ is "x has taken

y," the universe of discourse for x consists of all students in this class, and the universe of discourse for y consists of all computer science classes **d)** $\exists x \exists y P(x, y)$, where $P(x, y)$ and universes of discourse are the same as in part (c) **e)** $\forall x \forall y P(x, y)$, where $P(x, y)$ is "x has been in y," the universe of discourse for x consists of all students in this class, and the universe of discourse for y consists of all buildings on campus **f)** $\exists x \exists y \forall z (P(z, y) \rightarrow Q(x, z))$, where $P(z, y)$ is "z is in y" and $Q(x, z)$ is "x has been in z"; the universe of discourse for x consists of all students in the class, the universe of discourse for y consists of all buildings on campus, and the universe of discourse of z consists of all rooms. **g)** $\forall x \forall y \exists z (P(z, y) \land Q(x, z))$, with same environment as in part (f)   **17. a)** $\forall u \exists m (A(u, m) \land \forall n(n \neq m \rightarrow \neg A(u, n)))$, where $A(u, m)$ means that user u has access to mailbox m **b)** $\exists p \forall e (H(e) \land S(p,\ running)) \rightarrow S(kernel,\ working$ correctly), where $H(e)$ means that error condition e is in effect and $S(x, y)$ means that the status of x is y **c)** $\forall u \forall s (E(s, .edu) \rightarrow A(u, s))$, where $E(s, x)$ means that website s has extension x, and $A(u, s)$ means that user u can access website s **d)** $\exists x \exists y (x \neq y \land \forall z ((\forall s\ M(z, s)) \leftrightarrow (z = x \lor z = y)))$, where $M(a, b)$ means that system a monitors remote server b **19. a)** $\forall x \forall y ((x < 0) \land (y < 0) \rightarrow (x + y < 0))$ **b)** $\neg \forall x \forall y ((x > 0) \land (y > 0) \rightarrow (x - y > 0))$ **c)** $\forall x \forall y (x^2 + y^2 \geq (x + y)^2)$ **d)** $\forall x \forall y (|xy| = |x||y|)$ **21.** $\forall x \exists a \exists b \exists c \exists d ((x > 0) \rightarrow x = a^2 + b^2 + c^2 + d^2)$, where the universe of discourse consists of all integers   **23. a)** $\forall x \forall y ((x < 0) \land (y < 0) \rightarrow (xy > 0))$ **b)** $\forall x (x - x = 0)$ **c)** $\forall x \exists a \exists b (a \neq b \land \forall c (c^2 = x \leftrightarrow (c = a \lor c = b)))$ **d)** $\forall x ((x < 0) \rightarrow \neg \exists y (x = y^2))$ **25. a)** There is a multiplicative identity for the real numbers. **b)** The product of two negative real numbers is always a positive real number. **c)** There exist real numbers x and y such that x^2 exceeds y but x is less than y. **d)** The real numbers are closed under the operation of addition.   **27. a)** True **b)** True **c)** True **d)** True **e)** True **f)** False **g)** False **h)** True **i)** False **29. a)** $P(1, 1) \land P(1, 2) \land P(1, 3) \land P(2, 1) \land P(2, 2) \land P(2, 3) \land P(3, 1) \land P(3, 2) \land P(3, 3)$ **b)** $P(1, 1) \lor P(1, 2) \lor P(1, 3) \lor P(2, 1) \lor P(2, 2) \lor P(2, 3) \lor P(3, 1) \lor P(3, 2) \lor P(3, 3)$ **c)** $(P(1, 1) \land P(1, 2) \land P(1, 3)) \lor (P(2, 1) \land P(2, 2) \land P(2, 3)) \lor (P(3, 1) \land P(3, 2) \land P(3, 3))$ **d)** $(P(1, 1) \lor P(2, 1) \lor P(3, 1)) \land (P(1, 2) \lor P(2, 2) \lor P(3, 2)) \land (P(1, 3) \lor P(2, 3) \lor P(3, 3))$ **31. a)** $\exists x \forall y \exists z \neg T(x, y, z)$ **b)** $\exists x \forall y \neg P(x, y) \land \exists x \forall y \neg Q(x, y)$ **c)** $\exists x \forall y (\neg P(x, y) \lor \forall z \neg R(x, y, z))$ **d)** $\exists x \forall y (P(x, y) \land \neg Q(x, y))$ **33. a)** $\exists x \exists y \neg P(x, y)$ **b)** $\exists y \forall x \neg P(x, y)$ **c)** $\exists y \exists x (\neg P(x, y) \land \neg Q(x, y))$ **d)** $(\forall x \forall y P(x, y)) \lor (\exists x \exists y \neg Q(x, y))$ **e)** $\exists x (\forall y \exists z \neg P(x, y, z) \lor \forall z \exists y \neg P(x, y, z))$ **35. a)** There is someone in this class such that for every two different math courses, these are not the two and only two math courses this person has taken. **b)** Every person has either visited Libya or has not visited a country other than Libya. **c)** Someone has climbed every mountain in the Himalayas. **d)** There is someone who has neither been in a movie with Kevin Bacon nor has been in a movie

with someone who has been in a movie with Kevin Bacon. **37. a)** $x = 2, y = -2$ **b)** $x = -4$ **c)** $x = 17, y = -1$ **39.** $\forall x \forall y \forall z ((x \cdot y) \cdot z = x \cdot (y \cdot z))$ **41. a)** True **b)** False **c)** True   **43.** $\neg (\exists x \forall y P(x, y)) \leftrightarrow \forall x (\neg \forall y P(x, y)) \leftrightarrow \forall x \exists y \neg P(x, y)$ **45. a)** Suppose that $\forall x P(x) \land \exists x Q(x)$ is true. Then $P(x)$ is true for all x and there is an element y for which $Q(y)$ is true. Since $P(x) \land Q(y)$ is true for all x and there is a y for which $Q(y)$ is true, $\forall x \exists y (P(x) \land Q(y))$ is true. Conversely, suppose that the second proposition is true. Let x be an element in the universe of discourse. There is a y such that $Q(y)$ is true, so $\exists x Q(x)$ is true. Since $\forall x P(x)$ is also true, it follows that the first proposition is true. **b)** Suppose that $\forall x P(x) \lor \exists x Q(x)$ is true. Then either $P(x)$ is true for all x, or there exists a y for which $Q(y)$ is true. In the former case, $P(x) \lor Q(y)$ is true for all x, so $\forall x \exists y (P(x) \lor Q(y))$ is true. In the latter case, $Q(y)$ is true for a particular y, so $P(x) \lor Q(y)$ is true for all x and consequently $\forall x \exists y (P(x) \lor Q(y))$ is true. Conversely, suppose that the second proposition is true. If $P(x)$ is true for all x, then the first proposition is true. If not, $P(x)$ is false for some x, and for this x there must be a y such that $P(x) \lor Q(y)$ is true. Hence, $Q(y)$ must be true, so $\exists y Q(y)$ is true. It follows that the first proposition must hold. **47.** We will show how an expression can be put into prenex normal form (PNF) if subexpressions in it can be put into PNF. Then, working from the inside out, any expression can be put in PNF. (To formalize the argument, it is necessary to use the method of structural induction that will be discussed in Section 3.4.) By Exercise 39 of Section 1.2, we can assume that the proposition uses only $\lor$ and $\neg$ as logical connectives. Now note that any proposition with no quantifiers is already in PNF. (This is the basis case of the argument.) Now suppose that the proposition is of the form $Qx P(x)$, where Q is a quantifier. Since $P(x)$ is a shorter expression than the original proposition, we can put it into PNF. Then Qx followed by this PNF is again in PNF and is equivalent to the original proposition. Next, suppose that the proposition is of the form $\neg P$. If P is already in PNF, we slide the negation sign past all the quantifiers using the equivalences in Table 2 in Section 1.3. Finally, assume that proposition is of the form $P \lor Q$, where each of P and Q is in PNF. If only one of P and Q has quantifiers, then we can use Exercise 44 in Section 1.3 to bring the quantifier in front of both. If both P and Q have quantifiers, we can use Exercise 43 in Section 1.3, Exercise 44, or part (b) of Exercise 45 to rewrite $P \lor Q$ with two quantifiers preceding the disjunction of a proposition of the form $R \lor S$, and then put $R \lor S$ into PNF.   **49.** $\exists x P(x) \land \forall x \forall y ((P(x) \land P(y)) \rightarrow x = y)$ **51.** $\forall L \exists \epsilon \forall N \exists n (n > N \land |a_n - L| \geq \epsilon)$ **53.** $\forall \epsilon (\forall N \exists n (n > N \land a_n > L - \epsilon) \land \exists N \forall n (n > N \rightarrow a_n \leq L + \epsilon))$

SECTION 1.5

1. a) Addition   **b)** Simplification   **c)** Modus ponens **d)** Modus tollens **e)** Hypothetical syllogism   **3.** Let w

be "Randy works hard," let d be "Randy is a dull boy," and let j be "Randy will get the job." The hypotheses are $w, w \rightarrow d$, and $d \rightarrow \neg j$. Using modus ponens and the first two hypotheses, d follows. Using modus ponens and the last hypothesis, $\neg j$, which is the desired conclusion, "Randy will not get the job," follows.   **5.** Universal instantiation is used to conclude that "If Socrates is a man, then Socrates is mortal." Modus ponens is then used to conclude that Socrates is mortal.   **7. a)** Valid conclusions are "I did not take Tuesday off," "I took Thursday off," "It rained on Thursday."   **b)** "I did not eat spicy foods and it did not thunder" is a valid conclusion.   **c)** "I am clever" is a valid conclusion.   **d)** "Ralph is not a CS major" is a valid conclusion.   **e)** "That you buy lots of stuff is good for the U.S. and is good for you" is a valid conclusion.   **f)** "Mice gnaw their food" and "Rabbits are not rodents" are valid conclusions.   **9. a)** Let $c(x)$ be "x is in this class," $j(x)$ be "x knows how to write programs in JAVA," and $h(x)$ be "x can get a high-paying job." The premises are $c(\text{Doug}), j(\text{Doug}), \forall x(j(x) \rightarrow h(x))$. Using universal instantiation and the last premise, $j(\text{Doug}) \rightarrow h(\text{Doug})$ follows. Applying modus ponens to this conclusion and the second premise, $h(\text{Doug})$ follows. Using conjunction and the first premise, $c(\text{Doug}) \wedge h(\text{Doug})$ follows. Finally, using existential generalization, the desired conclusion, $\exists x(c(x) \wedge h(x))$ follows.   **b)** Let $c(x)$ be "x is in this class," $w(x)$ be "x enjoys whale watching," and $p(x)$ be "x cares about ocean pollution." The premises are $\exists x(c(x) \wedge w(x))$ and $\forall x(w(x) \rightarrow p(x))$. From the first premise, $c(y) \wedge w(y)$ for a particular person y. Using simplification, $w(y)$ follows. Using the second premise and universal instantiation, $w(y) \rightarrow p(y)$ follows. Using modus ponens, $p(y)$ follows, and by conjunction, $c(y) \wedge p(y)$ follows. Finally, by existential generalization, the desired conclusion, $\exists x(c(x) \wedge p(x))$, follows.   **c)** Let $c(x)$ be "x is in this class," $p(x)$ be "x owns a PC," and $w(x)$ be "x can use a word-processing program." The premises are $c(\text{Zeke}), \forall x(c(x) \rightarrow p(x))$, and $\forall x(p(x) \rightarrow w(x))$. Using the second premise and universal instantiation, $c(\text{Zeke}) \rightarrow p(\text{Zeke})$ follows. Using the first premise and modus ponens, $p(\text{Zeke})$ follows. Using the third premise and universal instantiation, $p(\text{Zeke}) \rightarrow w(\text{Zeke})$ follows. Finally, using modus ponens, $w(\text{Zeke})$, the desired conclusion, follows.   **d)** Let $j(x)$ be "x is in New Jersey," $f(x)$ be "x lives within 50 miles of the ocean," and $s(x)$ be "x has seen the ocean." The premises are $\forall x(j(x) \rightarrow f(x))$ and $\exists x(j(x) \wedge \neg s(x))$. The second hypothesis and existential instantiation imply that $j(y) \wedge \neg s(y)$ for a particular person y. By simplification, $j(y)$ for this person y. Using universal instantiation and the first premise, $j(y) \rightarrow f(y)$, and by modus ponens, $f(y)$ follows. By simplification, $\neg s(y)$ follows from $j(y) \wedge \neg s(y)$. So $f(y) \wedge \neg s(y)$ follows by conjunction. Finally, the desired conclusion, $\exists x(f(x) \wedge \neg s(x))$, follows by existential generalization.   **11. a)** Correct, using universal instantiation and modus ponens   **b)** Invalid; fallacy

of affirming the conclusion   **c)** Invalid; fallacy of denying the hypothesis   **d)** Correct, using universal instantiation and modus tollens   **13. a)** Fallacy of affirming the conclusion   **b)** Fallacy of begging the question   **c)** Valid argument using modus tollens   **d)** Fallacy of denying the hypothesis   **15.** We know that *some* x exists that makes $H(x)$ true, but we cannot conclude that Lola is one such x.   **17.** The proposition is vacuously true since 0 is not a positive integer. Vacuous proof.   **19.** $P(1)$ is true since $(a + b)^1 = a + b \geq a^1 + b^1 = a + b$. Direct proof.   **21. a)** Assume that n is odd, so $n = 2k + 1$ for some integer k. Then $n^3 + 5 = 2(4k^3 + 6k^2 + 3k + 3)$. Since $n^3 + 5$ is two times some integer, it is even.   **b)** Suppose that $n^3 + 5$ is odd and n is odd. Since n is odd and the product of two odd numbers is odd, it follows that n^2 is odd and then that n^3 is odd. But then $5 = (n^3 + 5) - n^3$ would have to be even since it is the difference of two odd numbers. Therefore, the supposition that $n^3 + 5$ and n were both odd is wrong.   **23.** Let $n = 2k + 1$ and $m = 2l + 1$ be odd integers. Then $n + m = 2(k + l + 1)$ is even.   **25.** Suppose that r is rational and i is irrational and $s = r + i$ is rational. Then by Example 18, $s + (-r) = i$ is rational, which is a contradiction.   **27.** Since $\sqrt{2} \cdot \sqrt{2} = 2$ is rational and $\sqrt{2}$ is irrational, the product of two irrational numbers is not necessarily irrational.   **29.** Indirect proof: If $1/x$ were rational, then by definition $1/x = p/q$ for some integers p and q with $q \neq 0$. Since $1/x$ cannot be 0 (if it were, then we'd have the contradiction $1 = x \cdot 0$ by multiplying both sides by x), we know that $p \neq 0$. Now $x = 1/(1/x) = 1/(p/q) = q/p$ by the usual rules of algebra and arithmetic. Hence x can be written as the quotient of two integers with the denominator nonzero. Thus by definition, x is rational.   **31.** If there were 9 or fewer days on each day of the week, this would account for at most $9 \cdot 7 = 63$ days. But we chose 64 days. This contradiction shows that at least 10 of the days must be on the same day of the week.   **33.** If $x \leq y$, then $\max(x, y) + \min(x, y) = y + x = x + y$. If $x \geq y$, then $\max(x, y) + \min(x, y) = x + y$. Since these are the only two cases, the equality always holds.   **35.** There are four cases. *Case 1:* $x \geq 0$ and $y \geq 0$. Then $|x| + |y| = x + y = |x + y|$. *Case 2:* $x < 0$ and $y < 0$. Then $|x| + |y| = -x + (-y) = -(x + y) = |x + y|$ since $x + y < 0$. *Case 3:* $x \geq 0$ and $y < 0$. Then $|x| + |y| = x + (-y)$. If $x \geq -y$, then $|x + y| = x + y$. But since $y < 0, -y > y$, so that $|x| + |y| = x + (-y) > x + y = |x + y|$. If $x < -y$, then $|x + y| = -(x + y) = -x + (-y)$. But since $x \geq 0$, $x \geq -x$, so that $|x| + |y| = x + (-y) \geq -x + (-y) = |x + y|$. *Case 4:* $x < 0$ and $y \geq 0$. Identical to Case 3 with the roles of x and y reversed.   **37.** Without loss of generality we can assume that n is nonnegative, since the fourth power of an integer and the fourth power of its negative are the same. Following the hint given in Exercise 36, we divide an arbitrary positive integer n by 10, obtaining a quotient k and remainder l, whence $n = 10k + l$, and l is an integer between 0 and 9, inclusive. Then we compute n^4 in each of these ten cases. We get the following values, where X is some integer that is a multiple of 10, whose exact value we do not care about. $(10k + 0)^4 = 10{,}000k^4 = 10{,}000k^4 + 0$, $(10k + 1)^4 = 10{,}000k^4 + X \cdot k^3 + X \cdot k^2 + X \cdot k + 1$, $(10k + 2)^4 = 10{,}000k^4 + X \cdot k^3 + X \cdot k^2 + X \cdot k + 16$, $(10k + 3)^4 = 10{,}000k^4 + X \cdot k^3 + X \cdot k^2 + X \cdot k + 81$, $(10k + 4)^4 = 10{,}000k^4 + X \cdot k^3 + X \cdot k^2 + X \cdot k + 256$, $(10k + 5)^4 = 10{,}000k^4 + X \cdot k^3 + X \cdot k^2 + X \cdot k + 625$, $(10k + 6)^4 = 10{,}000k^4 + X \cdot k^3 + X \cdot k^2 + X \cdot k + 1296$, $(10k + 7)^4 = 10{,}000k^4 + X \cdot k^3 + X \cdot k^2 + X \cdot k + 2401$, $(10k + 8)^4 = 10{,}000k^4 + X \cdot k^3 + X \cdot k^2 + X \cdot k + 4096$, $(10k + 9)^4 = 10{,}000k^4 + X \cdot k^3 + X \cdot k^2 + X \cdot k + 6561$. Since each coefficient indicated by X is a multiple of 10, the corresponding term has no effect on the ones digit of the answer. Therefore the ones digits are 0, 1, 6, 1, 6, 5, 6, 1, 6, 1, respectively, so it is always a 0, 1, 5, or 6. **39.** First, assume that n is odd, so that $n = 2k + 1$ for some integer k. Then $5n + 6 = 5(2k + 1) + 6 = 10k + 11 = 2(5k + 5) + 1$. Hence $5n + 6$ is odd. To prove the converse, suppose that n is even, so that $n = 2k$ for some integer k. Then $5n + 6 = 10k + 6 = 2(5k + 3)$, so that $5n + 6$ is even. Hence n is odd if and only if $5n + 6$ is odd. **41.** This proposition is true. Suppose that m is neither 1 nor -1. Then mn has a factor m larger than 1. On the other hand, $mn = 1$, and 1 has no such factor. Hence $m = 1$ or $m = -1$. In the first case $n = 1$, and in the second case $n = -1$, since $n = 1/m$. **43.** We prove that all these are equivalent to x being even. If x is even, then $x = 2k$ for some integer k. Therefore $3x + 2 = 3 \cdot 2k + 2 = 6k + 2 = 2(3k + 1)$, which is even, since it has been written in the form $2t$, where $t = 3k + 1$. Similarly, $x + 5 = 2k + 5 = 2k + 4 + 1 = 2(k + 2) + 1$, so $x + 5$ is odd; and $x^2 = (2k)^2 = 2(2k^2)$, so x^2 is even. For the converses, we will use an indirect proof. So assume that x is not even; thus x is odd and we can write $x = 2k + 1$ for some integer k. Then $3x + 2 = 3(2k + 1) + 2 = 6k + 5 = 2(3k + 2) + 1$, which is odd (i.e., not even), since it has been written in the form $2t + 1$, where $t = 3k + 2$. Similarly, $x + 5 = 2k + 1 + 5 = 2(k + 3)$, so $x + 5$ is even (i.e., not odd). That x^2 is odd was already proved in Example 14. **45.** We give indirect proofs of (i) $\rightarrow$ (ii), (ii) $\rightarrow$ (i), (i) $\rightarrow$ (iii), and (iii) $\rightarrow$ (i). For the first of these, suppose that $3x + 2$ is rational, namely, equal to p/q for some integers p and q with $q \neq 0$. Then we can write $x = ((p/q) - 2)/3 = (p - 2q)/(3q)$, where $3q \neq 0$. This shows that x is rational. For the second implication, suppose that x is rational, namely, equal to p/q for some integers p and q with $q \neq 0$. Then we can write $3x + 2 = (3p + 2q)/q$, where $q \neq 0$. This shows that $3x + 2$ is rational. For the third implication, suppose that $x/2$ is rational, namely, equal to p/q for some integers p and q with $q \neq 0$. Then we can write $x = 2p/q$, where $q \neq 0$. This shows that x is rational. And for the fourth implication, suppose that x is rational, namely, equal to p/q for some integers p and q with $q \neq 0$. Then we can write $x/2 = p/(2q)$, where $2q \neq 0$. This shows that $x/2$ is ra-

tional. **47.** No **49.** $10{,}001, 10{,}002, \ldots, 10{,}100$ are all nonsquares, since $100^2 = 10{,}000$ and $101^2 = 10{,}201$; constructive **51.** $8 = 2^3$ and $9 = 3^2$ **53.** **a)** This statement asserts the existence of x with a certain property. If we let $y = x$, then we see that $P(x)$ is true. If y is anything other than x, then $P(x)$ is not true. Thus x is the unique element that makes P true. **b)** The first clause here says that there is an element that makes P true. The second clause says that whenever two elements both make P true, they are in fact the same element. Together this says that P is satisfied by exactly one element. **c)** This statement asserts the existence of an x that makes P true and has the further property that whenever we find an element that makes P true, that element is x. In other words, x is the unique element that makes P true. **55.** The equation $|a - c| = |b - c|$ is equivalent to the disjunction of two equations: $a - c = b - c$ or $a - c = -b + c$. The first of these is equivalent to $a = b$, which contradicts the assumptions made in this problem, so the original equation is equivalent to $a - c = -b + c$. By adding $b + c$ to both sides and dividing by 2, we see that this equation is equivalent to $c = (a + b)/2$. Thus there is a unique solution. Furthermore, this c is an integer, because the sum of the odd integers a and b is even. **57.** We are being asked to solve $n = (k - 2) + (k + 3)$ for k. Using the usual, reversible, rules of algebra, we see that this equation is equivalent to $k = (n - 1)/2$. In other words, this is the one and only value of k that makes our equation true. Since n is odd, $n - 1$ is even, so k is an integer. **59.** If x is itself an integer, then we can take $n = x$ and $\epsilon = 0$. No other solution is possible in this case, since if the integer n is greater than x, then n is at least $x + 1$, which would make $\epsilon \geq 1$. If x is not an integer, then round it up to the next integer, and call that integer n. We let $\epsilon = n - x$. Clearly $0 \leq \epsilon < 1$, this is the only ϵ that will work with this n, and n cannot be any larger, since ϵ is constrained to be less than 1. **61.** Let p be "It is raining"; let q be "Yvette has her umbrella"; let r be "Yvette gets wet." Assumptions are $\neg p \lor q$, $\neg q \lor \neg r$, and $p \lor \neg r$. Resolution on the first two gives $\neg p \lor \neg r$. Resolution on this and the third assumption gives $\neg r$, as desired. **63.** Assume that this proposition is satisfiable. Using resolution on the first two clauses enables us to conclude $q \lor q$; in other words, we know that q has to be true. Using resolution on the last two clauses enables us to conclude $\neg q \lor \neg q$; in other words, we know that $\neg q$ has to be true. This is a contradiction. So this proposition is not satisfiable. **65.** Let $x = 2$ and $y = \sqrt{2}$. If $x^y = 2^{\sqrt{2}}$ is irrational, we are done. If not, then let $x = 2^{\sqrt{2}}$ and $y = \sqrt{2}/4$. Then $x^y = (2^{\sqrt{2}})^{\sqrt{2}/4} = 2^{\sqrt{2} \cdot (\sqrt{2})/4} = 2^{1/2} = \sqrt{2}$. **67.** Suppose that $p_1 \rightarrow p_4 \rightarrow p_2 \rightarrow p_5 \rightarrow p_3 \rightarrow p_1$. To prove that one of these propositions implies any of the others, just use hypothetical syllogism repeatedly. **69.** Every domino placed on a chessboard covers exactly one white and one black square. Hence a set of dominos covers exactly the same number of white squares and black squares.

Since removing opposite corners leaves a board with two more black squares than white squares or two more white squares than black squares, no set of dominos can cover the board with opposite corners removed. **71.** We will give a proof by contradiction. Suppose that $a_1, a_2, \ldots, a_n$ are all less than A, where A is the average of these numbers. Then $a_1 + a_2 + \cdots + a_n < nA$. Dividing both sides by n shows that $A = (a_1 + a_2 + \cdots + a_n)/n < A$, which is a contradiction. **73.** We will show that the four statements are equivalent by showing that (i) implies (ii), (ii) implies (iii), (iii) implies (iv), and (iv) implies (i). First, assume that n is even. Then $n = 2k$ for some integer k. Then $n + 1 = 2k + 1$, so that $n + 1$ is odd. This shows that (i) implies (ii). Next, suppose that $n + 1$ is odd, so that $n + 1 = 2k + 1$ for some integer k. Then $3n + 1 = 2n + (n + 1) = 2(n + k) + 1$, which shows that $3n + 1$ is odd, showing that (ii) implies (iii). Next, suppose that $3n + 1$ is odd, so that $3n + 1 = 2k + 1$ for some integer k. Then $3n = (2k + 1) - 1 = 2k$, so that $3n$ is even. This shows that (iii) implies (iv). Finally, suppose that n is not even. Then n is odd, so $n = 2k + 1$ for some integer k. Then $3n = 3(2k + 1) = 6k + 3 = 2(3k + 1) + 1$, so that $3n$ is odd. This completes an indirect proof that (iv) implies (i). **75.** By the second premise, there is some lion that does not drink coffee. Let Leo be such a creature. By simplification we know that Leo is a lion. By modus ponens we know from the first premise that Leo is fierce. Hence Leo is fierce and does not drink coffee. By the definition of the existential quantifier, there exist fierce creatures that do not drink coffee, that is, some fierce creatures do not drink coffee. **77.** Valid

SECTION 1.6

1. a) $\{-1, 1\}$ **b)** $\{1, 2, 3, 4, 5, 6, 7, 8, 9, 10, 11\}$ **c)** $\{0, 1, 4, 9, 16, 25, 36, 49, 64, 81\}$ **d)** $\emptyset$ **3. a)** Yes **b)** No **c)** No **5. a)** Yes **b)** No **c)** Yes **d)** No **e)** No **f)** No **7. a)** False **b)** False **c)** False **d)** True **e)** False **f)** False **g)** True **9. a)** True **b)** True **c)** False **d)** True **e)** True **f)** False **11.** Suppose that $x \in A$. Since $A \subseteq B$, this implies that $x \in B$. Since $B \subseteq C$, we see that $x \in C$. Since $x \in A$ implies that $x \in C$, it follows that $A \subseteq C$. **13. a)** 1 **b)** 1 **c)** 2 **d)** 3 **15. a)** $\{\emptyset, \{a\}\}$ **b)** $\{\emptyset, \{a\}, \{b\}, \{a, b\}\}$ **c)** $\{\emptyset, \{\emptyset\}, \{\{\emptyset\}\}, \{\emptyset, \{\emptyset\}\}\}$ **17. a)** 8 **b)** 16 **c)** 2 **19. a)** $\{(a, y), (b, y), (c, y), (d, y), (a, z), (b, z), (c, z), (d, z)\}$ **b)** $\{(y, a), (y, b), (y, c), (y, d), (z, a), (z, b), (z, c), (z, d)\}$ **21.** The set of triples (a, b, c), where a is an airline and b and c are cities. **23.** $\emptyset \times A = \{(x, y) \mid x \in \emptyset$ and $y \in A\} = \emptyset = \{(x, y) \mid x \in A$ and $y \in \emptyset\} = A \times \emptyset$ **25.** mn **27. a)** The square of a real number is never -1. True **b)** There exists an integer whose square is 2. False **c)** The square of every integer is positive. False **d)** There is a real number equal to its own square. True **29.** We must show that $\{\{a\}, \{a, b\}\} = \{\{c\}, \{c, d\}\}$ if and only if $a = c$ and $b = d$. The "if" part is immediate. So assume these two sets are equal. First, consider the case when $a \neq b$. Then $\{\{a\}, \{a, b\}\}$ contains exactly two elements, one of which contains one element. Thus, $\{\{c\}, \{c, d\}\}$ must have

the same property, so $c \neq d$ and $\{c\}$ is the element containing exactly one element. Hence, $\{a\} = \{c\}$, which implies that $a = c$. Also, the two-element sets $\{a, b\}$ and $\{c, d\}$ must be equal. Since $a = c$ and $a \neq b$, it follows that $b = d$. Second, suppose that $a = b$. Then $\{\{a\}, \{a, b\}\} = \{\{a\}\}$, a set with one element. Hence $\{\{c\}, \{c, d\}\}$ has only one element, which can happen only when $c = d$, and the set is $\{\{c\}\}$. It then follows that $a = c$ and $b = d$. **31.** Let $S = \{a_1, a_2, \ldots, a_n\}$. Represent each subset of S with a bit string of length n, where the ith bit is 1 if and only if $a_i \in S$. To generate all subsets of S, list all 2^n bit strings of length n (for instance, in increasing order), and write down the corresponding subsets.

SECTION 1.7

1. a) The set of students who live within 1 mile of school and who walk to classes. **b)** The set of students who live within 1 mile of school or who walk to classes (or who do both). **c)** The set of students who live within 1 mile of school but do not walk to classes. **d)** The set of students who walk to classes but live more than 1 mile away from school. **3. a)** $\{0, 1, 2, 3, 4, 5, 6\}$ **b)** $\{3\}$ **c)** $\{1, 2, 4, 5\}$ **d)** $\{0, 6\}$ **5.** $\overline{\overline{A}} = \{x \mid \neg(x \in \overline{A})\} = \{x \mid \neg(\neg x \in A)\} = \{x \mid x \in A\} = A$. **7. a)** $A \cup B = \{x \mid x \in A \vee x \in B\} = \{x \mid x \in B \vee x \in A\} = B \cup A$; **b)** $A \cap B = \{x \mid x \in A \wedge x \in B\} = \{x \mid x \in B \wedge x \in A\} = B \cap A$. **9.** Suppose $x \in A \cap (A \cup B)$. Then $x \in A$ and $x \in A \cup B$ by the definition of intersection. Since $x \in A$, we have proved that the left-hand side is a subset of the right-hand side. Conversely, let $x \in A$. Then by the definition of union, $x \in A \cup B$ as well. Therefore $x \in A \cap (A \cup B)$ by the definition of intersection, so the right-hand side is a subset of the left-hand side. **11. a)** $x \in \overline{(A \cup B)} \equiv x \notin (A \cup B) \equiv \neg(x \in A \vee x \in B) \equiv \neg(x \in A) \wedge \neg(x \in B) \equiv x \notin A \wedge x \notin B \equiv x \in \overline{A} \wedge x \in \overline{B} \equiv x \in \overline{A} \cap \overline{B}$.

b)

A	B	$A \cup B$	$\overline{(A \cup B)}$	$\overline{A}$	$\overline{B}$	$\overline{A} \cap \overline{B}$
1	1	1	0	0	0	0
1	0	1	0	0	1	0
0	1	1	0	1	0	0
0	0	0	1	1	1	1

13. a) $x \in \overline{A \cap B \cap C} \equiv x \notin A \cap B \cap C \equiv x \notin A \vee x \notin B \vee x \notin C \equiv x \in \overline{A} \vee x \in \overline{B} \vee x \in \overline{C} \equiv x \in \overline{A} \cup \overline{B} \cup \overline{C}$.

b)

A	B	C	$A \cap B \cap C$	$\overline{(A \cap B \cap C)}$	$\overline{A}$	$\overline{B}$	$\overline{C}$	$\overline{A} \cup \overline{B} \cup \overline{C}$
1	1	1	1	0	0	0	0	0
1	1	0	0	1	0	0	1	1
1	0	1	0	1	0	1	0	1
1	0	0	0	1	0	1	1	1
0	1	1	0	1	1	0	0	1
0	1	0	0	1	1	0	1	1
0	0	1	0	1	1	1	0	1
0	0	0	0	1	1	1	1	1

15. Both sides equal $\{x \mid x \in A \wedge x \notin B\}$. **17. a)** $x \in A \cup (B \cup C) \equiv (x \in A) \vee (x \in (B \cup C)) \equiv (x \in A) \vee (x \in B \vee x \in C) \equiv (x \in A \vee x \in B) \vee (x \in C) \equiv x \in (A \cup B) \cup C$ **b)** same as part (a) with $\cup$ replaced by $\cap$ and $\vee$ replaced by $\wedge$ **c)** $x \in A \cup (B \cap C) \equiv (x \in A) \vee (x \in (B \cap C)) \equiv (x \in A) \vee (x \in B \wedge x \in C) \equiv (x \in A \vee x \in B) \wedge (x \in A \vee x \in C) \equiv x \in (A \cup B) \cap (A \cup C)$ **19. a)** $\{4, 6\}$
b) $\{0, 1, 2, 3, 4, 5, 6, 7, 8, 9, 10\}$ **c)** $\{4, 5, 6, 8, 10\}$
d) $\{0, 2, 4, 5, 6, 7, 8, 9, 10\}$ **21. a)** $B \subseteq A$ **b)** $A \subseteq B$
c) $A \cap B = \emptyset$ **d)** nothing, since this is always true
e) $A = B$ **23.** $A \subseteq B \equiv \forall x(x \in A \rightarrow x \in B) \equiv \forall x(x \notin B \rightarrow x \notin A) \equiv \forall x(x \in \overline{B} \rightarrow x \in \overline{A}) \equiv \overline{B} \subseteq \overline{A}$
25. The set of students who are computer science majors but not mathematics majors or who are mathematics majors but not computer science majors. **27.** An element is in $(A \cup B) - (A \cap B)$ if it is in the union of A and B but not in the intersection of A and B, which means that it is in either A or B but not in both A and B. This is exactly what it means for an element to belong to $A \oplus B$. **29. a)** $A \oplus A = (A - A) \cup (A - A) = \emptyset \cup \emptyset = \emptyset$
b) $A \oplus \emptyset = (A - \emptyset) \cup (\emptyset - A) = A \cup \emptyset = A$
c) $A \oplus U = (A - U) \cup (U - A) = \emptyset \cup \overline{A} = \overline{A}$
d) $A \oplus \overline{A} = (A - \overline{A}) \cup (\overline{A} - A) = A \cup \overline{A} = U$ **31.** $B = \emptyset$
33. Yes. Suppose that $x \in A$ but $x \notin B$. If $x \in C$, then $x \notin A \oplus C$ but $x \in B \oplus C$, a contradiction. If $x \notin C$ then $x \in A \oplus C$ but $x \notin B \oplus C$, a contradiction. Hence, $A \subseteq B$. Similarly, $B \subseteq A$, so that $A = B$.
35. Yes. **37. a)** $\{1, 2, 3, \ldots, n\}$ **b)** $\{1\}$ **39. a)** A_n
b) $\{0, 1\}$ **41. a)** $\{1, 2, 3, 4, 7, 8, 9, 10\}$ **b)** $\{2, 4, 5, 6, 7\}$
c) $\{1, 10\}$ **43.** The bit in the ith position of the bit string of the difference of two sets is 1 if the ith bit of the first string is 1 and the ith bit of the second string is 0, and is 0 otherwise. **45. a)** 11 1110 0000 0000 0000 0000 $\vee$ 01 1100 1000 0000 0100 0101 0000 = 11 1110 1000 0000 0100 0101 0000, representing $\{a, b, c, d, e, g, p, t, v\}$
b) 11 1110 0000 0000 0000 0000 0000 $\wedge$ 01 1100 1000 0000 0100 0101 0000 = 01 1100 0000 0000 0000 0000 0000, representing $\{b, c, d\}$ **c)** (11 1110 0000 0000 0000 0000 0000 $\vee$ 00 0110 0110 0001 1000 0110 0110) $\wedge$ (01 1100 1000 0000 0100 0101 0000 $\vee$ 00 1010 0010 0000 1000 0010 0111) = 11 1110 0110 0001 1000 0110 0110 $\wedge$ 01 1110 1010 0000 1100 0111 0111 = 01 1110 0010 0000 1000 0110 0110, representing $\{b, c, d, e, i, o, t, u, x, y\}$ **d)** 11 1110 0000 0000 0000 0000 0000 $\vee$ 01 1100 1000 0000 0100 0101 0000 $\vee$ 00 1010 0010 0000 1000 0010 0111 $\vee$ 00 0110 0110 0001 1000 0110 0110 = 11 1110 1110 0001 1100 0111 0111, representing $\{a, b, c, d, e, g, h, i, n, o, p, t, u, v, x, y, z\}$
47. a) $\{1, 2, 3, \{1, 2, 3\}\}$ **b)** $\{\emptyset\}$ **c)** $\{\emptyset, \{\emptyset\}\}$ **d)** $\{\emptyset, \{\emptyset\}, \{\emptyset, \{\emptyset\}\}\}$ **49. a)** $\{3 \cdot a, \ 3 \cdot b, \ 1 \cdot c, \ 4 \cdot d\}$ **b)** $\{2 \cdot a, \ 2 \cdot b\}$
c) $\{1 \cdot a, \ 1 \cdot c\}$ **d)** $\{1 \cdot b, \ 4 \cdot d\}$ **e)** $\{5 \cdot a, \ 5 \cdot b, \ 1 \cdot c, \ 4 \cdot d\}$
51. $\overline{F} = \{0.4 \text{ Alice}, 0.1 \text{ Brian}, 0.6 \text{ Fred}, 0.9 \text{ Oscar}, 0.5 \text{ Rita}\}$, $\overline{R} = \{0.6 \text{ Alice}, 0.2 \text{ Brian}, 0.8 \text{ Fred}, 0.1 \text{ Oscar}, 0.3 \text{ Rita}\}$
53. $F \cap R = \{0.4 \text{ Alice}, 0.8 \text{ Brian}, 0.2 \text{ Fred}, 0.1 \text{ Oscar}, 0.5 \text{ Rita}\}$

SECTION 1.8

1. a) $f(0)$ is not defined. **b)** $f(x)$ is not defined for $x < 0$. **c)** $f(x)$ is not well-defined since there are two distinct values assigned to each x. **3. a)** Not a function **b)** A function **c)** Not a function **5. a)** The set of integers **b)** The set of even nonnegative integers **c)** The set of nonnegative integers not exceeding 7 **d)** The set of squares of integers $= \{0, 1, 4, 9, 16, \ldots\}$
7. a) Domain $\mathbf{Z}^+ \times \mathbf{Z}^+$; range $\mathbf{Z}^+$ **b)** Domain $\mathbf{Z}^+$; range $\{0, 1, 2, 3, 4, 5, 6, 7, 8, 9\}$ **c)** Domain the set of bit strings; range $\mathbf{N}$ **d)** Domain the set of bit strings; range $\mathbf{N}$
9. **a)** 1 **b)** 0 **c)** 0 **d)** -1 **e)** 3 **f)** -1 **g)** 2 **h)** 1
11. Only the function in part (a) **13.** Only the functions in parts (a) and (d) **15. a)** Onto **b)** Not onto
c) Onto **d)** Not onto **e)** Onto **17. a)** The function $f(x)$ with $f(x) = 3x + 1$ when $x \geq 0$ and $f(x) = -3x + 2$ when $x < 0$ **b)** $f(x) = |x| + 1$ **c)** The function $f(x)$ with $f(x) = 2x + 1$ when $x \geq 0$ and $f(x) = -2x$ when $x < 0$ **d)** $f(x) = x^2 + 1$ **19. a)** Yes **b)** No **c)** Yes
d) No **21.** Suppose that f is strictly decreasing. This means that $f(x) > f(y)$ whenever $x < y$. To show that g is strictly increasing, suppose that $x < y$. Then $g(x) = 1/f(x) < 1/f(y) = g(y)$. Conversely, suppose that g is strictly increasing. This means that $g(x) < g(y)$ whenever $x < y$. To show that f is strictly decreasing, suppose that $x < y$. Then $f(x) = 1/g(x) > 1/g(y) = f(y)$. **23. a)** $f(S) = \{0, 1, 3\}$ **b)** $f(S) = \{0, 1, 3, 5, 8\}$
c) $f(S) = \{0, 8, 16, 40\}$ **d)** $f(S) = \{1, 12, 33, 65\}$
25. a) Let x and y be distinct elements of A. Since g is one-to-one, $g(x)$ and $g(y)$ are distinct elements of B. Since f is one-to-one, $f(g(x)) = (f \circ g)(x)$ and $f(g(y)) = (f \circ g)(y)$ are distinct elements of C. Hence, $f \circ g$ is one-to-one. **b)** Let $y \in C$. Since f is onto, $y = f(b)$ for some $b \in B$. Now since g is onto, $b = g(x)$ for some $x \in A$. Hence, $y = f(b) = f(g(x)) = (f \circ g)(x)$. It follows that $f \circ g$ is onto. **27.** No. For example, suppose that $A = \{a\}$, $B = \{b, c\}$, and $C = \{d\}$. Let $g(a) = b$, $f(b) = d$, and $f(c) = d$. f and $f \circ g$ are onto, but g is not. **29.** $(f + g)(x) = x^2 + x + 3$, $(fg)(x) = x^3 + 2x^2 + x + 2$. **31.** f is one-to-one since $f(x_1) = f(x_2) \equiv ax_1 + b = ax_2 + b \equiv ax_1 = ax_2 \equiv x_1 = x_2$. f is onto since $f((y - b)/a) = y$. $f^{-1}(y) = (y - b)/a$.
33. Let $f(1) = a$, $f(2) = a$. Let $S = \{1\}$ and $T = \{2\}$. Then $f(S \cap T) = f(\emptyset) = \emptyset$, but $f(S) \cap f(T) = \{a\} \cap \{a\} = \{a\}$. **35. a)** $\{x \mid 0 \leq x < 1\}$ **b)** $\{x \mid -1 \leq x < 2\}$ **c)** $\emptyset$
37. $f^{-1}(\overline{S}) = \{x \in A \mid f(x) \notin S\} = \overline{\{x \in A \mid f(x) \in S\}} = \overline{f^{-1}(S)}$ **39.** Let $x = \lfloor x \rfloor + \epsilon$, where ϵ is a real number with $0 \leq \epsilon < 1$. If $\epsilon < \frac{1}{2}$, then $\lfloor x \rfloor - 1 < x - \frac{1}{2} < \lfloor x \rfloor$, so $\lceil x - \frac{1}{2} \rceil = \lfloor x \rfloor$ and this is the integer closest to x. If $\epsilon > \frac{1}{2}$, then $\lfloor x \rfloor < x - \frac{1}{2} < \lfloor x \rfloor + 1$, so $\lceil x - \frac{1}{2} \rceil = \lfloor x \rfloor + 1$ and this is the integer closest to x. If $\epsilon = \frac{1}{2}$, then $\lceil x - \frac{1}{2} \rceil = \lfloor x \rfloor$, which is the smaller of the two integers that surround x and are the same distance from x. **41.** Write the real number

x as $\lfloor x \rfloor + \epsilon$, where ϵ is a real number with $0 \le \epsilon < 1$. Since $\epsilon = x - \lfloor x \rfloor$, it follows that $0 \le -\lfloor x \rfloor < 1$. The first two inequalities, $x - 1 < \lfloor x \rfloor$ and $\lfloor x \rfloor \le x$, follow directly. For the other two inequalities, write $x = \lceil x \rceil - \epsilon'$, where $0 \le \epsilon' < 1$. Then $0 \le \lceil x \rceil - x < 1$, and the desired inequality follows. **43. a)** If $x < n$, since $\lfloor x \rfloor \le x$, it follows that $\lfloor x \rfloor < n$. Suppose that $x \ge n$. By the definition of the floor function, it follows that $\lfloor x \rfloor \ge n$. This means that if $\lfloor x \rfloor < n$, then $x < n$. **b)** If $n < x$, then since $x \le \lceil x \rceil$, it follows that $n \le \lceil x \rceil$. Suppose that $n \ge x$. By the definition of the ceiling function, it follows that $\lceil x \rceil \le n$. This means that if $n < \lceil x \rceil$, then $n < x$. **45.** If n is even, then $n = 2k$ for some integer k. Thus $\lfloor n/2 \rfloor = \lfloor k \rfloor = k = n/2$. If n is odd, then $n = 2k + 1$ for some integer k. Thus $\lfloor n/2 \rfloor = \lfloor k + \frac{1}{2} \rfloor = k = (n - 1)/2$. **47.** Assume that $x \ge 0$. The left-hand side is $\lceil -x \rceil$ and the right-hand side is $-\lfloor x \rfloor$. If x is an integer, then both sides equal $-x$. Otherwise, let $x = n + \epsilon$, where n is a natural number and ϵ is a real number with $0 \le \epsilon < 1$. Then $\lceil -x \rceil = \lceil -n - \epsilon \rceil = -n$ and $-\lfloor x \rfloor = -\lfloor n + \epsilon \rfloor = -n$ also. When $x < 0$, the equation also holds since it can be obtained by substituting $-x$ for x. **49.** $\lceil b \rceil - \lfloor a \rfloor - 1$ **51. a)** 1 **b)** 3 **c)** 126 **d)** 3600 **53. a)** 100 **b)** 256 **c)** 1030 **d)** 30,200

55.

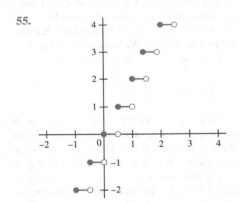

57.

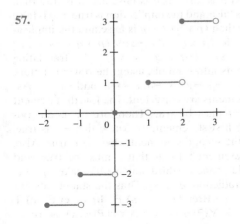

59. a)

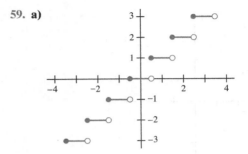

b)

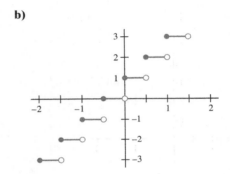

c)

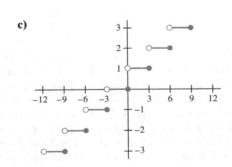

d)

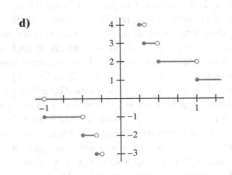

e)

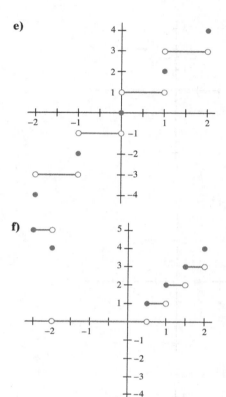

f)

g) See part (a).   **61.** $f^{-1}(y) = (y-1)^{1/3}$
63. a) $f_{A\cap B}(x) = 1 \equiv x \in A \cap B \equiv x \in A$ and
$x \in B \equiv f_A(x) = 1$ and $f_B(x) = 1 \equiv f_A(x)f_B(x) = 1$
b) $f_{A\cup B}(x) = 1 \equiv x \in A \cup B \equiv x \in A$ or $x \in B \equiv$
$f_A(x) = 1$ or $f_B(x) = 1 \equiv f_A(x) + f_B(x) - f_A(x)f_B(x) = 1$
c) $f_{\overline{A}}(x) = 1 \equiv x \in \overline{A} \equiv x \notin A \equiv f_A(x) = 0 \equiv 1 - f_A(x) =$
1 **d)** $f_{A\oplus B}(x) = 1 \equiv x \in A \oplus B \equiv (x \in A$ and $x \notin B)$ or
$(x \notin A$ and $x \in B) \equiv f_A(x) + f_B(x) - 2f_A(x)f_B(x) = 1$
65. a) True; since $\lfloor x \rfloor$ is already an integer, $\lceil \lfloor x \rfloor \rceil = \lfloor x \rfloor$.
b) False; $x = \frac{1}{2}$ is a counterexample.   **c)** True; if x or y
is an integer, then using property 4b in Table 1 of Sec-
tion 1.8, the difference is 0. If neither x nor y is an integer, then $x = n + \epsilon$ and $y = m + \delta$, where n and m
are integers and ϵ and δ are positive real numbers less
than 1. Then $m + n < x + y < m + n + 2$, so $\lceil x + y \rceil$ is
either $m + n + 1$ or $m + n + 2$. Therefore, the given expression is either $(n + 1) + (m + 1) - (m + n + 1) = 1$ or
$(n + 1) + (m + 1) - (m + n + 2) = 0$, as desired.   **d)** False;
$x = \frac{1}{4}$ and $y = 3$ is a counterexample.   **e)** False; $x = \frac{1}{2}$ is
a counterexample.   **67. a)** If x is a positive integer, then
the two sides are equal. So suppose that $x = n^2 + m + \epsilon$,
where n^2 is the largest perfect square less than x, m is a
nonnegative integer, and $0 < \epsilon \leq 1$. Then both $\sqrt{x}$ and
$\sqrt{\lceil x \rceil} = \sqrt{n^2 + m}$ are between n and $n + 1$, so both sides
equal n.   **b)** If x is a positive integer, then the two sides are

equal. So suppose that $x = n^2 - m - \epsilon$, where n^2 is the smallest perfect square greater than x, m is a nonnegative inte-
ger, and ϵ is a real number with $0 < \epsilon \leq 1$. Then both $\sqrt{x}$
and $\sqrt{\lceil x \rceil} = \sqrt{n^2 - m}$ are between $n - 1$ and n. Therefore,
both sides of the equation equal n.   **69. a)** Domain is **Z**;
codomain is **R**; domain of definition is the set of nonzero
integers; the set of values for which f is undefined is {0};
not a total function.   **b)** Domain is **Z**; codomain is **Z**; domain of definition is **Z**; set of values for which f is undefined is Ø; total function.   **c)** Domain is **Z** × **Z**; codomain
is **Q**; domain of definition is **Z** × (**Z** − {0}); set of values
for which f is undefined is **Z** × {0}; not a total function.
d) Domain is **Z** × **Z**; codomain is **Z**; domain of definition is **Z** × **Z**; set of values for which f is undefined is
Ø; total function.   **e)** Domain is **Z** × **Z**; codomain is **Z**;
domain of definitions is $\{(m, n) \mid m > n\}$; set of values
for which f is undefined is $\{(m, n) \mid m \leq n\}$; not a total function.   **71.** It is clear from the formula that the
range of values the function takes on for a fixed value
of $m + n$, say $m + n = x$, is $(x - 2)(x - 1)/2 + 1$ through
$(x - 2)(x - 1)/2 + (x - 1)$, since m can assume the values
$1, 2, 3, \ldots, (x - 1)$ under these conditions, and the first
term in the formula is a fixed positive integer when $m + n$
is fixed. To show that this function is one-to-one and onto,
we merely need to show that the range of values for $x + 1$
picks up precisely where the range of values for x left off,
i.e., that $f(x - 1, 1) + 1 = f(1, x)$. We have $f(x - 1, 1) + 1 =$
$\frac{(x-2)(x-1)}{2} + (x - 1) + 1 = \frac{x^2 - x + 2}{2} = \frac{(x-1)x}{2} + 1 = f(1, x)$.

SUPPLEMENTARY EXERCISES

1. a) $q \to p$ **b)** $q \wedge p$ **c)** $\neg q \vee \neg p$ **d)** $q \leftrightarrow p$
3. a) The proposition cannot be false unless $\neg p$ is false, so
that p is true. If p is true and q is true then $\neg q \wedge (p \to q)$
is false and the implication is true. If p is true and q is
false then $p \to q$ is false so that $\neg q \wedge (p \to q)$ is false
and the implication is true.   **b)** The proposition cannot
be false unless q is false. If q is false and p is true then
$(p \vee q) \wedge \neg p$ is false, and the implication is true. If q is false
and p is false then $(p \vee q) \wedge \neg p$ is false and the implica-
tion is true.   **5.** $(p \wedge q \wedge r \wedge \neg s) \vee (p \wedge q \wedge \neg r \wedge s) \vee$
$(p \wedge \neg q \wedge r \wedge s) \vee (\neg p \wedge q \wedge r \wedge s)$ **7.** Translating
these statements into symbols, using the obvious letters,
we have $\neg t \to \neg g$, $\neg g \to \neg q$, $r \to q$, and $\neg t \wedge r$. Assume the statements are consistent. The fourth statement
tells us that $\neg t$ must be true. Therefore by modus ponens with the first statement, we know that $\neg g$ is true,
hence (from the second statement) that $\neg q$ is true. Also,
the fourth statement tells us that r must be true, and
so again modus ponens (third statement) makes q true.
This is a contradiction: $q \wedge \neg q$. Thus the statements are
inconsistent.   **9.** Brenda   **11. a)** F **b)** T **c)** F **d)** T
e) F **f)** T   **13.** $\forall x \exists y \exists z (y \neq z \wedge \forall w (P(w, x) \leftrightarrow (w =$

$y \vee w = z)))$ **15.** Suppose that $\exists x(P(x) \rightarrow Q(x))$ is true. Then either $Q(x_0)$ is true for some x_0, in which case $\forall x P(x) \rightarrow \exists x Q(x)$ is true; or $P(x_0)$ is false for some x_0, in which case $\forall x P(x) \rightarrow \exists x Q(x)$ is true. Conversely, suppose that $\exists x(P(x) \rightarrow Q(x))$ is false. That means that $\forall x(P(x) \wedge \neg Q(x))$ is true, which implies $\forall x P(x)$ and $\forall x(\neg Q(x))$. This latter proposition is equivalent to $\neg \exists x Q(x)$. Thus, $\forall x P(x) \rightarrow \exists x Q(x)$ is false. **17.** No **19.** $\forall x \forall z \exists y T(x, y, z)$, where $T(x, y, z)$ is the statement that student x has taken class y in department z, where the universes of discourse are the set of students in the class, the set of courses at this university, and the set of departments in the school of mathematical sciences. **21. a)** $\overline{A}$ **b)** $A \cap B$ **c)** $A - B$ **d)** $\overline{A} \cap \overline{B}$ **e)** $A \oplus B$ **23.** The second use of existential instantiation cannot use the letter c, since that letter has already been used for something else. There is no guarantee that the x that makes P true is the same as the x that makes Q true, so we can't call them both c. **25.** Let x be given. We must show that $\neg R(x) \rightarrow P(x)$, so assume that $\neg R(x)$ is true. We apply universal instantiation to the second hypothesis and then take the contrapositive and apply De Morgan's law to obtain $\neg R(x) \rightarrow (P(x) \vee \neg Q(x))$. By modus ponens, this gives us $P(x) \vee \neg Q(x)$. The first hypothesis gives $P(x) \vee Q(x)$ by universal instantiation. Combining these by resolution, we have $P(x)$, as desired. **27.** We give an indirect proof that if $\sqrt{x}$ is rational, then x is rational, assuming throughout that $x \geq 0$. Suppose that $\sqrt{x} = p/q$ is rational, $q \neq 0$. Then $x = (\sqrt{x})^2 = p^2/q^2$ is also rational (q^2 is again nonzero). **29.** We can give a constructive proof by letting $m = 10^{500} + 1$. Then $m^2 = (10^{500} + 1)^2 > (10^{500})^2 = 10^{1000}$. **31.** 23 cannot be written as the sum of eight cubes. **33.** 223 cannot be written as the sum of 36 fifth powers. **35.** Yes **37. a)** $A \cap \overline{A} = \{x \mid x \in A \wedge x \notin A\} = \emptyset$ **b)** $A \cup \overline{A} = \{x \mid x \in A \vee x \notin A\} = U$ **39.** $A - (A - B) = A - (A \cap \overline{B}) = A \cap \overline{(A \cap \overline{B})} = A \cap (\overline{A} \cup B) = (A \cap \overline{A}) \cup (A \cap B) = \emptyset \cup (A \cap B) = A \cap B$ **41.** Let $A = \{1\}, B = \emptyset$, $C = \{1\}$. Then $(A - B) - C = \emptyset$ but $A - (B - C) = \{1\}$. **43.** No. For example, let $A = B = \{a, b\}, C = \emptyset$, and $D = \{a\}$. Then $(A - B) - (C - D) = \emptyset - \emptyset = \emptyset$, but $(A - C) - (B - D) = \{a, b\} - \{b\} = \{a\}$. **45. a)** $|\emptyset| \leq |A \cap B| \leq |A| \leq |A \cup B| \leq |U|$ **b)** $|\emptyset| \leq |A - B| \leq |A \oplus B| \leq |A \cup B| \leq |A| + |B|$ **47. a)** yes, no **b)** yes, no **c)** f has inverse with $f^{-1}(a) = 3, f^{-1}(b) = 4, f^{-1}(c) = 2$, $f^{-1}(d) = 1$; g has no inverse **49.** Let $f(a) = f(b) = 1$, $f(c) = f(d) = 2, S = \{a, c\}, T = \{b, d\}$. Then $f(S \cap T) = f(\emptyset) = \emptyset$, but $f(S) \cap f(T) = \{1, 2\} \cap \{1, 2\} = \{1, 2\}$. **51.** The equation is true if and only if the sum of the fractional parts of x and y is less than 1.

CHAPTER

3

Mathematical Reasoning, Induction, and Recursion

I n Chapter 1 we introduced rules of inference and methods of proof. In the later sections of Chapter 1 and in Chapter 2 we used these proof methods to prove a variety of results. However, we did not discuss the process of formulating conjectures and then attempting to determine whether these conjectures are correct. In this chapter we will briefly address this process and provide guidance for selecting techniques from our arsenal of proof methods and for constructing proofs using these methods. We will also discuss the role of counterexamples in this process.

We will discuss some important properties of sequences and strings in this chapter. We will define the notion of a countable set and prove that the set of rational numbers is countable. We will prove that the set of real numbers is not countable using a proof technique called the diagonalization argument.

Many mathematical statements assert that a property is true for all positive integers. Examples of such statements are that for every positive integer n: $n! \leq n^n$, $n^3 - n$ is divisible by 3, and the sum of the first n positive integers is $n(n + 1)/2$. A major goal of this chapter, and the book, is to give the student a thorough understanding of mathematical induction, which is used to prove results of this kind.

In Chapters 1 and 2 we explicitly defined sets and functions. That is, we described sets by listing their elements or by giving some property that characterizes these elements. We gave formulae for the values of functions. There is another important way to define such objects, based on mathematical induction. To define functions, some initial terms are specified, and a rule is given for finding subsequent values from values already known. Sets can be defined by listing some of their elements and giving rules for constructing elements from those already known to be in the set. Such definitions, called *recursive definitions,* are used throughout discrete mathematics and computer science. Once we have defined a set recursively, we can use a proof method called structural induction to prove results about this set.

When a procedure is specified for solving a problem, this procedure *always* solves the problem correctly. Just testing to see that the correct result is obtained for a set of input values does not show that the procedure always works correctly. The correctness of a procedure can be guaranteed only by proving that it always yields the correct result. The final section of this chapter contains an introduction to the techniques of program verification. This is a formal technique to verify that procedures are correct. Program verification serves as the basis for attempts under way to prove in a mechanical fashion that programs are correct.

3.1   Proof Strategy

INTRODUCTION

In Section 1.5 we introduced some of the most important methods of proof and illustrated how each method is used. In Sections 1.6–1.8 and in Chapter 2 we used these methods to prove many different theorems. However, we discussed only briefly the strategy behind constructing proofs. This strategy includes selecting a proof method and then successfully constructing an argument step by step, based on this method. In this section we will study some additional aspects of the art and science of proofs. We will provide advice on how to find a proof of a theorem. Because we already have a portfolio of proof methods, we can investigate more closely how proofs are actually constructed. In particular, we will describe some tricks of the trade, including how proofs can be found by working backward, by adapting existing proofs, and by taking advantage of the method of proof by cases.

When mathematicians work, they formulate conjectures and attempt to prove or disprove them. We will briefly describe this process here. Besides providing useful advice about constructing proofs and formulating conjectures, we will also supply some words of advice about counterexamples. We will describe the role counterexamples play in resolving some long-standing conjectures. Further, we discuss some interesting problems that remain unsolved.

Finally, we will present a proof by contradiction of an extremely important result in computer science. We will prove that no procedure exists that can determine, given a computer program and its input, whether this program will eventually stop when provided with this input.

PROOF STRATEGIES

Finding proofs can be a challenging business. When you are confronted with a statement to prove, you should first replace terms by their definitions and then carefully analyze what the hypotheses and the conclusion mean. After doing so, you can attempt to prove the result using one of the available methods of proof. Generally, if the statement is an implication, you should first try a direct proof; if this fails, you can try an indirect proof. If neither of these approaches works, you might try a proof by contradiction.

FORWARD AND BACKWARD REASONING Whichever method you choose, you need a starting point for your proof. To begin a direct proof of an implication, you can start with the hypotheses. Using these hypotheses, together with axioms and known theorems, you can construct a proof using a sequence of steps that leads to the conclusion. This type of reasoning, called *forward reasoning,* is the most common type of reasoning used to prove relatively simple results. Similarly, with indirect reasoning you can start with the negation of the conclusion and, using a sequence of steps, obtain the negation of the hypotheses.

Unfortunately, forward reasoning is often difficult to use to prove more complicated results, because the reasoning needed to reach the desired conclusion may be far from obvious. In such cases it may be helpful to use *backward reasoning.* To reason backward to prove a statement q, we find a statement p that we can prove with the property that $p \rightarrow q$. (Note that it is not helpful to find a statement r that you can prove such that

$q \rightarrow r$, because it is the fallacy of begging the question to conclude from $q \rightarrow r$ and r that q is true.) Backward reasoning is illustrated in Examples 1 and 2.

EXAMPLE 1

Extra Examples

Given two positive real numbers a and b, their **arithmetic mean** is $(a + b)/2$ and their **geometric mean** is $\sqrt{ab}$. When we compare the arithmetic and geometric means of pairs of distinct positive real numbers, we find that the arithmetic mean is always greater than the geometric mean. (For example, when $a = 4$ and $b = 6$, we have $5 = (4 + 6)/2 > \sqrt{4 \cdot 6} = \sqrt{24}$.) Can we prove that this inequality is always true?

Solution: To prove that $(a + b)/2 > \sqrt{ab}$ when a and b are distinct positive real numbers, we can work backwards. We construct a sequence of equivalent inequalities. (We leave it to the reader to show that each successive pair of these inequalities is equivalent, using the fact that a and b are positive real numbers.) The equivalent inequalities are

$$(a + b)/2 > \sqrt{ab},$$
$$(a + b)^2/4 > ab,$$
$$(a + b)^2 > 4\,ab,$$
$$a^2 + 2\,ab + b^2 > 4\,ab,$$
$$a^2 - 2\,ab + b^2 > 0,$$
$$(a - b)^2 > 0.$$

Because $(a - b)^2 > 0$ when $a \neq b$, it follows that the final inequality is true. Since all these inequalities are equivalent, it follows that $(a + b)/2 > \sqrt{ab}$ when $a \neq b$. Once we have constructed this proof, we can easily construct a proof using forward reasoning. We leave this to the reader. ◄

EXAMPLE 2

Suppose that two people play a game taking turns removing 1, 2, or 3 stones at a time from a pile that begins with 15 stones. The person who removes the last stone wins the game. Show that the first player can win the game no matter what the second player does.

Solution: To prove that the first player can always win the game, we work backwards. At the last step, the first player can win if this player is left with a pile containing 1, 2, or 3 stones. The second player will be forced to leave 1, 2, or 3 stones if this player has to remove stones from a pile containing 4 stones. Consequently, the next-to-last move of the first player should leave 4 stones for the second player. This can be done when there are 5, 6, or 7 stones left, which happens when the second player has to remove stones from a pile with 8 stones. Consequently, the first player should leave 8 stones for the second player at the second-to-last move for the first player. This means that there are 9, 10, or 11 stones when the first player makes this move. Similarly, the first player should leave 12 stones when this player makes the first move. We can reverse this argument to show that the first player can always make moves so this player wins the game no matter what the second player does. These moves successively leave 12, 8, and 4 stones for the second player. ◄

LEVERAGING PROOF BY CASES When it is not possible to consider all cases of a proof at the same time, a proof by cases (introduced in Section 1.5) should be considered. When should you use such a proof? Generally, look for a proof by cases when there is no obvious way to begin a proof, but when extra information in each case helps move the proof forward. For example, to prove results about the integers, it may be advantageous to consider odd and even integers in separate cases or positive and negative integers in separate cases (such as when absolute values of variables are involved). Similarly, you may want to separately consider cases when an integer is divisible by 5 and when it is not, or the five cases when an integer is of the form $5k$, $5k + 1$, $5k + 2$, $5k + 3$, or $5k + 4$ for some integer k. Beware of a common error in proofs by cases: many people forget to consider all cases so that a purported proof does not establish the result for all possible values. Example 3 illustrates a situation when a proof by cases is called for.

EXAMPLE 3   Prove that if n is an integer not divisible by 2 or 3, then $n^2 - 1$ is divisible by 24.

Solution: To attempt a proof without using cases, we first observe that $n^2 - 1 = (n - 1) \cdot (n + 1)$. Unfortunately, there seems to be no clear way to show this number is divisible by 24 when n is not divisible by either 2 or 3 without looking at different cases. A proof by cases seems to be the next reasonable approach, but which cases should be used? Because we want to prove a result about integers not divisible by either 2 or 3, looking separately at the cases where n is of the form $6k + j$ for $j = 0, 1, 2, 3, 4, 5$ may help. (By the division algorithm, every integer is of one of these forms.) Because we are interested only in integers not divisible by either 2 or 3, we can immediately eliminate the cases where $n = 6k$, $6k + 2$, $6k + 3$, or $6k + 4$ for some integer k. This leaves only two cases, where n is of the form $6k + 1$ and where it is of the form $6k + 5$. We now consider these two cases separately.

Suppose that $n = 6k + 1$ for some integer k. Then $n^2 - 1 = (n + 1)(n - 1) = (6k + 2)6k = 12(3k + 1)k$. Note that $(3k + 1)k$ is an even integer; when k is even, this follows immediately, and when k is odd, $3k + 1$ is even, so that $(3k + 1)k$ is also even. Because $(3k + 1)k$ is even, there is an integer q such that $(3k + 1)k = 2q$. Hence $n^2 - 1 = 12(3k + 1)k = 24q$. It follows that 24 divides $n^2 - 1$.

Next, suppose that $n = 6k + 5$ for some integer k. Then, $n^2 - 1 = (n + 1)(n - 1) = (6k + 6)(6k + 4) = 12(k + 1)(3k + 2)$. Note that $(k + 1)(3k + 2)$ is even because when k is even, $3k + 2$ is even, and when k is odd, $k + 1$ is even. Hence, there is an integer q such that $(k + 1)(3k + 2) = 2q$. It follows that $n^2 - 1 = 12 \cdot 2q = 24q$. We conclude that 24 divides $n^2 - 1$. This completes the proof.   ◄

A common error of reasoning is to draw incorrect conclusions from examples. (For instance, see Example 8.) No matter how many separate examples are considered, a theorem is not proved by considering examples unless every possible case is covered. The problem of proving a theorem is analogous to showing that a computer program always produces the output desired. No matter how many input values are tested, unless all input values are tested, we cannot conclude that the program always produces the correct output. Sometimes, however, we are lucky and we can prove a theorem by considering only a few special cases, as Example 4 demonstrates.

EXAMPLE 4   Show that there are no solutions in integers x and y of $x^2 + 3y^2 = 8$.

Solution: We can quickly reduce this problem to checking just a few cases since $x^2 > 8$ when $|x| \geq 3$ and $3y^2 > 8$ when $|y| \geq 2$. This leaves the cases when x takes on one of the values $-2, -1, 0, 1$, or 2 and y takes on one of the values $-1, 0$, or 1. To dispense with these cases, we note that possible values for x^2 are 0, 1, and 4, and possible values for $3y^2$ are 0 and 3, and the largest sum of possible values for x^2 and $3y^2$ is 7. Consequently, it is impossible for $x^2 + 3y^2 = 8$ to hold when x and y are integers.   ◄

ADAPTING EXISTING PROOFS   An excellent way to look for possible approaches that can be used to prove a statement is to take advantage of existing proofs. Often an existing proof can be adapted to prove a new result. Even when this is not the case, some of the ideas used in existing proofs may be helpful. Because existing proofs provide clues for new proofs, you should read and understand the proofs you encounter in your studies. Example 5 illustrates how to adapt a proof you have already seen to prove a new result.

EXAMPLE 5   Prove that there are infinitely many primes of the form $4k + 3$, where k is a nonnegative integer.

Extra Examples

Solution: A proof we might be able to adapt is the proof given in Section 2.4 that there are infinitely many primes. Recall that this proof assumes that there are only finitely many primes $p_1, p_2, \ldots, p_n$, and forms the number $p_1 p_2 \cdots p_n + 1$. This number is either prime or has a prime factor different from each of the primes $p_1, p_2, \ldots, p_n$, proving that there are infinitely many primes. So, let us suppose that there are only finitely many primes of the form $4k + 3$, namely, $q_1, q_2, \ldots, q_n$, where $q_1 = 3, q_2 = 7$, and so on.

What number can we form that is not divisible by any of these primes, but that must be divisible by a prime of the form $4k + 3$? We might consider the number $4q_1 q_2 \cdots q_n + 3$. Unfortunately, this number is not prime and it is divisible by 3. (This follows since $q_1 = 3$.) Instead, we consider the number

$$Q = 4q_1 q_2 \cdots q_n - 1.$$

Note that Q is of the form $4k + 3$ (where $k = q_1 q_2 \cdots q_n - 1$. If Q is prime, we have found a prime of the desired form different from all those listed. If Q is not prime, Q has at least one prime factor not in the list $q_1, q_2, q_3, \ldots$ because the remainder when Q is divided by q_j is $q_j - 1$, and $q_j - 1 \neq 0$, so $q_j \nmid Q$ for $j = 1, 2, \ldots, n$. Because all odd primes are either of the form $4k + 1$ or of the form $4k + 3$, and the product of primes of the form $4k + 1$ is also of this form (as the reader can verify), there must be a factor of Q of the form $4k + 3$ different from the primes we listed. This completes the proof. We were able to adapt a proof we already had, making some minor modifications to prove a new result.   ◀

A famous theorem from number theory, which has only been proved by advanced methods, states that there are infinitely many primes of the form $ak + b$ whenever a and b are relatively prime positive integers. We leave it to the reader to explore whether the proof we have constructed in Example 5 can be adapted to show that there are infinitely many primes of the form $ak + b$ for other pairs a, b besides $a = 4$ and $b = 3$. (See Exercises 29 and 30, for example.)

CONJECTURE AND PROOF

Mathematics is generally taught as if mathematical facts were carved in stone. Mathematics texts (including the bulk of this book) formally present theorems and their proofs. Such presentations do not convey the discovery process in mathematics. This process begins with the exploration of concepts and examples, the formulation of conjectures, and attempts to settle these conjectures either by proof or by counterexample. These are the day-to-day activities of mathematicians. Believe it or not, the material taught in textbooks was originally developed in this way.

People formulate conjectures on the basis of many types of possible evidence. The examination of special cases can lead to a conjecture, as can the identification of possible patterns. Altering the hypotheses and conclusions of known theorems also can lead to plausible conjectures. At other times, conjectures are made based on intuition or a belief that a result holds. No matter how a conjecture was made, once it has been formulated, the goal is to prove or disprove it. When mathematicians believe a conjecture may be true, they try to find a proof. If they cannot find a proof, they may look for a counterexample. When they cannot find a counterexample, they may switch gears and once again try to prove the conjecture. Although many conjectures are quickly settled, a few conjectures resist attack for hundreds of years and lead to the development of new parts of mathematics. We illustrate the process of formulating conjectures and attempting to prove them in Examples 6 and 7.

EXAMPLE 6 In Chapter 2 we mentioned that the largest primes known are Mersenne primes. Recall that these are primes of the form $2^p - 1$, where p is prime; that is, Mersenne primes are 1 less than a prime power of 2. Do other primes of the special form $a^n - 1$, where a and n are positive integers, exist? After some numerical explorations (such as noting that none of $2^6 - 1 = 63, 2^8 - 1 = 255, 3^4 - 1 = 80$, and $4^5 - 1 = 1023$ are prime) and finding no other primes of this form besides Mersenne primes, we conjecture that $a^n - 1$ is composite when $a > 2$ or when $a = 2$ and n is composite. Can we prove this conjecture?

If we can find a proper factor of $a^n - 1$ when $a > 2$ or $a = 2$ and n is composite, then we have proved this conjecture. A useful approach is to use the factorization $x^n - 1 = (x - 1)(x^{n-1} + x^{n-2} + \cdots + x + 1)$. (You may recall this factorization from your earlier studies. If you do not, you can look at reference books such as [Zw02] that list factorizations of special types of polynomials.) We let $x = a$ in this factorization, to conclude that $a - 1$ is a factor of $a^n - 1$. When $a = 2$ we have $a - 1 = 2 - 1 = 1$, so this factorization does not yield a proper factor of $a^n - 1$. However, when $a > 2$, the factor $a - 1$ satisfies $1 < a - 1 < a^n - 1$, which tells us that $a^n - 1$ is not prime.

The case when $a = 2$ remains. When n is not prime, there are positive integers r and s with $1 < r < n$ and $1 < s < n$ such that $n = rs$. Using the factorization $x^n - 1 = x^{rs} - 1 = (x^r - 1)(x^{r(s-1)} + \cdots + x^r + 1)$, setting $x = a$ shows that $a^r - 1$ is a factor of $a^n - 1$. When $a^r > 2$, $a^r - 1$ is a positive integer greater than 1. This produces a nontrivial factor of $2^n - 1$ when n is composite. ◄

Putting everything together, we can present a succinct direct proof of the conjecture we made in Example 6. We use a proof by cases, since the case when $a > 2$ needs to be considered separately from the case when $a = 2$.

THEOREM 1 The integer $a^n - 1$ is composite when $a > 2$ or when $a = 2$ and n is composite.

Proof: We use a proof by cases.

Case (i): When $a > 2$, the integer $a - 1$ is a factor of $a^n - 1$ because $a^n - 1 = (a - 1) \cdot (a^{n-1} + \cdots + a + 1)$ and $1 < a - 1 < a^n - 1$. Consequently, $a^n - 1$ is composite.

Case (ii): When $a = 2$ and n is composite, there exist integers r and s such that $n = rs$ with $1 < r \le s < n$. In this case, $2^r - 1$ is a factor of $2^n - 1$ because $2^n - 1 = (2^r - 1) \cdot (2^{r(s-1)} + \cdots + 2^r + 1)$ and $1 < 2^r - 1 < 2^n - 1$. This shows that $2^n - 1$ is composite. ◁

EXAMPLE 7 We can easily find long strings of consecutive composite integers, such as 24, 25, 26, 27, 28 and 90, 91, 92, 93, 94, 95, 96. From such evidence, we formulate the conjecture that given a positive integer n, there are n consecutive composite positive integers. How might we prove this conjecture?

Solution: One possible approach to proving this conjecture is to work backward. We reason that if there is an integer X such that $X, X + 1, X + 2, \ldots, X + (n - 1)$ are all composite, then we have proved the result. (This is simply what it means for these n integers to be consecutive.) Given n, can we find an integer X such that each of the integers $X + j, j = 0, 1, \ldots, n - 1$, has a nontrivial factor? One possibility is to let $X = n!$. Then $X = n!$ is composite, and, for $j = 2, 3, \ldots, n - 1$, we immediately see that each of the integers $X + j = n! + j$ is composite because j divides $n! + j$. However, we do not know whether $X + 1 = n! + 1$ is composite.

To get around this problem, we instead take $X = (n + 1)! + 1$. We see that the n consecutive integers $X + 1, X + 2, \ldots, X + n$, which are the integers

$$(n + 1)! + 2, (n + 1)! + 3, \ldots, (n + 1)! + (n + 1),$$

are all composite, because j divides $(n + 1)! + j$ for $j = 2, \ldots, n + 1$. Consequently, we have found n consecutive composite integers. It is a short task, which we will not do here, to rewrite the proof without showing our backward reasoning. ◀

CONJECTURE AND COUNTEREXAMPLES

Not all the plausible conjectures we make turn out to be true. To dispose of those that turn out to be false, we need to find counterexamples. Examples 8 and 9 illustrate this process.

EXAMPLE 8

Extra Examples

It would be useful to have a function $f(n)$ such that $f(n)$ is prime for all positive integers n. If we had such a function, we could find large primes for use in cryptography and other applications. Looking for such a function, we might check out different polynomial functions, as some mathematicians did several hundred years ago. After a lot of computation we may encounter the polynomial $f(n) = n^2 - n + 41$. This polynomial has the interesting property that $f(n)$ is prime for all positive integers n not exceeding 40. [We have $f(1) = 41$, $f(2) = 43$, $f(3) = 47$, $f(4) = 53$, and so on.] This can lead us to the conjecture that $f(n)$ is prime for all positive integers n. Can we settle this conjecture?

Solution: Perhaps not surprisingly, this conjecture turns out to be false; we do not have to look far to find a positive integer n for which $f(n)$ is composite, because $f(41) = 41^2 - 41 + 41 = 41^2$. Because $f(n) = n^2 - n + 41$ is prime for all positive integers n with $1 \le n \le 40$, we might be tempted to find a different polynomial with the property that $f(n)$ is prime for *all* positive integers n. However, there is no such polynomial. It can be shown that for every polynomial $f(n)$ with integer coefficients there is a positive integer y such that $f(y)$ is composite. (See Exercise 37.) ◀

Example 9 illustrates that surprisingly large counterexamples are sometimes needed. This reiterates the important point that even a vast amount of numerical calculation does not establish a theorem.

EXAMPLE 9

In the eighteenth century, the great Swiss mathematician Leonhard Euler conjectured that for every integer n with $n \ge 3$, the sum of $n - 1$ nth powers of positive integers cannot be an nth power. The numerical evidence found for close to two hundred years supported this conjecture. However, no proof could be found, even for a single value of n. Then in 1966, L. J. Lander and T. R. Parkin found a surprisingly small counterexample for $n = 5$. They showed that $27^5 + 84^5 + 110^5 + 133^5 = 144^5$.

This counterexample left open the possibility that the conjecture is true for other values of n with $n \geq 3$. But in 1988, Noam Elkies found a counterexample for $n = 4$. All known counterexamples are much larger than that found for the $n = 5$ case. The smallest counterexample known for $n = 4$ is $95,800^4 + 217,519^4 + 414,560^4 = 422,481^4$ (where by smallest we mean the smallest in terms of the sum of the integers whose fourth powers are being computed). All cases with $n \geq 6$ are still unsettled. Looking hard for a counterexample for the $n = 6$ case may pay off for someone, but it is possible (though considered unlikely by many) that the conjecture is true for $n = 6$.   ◄

THE ROLE OF OPEN PROBLEMS Many advances in mathematics have been made by people trying to solve famous unsolved problems. For instance, one famous problem unsolved for approximately three hundred years led to the development of an entire branch of number theory. This problem asked whether the statement known as **Fermat's Last Theorem** is true.

THEOREM 2

Links

FERMAT'S LAST THEOREM The equation

$$x^n + y^n = z^n$$

has no solutions in integers x, y, and z with $xyz \neq 0$ whenever n is an integer with $n > 2$.

Remark: The equation $x^2 + y^2 = z^2$ has infinitely many solutions in integers x, y, and z; these solutions are called Pythagorean triples and correspond to the lengths of the sides of right triangles with integer lengths. See Exercise 10.

This problem has a fascinating history. In the seventeenth century, Fermat jotted in the margin of his copy of the works of Diophantus that he had a "wondrous proof" that there are no nontrivial integer solutions of $x^n + y^n = z^n$ when n is an integer greater than 2. However, he never published a proof (Fermat published almost nothing) and no proof could be found in the papers he left when he died. Mathematicians looked for a proof for three centuries without success, although many people were convinced that a relatively simple proof could be found. (Proofs of special cases were found, such as the proof of the case when $n = 3$ by Euler and the proof of the $n = 4$ case by Fermat himself.) Over the years, several established mathematicians thought that they had proved this theorem. In the nineteenth century, one of these failed attempts led to the development of the part of number theory called algebraic number theory. A correct proof, requiring hundreds of pages of advanced mathematics, was not found until the 1990s, when Andrew Wiles used recently developed ideas from a sophisticated area of number theory called the theory of elliptic curves to prove Fermat's Last Theorem. Wiles's quest to find a proof of Fermat's Last Theorem using this powerful theory, documented in a program in the *Nova* series on public television, took close to ten years! (The interested reader should consult [Ro99] for more information about Fermat's Last Theorem and for additional references concerning this problem and its resolution.)

Many famous problems still await ultimate resolution by clever people. We describe a few of the most accessible and better known of these open problems in Examples 10–13.

EXAMPLE 10   **Goldbach's Conjecture** In 1742, Christian Goldbach, in a letter to Leonhard Euler, conjectured that every odd integer n, $n > 5$, is the sum of three primes. Euler replied that this conjecture is equivalent to the conjecture that every even integer n, $n > 2$, is the sum

Links

of two primes (see Exercise 39). The conjecture that every even integer $n, n > 2$, is the sum of two primes is now called **Goldbach's conjecture.** We can check this conjecture for small even numbers. For example, $4 = 2 + 2, 6 = 3 + 3, 8 = 5 + 3, 10 = 7 + 3, 12 = 7 + 5$, and so on. Goldbach's conjecture was verified by hand calculations for numbers up to the millions prior to the advent of computers. With computers it can be checked for extremely large numbers. As of mid-2002, the conjecture has been checked for all positive even integers up to $4 \cdot 10^{14}$.

Although no proof of Goldbach's conjecture has been found, most mathematicians believe it is true. Several theorems have been proved, using complicated methods from analytic number theory, establishing results weaker than Goldbach's conjecture. Among these are the result that every even positive integer greater than 2 is the sum of at most six primes (proved in 1995 by O. Ramaré) and that every sufficiently large positive integer is the sum of a prime and a number that is either prime or the product of two primes (proved in 1966 by J. R. Chen). Perhaps Goldbach's conjecture will be settled in the not too distant future. ◄

EXAMPLE 11   There are many conjectures asserting that there are infinitely many primes of certain forms. For example, there is a conjecture that there are infinitely many Mersenne primes.

Links

(Recall from Section 2.4 that these are primes of the form $2^p - 1$, where p is prime.) Another conjecture of this sort is the conjecture that there are infinitely many primes of the form $n^2 + 1$, where n is a positive integer. For example, $5 = 2^2 + 1, 17 = 4^2 + 1$, $37 = 6^2 + 1$, and so on. The best result currently known is that there are infinitely many positive integers n such that $n^2 + 1$ is prime or the product of at most two primes (proved by Henryk Iwaniec in 1973). ◄

EXAMPLE 12   **The Twin Prime Conjecture** **Twin primes** are primes that differ by 2, such as 3 and 5, 5 and 7, 11 and 13, 17 and 19, and 4967 and 4969. The twin prime conjecture asserts that

Links

there are infinitely many twin primes. The strongest result proved concerning twin primes is that there are infinitely many pairs p and $p + 2$, where p is prime and $p + 2$ is prime or the product of two primes (proved by J. R. Chen in 1966). The world's record for twin primes, as of mid-2002, consists of the numbers $318,032,361 \cdot 2^{107,001} \pm 1$, numbers with 32,220 digits. ◄

EXAMPLE 13   **The $3x + 1$ Conjecture** Let $f(x)$ be the function that maps an even integer x to $x/2$ and an odd integer x to $3x + 1$. There is a famous conjecture, sometimes known as the

Links

$3x + 1$ conjecture, that states that for all positive integers x, when we repeatedly apply the function f we will eventually reach the integer 1. For example, starting with $x = 13$, we find $f(13) = 3 \cdot 13 + 1 = 40, f(40) = 40/2 = 20, f(20) = 20/2 = 10, f(10) = 10/2 = 5$, $f(5) = 3 \cdot 5 + 1 = 16, f(16) = 8, f(8) = 4, f(4) = 2$, and $f(2) = 1$. The $3x + 1$ conjecture has been verified for all integers x up to $5.6 \cdot 10^{13}$.

The $3x + 1$ conjecture has an interesting history and has attracted the attention of mathematicians since the 1950s. The conjecture has been raised many times and goes by many other names, including the Collatz problem, Hasse's algorithm, Ulam's problem, the

Links

CHRISTIAN GOLDBACH (1690–1764) Christian Goldbach was born in Königsberg, Prussia, the city noted for its famous bridge problem (which will be studied in Section 8.5). He became professor of mathematics at the Academy in St. Petersburg in 1725. In 1728 Goldbach went to Moscow to tutor the son of the Tsar. He entered the world of politics when, in 1742, he became a staff member in the Russian Ministry of Foreign Affairs. Goldbach is best known for his correspondence with eminent mathematicians, including Euler and Bernoulli, for his famous conjectures in number theory, and for several contributions to analysis.

Syracuse problem, and Kakutani's problem. Many mathematicians have been diverted from their work to spend time attacking this conjecture. This led to the joke that this problem was part of a conspiracy to slow down American mathematical research. See the article by Jeffrey Lagarias [La85] for a fascinating discussion of this problem and the results that have been found by mathematicians attacking it. ◀

THE HALTING PROBLEM

We will now describe a proof of one of the most famous theorems in computer science. We will show that there is a problem that cannot be solved using any procedure. That is, we will show there are unsolvable problems, as was mentioned in Section 2.3. The problem we study is the **halting problem.** It asks whether there is a procedure that does this: It takes as input a computer program and input to the program and determines whether the program will eventually stop when run with this input. It would be convenient to have such a procedure, if it existed. Certainly being able to test whether a program entered into an infinite loop would be helpful when writing and debugging programs. However, in 1936 Alan Turing showed that no such procedure exists (see his biography in Section 11.4).

Before we present a proof that the halting problem is unsolvable, first note that we cannot simply run a program and observe what it does to determine whether it terminates when run with the given input. If the program halts, we have our answer, but if it is still running after any fixed length of time has elapsed, we do not know whether it will never halt or we just did not wait long enough for it to terminate. After all, it is not hard to design a program that will stop only after more than a billion years has elapsed.

We will describe Turing's proof that the halting problem is unsolvable; it is a proof by contradiction. (The reader should note that our proof is not completely rigorous, since we have not explicitly defined what a procedure is. To remedy this, the concept of a Turing machine is needed. This concept is introduced in Section 11.5.)

Proof: Assume there is a solution to the halting problem, a procedure called $H(P, I)$. The procedure $H(P, I)$ takes two inputs, one a program P and the other I, an input to the program P. $H(P, I)$ generates the string "halt" as output if H determines that P stops when given I as input. Otherwise, $H(P, I)$ generates the string "loops forever" as output. We will now derive a contradiction.

When a procedure is coded, it is expressed as a string of characters; this string can be interpreted as a sequence of bits. This means that a program itself can be used as data. Therefore a program can be thought of as input to another program, or even itself. Hence, H can take a program P as both of its inputs, which are a program and input to this program. H should be able to determine if P will halt when it is given a copy of itself as input.

To show that no procedure H exists that solves the halting problem, we construct a simple procedure $K(P)$, which works as follows, making use of the output $H(P, P)$. If the output of $H(P, P)$ is "loops forever," which means that P loops forever when given a copy of itself as input, then $K(P)$ halts. If the output of $H(P, P)$ is "halt," which means that P halts when given a copy of itself as input, then $K(P)$ loops forever. That is, $K(P)$ does the opposite of what the output of $H(P, P)$ specifies. (See Figure 1.)

Now suppose we provide K as input to K. We note that if the output of $H(K, K)$ is "loops forever," then by the definition of K we see that $K(K)$ halts. Otherwise, if the output of $H(K, K)$ is "halt," then by the definition of K we see that $K(K)$ loops forever, in violation of what H tells us. In both cases, we have a contradiction.

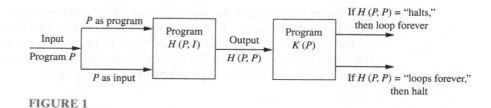

FIGURE 1

Thus, H cannot always give the correct answers. Consequently, there is no procedure that solves the halting problem.   ◁

ADDITIONAL PROOF METHODS

In Chapter 1 we introduced the basic methods used in proofs and in this section we described how to leverage these methods to prove a variety of results. However, there are many important proof methods besides those we have covered. We will introduce some of these methods later in this book. In particular, in Section 3.3 we will discuss mathematical induction, which is an extremely useful method for proving statements of the form $\forall n\, P(n)$, where the universe of discourse is the set of positive integers. In Section 3.4 we will introduce structural induction, which can be used to prove results about recursively defined sets. We will use the Cantor diagonalization method, which can be used to prove results about the size of infinite sets, in Section 3.2. Finally, in Chapter 4 we will introduce the notion of combinatorial proofs, which can be used to prove results by counting arguments. The reader should note that entire books have been devoted to the activities discussed in this section, including many excellent works by George Pólya ([Po61], [Po71], [Po90]).

Exercises

1. Prove that the product of any three consecutive integers is divisible by 6.
2. Prove that if n is an odd positive integer, then $n^2 \equiv 1$ (mod 8).
3. Prove that if n is an odd positive integer, then $n^4 \equiv 1$ (mod 16).
4. Prove that there are no solutions in integers x and y to the equation $2x^2 + 5y^2 = 14$.
5. Prove that there are no solutions in positive integers x and y to the equation $x^4 + y^4 = 625$.
6. Prove that there are no integers x and y such that $x^2 - 4y = 3$.
7. Prove that there are no integers x and y such that $3x^2 - 8y = 1$.
8. Prove that there are no solutions in integers x and y to the equation $x^2 - 5y^2 = 2$. (*Hint:* Consider this equation modulo 5.)

9. Prove that there are no solutions in integers x and y to the equation $x^4 - 16y^4 = 3$. (*Hint:* Look at the congruence obtained by considering this equation modulo 16 and use Exercise 3.)
10. Prove that there are infinitely many solutions in positive integers x, y, and z to the equation $x^2 + y^2 = z^2$. (*Hint:* Let $x = m^2 - n^2$, $y = 2mn$, and $z = m^2 + n^2$, where m and n are integers.)
11. The **harmonic mean** of two integers a and b equals $\frac{2ab}{a+b}$. By computing the harmonic and geometric means of different pairs of positive integers, formulate a conjecture about their relative sizes and prove your conjecture.
12. The **quadratic mean** of two integers a and b equals $\sqrt{\frac{a^2+b^2}{2}}$. By computing the arithmetic and quadratic means of different pairs of positive integers, formulate a conjecture about their relative sizes and prove your conjecture.

*13. Write the numbers $1, 2, \ldots, 2n$ on a blackboard, where n is an odd integer. Pick any two of the numbers, j and k, write $|j - k|$ on the board and erase j and k. Continue this process until only one integer is written on the board. Prove that this integer must be odd.

*14. Suppose that five ones and four zeros are arranged around a circle. Between any two equal bits you insert a 0 and between any two unequal bits you insert a 1 to produce nine new bits. Then you erase the nine original bits. Show that when you iterate this procedure, you can never get nine zeros. (*Hint:* Work backwards, assuming that you did end up with nine zeros.)

*15. Prove or disprove that $n^2 - 79n + 1601$ is prime whenever n is a positive integer.

16. Prove or disprove that $2^n + 1$ is prime for all non-negative integers n.

17. Prove or disprove that $\sqrt[3]{3}$ is irrational.

*18. Show that $\sqrt{n}$ is irrational if n is a positive integer that is not a perfect square.

*19. Prove or disprove that there is no rational number x such that $x^3 + x + 1 = 0$.

20. Prove that the square of an integer not divisible by 5 leaves a remainder of 1 or 4 when divided by 5. (*Hint:* Use a proof by cases.)

*21. Let p be prime. Prove that $a^2 \equiv b^2 \pmod{p}$ if and only if $a \equiv b \pmod{p}$ or $a \equiv -b \pmod{p}$.

22. Prove or disprove that $n^2 - 1$ is composite whenever n is a positive integer greater than 1.

☞ **23.** Prove that $(a \bmod m)(b \bmod m) \bmod m = ab \bmod m$ for all integers a and b whenever m is a positive integer.

24. Prove or disprove that $a \bmod m + b \bmod m = (a + b) \bmod m$ for all integers a and b whenever m is a positive integer.

25. Prove or disprove that there are three consecutive odd positive integers that are primes, that is, odd primes of the form p, $p + 2$, and $p + 4$.

26. Prove or disprove that given a positive integer n, there are n consecutive odd positive integers that are primes.

27. Give a constructive proof of the proposition: "For every positive integer n there is an integer divisible by more than n primes."

28. Find a counterexample to the proposition: "For every prime number n, $n + 2$ is prime."

29. Adapt the proof given in Example 5 to show that there are infinitely many primes of the form $6k + 5$.

30. What goes wrong when you try to adapt the proof that there are infinitely many primes to show that there are infinitely many primes of the form $4k + 1$?

*31. Prove that if x is a real number and n is a positive integer, then $\lfloor \frac{x}{3} \rfloor + \lfloor \frac{x+n}{3} \rfloor + \lfloor \frac{x+2n}{3} \rfloor = \gcd(3, n) \lfloor \frac{x}{\gcd(3,n)} \rfloor + (n - 1) + \frac{\gcd(3, n) - 1}{2}$.

32. Prove that $\lfloor n/2 \rfloor \lceil n/2 \rceil = \lfloor n^2/4 \rfloor$ for all integers n.

*33. Let $S = x_1 y_1 + x_2 y_2 + \cdots + x_n y_n$, where $x_1, x_2, \ldots, x_n$ and $y_1, y_2, \ldots, y_n$ are orderings of two different sequences of positive real numbers, each containing n elements.

a) Show that S takes its maximum value over all orderings of the two sequences when both sequences are sorted (so that the elements in each sequence are in nondecreasing order).

b) Show that S takes its minimum value over all orderings of the two sequences when one sequence is sorted into nondecreasing order and the other is sorted into nonincreasing order.

34. Prove that if m and n are positive integers and x is a real number, then
$$\left\lfloor \frac{\lfloor x \rfloor + n}{m} \right\rfloor = \left\lfloor \frac{x + n}{m} \right\rfloor.$$

*35. Prove that if m is a positive integer and x is a real number, then
$$\lfloor mx \rfloor = \lfloor x \rfloor + \left\lfloor x + \frac{1}{m} \right\rfloor + \left\lfloor x + \frac{2}{m} \right\rfloor + \cdots$$
$$+ \left\lfloor x + \frac{m - 1}{m} \right\rfloor.$$

**36. Show that if a and b are positive irrational numbers such that $1/a + 1/b = 1$, then every positive integer can be uniquely expressed as either $\lfloor ka \rfloor$ or $\lfloor kb \rfloor$ for some positive integer k.

*37. Prove that if $f(x)$ is a nonconstant polynomial with integer coefficients, then there is an integer y such that $f(y)$ is composite. [*Hint:* Assume that $f(x_0) = p$ is prime. Show that p divides $f(x_0 + kp)$ for all integers k. Obtain a contradiction of the fact that a polynomial of degree n, where $n > 1$, takes on each value at most n times.]

38. Prove that if n is a positive integer such that the sum of its divisors is $n + 1$, then n is prime.

39. Show that Goldbach's conjecture, which states that every even integer greater than 2 is the sum of two primes, is equivalent to the statement that every integer greater than 5 is the sum of three primes.

40. A conjecture known as **de Polignac's conjecture** asserts that every positive even integer can be written as the difference of two consecutive primes in infinitely many ways. Show that de Polignac's conjecture implies the twin prime conjecture.

41. Verify the $3x + 1$ conjecture for these integers.

a) 6 **b)** 7 **c)** 17 **d)** 21

42. Verify the $3x + 1$ conjecture for these integers.

a) 16 **b)** 11 **c)** 35 **d)** 113

A **perfect number** is a positive integer that equals the sum of its proper divisors (that is, divisors other than itself).

43. Show that 6, 28, and 496 are perfect.

44. Prove that if $\gcd(s, t) = 1$, where s and t are positive integers, then the sum of the divisors of st is the product of the sum of the divisors of s and the sum of the divisors of t.

45. Prove that the integer $2^{p-1}(2^p - 1)$ is perfect when $2^p - 1$ is a Mersenne prime.

**46. Prove that if n is an even integer that is perfect, then $n = 2^p(2^p - 1)$, where $2^p - 1$ is a Mersenne prime.

47. Prove or disprove that if you have an eight-gallon jug of water and two empty jugs with capacities of five gallons and three gallons, respectively, then you can measure four gallons by successively pouring some of or all of the water in a jug into another jug.

*48. Prove or disprove that if n is a positive integer, then $\lfloor \sqrt{n} + \sqrt{n+1} \rfloor = \lfloor \sqrt{4n+2} \rfloor$.

49. Show that the problem of determining whether a program with a given input ever prints the digit 1 is unsolvable.

50. Show that the problem of deciding whether a specific program with a specific input halts is solvable.

51. Show that the following problem is solvable. Given two programs with their inputs and the knowledge that exactly one of them halts, determine which halts.

3.2 Sequences and Summations

INTRODUCTION

Sequences are used to represent ordered lists of elements. Sequences are used in discrete mathematics in many ways. They can be used to represent solutions to certain counting problems, as we will see in Chapter 6. They are also an important data structure in computer science. This section contains a review of the concept of a function, as well as the notation used to represent sequences and sums of terms of sequences.

When the elements of an infinite set can be listed, the set is called countable. We will conclude this section with a discussion of both countable and uncountable sets. We will prove that the set of rational numbers is countable, but the set of real numbers is not.

SEQUENCES

A sequence is a discrete structure used to represent an ordered list.

DEFINITION 1

A *sequence* is a function from a subset of the set of integers (usually either the set $\{0, 1, 2, \ldots\}$ or the set $\{1, 2, 3, \ldots\}$) to a set S. We use the notation a_n to denote the image of the integer n. We call a_n a *term* of the sequence.

We use the notation $\{a_n\}$ to describe the sequence. (Note that a_n represents an individual term of the sequence $\{a_n\}$. Also note that the notation $\{a_n\}$ for a sequence conflicts with the notation for a set. However, the context in which we use this notation will always make it clear when we are dealing with sets and when we are dealing with sequences. Note also that the choice of the letter a is arbitrary.)

We describe sequences by listing the terms of the sequence in order of increasing subscripts.

EXAMPLE 1 Consider the sequence $\{a_n\}$, where

$$a_n = 1/n.$$

The list of the terms of this sequence, beginning with a_1, namely,

$$a_1, a_2, a_3, a_4, \ldots,$$

starts with

$$1, \frac{1}{2}, \frac{1}{3}, \frac{1}{4}, \ldots.$$ ◀

DEFINITION 2

A *geometric progression* is a sequence of the form

$$a, ar, ar^2, \ldots, ar^n,$$

where the *initial term a* and the *common ratio r* are real numbers.

Remark: A geometric progression is a discrete analogue of the exponential function $f(x) = ar^x$.

EXAMPLE 2 The sequences $\{b_n\}$ with $b_n = (-1)^n$, $\{c_n\}$ with $c_n = 2 \cdot 5^n$, and $\{d_n\}$ with $d_n = 6 \cdot (1/3)^n$ are geometric progressions with initial term and common ratio equal to -1 and -1; 10 and 5; and 2 and 1/3, respectively. The list of terms $b_1, b_2, b_3, b_4, \ldots$ begins with

$$-1, 1, -1, 1, \ldots;$$

the list of terms $c_1, c_2, c_3, c_4, \ldots$ begins with

$$10, 50, 250, 1250, \ldots;$$

and the list of terms $d_1, d_2, d_3, d_4, \ldots$ begins with

$$2, 2/3, 2/9, 2/27, \ldots.$$ ◀

DEFINITION 3

An *arithmetic progression* is a sequence of the form

$$a, a + d, a + 2d, \ldots, a + nd,$$

where the *initial term a* and the *common difference d* are real numbers.

Remark: An arithmetic progression is a discrete analogue of the linear function $f(x) = dx + a$.

EXAMPLE 3 The sequences $\{s_n\}$ with $s_n = -1 + 4n$ and $\{t_n\}$ with $t_n = 7 - 3n$ are both arithmetic progressions with initial terms and common differences equal to -1 and 4, and 7 and -3, respectively. The list of terms, starting with the term with $n = 0, s_0, s_1, s_2, s_3, \ldots$ begins with

$$-1, 3, 7, 11, \ldots,$$

and the list of terms $t_0, t_1, t_2, t_3, \ldots$ begins with

$$7, 4, 1, -2, \ldots.$$ ◀

Sequences of the form $a_1, a_2, \ldots, a_n$ are often used in computer science. These finite sequences are also called **strings.** This string is also denoted by $a_1 a_2 \cdots a_n$. (Recall that bit strings, which are finite sequences of bits, were introduced in Section 1.1.) The **length** of the string S is the number of terms in this string. The **empty string,** denoted by λ, is the string that has no terms. The empty string has length zero.

EXAMPLE 4 The string $abcd$ is a string of length four. ◀

SPECIAL INTEGER SEQUENCES

A common problem in discrete mathematics is finding a formula or a general rule for constructing the terms of a sequence. Sometimes only a few terms of a sequence solving a problem are known; the goal is to identify the sequence. Even though the initial terms of a sequence do not determine the entire sequence (after all, there are infinitely many different sequences that start with any finite set of initial terms), knowing the first few terms may help you make an educated conjecture about the identity of your sequence. Once you have made this conjecture, you can try to verify that you have the correct sequence.

When trying to deduce a possible formula or rule for the terms of a sequence from the initial terms, try to find a pattern in these terms. You might also see whether you can determine how a term might have been produced from those preceding it. There are many questions you could ask, but some of the more useful are:

- Are there runs of the same value?
- Are terms obtained from previous terms by adding the same amount or an amount that depends on the position in the sequence?
- Are terms obtained from previous terms by multiplying by a particular amount?
- Are terms obtained by combining previous terms in a certain way?
- Are there cycles among the terms?

EXAMPLE 5   Find formulas for the sequences with the following first five terms: (a) $1, 1/2, 1/4, 1/8,$ $1/16$ (b) $1, 3, 5, 7, 9$ (c) $1, -1, 1, -1, 1$.

Solution: (a) We recognize that the denominators are powers of 2. The sequence with $a_n = 1/2^{n-1}$ is a possible match. This proposed sequence is a geometric progression with $a = 1$ and $r = 1/2$.

(b) We note that each term is obtained by adding 2 to the previous term. The sequence with $a_n = 2n - 1$ is a possible match. This proposed sequence is an arithmetic progression with $a = 1$ and $d = 2$.

(c) The terms alternate between 1 and -1. The sequence with $a_n = (-1)^{n+1}$ is a possible match. This proposed sequence is a geometric progression with $a = 1$ and $r = -1$.   ◄

Examples 6 and 7 illustrate how we can analyze sequences to find how the terms are constructed.

EXAMPLE 6   How can we produce the terms of a sequence if the first 10 terms are $1, 2, 2, 3, 3, 3, 4, 4, 4, 4$?

Solution: Note that the integer 1 appears once, the integer 2 appears twice, the integer 3 appears three times, and the integer 4 appears four times. A reasonable rule for generating this sequence is that the integer n appears exactly n times, so the next five terms of the sequence would all be 5, the following six terms would all be 6, and so on. The sequence generated this way is a possible match.   ◄

EXAMPLE 7   How can we produce the terms of a sequence if the first 10 terms are $5, 11, 17, 23, 29, 35,$ $41, 47, 53, 59$?

Solution: Note that each of the first 10 terms of this sequence after the first is obtained by adding 6 to the previous term. (We could see this by noticing that the difference between consecutive terms is 6.) Consequently, the nth term could be produced by starting with 5 and adding 6 a total of $n - 1$ times; that is, a reasonable guess is that the nth term is $5 + 6(n - 1) = 6n - 1$. (This is an arithmetic progression with $a = 5$ and $d = 6$.) ◄

Another useful technique for finding a rule for generating the terms of a sequence is to compare the terms of a sequence of interest with the terms of a well-known integer sequence, such as terms of an arithmetic progression, terms of a geometric progression, perfect squares, perfect cubes, and so on. The first 10 terms of some sequences you may want to keep in mind are displayed in Table 1.

EXAMPLE 8   Conjecture a simple formula for a_n if the first 10 terms of the sequence $\{a_n\}$ are $1, 7, 25,$ $79, 241, 727, 2185, 6559, 19681, 59047$.

Solution: To attack this problem, we begin by looking at the difference of consecutive terms, but we do not see a pattern. When we form the ratio of consecutive terms to see whether each term is a multiple of the previous term, we find that this ratio, although not a constant, is close to 3. So it is reasonable to suspect that the terms of this sequence are generated by a formula involving 3^n. Comparing these terms with the corresponding terms of the sequence $\{3^n\}$, we notice that the nth term is 2 less than the corresponding power of 3. We see that $a_n = 3^n - 2$ for $1 \le n \le 10$ and conjecture that this formula holds for all n. ◄

We will see throughout this text that integer sequences appear in a wide range of contexts in discrete mathematics. Sequences we have or will encounter include the sequence of prime numbers (Chapter 2), the number of ways to order n discrete objects (Chapter 4), the number of the moves required to solve the famous Tower of Hanoi puzzle with n disks (Chapter 6), and the number of rabbits on an island after n months (Chapter 6).

Integer sequences appear in an amazingly wide range of subject areas besides discrete mathematics, including biology, engineering, chemistry, and physics, as well as in puzzles. A wonderfully diverse collection of over 8000 different integer sequences has been constructed over the past 20 years by the mathematician Neil Sloane, who has teamed up with Simon Plouffe, to produce *The Encyclopedia of Integer Sequences* ([SlPl95]). An extended list of the sequences is available on the Web, with new sequences added regularly. There is also a program accessible via the Web that you can use to find sequences from the encyclopedia that match initial terms you provide.

Links

TABLE 1 **Some Useful Sequences.**	
nth Term	*First 10 Terms*
n^2	$1, 4, 9, 16, 25, 36, 49, 64, 81, 100, \ldots$
n^3	$1, 8, 27, 64, 125, 216, 343, 512, 729, 1000, \ldots$
n^4	$1, 16, 81, 256, 625, 1296, 2401, 4096, 6561, 10000, \ldots$
2^n	$2, 4, 8, 16, 32, 64, 128, 256, 512, 1024, \ldots$
3^n	$3, 9, 27, 81, 243, 729, 2187, 6561, 19683, 59049, \ldots$
$n!$	$1, 2, 6, 24, 120, 720, 5040, 40320, 362880, 3628800, \ldots$

SUMMATIONS

Next, we introduce **summation notation.** We begin by describing the notation used to express the sum of the terms

$$a_m, a_{m+1}, \ldots, a_n$$

from the sequence $\{a_n\}$. We use the notation

$$\sum_{j=m}^{n} a_j \qquad \text{or} \qquad \sum_{j=m}^{n} a_j$$

to represent

$$a_m + a_{m+1} + \cdots + a_n.$$

Here, the variable j is called the **index of summation,** and the choice of the letter j as the variable is arbitrary; that is, we could have used any other letter, such as i or k. Or, in notation,

$$\sum_{j=m}^{n} a_j = \sum_{i=m}^{n} a_i = \sum_{k=m}^{n} a_k.$$

Here, the index of summation runs through all integers starting with its **lower limit** m and ending with its **upper limit** n. The uppercase Greek letter sigma, Σ, is used to denote summation. We give some examples of summation notation.

Links

NEIL SLOANE (BORN 1939) Neil Sloane studied mathematics and electrical engineering at the University of Melbourne on a scholarship from the Australian state telephone company. He mastered many telephone-related jobs, such as erecting telephone poles, in his summer work. After graduating, he designed minimal cost telephone networks in Australia. In 1962 he came to the United States and studied electrical engineering at Cornell University. His Ph.D. thesis was on what are now called neural networks. He took a job at Bell Labs in 1969, working in many areas, including network design, coding theory, and sphere packing. He now works for AT&T Labs, moving there from Bell Labs when AT&T split up in 1996. One of his favorite problems is the **kissing problem** (a name he coined), which asks how many spheres can be arranged in n dimensions so that they all touch a central sphere of the same size. (In two dimensions the answer is 6, since 6 pennies can be placed so that they touch a central penny. In three dimensions, 12 billiard balls can be placed so that they touch a central billiard ball. Two billiard balls that just touch are said to "kiss," giving rise to the terminology "kissing problem" and "kissing number.") Sloane, together with Andrew Odlyzko, showed that in 8 and 24 dimensions the optimal kissing numbers are, respectively, 240 and 196,560. The kissing number is known in dimensions 1, 2, 3, 8, and 24, but not in any other dimensions. Sloane's books include *Sphere Packings, Lattices and Groups,* 3d ed., with John Conway; *The Theory of Error-Correcting Codes* with Jessie MacWilliams; *The Encyclopedia of Integer Sequences* with Simon Plouffe; and *The Rock-Climbing Guide to New Jersey Crags* with Paul Nick. The last book demonstrates his interest in rock climbing; it includes more than 50 climbing sites in New Jersey.

EXAMPLE 9   Express the sum of the first 100 terms of the sequence $\{a_n\}$, where $a_n = 1/n$ for $n = 1, 2, 3, \ldots$.

Solution: The lower limit for the index of summation is 1, and the upper limit is 100. We write this sum as

$$\sum_{j=1}^{100} \frac{1}{j}.$$ ◀

EXAMPLE 10   What is the value of $\sum_{j=1}^{5} j^2$?

Solution: We have

$$\sum_{j=1}^{5} j^2 = 1^2 + 2^2 + 3^2 + 4^2 + 5^2$$
$$= 1 + 4 + 9 + 16 + 25$$
$$= 55.$$ ◀

EXAMPLE 11   What is the value of $\sum_{k=4}^{8} (-1)^k$?

Solution: We have

$$\sum_{k=4}^{8} (-1)^k = (-1)^4 + (-1)^5 + (-1)^6 + (-1)^7 + (-1)^8$$
$$= 1 + (-1) + 1 + (-1) + 1$$
$$= 1.$$ ◀

Sometimes it is useful to shift the index of summation in a sum. This is often done when two sums need to be added but their indices of summation do not match. When shifting an index of summation, it is important to make the appropriate changes in the corresponding summand. This is illustrated by the following example.

EXAMPLE 12   Suppose we have the sum

$$\sum_{j=1}^{5} j^2$$

but want the index of summation to run between 0 and 4 rather than from 1 to 5. To do this, we let $k = j - 1$. Then the new summation index runs from 0 to 4, and the term j^2 becomes $(k + 1)^2$. Hence

$$\sum_{j=1}^{5} j^2 = \sum_{k=0}^{4} (k + 1)^2.$$

It is easily checked that both sums are $1 + 4 + 9 + 16 + 25 = 55$. ◀

Sums of terms of geometric progressions commonly arise (such sums are called **geometric series**). Theorem 1 gives us a formula for the sum of terms of a geometric progression.

THEOREM 1

If a and r are real numbers and $r \neq 0$, then

$$\sum_{j=0}^{n} ar^j = \begin{cases} \dfrac{ar^{n+1} - a}{r - 1} & \text{if } r \neq 1 \\ (n+1)a & \text{if } r = 1. \end{cases}$$

Proof: Let

$$S = \sum_{j=0}^{n} ar^j.$$

To compute S, first multiply both sides of the equality by r and then manipulate the resulting sum as follows:

$$rS = r \sum_{j=0}^{n} ar^j$$

$$= \sum_{j=0}^{n} ar^{j+1}$$

$$= \sum_{k=1}^{n+1} ar^k$$

$$= \sum_{k=0}^{n} ar^k + (ar^{n+1} - a) \quad \text{We obtain this equality by shifting the index of summation, setting } k = j + 1.$$

$$= S + (ar^{n+1} - a).$$

From these equalities, we see that

$$rS = S + (ar^{n+1} - a).$$

Solving for S shows that if $r \neq 1$

$$S = \frac{ar^{n+1} - a}{r - 1}.$$

If $r = 1$, then clearly the sum equals $(n+1)a$. ◁

EXAMPLE 13

Double summations arise in many contexts (as in the analysis of nested loops in computer programs). An example of a double summation is

$$\sum_{i=1}^{4} \sum_{j=1}^{3} ij.$$

To evaluate the double sum, first expand the inner summation and then continue by computing the outer summation:

$$\sum_{i=1}^{4} \sum_{j=1}^{3} ij = \sum_{i=1}^{4} (i + 2i + 3i)$$

$$= \sum_{i=1}^{4} 6i$$

$$= 6 + 12 + 18 + 24 = 60.$$ ◀

We can also use summation notation to add all values of a function, or terms of an indexed set, where the index of summation runs over all values in a set. That is, we write

$$\sum_{s \in S} f(s)$$

to represent the sum of the values $f(s)$, for all members s of S.

EXAMPLE 14   What is the value of $\sum_{s \in \{0,2,4\}} s$?

Solution: Since $\sum_{s \in \{0,2,4\}} s$ represents the sum of the values of s for all the members of the set $\{0, 2, 4\}$, it follows that

$$\sum_{s \in \{0,2,4\}} s = 0 + 2 + 4 = 6.$$ ◀

Certain sums arise repeatedly throughout discrete mathematics. Having a collection of formulae for such sums can be useful, so Table 2 provides a small table of formulae for commonly occurring sums.

We derived the first formula in this table in Theorem 1. The next three formulae give us the sum of the first n positive integers, the sum of their squares, and the sum of their cubes. These three formulae can be derived in many different ways (for example, see Exercises 21 and 22 at the end of this section). Also note that each of these formulae, once known, can easily be proved using mathematical induction, the subject of Section 3.3. The last two formulae in the table involve infinite series and will be discussed shortly.

Example 15 illustrates how the formulae in Table 2 can be useful.

EXAMPLE 15   Find $\sum_{k=50}^{100} k^2$.

TABLE 2 Some Useful Summation Formulae.

Sum	Closed Form
$\sum_{k=0}^{n} ar^k \ (r \neq 0)$	$\dfrac{ar^{n+1} - a}{r - 1}, r \neq 1$
$\sum_{k=1}^{n} k$	$\dfrac{n(n + 1)}{2}$
$\sum_{k=1}^{n} k^2$	$\dfrac{n(n + 1)(2n + 1)}{6}$
$\sum_{k=1}^{n} k^3$	$\dfrac{n^2(n + 1)^2}{4}$
$\sum_{k=0}^{\infty} x^k, |x| < 1$	$\dfrac{1}{1 - x}$
$\sum_{k=1}^{\infty} kx^{k-1}, |x| < 1$	$\dfrac{1}{(1 - x)^2}$

Solution: First note that since $\sum_{k=1}^{100} k^2 = \sum_{k=1}^{49} k^2 + \sum_{k=50}^{100} k^2$, we have

$$\sum_{k=50}^{100} k^2 = \sum_{k=1}^{100} k^2 - \sum_{k=1}^{49} k^2.$$

Using the formula $\sum_{k=1}^{n} k^2 = n(n+1)(2n+1)/6$ from Table 2, we see that

$$\sum_{k=50}^{100} k^2 = \frac{100 \cdot 101 \cdot 201}{6} - \frac{49 \cdot 50 \cdot 99}{6} = 338,350 - 40,425 = 297,925. \quad \blacktriangleleft$$

SOME INFINITE SERIES   Although most of the summations in this book are finite sums, infinite series are important in some parts of discrete mathematics. The closed forms for the infinite series in Examples 16 and 17 are quite useful.

EXAMPLE 16   (Requires calculus) Let x be a real number with $|x| < 1$. Find $\sum_{n=0}^{\infty} x^n$.

> *Extra Examples*

Solution: By Theorem 1 with $a = 1$ and $r = x$ we see that $\sum_{n=0}^{k} x^n = \frac{x^{k+1}-1}{x-1}$. Because $|x| < 1$, x^{k+1} approaches 0 as k approaches infinity. It follows that

$$\sum_{n=0}^{\infty} x^n = \lim_{k \to \infty} \frac{x^{k+1}-1}{x-1} = \frac{-1}{x-1} = \frac{1}{1-x}. \quad \blacktriangleleft$$

We can produce new summation formulae by differentiating or integrating existing formulae.

EXAMPLE 17   (Requires calculus) Differentiating both sides of the equation

$$\sum_{k=0}^{\infty} x^k = \frac{1}{1-x},$$

from Example 16, we find that

$$\sum_{k=1}^{\infty} k x^{k-1} = \frac{1}{(1-x)^2}.$$

(This differentiation is valid for $|x| < 1$ by a theorem about infinite series.) $\blacktriangleleft$

CARDINALITY

Recall that in Section 1.6, the cardinality of a finite set was defined to be the number of elements in the set. It is possible to extend the concept of cardinality to all sets, both finite and infinite, with Definition 4.

DEFINITION 4   The sets A and B have the same *cardinality* if and only if there is a one-to-one correspondence from A to B.

To see that this definition agrees with the previous definition of the cardinality of a finite set as the number of elements in that set, note that there is a one-to-one correspondence between any two finite sets with n elements, where n is a nonnegative integer.

We will now split infinite sets into two groups, those with the same cardinality as the set of natural numbers and those with different cardinality.

DEFINITION 5

> A set that is either finite or has the same cardinality as the set of positive integers is called *countable*. A set that is not countable is called *uncountable*.

We now give examples of countable and uncountable sets.

EXAMPLE 18   Show that the set of odd positive integers is a countable set.

Solution: To show that the set of odd positive integers is countable, we will exhibit a one-to-one correspondence between this set and the set of positive integers. Consider the function

$$f(n) = 2n - 1$$

from $\mathbf{Z}^+$ to the set of odd positive integers. We show that f is a one-to-one correspondence by showing that it is both one-to-one and onto. To see that it is one-to-one, suppose that $f(n) = f(m)$. Then $2n - 1 = 2m - 1$, so that $n = m$. To see that it is onto, suppose that t is an odd positive integer. Then t is 1 less than an even integer $2k$, where k is a natural number. Hence $t = 2k - 1 = f(k)$. We display this one-to-one correspondence in Figure 1.   ◀

Extra Examples

An infinite set is countable if and only if it is possible to list the elements of the set in a sequence (indexed by the positive integers). The reason for this is that a one-to-one correspondence f from the set of positive integers to a set S can be expressed in terms of a sequence $a_1, a_2, \ldots, a_n, \ldots$, where $a_1 = f(1), a_2 = f(2), \ldots, a_n = f(n), \ldots$. For instance, the set of odd integers can be listed in a sequence $a_1, a_2, \ldots, a_n, \ldots$, where $a_n = 2n - 1$.

EXAMPLE 19   Show that the set of positive rational numbers is countable.

Solution: It may seem surprising that the set of positive rational numbers is countable, but we will show how we can list the positive rational numbers as a sequence $r_1, r_2, \ldots, r_n, \ldots$. First, note that every positive rational number is the quotient p/q of two positive integers. We can arrange the positive rational numbers by listing those with denominator $q = 1$ in the first row, those with denominator $q = 2$ in the second row, and so on, as displayed in Figure 2.

The key to listing the rational numbers in a sequence is to first list the positive rational numbers p/q with $p + q = 2$, followed by those with $p + q = 3$, followed by those with $p + q = 4$, and so on, following the path shown in Figure 2. Whenever we encounter a number p/q that is already listed, we do not list it again. For example, when we come to $2/2 = 1$ we do not list it since we have already listed $1/1 = 1$. The initial terms in the list of positive rational numbers we have constructed are 1, 1/2, 2, 3, 1/3, 1/4, 2/3, 3/2, 4, 5, and so on. Because all rational numbers are listed once, as the reader can verify, we have shown that the set of rational numbers is countable.   ◀

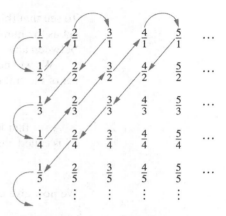

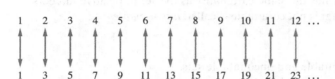

FIGURE 1   **A One-to-One Correspondence Between $\mathbf{Z}^+$ and the Set of Odd Positive Integers.**

FIGURE 2   **The Positive Rational Numbers Are Countable.**

Example 20 shows that the set of real numbers is uncountable. Georg Cantor discovered this fact in 1879. We use an important proof method, known as the **Cantor diagonalization argument,** to prove that the set of real numbers is not countable. This proof method is used extensively in mathematical logic and in the theory of computation.

EXAMPLE 20   Show that the set of real numbers is an uncountable set.

Solution: To show that the set of real numbers is uncountable, we suppose that the set of real numbers is countable and arrive at a contradiction. Then, the subset of all real numbers that fall between 0 and 1 would also be countable (since any subset of a countable set is also countable; see Exercise 34 at the end of the section). Under this assumption, the real numbers between 0 and 1 can be listed in some order, say, $r_1, r_2, r_3, \ldots$. Let the decimal representation of these real numbers be

$$r_1 = 0.d_{11}d_{12}d_{13}d_{14} \ldots$$
$$r_2 = 0.d_{21}d_{22}d_{23}d_{24} \ldots$$
$$r_3 = 0.d_{31}d_{32}d_{33}d_{34} \ldots$$
$$r_4 = 0.d_{41}d_{42}d_{43}d_{44} \ldots$$
$$\vdots$$

where $d_{ij} \in \{0, 1, 2, 3, 4, 5, 6, 7, 8, 9\}$. (For example, if $r_1 = 0.23794102\ldots$, we have $d_{11} = 2, d_{12} = 3, d_{13} = 7$, and so on.) Then, form a new real number with decimal expansion $r = 0.d_1d_2d_3d_4\ldots$, where the decimal digits are determined by the following rule:

$$d_i = \begin{cases} 4 & \text{if } d_{ii} \neq 4 \\ 5 & \text{if } d_{ii} = 4. \end{cases}$$

(As an example, suppose that $r_1 = 0.23794102\ldots$, $r_2 = 0.44590138\ldots$, $r_3 = 0.09118764\ldots$, $r_4 = 0.80553900\ldots$, and so on. Then we have $r = 0.d_1d_2d_3d_4\ldots = 0.4544\ldots$, where $d_1 = 4$ since $d_{11} \neq 4$, $d_2 = 5$ since $d_{22} = 4$, $d_3 = 4$ since $d_{33} \neq 4$, $d_4 = 4$ since $d_{44} \neq 4$, and so on.)

Every real number has a unique decimal expansion (when the possibility that the expansion has a tail end that consists entirely of the digit 9 is excluded). Then, the real number r is not equal to any of $r_1, r_2, \ldots$, since the decimal expansion of r differs from the decimal expansion of r_i in the ith place to the right of the decimal point, for each i.

Since there is a real number r between 0 and 1 that is not in the list, the assumption that all the real numbers between 0 and 1 could be listed must be false. Therefore, all the real numbers between 0 and 1 cannot be listed, so that the set of real numbers between 0 and 1 is uncountable. Any set with an uncountable subset is uncountable (see Exercise 35 at the end of this section). Hence, the set of real numbers is uncountable. ◀

Exercises

1. Find these terms of the sequence $\{a_n\}$ where $a_n = 2 \cdot (-3)^n + 5^n$.

   a) a_0 **b)** a_1 **c)** a_4 **d)** a_5

2. What is the term a_8 of the sequence $\{a_n\}$ if a_n equals

   a) 2^{n-1}?   **b)** 7?
   c) $1 + (-1)^n$?   **d)** $-(-2)^n$?

3. What are the terms a_0, a_1, a_2, and a_3 of the sequence $\{a_n\}$, where a_n equals

   a) $2^n + 1$?   **b)** $(n+1)^{n+1}$?
   c) $\lfloor n/2 \rfloor$?   **d)** $\lfloor n/2 \rfloor + \lceil n/2 \rceil$?

4. What are the terms a_0, a_1, a_2, and a_3 of the sequence $\{a_n\}$, where a_n equals

   a) $(-2)^n$?   **b)** 3?
   c) $7 + 4^n$?   **d)** $2^n + (-2)^n$?

5. List the first 10 terms of each of these sequences.

   a) the sequence that begins with 2 and in which each successive term is 3 more than the preceding term
   b) the sequence that lists each positive integer three times, in increasing order
   c) the sequence that lists the odd positive integers in increasing order, listing each odd integer twice
   d) the sequence whose nth term is $n! - 2^n$
   e) the sequence that begins with 3, where each succeeding term is twice the preceding term
   f) the sequence whose first two terms are 1 and each succeeding term is the sum of the two preceding terms (This is the famous Fibonacci sequence, which we will study later in this text.)
   g) the sequence whose nth term is the number of bits in the binary expansion of the number n (defined in Section 2.5)
   h) the sequence where the nth term is the number of letters in the English word for the index n

6. List the first 10 terms of each of these sequences.

   a) the sequence obtained by starting with 10 and obtaining each term by subtracting 3 from the previous term
   b) the sequence whose nth term is the sum of the first n positive integers

   c) the sequence whose nth term is $3^n - 2^n$
   d) the sequence whose nth term is $\lfloor \sqrt{n} \rfloor$
   e) the sequence whose first two terms are 1 and 2 and each succeeding term is the sum of the two previous terms
   f) the sequence whose nth term is the largest integer whose binary expansion (defined in Section 2.5) has n bits (Write your answer in decimal notation.)
   g) the sequence whose terms are constructed sequentially as follows: start with 1, then add 1, then multiply by 1, then add 2, then multiply by 2, and so on
   h) the sequence whose nth term is the largest integer k such that $k! \leq n$

7. Find at least three different sequences beginning with the terms 1, 2, 4 whose terms are generated by a simple formula or rule.

8. Find at least three different sequences beginning with the terms 3, 5, 7 whose terms are generated by a simple formula or rule.

9. For each of these lists of integers, provide a simple formula or rule that generates the terms of an integer sequence that begins with the given list.

   a) $1, 0, 1, 1, 0, 0, 1, 1, 1, 0, 0, 0, 1, \ldots$
   b) $1, 2, 2, 3, 4, 4, 5, 6, 6, 7, 8, 8, \ldots$
   c) $1, 0, 2, 0, 4, 0, 8, 0, 16, 0, \ldots$
   d) $3, 6, 12, 24, 48, 96, 192, \ldots$
   e) $15, 8, 1, -6, -13, -20, -27, \ldots$
   f) $3, 5, 8, 12, 17, 23, 30, 38, 47, \ldots$
   g) $2, 16, 54, 128, 250, 432, 686, \ldots$
   h) $2, 3, 7, 25, 121, 721, 5041, 40321, \ldots$

10. For each of these lists of integers, provide a simple formula or rule that generates the terms of an integer sequence that begins with the given list.

   a) $3, 6, 11, 18, 27, 38, 51, 66, 83, 102, \ldots$
   b) $7, 11, 15, 19, 23, 27, 31, 35, 39, 43, \ldots$
   c) $1, 10, 11, 100, 101, 110, 111, 1000, 1001, 1010, 1011, \ldots$
   d) $1, 2, 2, 2, 3, 3, 3, 3, 3, 5, 5, 5, 5, 5, 5, 5, \ldots$
   e) $0, 2, 8, 26, 80, 242, 728, 2186, 6560, 19682, \ldots$

f) 1, 3, 15, 105, 945, 10395, 135135, 2027025, 34459425, ...

g) 1, 0, 0, 1, 1, 1, 0, 0, 0, 0, 1, 1, 1, 1, 1, ...

h) 2, 4, 16, 256, 65536, 4294967296, ...

*11. Show that if a_n denotes the nth positive integer that is not a perfect square, then $a_n = n + \{\sqrt{n}\}$, where $\{x\}$ denotes the integer closest to the real number x.

*12. Let a_n be the nth term of the sequence 1, 2, 2, 3, 3, 3, 4, 4, 4, 4, 5, 5, 5, 5, 5, 6, 6, 6, 6, 6, 6, ..., constructed by including the integer k exactly k times. Show that $a_n = \lfloor \sqrt{2n} + \frac{1}{2} \rfloor$.

13. What are the values of these sums?

a) $\sum_{k=1}^{5} (k+1)$

b) $\sum_{j=0}^{4} (-2)^j$

c) $\sum_{i=1}^{10} 3$

d) $\sum_{j=0}^{8} (2^{j+1} - 2^j)$

14. What are the values of these sums, where $S = \{1, 3, 5, 7\}$?

a) $\sum_{j \in S} j$

b) $\sum_{j \in S} j^2$

c) $\sum_{j \in S} (1/j)$

d) $\sum_{j \in S} 1$

15. What is the value of each of these sums of terms of a geometric progression?

a) $\sum_{j=0}^{8} 3 \cdot 2^j$

b) $\sum_{j=1}^{8} 2^j$

c) $\sum_{j=2}^{8} (-3)^j$

d) $\sum_{j=0}^{8} 2 \cdot (-3)^j$

16. Find the value of each of these sums.

a) $\sum_{j=0}^{8} (1 + (-1)^j)$

b) $\sum_{j=0}^{8} (3^j - 2^j)$

c) $\sum_{j=0}^{8} (2 \cdot 3^j + 3 \cdot 2^j)$

d) $\sum_{j=0}^{8} (2^{j+1} - 2^j)$

17. Compute each of these double sums.

a) $\sum_{i=1}^{2} \sum_{j=1}^{3} (i+j)$

b) $\sum_{i=0}^{2} \sum_{j=0}^{3} (2i + 3j)$

c) $\sum_{i=1}^{3} \sum_{j=0}^{2} i$

d) $\sum_{i=0}^{2} \sum_{j=1}^{3} ij$

18. Compute each of these double sums.

a) $\sum_{i=1}^{3} \sum_{j=1}^{2} (i-j)$

b) $\sum_{i=0}^{3} \sum_{j=0}^{2} (3i + 2j)$

c) $\sum_{i=1}^{3} \sum_{j=0}^{2} j$

d) $\sum_{i=0}^{2} \sum_{j=0}^{3} i^2 j^3$

19. Show that $\sum_{j=1}^{n} (a_j - a_{j-1}) = a_n - a_0$ where $a_0, a_1, \ldots, a_n$ is a sequence of real numbers. This type of sum is called **telescoping.**

20. Use the identity $1/(k(k+1)) = 1/k - 1/(k+1)$ and Exercise 19 to compute $\sum_{k=1}^{n} 1/(k(k+1))$.

21. Sum both sides of the identity $k^2 - (k-1)^2 = 2k - 1$ from $k = 1$ to $k = n$ and use Exercise 19 to find

a) a formula for $\sum_{k=1}^{n} (2k-1)$ (the sum of the first n odd natural numbers).

b) a formula for $\sum_{k=1}^{n} k$.

*22. Use the technique given in Exercise 19, together with the result of Exercise 21b, to find a formula for $\sum_{k=1}^{n} k^2$.

23. Find $\sum_{k=100}^{200} k$. (Use Table 2.)

24. Find $\sum_{k=99}^{200} k^3$. (Use Table 2.)

*25. Find a formula for $\sum_{k=0}^{m} \lfloor \sqrt{k} \rfloor$, when m is a positive integer. (*Hint:* Use the formula for $\sum_{k=1}^{n} k^2$.)

*26. Find a formula for $\sum_{k=0}^{m} \lfloor \sqrt[3]{k} \rfloor$, when m is a positive integer. (*Hint:* Use the formula for $\sum_{k=1}^{n} k^3$.)

There is also a special notation for products. The product of $a_m, a_{m+1}, \ldots, a_n$ is represented by

$$\prod_{j=m}^{n} a_j.$$

27. What are the values of the following products?

a) $\prod_{i=0}^{10} i$

b) $\prod_{i=5}^{8} i$

c) $\prod_{i=1}^{100} (-1)^i$

d) $\prod_{i=1}^{10} 2$

Recall that the value of the factorial function at a positive integer n, denoted by $n!$, is the product of the positive integers from 1 to n, inclusive. Also, we specify that $0! = 1$.

28. Express $n!$ using product notation.

29. Find $\sum_{j=0}^{4} j!$.

30. Find $\prod_{j=0}^{4} j!$.

31. Determine whether each of these sets is countable or uncountable. For those that are countable, exhibit a one-to-one correspondence between the set of natural numbers and that set.

a) the negative integers

b) the even integers

c) the real numbers between 0 and $\frac{1}{2}$

d) integers that are multiples of 7

*32. Determine whether each of these sets is countable or uncountable. For those that are countable, exhibit a one-to-one correspondence between the set of natural numbers and that set.

a) integers not divisible by 3

b) integers divisible by 5 but not by 7

c) the real numbers with decimal representations consisting of all 1s

d) the real numbers with decimal representations of all 1s or 9s

33. If A is an uncountable set and B is a countable set, must $A - B$ be uncountable?

34. Show that a subset of a countable set is also countable.

35. Show that if A is an uncountable set and $A \subseteq B$, then B is uncountable.

36. Show that the union of two countable sets is countable.

**37. Show that the union of a countable number of countable sets is countable.

38. Show that the set $\mathbf{Z}^+ \times \mathbf{Z}^+$ is countable.

*39. Show that the set of all bit strings is countable.

*40. Show that the set of real numbers that are solutions of quadratic equations $ax^2 + bx + c = 0$, where a, b, and c are integers, is countable.

*41. Show that the set of all computer programs in a particular programming language is countable. (*Hint:* A computer program written in a programming language can be thought of as a string of symbols from a finite alphabet.)

*42. Show that the set of functions from the positive integers to the set $\{0, 1, 2, 3, 4, 5, 6, 7, 8, 9\}$ is uncountable. [*Hint:* First set up a one-to-one correspondence between the set of real numbers between 0 and 1 and a subset of these functions. Do this by associating to the real number $0.d_1 d_2 \ldots d_n \ldots$ the function f with $f(n) = d_n$.]

*43. We say that a function is **computable** if there is a computer program that finds the values of this function. Use Exercises 41 and 42 to show that there are functions that are not computable.

*44. Prove that the set of positive rational numbers is countable by setting up a function that assigns to a rational number p/q with $\gcd(p, q) = 1$ the base 11 number formed from the decimal representation of p followed by the base 11 digit A, which corresponds to the decimal number 10, followed by the decimal representation of q.

*45. Prove that the set of positive rational numbers is countable by showing that the function K is a one-to-one correspondence between the set of positive rational numbers and the set of positive integers if $K(m/n) = p_1^{2a_1} p_2^{2a_2} \cdots p_s^{2a_s} q_1^{2b_1-1} q_2^{2b_2-1} \cdots q_t^{2b_t-1}$, where $\gcd(m, n) = 1$ and the prime-power factorizations of m and n are $m = p_1^{a_1} p_2^{a_2} \cdots p_s^{a_s}$ and $n = q_1^{b_1} q_2^{b_2} \cdots q_t^{b_t}$.

3.3 Mathematical Induction

INTRODUCTION

Links

What is a formula for the sum of the first n positive odd integers? The sums of the first n positive odd integers for $n = 1, 2, 3, 4, 5$ are

$$1 = 1, \qquad\qquad 1 + 3 = 4, \qquad\qquad 1 + 3 + 5 = 9,$$
$$1 + 3 + 5 + 7 = 16, \quad 1 + 3 + 5 + 7 + 9 = 25.$$

From these values it is reasonable to guess that the sum of the first n positive odd integers is n^2. We need a method to *prove* that this *guess* is correct, if in fact it is.

Mathematical induction is an extremely important proof technique that can be used to prove assertions of this type. As we will see in this section and in subsequent chapters, mathematical induction is used extensively to prove results about a large variety of discrete objects. For example, it is used to prove results about the complexity of algorithms, the correctness of certain types of computer programs, theorems about graphs and trees, as well as a wide range of identities and inequalities.

In this section we will describe how mathematical induction can be used and why it is a valid proof technique. It is extremely important to note that mathematical induction can be used only to prove results obtained in some other way. It is *not* a tool for discovering formulae or theorems.

There are several useful illustrations of mathematical induction that can help you remember how this principle works. One of these involves a line of people, person one, person two, and so on. A secret is told to person one, and each person tells the secret to the next person in line, if the former person hears it. Let $P(n)$ be the proposition that person n knows the secret. Then $P(1)$ is true, since the secret is told to person one; $P(2)$ is true, since person one tells person two the secret; $P(3)$ is true, since person two tells person three the secret; and so on. By the principle of mathematical induction, every person in line learns the secret. This is illustrated in Figure 1. (Of course, it has been assumed that each person relays the secret in an unchanged manner to the next person, which is usually not true in real life.)

FIGURE 1   People Telling Secrets.

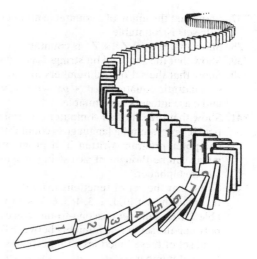

FIGURE 2   Illustrating How Mathematical Induction Works Using Dominos.

Another way to illustrate the principle of mathematical induction is to consider an infinite row of dominos, labeled $1, 2, 3, \ldots, n$, where each domino is standing up. Let $P(n)$ be the proposition that domino n is knocked over. If the first domino is knocked over—i.e., if $P(1)$ is true—and if, whenever the nth domino is knocked over, it also knocks the $(n + 1)$th domino over—i.e., if $P(n) \rightarrow P(n + 1)$ is true—then all the dominos are knocked over. This is illustrated in Figure 2.

MATHEMATICAL INDUCTION

Many theorems state that $P(n)$ is true for all positive integers n, where $P(n)$ is a propositional function, such as the statement that $1 + 2 + \cdots + n = n(n + 1)/2$ or the statement that $n \leq 2^n$. Mathematical induction is a technique for proving theorems of this kind. In other words, mathematical induction is used to prove propositions of the form $\forall n\, P(n)$, where the universe of discourse is the set of positive integers.

A proof by mathematical induction that $P(n)$ is true for every positive integer n consists of two steps:

BASIS STEP: The proposition $P(1)$ is shown to be true.

INDUCTIVE STEP: The implication $P(k) \rightarrow P(k + 1)$ is shown to be true for every positive integer k.

Here, the statement $P(k)$ for a fixed positive integer k is called the **inductive hypothesis.** When we complete both steps of a proof by mathematical induction, we have proved that $P(n)$ is true for all positive integers n; that is, we have shown that $\forall n\, P(n)$ is true.

Expressed as a rule of inference, this proof technique can be stated as

$$[P(1) \wedge \forall k\, (P(k) \rightarrow P(k + 1))] \rightarrow \forall n\, P(n).$$

Since mathematical induction is such an important technique, it is worthwhile to explain in detail the steps of a proof using this technique. The first thing we do to prove that $P(n)$

is true for all positive integers n is to show that $P(1)$ is true. This amounts to showing that the particular statement obtained when n is replaced by 1 in $P(n)$ is true. Then we must show that $P(k) \to P(k + 1)$ is true for every positive integer k. To prove that this implication is true for every positive integer k, we need to show that $P(k + 1)$ cannot be false when $P(k)$ is true. This can be accomplished by assuming that $P(k)$ is true and showing that *under this hypothesis* $P(k + 1)$ must also be true.

Remark: In a proof by mathematical induction it is *not* assumed that $P(k)$ is true for all positive integers! It is only shown that *if it is assumed* that $P(k)$ is true, then $P(k + 1)$ is also true. Thus, a proof by mathematical induction is not a case of begging the question, or circular reasoning.

When we use mathematical induction to prove a theorem, we first show that $P(1)$ is true. Then we know that $P(2)$ is true, since $P(1)$ implies $P(2)$. Further, we know that $P(3)$ is true, since $P(2)$ implies $P(3)$. Continuing along these lines, we see that $P(n)$ is true, for every positive integer n.

EXAMPLES OF PROOFS BY MATHEMATICAL INDUCTION

Links

Extra Examples

We will use a variety of examples to illustrate how theorems are proved using mathematical induction. We begin by proving a formula for the sum of the first n odd positive integers. (Many theorems proved in this section via mathematical induction can be proved using different methods. However, it is worthwhile to try to prove a theorem in more than one way, since one method of attack may succeed whereas another approach may not.)

EXAMPLE 1   Use mathematical induction to prove that the sum of the first n odd positive integers is n^2.

Solution: Let $P(n)$ denote the proposition that the sum of the first n odd positive integers is n^2. We must first complete the basis step; that is, we must show that $P(1)$ is true. Then we must carry out the inductive step; that is, we must show that $P(k + 1)$ is true when $P(k)$ is assumed to be true.

BASIS STEP: $P(1)$ states that the sum of the first one odd positive integer is 1^2. This is true since the sum of the first odd positive integer is 1.

INDUCTIVE STEP: To complete the inductive step we must show that the proposition $P(k) \to P(k + 1)$ is true for every positive integer k. To do this, suppose that $P(k)$ is true for a positive integer k; that is,

$$1 + 3 + 5 + \cdots + (2k - 1) = k^2.$$

Links

HISTORICAL NOTE   The first known use of mathematical induction is in the work of the sixteenth-century mathematician Francesco Maurolico (1494–1575). Maurolico wrote extensively on the works of classical mathematics and made many contributions to geometry and optics. In his book *Arithmeticorum Libri Duo*, Maurolico presented a variety of properties of the integers together with proofs of these properties. To prove some of these properties he devised the method of mathematical induction. His first use of mathematical induction in this book was to prove that the sum of the first n odd positive integers equals n^2.

[Note that the kth odd positive integer is $(2k-1)$, since this integer is obtained by adding 2 a total of $k-1$ times to 1.] We must show that $P(k+1)$ is true, assuming that $P(k)$ is true. Note that $P(k+1)$ is the statement that

$$1 + 3 + 5 + \cdots + (2k-1) + (2k+1) = (k+1)^2.$$

So, assuming that $P(k)$ is true, it follows that

$$1 + 3 + 5 + \cdots + (2k-1) + (2k+1) = [1 + 3 + \cdots + (2k-1)] + (2k+1)$$
$$= k^2 + (2k+1)$$
$$= k^2 + 2k + 1$$
$$= (k+1)^2.$$

This shows that $P(k+1)$ follows from $P(k)$. Note that we used the inductive hypothesis $P(k)$ in the second equality to replace the sum of the first k odd positive integers by k^2.

Since $P(1)$ is true and the implication $P(k) \to P(k+1)$ is true for all positive integers k, the principle of mathematical induction shows that $P(n)$ is true for all positive integers n. ◀

Example 2 uses the principle of mathematical induction to prove an inequality.

EXAMPLE 2   Use mathematical induction to prove the inequality

$$n < 2^n$$

for all positive integers n.

Solution: Let $P(n)$ be the proposition "$n < 2^n$."

BASIS STEP: $P(1)$ is true, since $1 < 2^1 = 2$.

INDUCTIVE STEP: Assume that $P(k)$ is true for the positive integer k. That is, assume that $k < 2^k$. We need to show that $P(k+1)$ is true. That is, we need to show that $k+1 < 2^{k+1}$. Adding 1 to both sides of $k < 2^k$, and then noting that $1 \le 2^k$, gives

$$k + 1 < 2^k + 1 \le 2^k + 2^k = 2^{k+1}.$$

We have shown that $P(k+1)$ is true, namely, that $k+1 < 2^{k+1}$, based on the assumption that $P(k)$ is true. The induction step is complete.

Therefore, by the principle of mathematical induction, it has been shown that $n < 2^n$ is true for all positive integers n. ◀

We will now use mathematical induction to prove a theorem involving the divisibility of integers.

EXAMPLE 3   Use mathematical induction to prove that $n^3 - n$ is divisible by 3 whenever n is a positive integer.

Solution: To construct the proof, let $P(n)$ denote the proposition: "$n^3 - n$ is divisible by 3."

BASIS STEP: $P(1)$ is true, since $1^3 - 1 = 0$ is divisible by 3.

INDUCTIVE STEP: Assume that $P(k)$ is true; that is, $k^3 - k$ is divisible by 3. We must show that $P(k+1)$ is true. That is, we must show that $(k+1)^3 - (k+1)$ is divisible by 3. Note that

$$(k+1)^3 - (k+1) = (k^3 + 3k^2 + 3k + 1) - (k+1)$$
$$= (k^3 - k) + 3(k^2 + k).$$

Since both terms in this sum are divisible by 3 (the first by the assumption of the inductive step, and the second because it is 3 times an integer), it follows that $(k+1)^3 - (k+1)$ is also divisible by 3. This completes the induction step. Thus, by the principle of mathematical induction, $n^3 - n$ is divisible by 3 whenever n is a positive integer. ◀

Sometimes we need to show that $P(n)$ is true for $n = b, b+1, b+2, \ldots$, where b is an integer other than 1. We can use mathematical induction to accomplish this as long as we change the basis step. For instance, consider Example 4, which proves that a summation formula is valid for all nonnegative integers, so that we need to prove that $P(n)$ is true for $n = 0, 1, 2, \ldots$.

EXAMPLE 4   Use mathematical induction to show that

$$1 + 2 + 2^2 + \cdots + 2^n = 2^{n+1} - 1$$

for all nonnegative integers n.

Solution: Let $P(n)$ be the proposition that this formula is correct for the integer n.

BASIS STEP: $P(0)$ is true since $2^0 = 1 = 2^1 - 1$.

INDUCTIVE STEP: Assume that $P(k)$ is true. To carry out the inductive step using this assumption, it must be shown that $P(k+1)$ is true, namely,

$$1 + 2 + 2^2 + \cdots + 2^k + 2^{k+1} = 2^{(k+1)+1} - 1 = 2^{k+2} - 1.$$

Using the inductive hypothesis $P(k)$, it follows that

$$1 + 2 + 2^2 + \cdots + 2^k + 2^{k+1} = (1 + 2 + 2^2 + \cdots + 2^k) + 2^{k+1}$$
$$= (2^{k+1} - 1) + 2^{k+1}$$
$$= 2 \cdot 2^{k+1} - 1$$
$$= 2^{k+2} - 1.$$

This finishes the inductive step, which completes the proof. ◀

As Example 4 demonstrates, to use mathematical induction to show that $P(n)$ is true for $n = b, b+1, b+2, \ldots$, where b is an integer other than 1, we show that $P(b)$ is true (the basis step) and then show that the implication $P(k) \to P(k+1)$ is true for $k = b, b+1, b+2, \ldots$ (the inductive step). Note that b can be negative, zero, or positive. Following the domino analogy we used earlier, imagine that we begin by knocking down the bth domino (the basis step), and as each domino falls, it knocks down the next domino (the inductive step). We leave it to the reader to show that this form of induction is valid (see Exercise 76).

The formula given in Example 4 is a special case of a general result for the sum of terms of a geometric progression (Theorem 1 in Section 3.2). We will use mathematical induction to provide an alternate proof of this formula.

EXAMPLE 5   **Sums of Geometric Progressions**   Use mathematical induction to prove this formula for the sum of a finite number of terms of a geometric progression:

$$\sum_{j=0}^{n} ar^j = a + ar + ar^2 + \cdots + ar^n = \frac{ar^{n+1} - a}{r - 1}, \qquad \text{when } r \neq 1.$$

Solution: To prove this formula using mathematical induction, let $P(n)$ be the proposition that the sum of the first $n + 1$ terms of a geometric progression in this formula is correct.

BASIS STEP: $P(0)$ is true, since

$$a = \frac{ar - a}{r - 1}.$$

INDUCTIVE STEP: Assume that $P(k)$ is true. That is, assume

$$a + ar + ar^2 + \cdots + ar^k = \frac{ar^{k+1} - a}{r - 1}.$$

To show that this implies that $P(k + 1)$ is true, add ar^{k+1} to both sides of this equation to obtain

$$a + ar + ar^2 + \cdots + ar^k + ar^{k+1} = \frac{ar^{k+1} - a}{r - 1} + ar^{k+1}.$$

Rewriting the right-hand side of this equation shows that

$$\frac{ar^{k+1} - a}{r - 1} + ar^{k+1} = \frac{ar^{k+1} - a}{r - 1} + \frac{ar^{k+2} - ar^{k+1}}{r - 1}$$

$$= \frac{ar^{k+2} - a}{r - 1}.$$

Combining these last two equations gives

$$a + ar + ar^2 + \cdots + ar^k + ar^{k+1} = \frac{ar^{k+2} - a}{r - 1}.$$

This shows that if $P(k)$ is true, then $P(k + 1)$ must also be true. This completes the inductive argument and shows that the formula for the sum of the terms of a geometric series is correct. ◀

As previously mentioned, the formula in Example 4 is the case of the formula in Example 5 with $a = 1$ and $r = 2$. The reader should verify that putting these values for a and r in the general formula gives the same formula as in Example 4.

An important inequality for the sum of the reciprocals of a set of positive integers will be proved in the next example.

EXAMPLE 6   **An Inequality for Harmonic Numbers**   The **harmonic numbers** H_j, $j = 1, 2, 3, \ldots,$ are defined by

$$H_j = 1 + \frac{1}{2} + \frac{1}{3} + \cdots + \frac{1}{j}.$$

For instance,

$$H_4 = 1 + \frac{1}{2} + \frac{1}{3} + \frac{1}{4} = \frac{25}{12}.$$

Use mathematical induction to show that

$$H_{2^n} \geq 1 + \frac{n}{2},$$

whenever n is a nonnegative integer.

Solution: To carry out the proof, let $P(n)$ be the proposition that $H_{2^n} \geq 1 + n/2$.

BASIS STEP: $P(0)$ is true, since $H_{2^0} = H_1 = 1 \geq 1 + 0/2$.

INDUCTIVE STEP: Assume that $P(k)$ is true, so that $H_{2^k} \geq 1 + k/2$. It must be shown that $P(k+1)$, which states that $H_{2^{k+1}} \geq 1 + (k+1)/2$, must also be true under this assumption. This can be done since

$$H_{2^{k+1}} = 1 + \frac{1}{2} + \frac{1}{3} + \cdots + \frac{1}{2^k} + \frac{1}{2^k + 1} + \cdots + \frac{1}{2^{k+1}} \quad \text{definition of harmonic number}$$

$$= H_{2^k} + \frac{1}{2^k + 1} + \cdots + \frac{1}{2^{k+1}} \quad \text{definition of harmonic number}$$

$$\geq \left(1 + \frac{k}{2}\right) + \frac{1}{2^k + 1} + \cdots + \frac{1}{2^{k+1}} \quad \text{by the inductive hypothesis}$$

$$\geq \left(1 + \frac{k}{2}\right) + 2^k \cdot \frac{1}{2^{k+1}} \quad \text{since there are } 2^k \text{ terms each not less than } 1/2^{k+1}$$

$$\geq \left(1 + \frac{k}{2}\right) + \frac{1}{2}$$

$$= 1 + \frac{k+1}{2}.$$

This establishes the inductive step of the proof. Thus, the inequality for the harmonic numbers is valid for all nonnegative integers n.   ◀

Remark: The inequality established here shows that the **harmonic series**

$$1 + \frac{1}{2} + \frac{1}{3} + \cdots + \frac{1}{n} + \cdots$$

is a divergent infinite series. This is an important example in the study of infinite series.

Example 7 shows how mathematical induction can be used to verify a formula for the number of subsets of a finite set.

EXAMPLE 7   **The Number of Subsets of a Finite Set** Use mathematical induction to show that if S is a finite set with n elements, then S has 2^n subsets. (We will prove this result directly in several ways in Chapter 4.)

Solution: Let $P(n)$ be the proposition that a set with n elements has 2^n subsets.

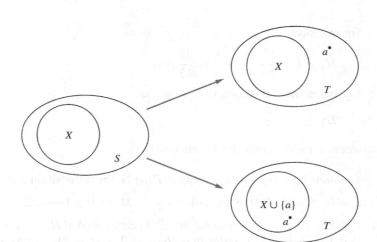

**FIGURE 3   Generating Subsets of a Set with $k + 1$ Elements.
Here $T = S \cup \{a\}$.**

BASIS STEP: $P(0)$ is true, since a set with zero elements, the empty set, has exactly $2^0 = 1$ subsets, since it has one subset, namely, itself.

INDUCTIVE STEP: Assume that $P(k)$ is true, that is, that every set with k elements has 2^k subsets. It must be shown that under this assumption $P(k + 1)$, which is the statement that every set with $k + 1$ elements has 2^{k+1} subsets, must also be true. To show this, let T be a set with $k + 1$ elements. Then, it is possible to write $T = S \cup \{a\}$ where a is one of the elements of T and $S = T - \{a\}$. The subsets of T can be obtained in the following way. For each subset X of S there are exactly two subsets of T, namely, X and $X \cup \{a\}$. (This is illustrated in Figure 3.) These constitute all the subsets of T and are all distinct. Since there are 2^k subsets of S, there are $2 \cdot 2^k = 2^{k+1}$ subsets of T. This finishes the induction argument.   ◀

EXAMPLE 8   Show that if n is a positive integer,

$$1 + 2 + \cdots + n = n(n + 1)/2 \,.$$

Solution: Let $P(n)$ be the proposition that the sum of the first n positive integers is $n(n + 1)/2$. We must do two things to prove that $P(n)$ is true for $n = 1, 2, 3, \ldots$. Namely, we must show that $P(1)$ is true and that the implication $P(k)$ implies $P(k + 1)$ is true for $k = 1, 2, 3, \ldots$.

BASIS STEP: $P(1)$ is true, since $1 = 1(1 + 1)/2$.

INDUCTIVE STEP: Assume that $P(k)$ holds so that

$$1 + 2 + \cdots + k = k(k + 1)/2.$$

Under this assumption, it must be shown that $P(k + 1)$ is true, namely, that

$$1 + 2 + \cdots + k + (k + 1) = (k + 1)[(k + 1) + 1]/2 = (k + 1)(k + 2)/2$$

is also true. Add $k + 1$ to both sides of the equation in $P(k)$ to obtain

$$1 + 2 + \cdots + k + (k + 1) = k(k + 1)/2 + (k + 1)$$
$$= [(k/2) + 1](k + 1)$$
$$= (k + 1)(k + 2)/2.$$

This last equation shows that $P(k + 1)$ is true. This completes the inductive step and completes the proof. ◀

EXAMPLE 9   Use mathematical induction to prove that $2^n < n!$ for every positive integer n with $n \geq 4$.

Solution: Let $P(n)$ be the proposition that $2^n < n!$.

BASIS STEP: To prove the inequality for $n \geq 4$ requires that the basis step be $P(4)$. Note that $P(4)$ is true, since $2^4 = 16 < 4! = 24$.

INDUCTIVE STEP: Assume that $P(k)$ is true. That is, assume that $2^k < k!$. We must show that $P(k + 1)$ is true. That is, we must show that $2^{k+1} < (k + 1)!$. Multiplying both sides of the inequality $2^k < k!$ by 2, it follows that

$$2 \cdot 2^k < 2 \cdot k!$$
$$< (k + 1) \cdot k!$$
$$= (k + 1)!.$$

This shows that $P(k + 1)$ is true when $P(k)$ is true. This completes the inductive step of the proof. Hence, it follows that $2^n < n!$ is true for all integers n with $n \geq 4$. ◀

EXAMPLE 10   Use mathematical induction to prove the following generalization of one of De Morgan's laws:

$$\overline{\bigcap_{j=1}^{n} A_j} = \bigcup_{j=1}^{n} \overline{A_j},$$

whenever $A_1, A_2, \ldots, A_n$ are subsets of a universal set U and $n \geq 2$.

Solution: Let $P(n)$ be the identity for n sets.

BASIS STEP: The statement $P(2)$ asserts that $\overline{A_1 \cap A_2} = \overline{A_1} \cup \overline{A_2}$. This is one of De Morgan's laws; it was proved in Section 1.7.

INDUCTIVE STEP: Assume that $P(k)$ is true, that is,

$$\overline{\bigcap_{j=1}^{k} A_j} = \bigcup_{j=1}^{k} \overline{A_j}$$

whenever $A_1, A_2, \ldots, A_k$ are subsets of the universal set U. To carry out the inductive step it must be shown that if this equality holds for any k subsets of U, it must also be valid for any $k + 1$ subsets of U. Suppose that $A_1, A_2, \ldots, A_k, A_{k+1}$ are subsets of U. When the inductive hypothesis is assumed to hold, it follows that

$$\overline{\bigcap_{j=1}^{k+1} A_j} = \overline{\left(\bigcap_{j=1}^{k} A_j\right) \cap A_{k+1}}$$

$$= \overline{\left(\bigcap_{j=1}^{k} A_j\right)} \cup \overline{A_{k+1}} \quad \text{by De Morgan's law}$$

$$= \left(\bigcup_{j=1}^{k} \overline{A_j}\right) \cup \overline{A_{k+1}} \quad \text{by the inductive hypothesis}$$

$$= \bigcup_{j=1}^{k+1} \overline{A_j}.$$

This completes the proof by induction.   ◄

Example 11 illustrates how mathematical induction can be used to prove a result about covering chessboards with pieces shaped like the letter "L."

EXAMPLE 11   Let n be a positive integer. Show that any $2^n \times 2^n$ chessboard with one square removed can be tiled using L-shaped pieces, where these pieces cover three squares at a time, as shown in Figure 4.

Solution: Let $P(n)$ be the proposition that any $2^n \times 2^n$ chessboard with one square removed can be tiled using L-shaped pieces. We can use mathematical induction to prove that $P(n)$ is true for all positive integers n.

BASIS STEP: $P(1)$ is true, since any of the four 2×2 chessboards with one square removed can be tiled using one L-shaped piece, as shown in Figure 5.

FIGURE 4   An L-Shaped Piece.

INDUCTIVE STEP: Assume that $P(k)$ is true; that is, assume that any $2^k \times 2^k$ chessboard with one square removed can be tiled using L-shaped pieces. It must be shown that under this assumption $P(k + 1)$ must also be true; that is, any $2^{k+1} \times 2^{k+1}$ chessboard with one square removed can be tiled using L-shaped pieces.

To see this, consider a $2^{k+1} \times 2^{k+1}$ chessboard with one square removed. Split this chessboard into four chessboards of size $2^k \times 2^k$, by dividing it in half in both directions. This is illustrated in Figure 6. No square has been removed from three of these four

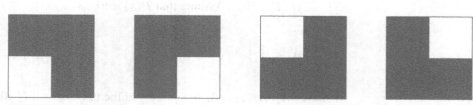

FIGURE 5   Tiling 2 × 2 Chessboards with One Square Removed.

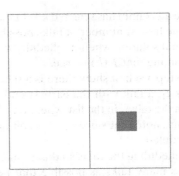

FIGURE 6 **Dividing a** $2^{k+1} \times 2^{k+1}$ **Chessboard into Four** $2^k \times 2^k$ **Chessboards.**

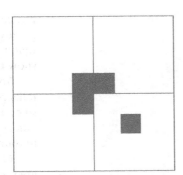

FIGURE 7 **Tiling the** $2^{k+1} \times 2^{k+1}$ **Chessboard with One Square Removed.**

chessboards. The fourth $2^k \times 2^k$ chessboard has one square removed, so by the inductive hypothesis, it can be covered by L-shaped pieces. Now temporarily remove the square from each of the other three $2^k \times 2^k$ chessboards that has the center of the original, larger chessboard as one of its corners, as shown in Figure 7. By the inductive hypothesis, each of these three $2^k \times 2^k$ chessboards with a square removed can be tiled by L-shaped pieces. Furthermore, the three squares that were temporarily removed can be covered by one L-shaped piece. Hence, the entire $2^{k+1} \times 2^{k+1}$ chessboard can be tiled with L-shaped pieces. This completes the proof. ◀

Next, we provide an example that illustrates one of many ways mathematical induction is used in the study of algorithms. We will show how mathematical induction can be used to prove that a greedy algorithm yields an optimal solution. (For an introduction to greedy algorithms, see Section 2.1.)

EXAMPLE 12   We can use a greedy algorithm to schedule a subset of m proposed talks $t_1, t_2, \ldots, t_m$ in a single lecture hall. Suppose that talk t_j begins at time b_j and ends at time e_j. (No two lectures can proceed at the same time and a lecture can begin at the same time one ends.) We assume that the talks are listed in order of nondecreasing ending time, so that $e_1 \le e_2 \le \cdots \le e_m$. The greedy algorithm proceeds by selecting at each stage a talk with the earliest ending time among all those talks that begin after all talks already scheduled end. (A lecture with an earliest end time is always added first by the algorithm.) We will show that this greedy algorithm is optimal in the sense that it always schedules the most talks possible. To prove the optimality of this algorithm we use mathematical induction on the variable n, the number of talks scheduled by the algorithm. We let $P(n)$ be the proposition that if the greedy algorithm schedules n talks, then it is not possible to schedule more than n talks.

BASIS STEP: Suppose that the greedy algorithm managed to schedule just one talk, t_1. This means that every other talk cannot start after e_1, the ending time of t_1. Otherwise, the first such talk we come to as we go through the talks in order of nondecreasing end time could be added. Hence, at time e_1 each of the remaining talks needs to use the lecture hall since they all start at or before e_1 and end after e_1. It follows that no two talks can be scheduled since both need to use the lecture hall at time e_1. This shows that $P(1)$ is true and completes the basis step.

INDUCTIVE STEP: Assume that $P(k)$ is true, that is, that the greedy algorithm always schedules the most possible talks when it selects k talks, given any set of talks (no matter how large). Now assume that the algorithm has selected $k + 1$ talks. We must show that the greedy algorithm has selected the largest number of talks possible, given the assumption that it always produces an optimal solution when it schedules k talks. That is, we need to show that $P(k + 1)$ is true, assuming that $P(k)$ is true.

To complete the inductive step, we first show there is a schedule including the most talks possible that contains talk t_1, a talk with the earliest end time. This is easy to see since a schedule that begins with the talk t_i in the list, where $i > 1$, can be changed so that talk t_1 replaces talk t_i. To see this, note that since $e_1 \leq e_i$, all talks that were scheduled to follow talk t_i can still be scheduled.

Once we included talk t_1, scheduling the talks so that as many as possible are scheduled is reduced to scheduling as many talks as possible that begin at or after time e_1. So, if we have scheduled as many talks as possible, the schedule of talks other than talk t_1 is an optimal schedule of the original talks that begin once talk t_1 has ended. Since the greedy algorithm schedules k talks when it creates this schedule, we can apply the induction hypothesis to conclude that it has scheduled the most possible talks. It follows that the greedy algorithm has scheduled the most possible talks, $k + 1$, when it produced a schedule with $k + 1$ talks, so that $P(k + 1)$ is true. This completes the induction step, finishing the proof that $P(n)$ is true for all positive integers n, and completes the proof of optimality.   ◀

STRONG INDUCTION

There is another form of mathematical induction that is often useful in proofs. With this form we use the same basis step as before, but we use a different inductive step. We assume that $P(j)$ is true for $j = 1, \ldots, k$ and show that $P(k + 1)$ must also be true based on this assumption. This is called **strong induction** (and is sometimes also known as the **second principle of mathematical induction**).

We summarize the two steps used to show that $P(n)$ is true for all positive integers n:

BASIS STEP: The proposition $P(1)$ is shown to be true.

INDUCTIVE STEP: It is shown that $[P(1) \land P(2) \land \cdots \land P(k)] \to P(k + 1)$ is true for every positive integer k.

The two forms of mathematical induction are equivalent; that is, each can be shown to be a valid proof technique assuming the other. We leave it as an exercise for the reader to show this. We now give three examples that show how the strong induction is used.

EXAMPLE 13   Consider a game in which two players take turns removing any number of matches they want from one of two piles of matches. The player who removes the last match wins the game. Show that if the two piles contain the same number of matches initially, the second player can always guarantee a win.

Solution: Let n be the number of matches in each pile. We will use strong induction to prove $P(n)$, the statement that the second player can win when there are initially n matches in each pile.

BASIS STEP: When $n = 1$, the first player has only one choice, removing one match from one of the piles, leaving a single pile with a single match, which the second player can remove to win the game.

INDUCTIVE STEP: Suppose that $P(j)$ is true for all j with $1 \leq j \leq k$, that is, that the second player can always win whenever there are j matches where $1 \leq j \leq k$ in each of the two piles at the start of the game. Now suppose that there are $k + 1$ matches in each of the two piles at the start of the game and suppose that the first player removes j matches $(1 \leq j \leq k)$ from one of the piles, leaving $k + 1 - j$ matches in this pile. By removing the same number of matches from the other pile, player two creates the situation where there are two piles each with $k + 1 - j$ matches. Because $1 \leq k + 1 - j \leq k$ the second player can always win by the induction hypothesis. We complete the proof by noting that if the first player removes all $k + 1$ matches from one of the piles, the second player can win by removing all the remaining matches. ◀

EXAMPLE 14 Show that if n is an integer greater than 1, then n can be written as the product of primes.

Solution: Let $P(n)$ be the proposition that n can be written as the product of primes.

BASIS STEP: $P(2)$ is true, since 2 can be written as the product of one prime, itself. [Note that $P(2)$ is the first case we need to establish.]

INDUCTIVE STEP: Assume that $P(j)$ is true for all positive integers j with $j \leq k$. To complete the inductive step, it must be shown that $P(k + 1)$ is true under this assumption.

There are two cases to consider, namely, when $k + 1$ is prime and when $k + 1$ is composite. If $k + 1$ is prime, we immediately see that $P(k + 1)$ is true. Otherwise, $k + 1$ is composite and can be written as the product of two positive integers a and b with $2 \leq a \leq b < k + 1$. By the induction hypothesis, both a and b can be written as the product of primes. Thus, if $k + 1$ is composite, it can be written as the product of primes, namely, those primes in the factorization of a and those in the factorization of b. ◀

Remark: Since 1 is a product of primes, namely, the *empty* product of no primes, we could have started the proof in Example 14 with $P(1)$ as the basis step. We chose not to do this because many people find this confusing.

Note that Example 14 completes the proof of the Fundamental Theorem of Arithmetic, which asserts that every nonnegative integer can be written uniquely as the product of primes in nondecreasing order. We showed in Section 2.6 (see page 183) that an integer has at most one such factorization into primes. Example 14 shows there is at least one such factorization.

Using the principle of mathematical induction, instead of strong induction, to prove the result in Example 14 is difficult. However, as Example 15 shows, some results can be readily proved using either the principle of mathematical induction or strong induction.

EXAMPLE 15 Prove that every amount of postage of 12 cents or more can be formed using just 4-cent and 5-cent stamps.

Solution: We will prove this result using the principle of mathematical induction. Then we will present a proof using strong induction. Let $P(n)$ be the statement that postage of n cents can be formed using 4-cent and 5-cent stamps.

We begin by using the principle of mathematical induction.

BASIS STEP: Postage of 12 cents can be formed using three 4-cent stamps.

INDUCTIVE STEP: Assume that $P(k)$ is true, so that postage of k cents can be formed using 4-cent and 5-cent stamps. If at least one 4-cent stamp was used, replace it with a 5-cent stamp to form postage of $k + 1$ cents. If no 4-cent stamps were used, postage of k cents was formed using just 5-cent stamps. Since $k \geq 12$, at least three 5-cent stamps were used. So, replace three 5-cent stamps with four 4-cent stamps to form postage of $k + 1$ cents. This completes the inductive step, as well as the proof by the principle of mathematical induction.

Next, we will use strong induction. We will show that postage of 12, 13, 14, and 15 cents can be formed and then show how to get postage of $k + 1$ cents for $k \geq 15$ from postage of $k - 3$ cents.

BASIS STEP: We can form postage of 12, 13, 14, and 15 cents using three 4-cent stamps, two 4-cent stamps and one 5-cent stamp, one 4-cent stamp and two 5-cent stamps, and three 5-cent stamps, respectively.

INDUCTIVE STEP: Let $k \geq 15$. Assume that we can form postage of j cents, where $12 \leq j \leq k$. To form postage of $k + 1$ cents, use the stamps that form postage of $k - 3$ cents together with a 4-cent stamp. This completes the inductive step, as well as the proof by strong induction.

(There are other ways to approach this problem besides those described here. Can you find a solution that does not use mathematical induction?)   ◀

Remark: Example 15 shows how we can adapt strong induction to handle cases where the inductive step is valid only for sufficiently large values of k. In particular, to prove that $P(n)$ is true for $n = j, j + 1, j + 2, \ldots$, where j is an integer, we first show that $P(j), P(j + 1), P(j + 2), \ldots, P(l)$ are true (the basis step), and then we show that $[P(j) \wedge P(j + 1) \wedge P(j + 2) \wedge \cdots \wedge P(k)] \rightarrow P(k + 1)$ is true for every integer $k \geq l$ (the inductive step). For example, the basis step of the second proof in the solution of Example 15 shows that $P(12), P(13), P(14)$, and $P(15)$ are true. We need to prove these cases separately since the inductive step, which shows that $[P(12) \wedge P(13) \wedge \cdots \wedge P(k)] \rightarrow P(k + 1)$, holds only when $k \geq 15$.

THE WELL-ORDERING PROPERTY

The validity of mathematical induction follows from the following fundamental axiom about the set of integers.

THE WELL-ORDERING PROPERTY Every nonempty set of nonnegative integers has a least element.

The well-ordering property can often be used directly in proofs.

EXAMPLE 16 Use the well-ordering property to prove the division algorithm. Recall that the division algorithm states that if a is an integer and d is a positive integer, then there are unique integers q and r with $0 \leq r < d$ and $a = dq + r$.

Solution: Let S be the set of nonnegative integers of the form $a - dq$ where q is an integer. This set is nonempty since $-dq$ can be made as large as desired (taking q to be a negative integer with large absolute value). By the well-ordering property S has a least element $r = a - dq_0$.

The integer r is nonnegative. It is also the case that $r < d$. If it were not, then there would be a smaller nonnegative element in S, namely, $a - d(q_0 + 1)$. To see this, suppose that $r \geq d$. Since $a = dq_0 + r$, it follows that $a - d(q_0 + 1) = (a - dq_0) - d = r - d \geq 0$.

Consequently, there are integers q and r with $0 \leq r < d$. The proof that q and r are unique is left as an exercise for the reader.   ◄

EXAMPLE 17   In a round-robin tournament every player plays every other player exactly once and each match has a winner and loser. We say that the players $p_1, p_2, \ldots, p_m$ form a *cycle* if p_1 beats p_2, p_2 beats p_3, $\ldots$, p_{m-1} beats p_m, and p_m beats p_1. Use the well-ordering principle to show that if there is a cycle of length m ($m \geq 3$) among the players in a round-robin tournament, there must be a cycle of three of these players.

Solution: We assume that there is no cycle of three players. Since there is at least one cycle in the round-robin tournament, the set of all positive integers n for which there is a cycle of length n is nonempty. By the well-ordering property, this set of positive integers has a least element k, which by assumption must be greater than three. Consequently, there exists a cycle of players $p_1, p_2, p_3, \ldots, p_k$ and no shorter cycle exists.

Now suppose that there is no cycle of three of these players, so that $k > 3$. Consider the first three elements of this cycle, p_1, p_2, p_3. There are two possible outcomes of the match between p_1 and p_3. If p_3 beats p_1, it follows that p_1, p_2, p_3 is a cycle of length three, contradicting our assumption that there is no cycle of three players. Consequently, it must be the case that p_1 beats p_3. This means that we can omit p_2 from the cycle $p_1, p_2, p_3, \ldots, p_k$ to obtain the cycle $p_1, p_3, p_4, \ldots, p_k$ of length $k - 1$, contradicting the assumption that the smallest cycle has length k. We conclude that there must be a cycle of length three.   ◄

INFINITE DESCENT We will now describe a proof method, the **method of infinite descent**, introduced by Pierre de Fermat in the 1600s. The method of infinite descent is often used to show that for a propositional function $P(n)$, $P(k)$ is false for all positive integers k. The method is based on the observation that if $P(k)$ is true for at least one integer k, then the well-ordering property implies that there is a least positive integer s such that $P(s)$ is true. The method proceeds by finding a positive integer s' with $s' < s$ for which $P(s')$ is true. It follows that $P(n)$ must be false for all positive integers. (This technique is called the method of *infinite* descent since the procedure of finding smaller integers for which the propositional function is true could be continued indefinitely, producing an infinite sequence of decreasing positive integers, which is impossible by the well-ordering property.) The method of infinite descent is often used to show that there are no solutions in integers to certain equations. In particular, Fermat used it to prove the $n = 4$ case of Fermat's Last Theorem, which states that the equation $x^4 + y^4 = z^4$ has no solutions in positive integers. We illustrate the use of infinite descent in Example 18.

EXAMPLE 18   In Example 21 in Section 1.5 we showed that $\sqrt{2}$ is irrational. Here we will provide a different proof of this fact using infinite descent. First, suppose that $\sqrt{2}$ is rational. Then there exist positive integers m and n such that $\sqrt{2} = m/n$. By the well-ordering property, there is a least positive integer N such that $\sqrt{2} = M/N$ for some positive integer M. (This would make N the smallest possible denominator of ratios of two positive integers that equal $\sqrt{2}$.)

To carry out the proof by infinite descent, we will show that $\sqrt{2} = (2N - M)/(M - N)$ and $0 < M - N < N$. This contradicts the choice of N as the least positive integer such that $\sqrt{2} = M/N$ for some positive integer M. To show that $\sqrt{2} = (2N - M)/(M - N)$ we need only show that $(2N - M)/(M - N) = M/N$. To show this, first note that because $(M/N)^2 = 2$, it follows that $M^2 = 2N^2$. Consequently,

$$\frac{2N - M}{M - N} = \frac{(2N - M)N}{(M - N)N} = \frac{2N^2 - MN}{(M - N)N} = \frac{M^2 - MN}{(M - N)N} = \frac{(M - N)M}{(M - N)N} = \frac{M}{N}.$$

To finish the proof, we need only show that the denominator, $M - N$, is positive and smaller than N. To see this, note that because $1 < \sqrt{2} < 2$ and $\sqrt{2} = M/N$, it follows that $1 < M/N < 2$, and hence, that $N < M < 2N$. Subtracting N, we conclude that $0 < M - N < N$.   ◄

WHY MATHEMATICAL INDUCTION IS VALID

Why is mathematical induction a valid proof technique? The reason comes from the well-ordering property. Suppose we know that $P(1)$ is true and that the proposition $P(k) \rightarrow P(k + 1)$ is true for all positive integers k. To show that $P(n)$ must be true for all positive integers, assume that there is at least one positive integer for which $P(n)$ is false. Then the set S of positive integers for which $P(n)$ is false is nonempty. Thus, by the well-ordering property, S has a least element, which will be denoted by m. We know that m cannot be 1, since $P(1)$ is true. Since m is positive and greater than 1, $m - 1$ is a positive integer. Furthermore, since $m - 1$ is less than m, it is not in S, so $P(m - 1)$ must be true. Since the implication $P(m - 1) \rightarrow P(m)$ is also true, it must be the case that $P(m)$ is true. This contradicts the choice of m. Hence, $P(n)$ must be true for every positive integer n.

Exercises

1. Find a formula for the sum of the first n even positive integers.

2. Use mathematical induction to prove the formula that you found in Exercise 1.

3. Use mathematical induction to prove that $3 + 3 \cdot 5 + 3 \cdot 5^2 + \cdots + 3 \cdot 5^n = 3(5^{n+1} - 1)/4$ whenever n is a nonnegative integer.

4. Use mathematical induction to prove that $2 - 2 \cdot 7 + 2 \cdot 7^2 - \cdots + 2(-7)^n = (1 - (-7)^{n+1})/4$ whenever n is a nonnegative integer.

5. Find a formula for
$$\frac{1}{2} + \frac{1}{4} + \frac{1}{8} + \cdots + \frac{1}{2^n}$$
by examining the values of this expression for small values of n. Use mathematical induction to prove your result.

6. Find a formula for
$$\frac{1}{1 \cdot 2} + \frac{1}{2 \cdot 3} + \cdots + \frac{1}{n(n + 1)}$$
by examining the values of this expression for small values of n. Use mathematical induction to prove your result.

7. Show that $1^2 + 2^2 + \cdots + n^2 = n(n + 1)(2n + 1)/6$ whenever n is a positive integer.

8. Show that $1^3 + 2^3 + \cdots + n^3 = [n(n + 1)/2]^2$ whenever n is a positive integer.

9. Prove that $1^2 + 3^2 + 5^2 + \cdots + (2n + 1)^2 = (n + 1)(2n + 1)(2n + 3)/3$ whenever n is a nonnegative integer.

10. Prove that $1 \cdot 1! + 2 \cdot 2! + \cdots + n \cdot n! = (n + 1)! - 1$ whenever n is a positive integer.

*11. Show by mathematical induction that if $h > -1$, then $1 + nh \leq (1 + h)^n$ for all nonnegative integers n. This is called **Bernoulli's inequality.**

12. Prove that $3^n < n!$ whenever n is a positive integer greater than 6.

13. Show that $2^n > n^2$ whenever n is an integer greater than 4.

14. Use mathematical induction to prove that $n! < n^n$ whenever n is a positive integer greater than 1.

15. Prove using mathematical induction that
$$1 \cdot 2 + 2 \cdot 3 + \cdots + n(n + 1) = n(n + 1)(n + 2)/3$$
whenever n is a positive integer.

16. Use mathematical induction to prove that
$$1 \cdot 2 \cdot 3 + 2 \cdot 3 \cdot 4 + \cdots + n(n + 1)(n + 2)$$
$$= n(n + 1)(n + 2)(n + 3)/4.$$

17. Show that $1^2 - 2^2 + 3^2 - \cdots + (-1)^{n-1}n^2 = (-1)^{n-1}n(n + 1)/2$ whenever n is a positive integer.

18. Prove that
$$1 + \frac{1}{4} + \frac{1}{9} + \cdots + \frac{1}{n^2} < 2 - \frac{1}{n}$$
whenever n is a positive integer greater than 1.

19. Show that any postage that is a positive integer number of cents greater than 7 cents can be formed using just 3-cent stamps and 5-cent stamps.

20. Use mathematical induction to show that 3 divides $n^3 + 2n$ whenever n is a nonnegative integer.

21. Use mathematical induction to show that 5 divides $n^5 - n$ whenever n is a nonnegative integer.

22. Use mathematical induction to show that 6 divides $n^3 - n$ whenever n is a nonnegative integer.

*23. Use mathematical induction to show that $n^2 - 1$ is divisible by 8 whenever n is an odd positive integer.

24. Use mathematical induction to show that $n^2 - 7n + 12$ is nonnegative if n is an integer greater than 3.

25. Use mathematical induction to prove that a set with n elements has $n(n - 1)/2$ subsets containing exactly two elements whenever n is an integer greater than or equal to 2.

*26. Use mathematical induction to prove that a set with n elements has $n(n - 1)(n - 2)/6$ subsets containing exactly three elements whenever n is an integer greater than or equal to 3.

27. Use mathematical induction to prove that $\sum_{j=1}^{n} j^4 = n(n+1)(2n+1)(3n^2+3n-1)/30$ whenever n is a positive integer.

28. For which nonnegative integers n is $n^2 \le n!$? Prove your answer using mathematical induction.

29. For which nonnegative integers n is $2n + 3 \le 2^n$? Prove your answer using mathematical induction.

30. Use mathematical induction to show that $1/(2n) \le [1 \cdot 3 \cdot 5 \cdots \cdot (2n - 1)]/(2 \cdot 4 \cdots \cdot 2n)$ whenever n is a positive integer.

31. a) Determine which amounts of postage can be formed using just 5-cent and 6-cent stamps.
b) Prove your answer to (a) using the principle of mathematical induction.
c) Prove your answer to (a) using the second principle of mathematical induction.

32. Which amounts of money can be formed using just dimes and quarters? Prove your answer using a form of mathematical induction.

33. An automatic teller machine has only \$20 bills and \$50 bills. Which amounts of money can the machine dispense, assuming the machine has a limitless supply of these two denominations of bills? Prove your answer using a form of mathematical induction.

34. Assume that a chocolate bar consists of n squares arranged in a rectangular pattern. The bar or a smaller rectangular piece of the bar can be broken along a vertical or a horizontal line separating the squares. Assuming that only one piece can be broken at a time, determine how many breaks you must successively make to break the bar into n separate squares. Use strong induction to prove your answer.

35. Consider this variation of the game of Nim. The game begins with n matches. Two players take turns removing matches, one, two, or three at a time. The player removing the last match loses. Use strong induction to show that if each player plays the best strategy pos-

sible, the first player wins if $n = 4j, 4j + 2$, or $4j + 3$ for some nonnegative integer j and the second player wins in the remaining case when $n = 4j + 1$ for some nonnegative integer j.

36. Prove that $\sum_{k=1}^{n} k2^k = (n - 1)2^{n+1} + 2$ using mathematical induction.

37. Show that if n is a positive integer, then

$$\sum_{\{a_1, \ldots, a_k\} \subseteq \{1, 2, \ldots, n\}} \frac{1}{a_1 a_2 \cdots a_k} = n.$$

(Here the sum is over all nonempty subsets of the set of the n smallest positive integers.)

38. Use mathematical induction to show that given a set of $n + 1$ positive integers, none exceeding $2n$, there is at least one integer in this set that divides another integer in the set.

*39. A knight on a chessboard can move one space horizontally (in either direction) and two spaces vertically (in either direction) or two spaces horizontally (in either direction) and one space vertically (in either direction). Use mathematical induction to show that for every square a knight starting at $(0, 0)$, the corner of an infinite chessboard made up of all squares (m, n), where m and n are nonnegative integers, can visit this square using a finite sequence of moves. (*Hint:* Use induction on the variable $s = m + n$.)

40. Suppose you begin with a pile of n stones and split this pile into n piles of one stone each by successively splitting a pile of stones into two smaller piles. Each time you split a pile you multiply the number of stones in each of the two smaller piles you form, so that if these piles have r and s stones in them, respectively, you compute rs. Show that no matter how you split the piles, the sum of the products computed at each step equals $n(n - 1)/2$.

41. (Calculus required) Use mathematical induction to prove that the derivative of $f(x) = x^n$ equals nx^{n-1} whenever n is a positive integer. (For the inductive step, use the product rule for derivatives.)

42. Suppose that

$$\mathbf{A} = \begin{bmatrix} a & 0 \\ 0 & b \end{bmatrix}$$

where a and b are real numbers. Show that

$$\mathbf{A}^n = \begin{bmatrix} a^n & 0 \\ 0 & b^n \end{bmatrix}$$

for every positive integer n.

43. Suppose that $\mathbf{A}$ and $\mathbf{B}$ are square matrices with the property $\mathbf{AB} = \mathbf{BA}$. Show that $\mathbf{AB}^n = \mathbf{B}^n\mathbf{A}$ for every positive integer n.

44. Suppose that m is a positive integer. Use mathematical induction to prove that if a and b are integers with $a \equiv b \pmod{m}$, then $a^k \equiv b^k \pmod{m}$ whenever k is a nonnegative integer.

45. Use mathematical induction to show that if A_1, $A_2, \ldots, A_n$ and B are sets, then

$$(A_1 \cup A_2 \cup \cdots \cup A_n) \cap B$$

$$= (A_1 \cap B) \cup (A_2 \cap B) \cup \cdots \cup (A_n \cap B).$$

46. Prove that if $A_1, A_2, \ldots, A_n$ and $B_1, B_2, \ldots, B_n$ are sets such that $A_k \subseteq B_k$ for $k = 1, 2, \ldots, n$, then

a) $\displaystyle\bigcup_{k=1}^{n} A_k \subseteq \bigcup_{k=1}^{n} B_k.$ **b)** $\displaystyle\bigcap_{k=1}^{n} A_k \subseteq \bigcap_{k=1}^{n} B_k.$

47. Use mathematical induction to prove that if A_1, $A_2, \ldots, A_n$ are subsets of a universal set U, then

$$\overline{\bigcup_{k=1}^{n} A_k} = \bigcap_{k=1}^{n} \overline{A_k}.$$

48. Use mathematical induction to show that $\neg(p_1 \vee p_2 \vee \cdots \vee p_n)$ is equivalent to $\neg p_1 \wedge \neg p_2 \wedge \cdots \wedge \neg p_n$ whenever $p_1, p_2, \ldots, p_n$ are propositions.

*49. Show that

$$[(p_1 \rightarrow p_2) \wedge (p_2 \rightarrow p_3) \wedge \cdots \wedge (p_{n-1} \rightarrow p_n)]$$
$$\rightarrow [(p_1 \wedge p_2 \wedge \cdots \wedge p_{n-1}) \rightarrow p_n]$$

is a tautology whenever $p_1, p_2, \ldots, p_n$ are propositions.

50. What is wrong with this "proof"?

"Theorem" For every positive integer n, $\sum_{i=1}^{n} i = (n + \frac{1}{2})^2/2$.

Basis Step: The formula is true for $n = 1$.

Inductive Step: Suppose that $\sum_{i=1}^{n} i = (n + \frac{1}{2})^2/2$. Then $\sum_{i=1}^{n+1} i = (\sum_{i=1}^{n} i) + (n + 1)$. By the inductive hypothesis, $\sum_{i=1}^{n+1} i = (n + \frac{1}{2})^2/2 + n + 1 = (n^2 + n + \frac{1}{4})/2 + n + 1 = (n^2 + 3n + \frac{9}{4})/2 = (n + \frac{3}{2})^2/2 = [(n + 1) + \frac{1}{2}]^2/2$, completing the inductive step.

51. What is wrong with this "proof" that all horses are the same color?

Let $P(n)$ be the proposition that all the horses in a set of n horses are the same color.

Basis Step: Clearly, $P(1)$ is true.

Inductive Step: Assume that $P(k)$ is true, so that all the horses in any set of k horses are the same color. Consider any $k + 1$ horses; number these as horses $1, 2, 3, \ldots, k, k + 1$. Now the first k of these horses all must have the same color, and the last k of these must also have the same color. Since the set of the first k horses and the set of the last k horses overlap, all $k + 1$ must be the same color. This shows that $P(k + 1)$ is true and finishes the proof by induction.

52. What is wrong with this "proof"?

"Theorem" For every positive integer n, if x and y are positive integers with $\max(x, y) = n$, then $x = y$.

Basis Step: Suppose that $n = 1$. If $\max(x, y) = 1$ and x and y are positive integers, we have $x = 1$ and $y = 1$.

Inductive Step: Let k be a positive integer. Assume that whenever $\max(x, y) = k$ and x and y are positive integers, then $x = y$. Now let $\max(x, y) = k + 1$, where x and y are positive integers. Then $\max(x - 1, y - 1) = k$, so by the inductive hypothesis, $x - 1 = y - 1$. It follows that $x = y$, completing the inductive step.

53. What is wrong with this "proof" by strong induction?

"Theorem" For every nonnegative integer n, $5n = 0$.

Basis Step: $5 \cdot 0 = 0$.

Inductive Step: Suppose that $5j = 0$ for all nonnegative integers j with $0 \le j \le k$. Write $k + 1 = i + j$, where i and j are natural numbers less than $k + 1$. By the induction hypothesis, $5(k + 1) = 5(i + j) = 5i + 5j = 0 + 0 = 0$.

*54. Find the flaw with the following "proof" that $a^n = 1$ for all nonnegative integers n, whenever a is a nonzero real number.

Basis Step: $a^0 = 1$ is true by the definition of a^0.

Inductive Step: Assume that $a^j = 1$ for all nonnegative integers j with $j \le k$. Then note that

$$a^{k+1} = \frac{a^k \cdot a^k}{a^{k-1}} = \frac{1 \cdot 1}{1} = 1.$$

*55. Show that strong induction is a valid method of proof by showing that it follows from the well-ordering property.

*56. Show that the following form of mathematical induction is a valid method to prove that $P(n)$ is true for all positive integers n.

Basis Step: $P(1)$ and $P(2)$ are true.

Inductive Step: For each positive integer k, if $P(k)$ and $P(k + 1)$ are both true, then $P(k + 2)$ is true.

In Exercises 57 and 58, H_n denotes the nth harmonic number.

*57. Use mathematical induction to show that $H_{2^n} \le 1 + n$ whenever n is a nonnegative integer.

*58. Use mathematical induction to prove that

$$H_1 + H_2 + \cdots + H_n = (n + 1)H_n - n.$$

*59. Prove that

$$1 + \frac{1}{\sqrt{2}} + \frac{1}{\sqrt{3}} + \cdots + \frac{1}{\sqrt{n}} > 2(\sqrt{n + 1} - 1).$$

*60. Show that n lines separate the plane into $(n^2 + n + 2)/2$ regions if no two of these lines are parallel and no three pass through a common point.

61. Let $a_1, a_2, \ldots, a_n$ be positive real numbers. The **arithmetic mean of these numbers is defined by

$$A = (a_1 + a_2 + \cdots + a_n)/n,$$

and the **geometric mean** of these numbers is defined by

$$G = (a_1 a_2 \cdots a_n)^{1/n}.$$

Use mathematical induction to prove that $A \geq G$.

*62. Use mathematical induction to show that 21 divides $4^{n+1} + 5^{2n-1}$ whenever n is a positive integer.

63. Use mathematical induction to prove Lemma 2 of Section 2.6, which states that if p is a prime and $p \mid a_1 a_2 \cdots a_n$, where a_i is an integer for $i = 1, 2, 3, \ldots, n$, then $p \mid a_i$ for some integer i.

64. Use infinite descent to show that the equation $8x^4 + 4y^4 + 2z^4 = w^4$ has no solutions in positive integers x, y, z, and w.

65. Use infinite descent to show that there are no solutions in positive integers w, x, y, and z to $w^2 + x^2 + y^2 + z^2 = 2wxyz$. (*Hint:* First show that if this equation holds, then all of w, x, y, and z must be even. Then show that all four of these integers must be divisible by 4, by 8, and so on.)

*66. The well-ordering property can be used to show that there is a unique greatest common divisor of two positive integers. Let a and b be positive integers, and let S be the set of positive integers of the form $as + bt$, where s and t are integers.

a) Show that S is nonempty.

b) Use the well-ordering property to show that S has a smallest element c.

c) Show that if d is a common divisor of a and b, then d is a divisor of c.

d) Show that $c \mid a$ and $c \mid b$. (*Hint:* First, assume that $c \nmid a$. Then $a = qc + r$, where $0 < r < c$. Show that $r \in S$, contradicting the choice of c.)

e) Conclude from (c) and (d) that the greatest common divisor of a and b exists. Finish the proof by showing that this greatest common divisor of two positive integers is unique.

*67. Show that if $a_1, a_2, \ldots, a_n$ are n distinct real numbers, exactly $n - 1$ multiplications are used to compute the product of these n numbers no matter how parenthe-

ses are inserted into their product. (*Hint:* Use strong induction and consider the last multiplication.)

68. Construct a tiling using L-shaped pieces of the 4×4 chessboard with the square in the upper left corner removed.

69. Construct a tiling using L-shaped pieces of the 8×8 chessboard with the square in the upper left corner removed.

70. Prove or disprove that all chessboards of these shapes can be completely covered using L-shaped pieces whenever n is a positive integer.

a) 3×2^n **b)** 6×2^n

c) $3^n \times 3^n$ **d)** $6^n \times 6^n$

*71. Show that a three-dimensional $2^n \times 2^n \times 2^n$ chessboard with one $1 \times 1 \times 1$ cube missing can be completely covered by $2 \times 2 \times 2$ cubes with one $1 \times 1 \times 1$ cube removed.

*72. Show that an $n \times n$ chessboard with one square removed can be completely covered using L-shaped pieces if $n > 5, n$ is odd, and $3 \nmid n$.

73. Show that a 5×5 chessboard with a corner square removed can be tiled using L-shaped pieces.

*74. Find a 5×5 chessboard with a square removed that cannot be tiled using L-shaped pieces. Prove that such a tiling does not exist for this board.

75. Let a be an integer and d be a positive integer. Show that the integers q and r with $a = dq + r$ and $0 \leq r < d$, which were shown to exist in Example 16, are unique.

☞ 76. Use the principle of mathematical induction to show that $P(n)$ is true for $n = b, b + 1, b + 2, \ldots$, where b is an integer, if $P(b)$ is true and the implication $P(k) \rightarrow P(k + 1)$ is true for all positive integers k with $k \geq b$.

**77. Can you use the well-ordering property to prove this statement? "Every positive integer can be described using no more than 15 English words"?

78. Use the well-ordering principle to show that if x and y are real numbers with $x < y$, then there is a rational number r with $x < r < y$. [*Hint:* Show that there exists a positive integer A with $A > 1/(y - x)$. Then show that there is a rational number r with denominator A between x and y by looking at the numbers $\lfloor x \rfloor + j/A$, where j is a positive integer.]

3.4   Recursive Definitions and Structural Induction

INTRODUCTION

Sometimes it is difficult to define an object explicitly. However, it may be easy to define this object in terms of itself. This process is called **recursion.** For instance, the picture shown in Figure 1 is produced recursively. First, an original picture is given. Then a process of

FIGURE 1   A Recursively Defined Picture.

successively superimposing centered smaller pictures on top of the previous pictures is carried out.

We can use recursion to define sequences, functions, and sets. In previous discussions, we specified the terms of a sequence using an explicit formula. For instance, the sequence of powers of 2 is given by $a_n = 2^n$ for $n = 0, 1, 2, \ldots$. However, this sequence can also be defined by giving the first term of the sequence, namely, $a_0 = 1$, and a rule for finding a term of the sequence from the previous one, namely, $a_{n+1} = 2a_n$ for $n = 0, 1, 2, \ldots$. When we define a sequence *recursively* by specifying how terms of the sequence are found from previous terms, we can use induction to prove results about the sequence.

When we define sets recursively, we specify some initial elements in a basis step and provide a rule for constructing new elements from those we already have in the recursive step. To prove results about recursively defined sets we use a method called *structural induction*.

RECURSIVELY DEFINED FUNCTIONS

We use two steps to define a function with the set of nonnegative integers as its domain:

BASIS STEP: Specify the value of the function at zero.

RECURSIVE STEP: Give a rule for finding its value at an integer from its values at smaller integers.

Such a definition is called a **recursive** or **inductive definition**.

EXAMPLE 1   Suppose that f is defined recursively by

$$f(0) = 3,$$
$$f(n + 1) = 2f(n) + 3.$$

Find $f(1), f(2), f(3)$, and $f(4)$.

Solution: From the recursive definition it follows that

$$f(1) = 2f(0) + 3 = 2 \cdot 3 + 3 = 9,$$
$$f(2) = 2f(1) + 3 = 2 \cdot 9 + 3 = 21,$$
$$f(3) = 2f(2) + 3 = 2 \cdot 21 + 3 = 45,$$
$$f(4) = 2f(3) + 3 = 2 \cdot 45 + 3 = 93.$$

◀

Many functions can be studied using their recursive definitions. The factorial function is one such example.

EXAMPLE 2   Give an inductive definition of the factorial function $F(n) = n!$.

Solution: We can define the factorial function by specifying the initial value of this function, namely, $F(0) = 1$, and giving a rule for finding $F(n + 1)$ from $F(n)$. This is obtained by noting that $(n + 1)!$ is computed from $n!$ by multiplying by $n + 1$. Hence, the desired rule is

$$F(n + 1) = (n + 1)F(n).$$

◀

To determine a value of the factorial function, such as $F(5) = 5!$, from the recursive definition found in Example 2, it is necessary to use the rule that shows how to express $F(n + 1)$ in terms of $F(n)$ several times:

$$F(5) = 5F(4) = 5 \cdot 4F(3) = 5 \cdot 4 \cdot 3F(2) = 5 \cdot 4 \cdot 3 \cdot 2F(1)$$
$$= 5 \cdot 4 \cdot 3 \cdot 2 \cdot 1 \cdot F(0) = 5 \cdot 4 \cdot 3 \cdot 2 \cdot 1 \cdot 1 = 120.$$

Once $F(0)$ is the only value of the function that occurs, no more reductions are necessary. The only thing left to do is to insert the value of $F(0)$ into the formula.

Recursively defined functions are well defined. This is a consequence of the principle of mathematical induction. (See Exercise 56 at the end of this section.) Additional examples of recursive definitions are given in the following examples.

EXAMPLE 3   Give a recursive definition of a^n, where a is a nonzero real number and n is a nonnegative integer.

Solution: The recursive definition contains two parts. First a^0 is specified, namely, $a^0 = 1$. Then the rule for finding a^{n+1} from a^n, namely, $a^{n+1} = a \cdot a^n$, for $n = 0, 1, 2, 3, \ldots,$ is given. These two equations uniquely define a^n for all nonnegative integers n. ◀

EXAMPLE 4   Give a recursive definition of

$$\sum_{k=0}^{n} a_k.$$

Solution: The first part of the recursive definition is

$$\sum_{k=0}^{0} a_k = a_0.$$

The second part is

$$\sum_{k=0}^{n+1} a_k = \left(\sum_{k=0}^{n} a_k \right) + a_{n+1}. \qquad \blacktriangleleft$$

In some recursive definitions of functions, the values of the function at the first k positive integers are specified, and a rule is given for determining the value of the function at larger integers from its values at some or all of the preceding k integers. That such definitions produce well-defined functions follows from strong induction (see Exercise 57 at the end of this section).

DEFINITION 1

The *Fibonacci numbers*, $f_0, f_1, f_2, \ldots,$ are defined by the equations $f_0 = 0$, $f_1 = 1$, and

$$f_n = f_{n-1} + f_{n-2}$$

for $n = 2, 3, 4, \ldots$.

Links

EXAMPLE 5   Find the Fibonacci numbers $f_2, f_3, f_4, f_5,$ and f_6.

Solution: Since the first part of the definition states that $f_0 = 0$ and $f_1 = 1$, it follows from the second part of the definition that

$$f_2 = f_1 + f_0 = 1 + 0 = 1,$$
$$f_3 = f_2 + f_1 = 1 + 1 = 2,$$
$$f_4 = f_3 + f_2 = 2 + 1 = 3,$$
$$f_5 = f_4 + f_3 = 3 + 2 = 5,$$
$$f_6 = f_5 + f_4 = 5 + 3 = 8.$$

$\blacktriangleleft$

We can use the recursive definition of the Fibonacci numbers to prove many properties of these numbers. We give one such property in Example 6.

Links

FIBONACCI (1170–1250) Fibonacci (short for *filius Bonacci*, or "son of Bonacci") was also known as Leonardo of Pisa. He was born in the Italian commercial center of Pisa. Fibonacci was a merchant who traveled extensively throughout the Mideast, where he came into contact with Arabian mathematics. In his book *Liber Abaci*, Fibonacci introduced the European world to Arabic notation for numerals and algorithms for arithmetic. It was in this book that his famous rabbit problem (described in Section 6.1) appeared. Fibonacci also wrote books on geometry and trigonometry and on Diophantine equations, which involve finding integer solutions to equations.

EXAMPLE 6   Show that whenever $n \geq 3$, $f_n > \alpha^{n-2}$, where $\alpha = (1 + \sqrt{5})/2$.

Extra
Examples

Solution: We can use strong induction to prove this inequality. Let $P(n)$ be the statement $f_n > \alpha^{n-2}$. We want to show that $P(n)$ is true whenever n is an integer greater than or equal to 3.

BASIS STEP: First, note that

$$\alpha < 2 = f_3, \qquad \alpha^2 = (3 + \sqrt{5})/2 < 3 = f_4,$$

so that $P(3)$ and $P(4)$ are true.

INDUCTIVE STEP: Assume that $P(j)$ is true, namely, that $f_j > \alpha^{j-2}$, for all integers j with $3 \leq j \leq k$, where $k \geq 4$. We must show that $P(k + 1)$ is true, that is, that $f_{k+1} > \alpha^{k-1}$. Since α is a solution of $x^2 - x - 1 = 0$ (as the quadratic formula shows), it follows that $\alpha^2 = \alpha + 1$. Therefore,

$$\alpha^{k-1} = \alpha^2 \cdot \alpha^{k-3} = (\alpha + 1)\alpha^{k-3} = \alpha \cdot \alpha^{k-3} + 1 \cdot \alpha^{k-3} = \alpha^{k-2} + \alpha^{k-3}.$$

By the inductive hypothesis, if $k \geq 4$, it follows that

$$f_{k-1} > \alpha^{k-3}, \qquad f_k > \alpha^{k-2}.$$

Therefore, we have

$$f_{k+1} = f_k + f_{k-1} > \alpha^{k-2} + \alpha^{k-3} = \alpha^{k-1}.$$

It follows that $P(k + 1)$ is true. This completes the proof.   ◄

Remark: The inductive step shows that whenever $k \geq 4$, $P(k + 1)$ follows from the assumption that $P(j)$ is true for $3 \leq j \leq k$. Hence, the inductive step does *not* show that $P(3) \rightarrow P(4)$. Therefore, we had to show that $P(4)$ is true separately.

We can now show that the Euclidean algorithm uses $O(\log b)$ divisions to find the greatest common divisor of the positive integers a and b, where $a \geq b$.

THEOREM 1

LAMÉ'S THEOREM   Let a and b be positive integers with $a \geq b$. Then the number of divisions used by the Euclidean algorithm to find $\gcd(a, b)$ is less than or equal to five times the number of decimal digits in b.

Links

GABRIEL LAMÉ (1795–1870)   Gabriel Lamé entered the École Polytechnique in 1813, graduating in 1817. He continued his education at the École des Mines, graduating in 1820.

In 1820 Lamé went to Russia, where he was appointed director of the Schools of Highways and Transportation in St. Petersburg. Not only did he teach, but he also planned roads and bridges while in Russia. He returned to Paris in 1832, where he helped found an engineering firm. However, he soon left the firm, accepting the chair of physics at the École Polytechnique, which he held until 1844. While holding this position, he was active outside academia as an engineering consultant, serving as chief engineer of mines and participating in the building of railways.

Lamé contributed original work to number theory, applied mathematics, and thermodynamics. His best-known work involves the introduction of curvilinear coordinates. His work on number theory includes proving Fermat's Last Theorem for $n = 7$, as well as providing the upper bound for the number of divisions used by the Euclidean algorithm given in this text.

In the opinion of Gauss, one of the most important mathematicians of all time, Lamé was the foremost French mathematician of his time. However, French mathematicians considered him too practical, whereas French scientists considered him too theoretical.

Proof: Recall that when the Euclidean algorithm is applied to find $\gcd(a, b)$ with $a \geq b$, this sequence of equations (where $a = r_0$ and $b = r_1$) is obtained.

$$r_0 = r_1 q_1 + r_2 \qquad 0 \leq r_2 < r_1$$
$$r_1 = r_2 q_2 + r_3 \qquad 0 \leq r_3 < r_2$$
$$\vdots$$
$$r_{n-2} = r_{n-1} q_{n-1} + r_n \qquad 0 \leq r_n < r_{n-1}$$
$$r_{n-1} = r_n q_n.$$

Here n divisions have been used to find $r_n = \gcd(a, b)$. Note that the quotients $q_1, q_2, \ldots, q_{n-1}$ are all at least 1. Moreover, $q_n \geq 2$, since $r_n < r_{n-1}$. This implies that

$$r_n \geq 1 = f_2,$$
$$r_{n-1} \geq 2r_n \geq 2f_2 = f_3,$$
$$r_{n-2} \geq r_{n-1} + r_n \geq f_3 + f_2 = f_4,$$
$$\vdots$$
$$r_2 \geq r_3 + r_4 \geq f_{n-1} + f_{n-2} = f_n,$$
$$b = r_1 \geq r_2 + r_3 \geq f_n + f_{n-1} = f_{n+1}.$$

It follows that if n divisions are used by the Euclidean algorithm to find $\gcd(a, b)$ with $a \geq b$, then $b \geq f_{n+1}$. From Example 6 we know that $f_{n+1} > \alpha^{n-1}$ for $n > 2$, where $\alpha = (1 + \sqrt{5})/2$. Therefore, it follows that $b > \alpha^{n-1}$. Furthermore, since $\log_{10} \alpha \sim 0.208 > 1/5$, we see that

$$\log_{10} b > (n - 1) \log_{10} \alpha > (n - 1)/5.$$

Hence, $n - 1 < 5 \cdot \log_{10} b$. Now suppose that b has k decimal digits. Then $b < 10^k$ and $\log_{10} b < k$. It follows that $n - 1 < 5k$, and since k is an integer, it follows that $n \leq 5k$. This finishes the proof. $\triangleleft$

Since the number of decimal digits in b, which equals $\lfloor \log_{10} b \rfloor + 1$, is less than or equal to $\log_{10} b + 1$, Theorem 1 tells us that the number of divisions required to find $\gcd(a, b)$ with $a > b$ is less than or equal to $5(\log_{10} b + 1)$. Since $5(\log_{10} b + 1)$ is $O(\log b)$, we see that $O(\log b)$ divisions are used by the Euclidean algorithm to find $\gcd(a, b)$ whenever $a > b$.

RECURSIVELY DEFINED SETS AND STRUCTURES

We have explored how functions can be defined recursively. We now turn our attention to how sets can be defined recursively. Just as in the recursive definition of functions, recursive definitions of sets have two parts, a **basis step** and a **recursive step.** In the basis step, an initial collection of elements is specified. In the recursive step, rules for forming new elements in the set from those already known to be in the set are provided. Recursive definitions may also include an **exclusion rule,** which specifies that a recursively defined set contains nothing other than those elements specified in the basis step or generated by applications of the recursive step. In our discussions, we will always tacitly assume that the exclusion rule holds and no element belongs to a recursively defined set unless it is in the initial collection specified in the basis step or can be generated using the recursive step one or more times. Later we will see how we can use a technique known as structural induction to prove results about recursively defined sets.

Examples 7, 8, 10, and 11 illustrate the recursive definition of sets. In each example, we show those elements generated by the first few applications of the recursive step.

EXAMPLE 7   Consider the subset S of the set of integers defined by

BASIS STEP: $3 \in S$.

RECURSIVE STEP: If $x \in S$ and $y \in S$, then $x + y \in S$.

The new elements found to be in S are 3 by the basis step, $3 + 3 = 6$ at the first application of the recursive step, $3 + 6 = 6 + 3 = 9$ and $6 + 6 = 12$ at the second application of the recursive step, and so on.   ◄

Recursive definitions play an important role in the study of strings. (See Chapter 11 for an introduction to the theory of formal languages, for example.) Recall from Section 3.2 that a string over an alphabet Σ is a finite sequence of symbols from Σ. We can define Σ^*, the set of strings over Σ, recursively, as Definition 2 shows.

DEFINITION 2   The set Σ^* of *strings* over the alphabet Σ can be defined recursively by

BASIS STEP: $\lambda \in \Sigma^*$ (where λ is the empty string containing no symbols).

RECURSIVE STEP: If $w \in \Sigma^*$ and $x \in \Sigma$, then $wx \in \Sigma^*$.

The basis step of the recursive definition of strings says that the empty string belongs to Σ^*. The recursive step states that new strings are produced by adding a symbol from Σ to the end of strings in Σ^*. At each application of the recursive step, strings containing one additional symbol are generated.

EXAMPLE 8   If $\Sigma = \{0, 1\}$, the strings found to be in Σ^*, the set of all bit strings, are λ, specified to be in Σ^* in the basis step, 0 and 1 formed during the first application of the recursive step, 00, 01, 10, and 11 formed during the second application of the recursive step, and so on.   ◄

Recursive definitions can be used to define operations or functions on the elements of recursively defined sets. This is illustrated in Definition 3 of the concatenation of two strings and Example 9 concerning the length of a string.

DEFINITION 3

Two strings can be combined via the operation of *concatenation*. Let Σ be a set of symbols and Σ^* the set of strings formed from symbols in Σ. We can define the concatenation of two strings, denoted by $\cdot$, recursively as follows.

BASIS STEP: If $w \in \Sigma^*$, then $w \cdot \lambda = w$, where λ is the empty string.

RECURSIVE STEP: If $w_1 \in \Sigma^*$ and $w_2 \in \Sigma^*$ and $x \in \Sigma$, then $w_1 \cdot (w_2 x) = (w_1 \cdot w_2) x$.

The concatenation of the strings w_1 and w_2 is often written as $w_1 w_2$ rather than $w_1 \cdot w_2$. By repeated application of the recursive definition, it follows that the concatenation of two strings w_1 and w_2 consists of the symbols in w_1 followed by the symbols in w_2. For instance, the concatenation of $w_1 = abra$ and $w_2 = cadabra$ is $w_1 w_2 = abracadabra$.

EXAMPLE 9 **Length of a String** Give a recursive definition of $l(w)$, the length of the string w.

Solution: The length of a string can be defined by

$$l(\lambda) = 0;$$
$$l(wx) = l(w) + 1 \text{ if } w \in \Sigma^* \text{ and } x \in \Sigma. \qquad \blacktriangleleft$$

Another important use of recursive definitions is to define **well-formed formulae** of various types. This is illustrated in Examples 10 and 11.

EXAMPLE 10 **Well-Formed Formulae for Compound Propositions** We can define the set of well-formed formulae for compound propositions involving **T**, **F**, propositional variables, and operators from the set $\{\neg, \wedge, \vee, \rightarrow, \leftrightarrow\}$.

BASIS STEP: **T**, **F**, and p, where p is a propositional variable, are well-formed formulae.

RECURSIVE STEP: If E and F are well-formed formulae, then $(\neg E), (E \wedge F), (E \vee F), (E \rightarrow F)$, and $(E \leftrightarrow F)$ are well-formed formulae.

For example, by the basis step we know that **T**, **F**, p, and q are well-formed formulae, where p and q are propositional variables. From an initial application of the recursive step, we know that $(p \vee q), (p \rightarrow \mathbf{F}), (\mathbf{F} \rightarrow q)$, and $(q \wedge \mathbf{F})$ are well-formed formulae. A second application of the recursive step shows that $((p \vee q) \rightarrow (q \wedge \mathbf{F})), (q \vee (p \vee q))$, and $((p \rightarrow \mathbf{F}) \rightarrow \mathbf{T})$ are well-formed formulae. $\qquad \blacktriangleleft$

EXAMPLE 11 **Well-Formed Formulae of Operators and Operands** We can define the set of well-formed formulae consisting of variables, numerals, and operators from the set $\{+, -, *, /, \uparrow\}$ (where $*$ denotes multiplication and $\uparrow$ denotes exponentiation) recursively.

BASIS STEP: x is a well-formed formula if x is a numeral or variable.

RECURSIVE STEP: If F and G are well-formed formulae, then $(F + G)$, $(F - G)$, $(F * G)$, (F/G), and $(F \uparrow G)$ are well-formed formulae.

For example, by the basis step we see that $x, y, 0,$ and 3 are well-formed formulae (as is any variable or numeral). Well-formed formulae generated by applying the recursive step once include $(x + 3), (3 + y), (x - y), (3 - 0), (x * 3), (3 * y), (3/0), (x/y), (3 \uparrow x)$, and $(0 \uparrow 3)$. Applying the recursive step twice shows that formulae such as $((x + 3) + 3)$ and $(x - (3 * y))$ are well-formed formulae. [Note that $(3/0)$ is a well-formed formula since we are concerned only with syntax matters here.] ◀

We will study trees extensively in Chapter 9. A tree is a special type of a graph; a graph is made up of vertices and edges connecting some pairs of vertices. We will study graphs in Chapter 8. We will briefly introduce them here to illustrate how they can be defined recursively.

DEFINITION 4

The set of *rooted trees,* where a rooted tree consists of a set of vertices containing a distinguished vertex called the *root,* and edges connecting these vertices, can be defined recursively by these steps:

BASIS STEP: A single vertex r is a rooted tree.

RECURSIVE STEP: Suppose that $T_1, T_2, \ldots, T_n$ are rooted trees with roots $r_1, r_2, \ldots, r_n$, respectively. Then the graph formed by starting with a root r, which is not in any of the rooted trees $T_1, T_2, \ldots, T_n$, and adding an edge from r to each of the vertices $r_1, r_2, \ldots, r_n$, is also a rooted tree.

In Figure 2 we illustrate some of the rooted trees formed starting with the basis step and applying the recursive step one time and two times. Note that infinitely many rooted trees are formed at each application of the recursive definition.

Rooted trees are a special type of binary trees. We will provide recursive definitions of two types of binary trees, full binary trees and extended binary trees. In the recursive step

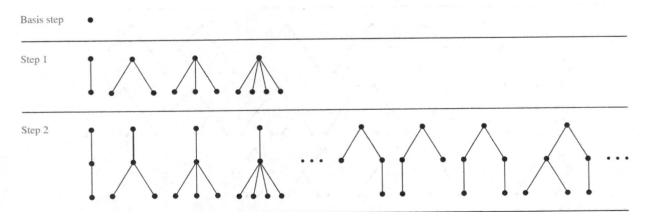

FIGURE 2   Building Up Rooted Trees.

of the definition of each type of binary tree, two binary trees are combined to form a new tree with one of these trees designated the left subtree and the other the right subtree. In extended binary trees, the left subtree or the right subtree can be empty, but in full binary trees this is not possible. Binary trees are one of the most important types of structures in computer science. In Chapter 9 we will see how they can be used in searching and sorting algorithms, in algorithms for compressing data, and in many other applications. We first define extended binary trees.

DEFINITION 5   The set of *extended binary trees* can be defined recursively by these steps:

BASIS STEP: The empty set is an extended binary tree.

RECURSIVE STEP: If T_1 and T_2 are extended binary trees, there is an extended binary tree, denoted by $T_1 \cdot T_2$, consisting of a root r together with edges connecting the root to each of the roots of the left subtree T_1 and the right subtree T_2 when these trees are nonempty.

Figure 3 shows how extended binary trees are built up by applying the recursive step from one to three times.

We now show how to define the set of full binary trees. Note that the difference between this recursive definition and that of extended binary trees lies entirely in the basis step.

Basis step ϕ

Step 1

Step 2

Step 3

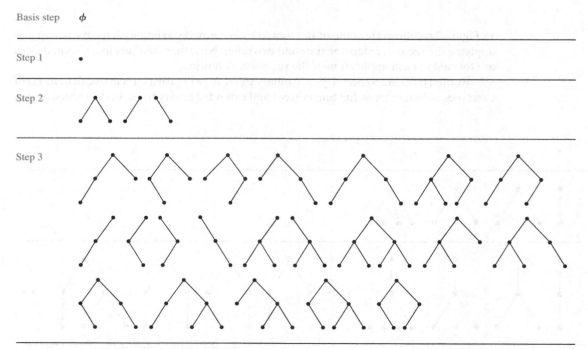

FIGURE 3   Building Up Extended Binary Trees.

Basis step

Step 1

Step 2

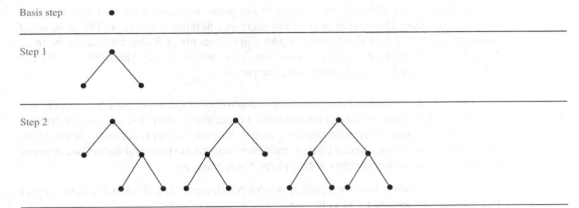

FIGURE 4   Building Up Full Binary Trees.

DEFINITION 6	The set of full binary trees can be defined recursively by these steps: *BASIS STEP:* There is a full binary tree consisting only of a single vertex r. *RECURSIVE STEP:* If T_1 and T_2 are full binary trees, there is a full binary tree, denoted by $T_1 \cdot T_2$, consisting of a root r together with edges connecting the root to each of the roots of the left subtree T_1 and the right subtree T_2.

Figure 4 shows how full binary trees are built up by applying the recursive step one and two times.

STRUCTURAL INDUCTION

To prove results about recursively defined sets we generally use some form of mathematical induction. Example 12 illustrates the connection between recursively defined sets and mathematical induction.

EXAMPLE 12   Show that the set S defined in Example 7 is the set of all positive integers that are multiples of 3.

Solution: Let A be the set of all positive integers divisible by 3. To prove that $A = S$, we must show that A is a subset of S and that S is a subset of A. To prove that A is a subset of S, we must show that every positive integer divisible by 3 is in S. We will use mathematical induction to prove this.

Let $P(n)$ be the statement that $3n$ belongs to S. The basis step holds since by the first part of the recursive definition of S, $3 \cdot 1 = 3$ is in S. To establish the inductive step, assume that $P(k)$ is true, namely, that $3k$ is in S. Since $3k$ is in S and since 3 is in S, it follows from the second part of the recursive definition of S that $3k + 3 = 3(k + 1)$ is also in S.

To prove that S is a subset of A, we use the recursive definition of S. First, the basis step of the definition specifies that 3 is in S. Since $3 = 3 \cdot 1$, all elements specified to be in S in this step are divisible by 3. To finish the proof, we must show that all integers in S generated using the second part of the recursive definition are in A. This consists of showing that $x + y$ is in A whenever x and y are elements of S also assumed to be in A. Now if x and y are both in A, it follows that $3 \mid x$ and $3 \mid y$. By Theorem 1 of Section 2.4, it follows that $3 \mid x + y$, completing the proof.   ◄

In Example 12 we used mathematical induction over the set of positive integers and a recursive definition to prove a result about a recursively defined set. However, instead of using mathematical induction directly to prove results about recursively defined sets, we can use a more convenient form of induction known as **structural induction.** A proof by structural induction consists of two parts. These parts are

BASIS STEP: Show that the result holds for all elements specified in the basis step of the recursive definition to be in the set.

RECURSIVE STEP: Show that if the statement is true for each of the elements used to construct new elements in the recursive step of the definition, the result holds for these new elements.

The validity of structural induction follows from the principle of mathematical induction for the nonnegative integers. To see this, let $P(n)$ state that the claim is true for all elements of the set that are generated by n or fewer applications of the rules in the recursive step of a recursive definition. We will have established that the principle of mathematical induction implies the principle of structural induction if we can show that $P(n)$ is true whenever n is a positive integer. In the basis step of a proof by structural induction we show that $P(0)$ is true. That is, we show that the result is true of all elements specified to be in the set in the basis step of the definition. A consequence of the inductive step is that if we assume $P(k)$ is true, it follows that $P(k + 1)$ is true. When we have completed a proof using structural induction, we have shown that $P(0)$ is true and that $P(k)$ implies $P(k + 1)$. By mathematical induction it follows that $P(n)$ is true for all nonnegative integers n. This also shows that the result is true for all elements generated by the recursive definition, and shows that structural induction is a valid proof technique.

EXAMPLES OF PROOFS USING STRUCTURAL INDUCTION To use structural induction to prove a result about the set of well-formed expressions defined in Example 10, we need to complete this basis step and this recursive step.

BASIS STEP: Show that the result is true for $\mathbf{T}, \mathbf{F}$, and p whenever p is a propositional variable.

RECURSIVE STEP: Show that if the result is true for the compound propositions p and q, it is also true for $(\neg p), (p \vee q), (p \wedge q), (p \rightarrow q)$, and $(p \leftrightarrow q)$.

Example 13 illustrates how we can prove results about well-formed formulae using structural induction.

EXAMPLE 13   Show that every well-formed formula for compound propositions, as defined in Example 10, contains an equal number of left and right parentheses.   ◄

Proof:

BASIS STEP: Each of the formulae $\mathbf{T}, \mathbf{F}$, and p contains no parentheses, so clearly they contain an equal number of left and right parentheses.

RECURSIVE STEP: Assume p and q are well-formed formulae each containing an equal number of left and right parentheses. That is, if l_p and l_q are the number of left parentheses in p and q, respectively, and r_p and r_q are the number of right parentheses in p and q, respectively, then $l_p = r_p$ and $l_q = r_q$. To complete the inductive step, we need to show that each of $(\neg p)$, $(p \vee q)$, $(p \wedge q)$, $(p \rightarrow q)$, and $(p \leftrightarrow q)$ also contains an equal number of left and right parentheses. The number of left parentheses in the first of these compound propositions equals $l_p + 1$ and in each of the other compound propositions equals $l_p + l_q + 1$. Similarly, the number of right parentheses in the first of these compound propositions equals $r_p + 1$ and in each of the other compound propositions equals $r_p + r_q + 1$. Since $l_p = r_p$ and $l_q = r_q$, it follows that each of these compound expressions contains the same number of left and right parentheses. This completes the inductive proof.   ◁

Suppose that $P(w)$ is a propositional function over the set of strings $w \in \Sigma^*$. To use structural induction to prove that $P(w)$ holds for all strings $w \in \Sigma^*$, we need to complete both a basis step and a recursive step. These steps are:

BASIS STEP: Show that $P(\lambda)$ is true.

RECURSIVE STEP: Assume that $P(w)$ is true, where $w \in \Sigma^*$. Show that if $x \in \Sigma$, then $P(wx)$ must also be true.

Example 14 illustrates how structural induction can be used in proofs about strings.

EXAMPLE 14   Use structural induction to prove that $l(xy) = l(x) + l(y)$, where x and y belong to Σ^*, the set of strings over the alphabet Σ.

Solution: We will base our proof on the recursive definition of the set Σ^* given in Definition 2 and the definition of the length of a string in Example 9. Let $P(y)$ be the statement that $l(xy) = l(x) + l(y)$ whenever x belongs to Σ^*.

BASIS STEP: To complete the basis step, we must show that $P(\lambda)$ is true. That is, we must show that $l(x\lambda) = l(x) + l(\lambda)$ for all $x \in \Sigma^*$. Since $l(x\lambda) = l(x) = l(x) + 0 = l(x) + l(\lambda)$ for every string x, it follows that $P(\lambda)$ is true.

RECURSIVE STEP: To complete the inductive step, we assume that $P(y)$ is true and show that this implies that $P(ya)$ is true whenever $a \in \Sigma$. What we need to show is that $l(xya) = l(x) + l(ya)$ for every $a \in \Sigma$. To show this, note that by the recursive definition of $l(w)$ (given in Example 9), we have $l(xya) = l(xy) + 1$ and $l(ya) = l(y) + 1$. And, by the inductive hypothesis, $l(xy) = l(x) + l(y)$. We conclude that $l(xya) = l(x) + l(y) + 1 = l(x) + l(ya)$.   ◀

We can prove results about trees or special classes of trees using structural induction. For example, to prove a result about full binary trees using structural induction we need to complete this basis step and this recursive step.

BASIS STEP: Show that the result is true for the tree consisting of a single vertex.

RECURSIVE STEP: Show that if the result is true for the trees T_1 and T_2, then it is true for tree $T_1 \cdot T_2$ consisting of a root r, which has T_1 as its left subtree and T_2 as its right subtree.

Before we provide an example showing how structural induction can be used to prove a result about full binary trees, we need some definitions. We will recursively define the height $h(T)$ and the number of vertices $n(T)$ of a full binary tree T. We begin by defining the height of a full binary tree.

DEFINITION 7

We define the height $h(T)$ of a full binary tree T recursively.

BASIS STEP: The height of the full binary tree T consisting of only a root r is $h(T) = 0$.

RECURSIVE STEP: If T_1 and T_2 are full binary trees, then the full binary tree $T = T_1 \cdot T_2$ has height $h(T) = 1 + \max(h(T_1), h(T_2))$.

If we let $n(T)$ denote the number of vertices in a full binary tree, we observe that $n(T)$ satisfies the following recursive formula:

BASIS STEP: The number of vertices $n(T)$ of the full binary tree T consisting of only a root r is $n(T) = 1$.

RECURSIVE STEP: If T_1 and T_2 are full binary trees, then the number of vertices of the full binary tree $T = T_1 \cdot T_2$ is $n(T) = 1 + n(T_1) + n(T_2)$.

We now show how structural induction can be used to prove a result about full binary trees.

THEOREM 2

If T is a full binary tree T, then $n(T) \leq 2^{h(T)+1} - 1$.

Proof: We prove this inequality using structural induction.

BASIS STEP: For the full binary tree consisting of just the root r the result is true since $n(T) = 1$ and $h(T) = 0$, so that $n(T) = 1 \leq 2^{0+1} - 1 = 1$.

INDUCTIVE STEP: For the inductive hypothesis we assume that $n(T_1) \leq 2^{h(T_1)+1} - 1$ and $n(T_2) \leq 2^{h(T_2)+1} - 1$ whenever T_1 and T_2 are full binary trees. By the recursive formulae for $n(T)$ and $h(T)$ we have $n(T) = 1 + n(T_1) + n(T_2)$ and $h(T) = 1 + \max(h(T_1), h(T_2))$.

We find that

$$n(T) = 1 + n(T_1) + n(T_2) \quad \text{by the recursive formula for } n(T)$$
$$\leq 1 + (2^{h(T_1)+1} - 1) + (2^{h(T_2)+1} - 1) \quad \text{by the inductive hypothesis}$$
$$= 2 \cdot \max(2^{h(T_1)+1}, 2^{h(T_2)+1}) - 1 \quad \text{since the sum of two terms is at most 2 times the larger}$$
$$= 2 \cdot 2^{\max(h(T_1), h(T_2))+1} - 1$$
$$= 2 \cdot 2^{h(T)} - 1 \quad \text{by the recursive definition of } h(T)$$
$$= 2^{h(T)+1} - 1.$$

This completes the inductive step.   ◁

GENERALIZED INDUCTION

We can extend mathematical induction to prove results about other sets that have the well-ordering property besides the set of integers. Although we will discuss this concept in detail in Section 7.6, we provide an example here to illustrate the usefulness of such an approach.

As an example, note that we can define an ordering on $\mathbf{N} \times \mathbf{N}$, the ordered pairs of nonnegative integers, by specifying that (x_1, y_1) is less than or equal to (x_2, y_2) if either $x_1 < x_2$, or $x_1 = x_2$ and $y_1 < y_2$; this is called the **lexicographic ordering.** The set $\mathbf{N} \times \mathbf{N}$ with this ordering has the property that every subset of $\mathbf{N} \times \mathbf{N}$ has a least element (see Supplementary Exercise 47 in Chapter 7). This implies that we can recursively define the terms $a_{m,n}$, with $m \in \mathbf{N}$ and $n \in \mathbf{N}$, and prove results about them using a variant of mathematical induction, as illustrated in Example 15.

EXAMPLE 15   Suppose that $a_{m,n}$ is defined recursively for $(m, n) \in \mathbf{N} \times \mathbf{N}$ by $a_{0,0} = 0$ and

$$a_{m,n} = \begin{cases} a_{m-1,n} + 1 & \text{if } n = 0 \text{ and } m > 0 \\ a_{m,n-1} + n & \text{if } n > 0. \end{cases}$$

Show that $a_{m,n} = m + n(n + 1)/2$ for all $(m, n) \in \mathbf{N} \times \mathbf{N}$, that is, for all pairs of nonnegative integers.

Solution: We can prove that $a_{m,n} = m + n(n+1)/2$ using a generalized version of mathematical induction. The basis step requires that we show that this formula is valid when $(m, n) = (0, 0)$. The induction step requires that we show that if the formula holds for all pairs smaller than (m, n) in the lexicographic ordering of $\mathbf{N} \times \mathbf{N}$, then it also holds for (m, n).

BASIS STEP: Let $(m, n) = (0, 0)$. Then by the basis case of the recursive definition of $a_{m,n}$ we have $a_{0,0} = 0$. Furthermore, when $m = n = 0$, $m + n(n + 1)/2 = 0 + (0 \cdot 1)/2 = 0$. This completes the basis step.

INDUCTIVE STEP: Suppose that $a_{m',n'} = m' + n'(n' + 1)/2$ whenever (m', n') is less than (m, n) in the lexicographic ordering of $\mathbf{N} \times \mathbf{N}$. By the recursive definition, if $n = 0$, then $a_{m,n} = a_{m-1,n} + 1$. Because $(m - 1, n)$ is smaller than (m, n), the induction hypothesis tells us that $a_{m-1,n} = m - 1 + n(n + 1)/2$, so that $a_{m,n} = m - 1 + n(n + 1)/2 + 1 = m + n(n + 1)/2$, giving us the desired equality. Now suppose that $n > 0$, so $a_{m,n} = a_{m,n-1} + n$. Since $(m, n - 1)$ is smaller than (m, n), the induction hypothesis tells us that $a_{m,n-1} = m + (n - 1)n/2$, so $a_{m,n} = m + (n - 1)n/2 + n = m + (n^2 - n + 2n)/2 = m + n(n + 1)/2$. This finishes the inductive step.   ◀

As mentioned, we will justify this proof technique in Section 7.6.

Exercises

1. Find $f(1)$, $f(2)$, $f(3)$, and $f(4)$ if $f(n)$ is defined recursively by $f(0) = 1$ and for $n = 0, 1, 2, \ldots$

  a) $f(n + 1) = f(n) + 2$.
  b) $f(n + 1) = 3f(n)$.
  c) $f(n + 1) = 2^{f(n)}$.
  d) $f(n + 1) = f(n)^2 + f(n) + 1$.

2. Find $f(1)$, $f(2)$, $f(3)$, $f(4)$, and $f(5)$ if $f(n)$ is defined recursively by $f(0) = 3$ and for $n = 0, 1, 2, \ldots$

  a) $f(n + 1) = -2f(n)$.
  b) $f(n + 1) = 3f(n) + 7$.
  c) $f(n + 1) = f(n)^2 - 2f(n) - 2$.
  d) $f(n + 1) = 3^{f(n)/3}$.

3. Find $f(2)$, $f(3)$, $f(4)$, and $f(5)$ if f is defined recursively by $f(0) = -1$, $f(1) = 2$ and for $n = 1, 2, \ldots$

  a) $f(n + 1) = f(n) + 3f(n - 1)$.
  b) $f(n + 1) = f(n)^2 f(n - 1)$.

c) $f(n+1) = 3f(n)^2 - 4f(n-1)^2$.
d) $f(n+1) = f(n-1)/f(n)$.

4. Find $f(2)$, $f(3)$, $f(4)$, and $f(5)$ if f is defined recursively by $f(0) = f(1) = 1$ and for $n = 1, 2, \ldots$
   a) $f(n+1) = f(n) - f(n-1)$.
   b) $f(n+1) = f(n)f(n-1)$.
   c) $f(n+1) = f(n)^2 + f(n-1)^3$.
   d) $f(n+1) = f(n)/f(n-1)$.

5. Determine whether each of these proposed definitions is a valid recursive definition of a function f from the set of nonnegative integers to the set of integers. If f is well defined, find a formula for $f(n)$ when n is a nonnegative integer and prove that your formula is valid.
   a) $f(0) = 0$, $f(n) = 2f(n-2)$ for $n \geq 1$
   b) $f(0) = 1$, $f(n) = f(n-1) - 1$ for $n \geq 1$
   c) $f(0) = 2$, $f(1) = 3$, $f(n) = f(n-1) - 1$ for $n \geq 2$
   d) $f(0) = 1$, $f(1) = 2$, $f(n) = 2f(n-2)$ for $n \geq 2$
   e) $f(0) = 1$, $f(n) = 3f(n-1)$ if n is odd and $n \geq 1$ and $f(n) = 9f(n-2)$ if n is even and $n \geq 2$

6. Determine whether each of these proposed definitions is a valid recursive definition of a function f from the set of nonnegative integers to the set of integers. If f is well defined, find a formula for $f(n)$ when n is a nonnegative integer and prove that your formula is valid.
   a) $f(0) = 1$, $f(n) = -f(n-1)$ for $n \geq 1$
   b) $f(0) = 1$, $f(1) = 0$, $f(2) = 2$, $f(n) = 2f(n-3)$ for $n \geq 3$
   c) $f(0) = 0$, $f(1) = 1$, $f(n) = 2f(n+1)$ for $n \geq 2$
   d) $f(0) = 0$, $f(1) = 1$, $f(n) = 2f(n-1)$ for $n \geq 1$
   e) $f(0) = 2$, $f(n) = f(n-1)$ if n is odd and $n \geq 1$ and $f(n) = 2f(n-2)$ if $n \geq 2$

7. Give a recursive definition of the sequence $\{a_n\}$, $n = 1, 2, 3, \ldots$ if
   a) $a_n = 6n$.   **b)** $a_n = 2n + 1$.
   c) $a_n = 10^n$.   **d)** $a_n = 5$.

8. Give a recursive definition of the sequence $\{a_n\}$, $n = 1, 2, 3, \ldots$ if
   a) $a_n = 4n - 2$.   **b)** $a_n = 1 + (-1)^n$.
   c) $a_n = n(n+1)$.   **d)** $a_n = n^2$.

9. Let F be the function such that $F(n)$ is the sum of the first n positive integers. Give a recursive definition of $F(n)$.

10. Give a recursive definition of $S_m(n)$, the sum of the integer m and the nonnegative integer n.

11. Give a recursive definition of $P_m(n)$, the product of the integer m and the nonnegative integer n.

In Exercises 12–19 f_n is the nth Fibonacci number.

12. Prove that $f_1^2 + f_2^2 + \cdots + f_n^2 = f_n f_{n+1}$ whenever n is a positive integer.

13. Prove that $f_1 + f_3 + \cdots + f_{2n-1} = f_{2n}$ whenever n is a positive integer.

*14. Show that $f_{n+1}f_{n-1} - f_n^2 = (-1)^n$ whenever n is a positive integer.

*15. Show that $f_0 f_1 + f_1 f_2 + \cdots + f_{2n-1}f_{2n} = f_{2n}^2$ whenever n is a positive integer.

*16. Show that $f_0 - f_1 + f_2 - \cdots - f_{2n-1} + f_{2n} = f_{2n-1} - 1$ whenever n is a positive integer.

17. Determine the number of divisions used by the Euclidean algorithm to find the greatest common divisor of the Fibonacci numbers f_n and f_{n+1} where n is a nonnegative integer. Verify your answer using mathematical induction.

18. Let
$$\mathbf{A} = \begin{bmatrix} 1 & 1 \\ 1 & 0 \end{bmatrix}$$
Show that
$$\mathbf{A}^n = \begin{bmatrix} f_{n+1} & f_n \\ f_n & f_{n-1} \end{bmatrix}$$
whenever n is a positive integer.

19. By taking determinants of both sides of the equation in Exercise 18, prove the identity given in Exercise 14. (This exercise depends on the notion of the determinant of a 2×2 matrix.)

*20. Give a recursive definition of the functions max and min so that $\max(a_1, a_2, \ldots, a_n)$ and $\min(a_1, a_2, \ldots, a_n)$ are the maximum and minimum of the n numbers $a_1, a_2, \ldots, a_n$, respectively.

*21. Let $a_1, a_2, \ldots, a_n$, and $b_1, b_2, \ldots, b_n$ be real numbers. Use the recursive definitions that you gave in Exercise 20 to prove these.
   a) $\max(-a_1, -a_2, \ldots, -a_n) = -\min(a_1, a_2, \ldots, a_n)$
   b) $\max(a_1 + b_1, a_2 + b_2, \ldots, a_n + b_n)$
        $\leq \max(a_1, a_2, \ldots, a_n) + \max(b_1, b_2, \ldots, b_n)$
   c) $\min(a_1 + b_1, a_2 + b_2, \ldots, a_n + b_n)$
        $\geq \min(a_1, a_2, \ldots, a_n) + \min(b_1, b_2, \ldots, b_n)$

22. Show that the set S defined by $1 \in S$ and $s + t \in S$ whenever $s \in S$ and $t \in S$ is the set of positive integers.

23. Give a recursive definition of the set of positive integers that are multiples of 5.

24. Give a recursive definition of
   a) the set of odd positive integers.
   b) the set of positive integer powers of 3.
   c) the set of polynomials with integer coefficients.

25. Give a recursive definition of
   a) the set of even integers.
   b) the set of positive integers congruent to 2 modulo 3.
   c) the set of positive integers not divisible by 5.

26. Let S be the subset of the set of ordered pairs of integers defined recursively by

Basis step: $(0, 0) \in S$.

Recursive step: If $(a, b) \in S$, then $(a + 2, b + 3) \in S$ and $(a + 3, b + 2) \in S$.

a) List the elements of S produced by the first five applications of the recursive definition.

b) Use strong induction on the number of applications of the recursive step of the definition to show that $5 \mid a + b$ when $(a, b) \in S$.

c) Use structural induction to show that $5 \mid a + b$ when $(a, b) \in S$.

27. Let S be the subset of the set of ordered pairs of integers defined recursively by

Basis step: $(0, 0) \in S$.

Recursive step: If $(a, b) \in S$, then $(a, b + 1) \in S$, $(a + 1, b + 1) \in S$, and $(a + 2, b + 1) \in S$.

a) List the elements of S produced by the first four applications of the recursive definition.

b) Use strong induction on the number of applications of the recursive step of the definition to show that $a \le 2b$ whenever $(a, b) \in S$.

c) Use structural induction to show that $a \le 2b$ whenever $(a, b) \in S$.

28. Give a recursive definition of each of these sets of ordered pairs of positive integers. (*Hint:* Plot the points in the set in the plane and look for lines containing points in the set.)

a) $S = \{(a, b) \mid a \in \mathbf{Z}^+, b \in \mathbf{Z}^+, \text{ and } a + b \text{ is odd}\}$

b) $S = \{(a, b) \mid a \in \mathbf{Z}^+, b \in \mathbf{Z}^+, \text{ and } a \mid b\}$

c) $S = \{(a, b) \mid a \in \mathbf{Z}^+, b \in \mathbf{Z}^+, \text{ and } 3 \mid a + b\}$

29. Give a recursive definition of each of these sets of ordered pairs of positive integers. Use structural induction to prove that the recursive definition you found is correct. (*Hint:* To find a recursive definition plot the points in the set in the plane and look for patterns.)

a) $S = \{(a, b) \mid a \in \mathbf{Z}^+, b \in \mathbf{Z}^+, \text{ and } a + b \text{ is even}\}$

b) $S = \{(a, b) \mid a \in \mathbf{Z}^+, b \in \mathbf{Z}^+, \text{ and } a \text{ or } b \text{ is odd}\}$

c) $S = \{(a, b) \mid a \in \mathbf{Z}^+, b \in \mathbf{Z}^+, \text{ and } a + b \text{ is odd and } 3 \mid b\}$

30. Prove that in a bit string, the string 01 occurs at most one more time than the string 10.

31. Define well-formed formulae of sets, variables representing sets, and operators from $\{^-, \cup, \cap, -\}$.

32. a) Give a recursive definition of the function *ones(s)*, which counts the number of ones in a bit string s.

b) Use structural induction to prove that *ones(st)* = *ones(s)* + *ones(t)*.

33. a) Give a recursive definition of the function $m(s)$, which equals the smallest digit in a nonempty string of decimal digits.

b) Use structural induction to prove that $m(st)$ = $\min(m(s), m(t))$.

The **reversal** of a string is the string consisting of the symbols of the string in reverse order. The reversal of the string w is denoted by w^R.

34. Find the reversal of the following bit strings.

a) 0101   b) 1 1011   c) 1000 1001 0111

35. Give a recursive definition of the reversal of a string. (*Hint:* First define the reversal of the empty string. Then write a string w of length $n + 1$ as xy, where x is a string of length n, and express the reversal of w in terms of x^R and y.)

*36. Use structural induction to prove that $(w_1 w_2)^R = w_2^R w_1^R$.

37. Give a recursive definition of w^i where w is a string and i is a nonnegative integer. (Here w^i represents the concatenation of i copies of the string w.)

*38. Give a recursive definition of the set of bit strings that are palindromes.

39. When does a string belong to the set A of bit strings defined recursively by

$\lambda \in A$
$0x1 \in A$ if $x \in A$,

where λ is the empty string?

*40. Recursively define the set of bit strings that have more zeros than ones.

41. Use Exercise 37 and mathematical induction to show that $l(w^i) = i \cdot l(w)$, where w is a string and i is a nonnegative integer.

*42. Show that $(w^R)^i = (w^i)^R$ whenever w is a string and i is a nonnegative integer; that is, show that the ith power of the reversal of a string is the reversal of the ith power of the string.

43. Use structural induction to show that $n(T) \ge 2h(T) + 1$, where T is a full binary tree, $n(T)$ equals the number of vertices of T, and $h(T)$ is the height of T.

The set of leaves and the set of internal vertices of a full binary tree can be defined recursively.

Basis step: The root r is a leaf of the full binary tree with exactly one vertex r. This tree has no internal vertices.

Recursive step: The set of leaves of the tree $T = T_1 \cdot T_2$ is the union of the set of leaves of T_1 and the set of leaves of T_2. The internal vertices of T are the root r of T and the union of the set of internal vertices of T_1 and the set of internal vertices of T_2.

44. Use structural induction to show that $l(T)$, the number of leaves of a full binary tree T, is 1 more than $i(T)$, the number of internal vertices of T.

45. Use generalized induction as was done in Example 15 to show that if $a_{m,n}$ is defined recursively by $a_{0,0} = 0$ and

$$a_{m,n} = \begin{cases} a_{m-1,n} + 1 & \text{if } n = 0 \text{ and } m > 0 \\ a_{m,n-1} + 1 & \text{if } n > 0, \end{cases}$$

then $a_{m,n} = m + n$ for all $(m, n) \in \mathbf{N} \times \mathbf{N}$.

46. Use generalized induction as was done in Example 15 to show that if $a_{m,n}$ is defined recursively by $a_{1,1} = 5$ and

$$a_{m,n} = \begin{cases} a_{m-1,n} + 2 & \text{if } n = 1 \text{ and } m > 1 \\ a_{m,n-1} + 2 & \text{if } n > 1, \end{cases}$$

then $a_{m,n} = 2(m+n) + 1$ for all $(m, n) \in \mathbf{Z}^+ \times \mathbf{Z}^+$.

*47. A **partition** of a positive integer n is a way to write n as a sum of positive integers. For instance, $7 = 3 + 2 + 1 + 1$ is a partition of 7. Let P_m equal the number of different partitions of m, where the order of terms in the sum does not matter, and let $P_{m,n}$ be the number of different ways to express m as the sum of positive integers not exceeding n.

a) Show that $P_{m,m} = P_m$.

b) Show that the following recursive definition for $P_{m,n}$ is correct:

$$P_{m,n} = \begin{cases} 1 & \text{if } m = 1 \\ 1 & \text{if } n = 1 \\ P_{m,m} & \text{if } m < n \\ 1 + P_{m,m-1} & \text{if } m = n > 1 \\ P_{m,n-1} + P_{m-n,n} & \text{if } m > n > 1. \end{cases}$$

c) Find the number of partitions of 5 and of 6 using this recursive definition.

Consider an inductive definition of a version of **Ackermann's function.** This function was named after Wilhelm Ackermann, a German mathematician who was a student of the great mathematician David Hilbert. Ackermann's function plays an important role in the theory of recursive functions and in the study of the complexity of certain algorithms involving set unions. (There are several different variants of this function. All are called Ackermann's function and have similar properties even though their values do not always agree.)

$$A(m, n) = \begin{cases} 2n & \text{if } m = 0 \\ 0 & \text{if } m \geq 1 \text{ and } n = 0 \\ 2 & \text{if } m \geq 1 \text{ and } n = 1 \\ A(m-1, A(m, n-1)) & \\ & \text{if } m \geq 1 \text{ and } n \geq 2 \end{cases}$$

Exercises 48–55 involve this version of Ackermann's function.

48. Find these values of Ackermann's function.

a) $A(1, 0)$ **b)** $A(0, 1)$
c) $A(1, 1)$ **d)** $A(2, 2)$

49. Show that $A(m, 2) = 4$ whenever $m \geq 1$.
50. Show that $A(1, n) = 2^n$ whenever $n \geq 1$.
51. Find these values of Ackermann's function.

a) $A(2, 3)$ ***b)** $A(3, 3)$

*52. Find $A(3, 4)$.
**53. Prove that $A(m, n+1) > A(m, n)$ whenever m and n are nonnegative integers.
*54. Prove that $A(m+1, n) \geq A(m, n)$ whenever m and n are nonnegative integers.

55. Prove that $A(i, j) \geq j$ whenever i and j are nonnegative integers.
56. Use mathematical induction to prove that a function F defined by specifying $F(0)$ and a rule for obtaining $F(n + 1)$ from $F(n)$ is well defined.
57. Use strong induction to prove that a function F defined by specifying $F(0)$ and a rule for obtaining $F(n+1)$ from the values $F(k)$ for $k = 0, 1, 2, \ldots, n$ is well defined.
58. Show that each of these proposed recursive definitions of a function on the set of positive integers does not produce a well-defined function.

a) $F(n) = 1 + F(\lfloor n/2 \rfloor)$ for $n \geq 1$ and $F(1) = 1$.
b) $F(n) = 1 + F(n - 3)$ for $n \geq 2$, $F(1) = 2$, and $F(2) = 3$.
c) $F(n) = 1 + F(n/2)$ for $n \geq 2$, $F(1) = 1$, and $F(2) = 2$.
d) $F(n) = 1 + F(n/2)$ if n is even and $n \geq 2$, $F(n) = 1 - F(n - 1)$ if n is odd, and $F(1) = 1$.
e) $F(n) = 1 + F(n/2)$ if n is even and $n \geq 2$, $F(n) = F(3n - 1)$ if n is odd and $n \geq 3$, and $F(1) = 1$.

59. Show that each of these proposed recursive definitions of a function on the set of positive integers does not produce a well-defined function.

a) $F(n) = 1 + F(\lfloor (n+1)/2 \rfloor)$ for $n \geq 1$ and $F(1) = 1$.
b) $F(n) = 1 + F(n - 2)$ for $n \geq 2$ and $F(1) = 0$.
c) $F(n) = 1 + F(n/3)$ for $n \geq 3$, $F(1) = 1$, $F(2) = 2$, and $F(3) = 3$.
d) $F(n) = 1 + F(n/2)$ if n is even and $n \geq 2$, $F(n) = 1 + F(n - 2)$ if n is odd, and $F(1) = 1$.
e) $F(n) = 1 + F(F(n - 1))$ if $n \geq 2$ and $F(1) = 2$.

Exercises 60–62 deal with iterations of the logarithm function. Let $\log n$ denote the logarithm of n to the base 2, as usual. The function $\log^{(k)} n$ is defined recursively by

$$\log^{(k)} n = \begin{cases} n & \text{if } k = 0 \\ \log(\log^{(k-1)} n) & \text{if } \log^{(k-1)} n \text{ is defined} \\ & \text{and positive} \\ \text{undefined} & \text{otherwise.} \end{cases}$$

The **iterated logarithm** is the function $\log^* n$ whose value at n is the smallest nonnegative integer k such that $\log^{(k)} n \leq 1$.

60. Find each of these values:

a) $\log^{(2)} 16$
b) $\log^{(3)} 256$
c) $\log^{(3)} 2^{65536}$
d) $\log^{(4)} 2^{2^{65536}}$

61. Find the value of $\log^* n$ for each of these values of n:

a) 2   **b)** 4   **c)** 8   **d)** 16
e) 256   **f)** 65536   **g)** 2^{2048}

62. Find the largest integer n such that $\log^* n = 5$. Determine the number of decimal digits in this number.

Exercises 63–65 deal with values of iterated functions. Suppose that $f(n)$ is a function from the set of real numbers, or positive real numbers, or some other set of real numbers, to the set of real numbers such that $f(n)$ is monotonically increasing [that is, $f(n) < f(m)$ when $n < m$) and $f(n) < n$ for all n in the domain of f.] The function $f^{(k)}(n)$ is defined recursively by

$$f^{(k)}(n) = \begin{cases} n & \text{if } k = 0 \\ f(f^{(k-1)}(n)) & \text{if } k > 0. \end{cases}$$

Furthermore, let c be a positive real number. The **iterated** function f_c^* is the number of iterations of f required to reduce its argument to c or less, so that $f_c^*(n)$ is the smallest nonnegative integer k such that $f^k(n) \leq c$.

63. Let $f(n) = n - a$, where a is a positive integer. Find a formula for $f^{(k)}(n)$. What is the value of $f_0^*(n)$ when n is a positive integer?

64. Let $f(n) = n/2$. Find a formula for $f^{(k)}(n)$. What is the value of $f_1^*(n)$ when n is a positive integer?

65. Let $f(n) = \sqrt{n}$. Find a formula for $f^{(k)}(n)$. What is the value of $f_2^*(n)$ when n is a positive integer?

3.5 Recursive Algorithms

INTRODUCTION

Sometimes we can reduce the solution to a problem with a particular set of input to the solution of the same problem with smaller input values. For instance, the problem of finding the greatest common divisor of two positive integers a and b where $b > a$ can be reduced to finding the greatest common divisor of a pair of smaller integers, namely, $b \bmod a$ and a, since $\gcd(b \bmod a, a) = \gcd(a, b)$. When such a reduction can be done, the solution to the original problem can be found with a sequence of reductions, until the problem has been reduced to some initial case for which the solution is known. For instance, for finding the greatest common divisor, the reduction continues until the smaller of the two numbers is zero, since $\gcd(a, 0) = a$ when $a > 0$.

We will see that algorithms that successively reduce a problem to the same problem with smaller input are used to solve a wide variety of problems.

DEFINITION 1   An algorithm is called *recursive* if it solves a problem by reducing it to an instance of the same problem with smaller input.

Links

We will describe several different recursive algorithms in Examples 1, 2, 4, 5, and 6. The first example shows how a recursive algorithm can be constructed to evaluate a function from its recursive definition.

EXAMPLE 1   Give a recursive algorithm for computing a^n where a is a nonzero real number and n is a nonnegative integer.

Solution: We can base a recursive algorithm on the recursive definition of a^n. This definition states that $a^{n+1} = a \cdot a^n$ for $n > 0$ and the initial condition $a^0 = 1$. To find a^n, successively use the recursive condition to reduce the exponent until it becomes zero. We give this procedure in Algorithm 1. ◄

ALGORITHM 1 **A Recursive Algorithm for Computing a^n.**

---

procedure *power*(a: nonzero real number, n: nonnegative integer)
if $n = 0$ **then** *power*(a, n) := 1
else *power*(a, n) := $a \cdot$ *power*($a, n - 1$)

EXAMPLE 2　Devise a recursive algorithm for computing b^n **mod** m, where b, n, and m are integers with $m \geq 2, n \geq 0$, and $1 \leq b < m$.

Solution: We can base a recursive algorithm on the fact that b^n **mod** $m = (b \cdot (b^{n-1}$ **mod** $m))$ **mod** m, which follows by Exercise 23 in Section 3.1, and the initial condition b^0 **mod** $m = 1$. We leave this as Exercise 6 for the reader at the end of the section.

However, we can devise a much more efficient recursive algorithm, which we describe in pseudocode as Algorithm 2.　◀

ALGORITHM 2 **Recursive Modular Exponentiation.**

---

procedure *mpower*(b, n, m: integers with $m \geq 2, n \geq 0; 1 \leq b < m$)
if $n = 0$ **then**
　　mpower(b, n, m) = 1
else if n is even **then**
　　mpower(b, n, m) = *mpower*($b, n/2, m$)^2 **mod** m
else
　　mpower(b, n, m) = (*mpower*($b, \lfloor n/2 \rfloor, m$)^2 **mod** $m \cdot b$ **mod** m) **mod** m
{*mpower*(b, n, m) = b^n **mod** m}

Strong induction can be used to prove that a recursive algorithm is correct, that is, that it produces the desired output for all possible input values. We illustrate how this is done in Example 3 by proving that Algorithm 2 is correct.

EXAMPLE 3　Prove that Algorithm 2, which computes modular powers, is correct.

Extra Examples

Solution: We use strong induction on the exponent n.

BASIS STEP: When $n = 0$, *mpower*(b, n, m) = 1. Because b^0 **mod** $m = 1$ whenever b is an integer, m is an integer with $m \geq 2$, and $1 \leq b < m$, the basis step is complete.

INDUCTIVE STEP: The inductive hypothesis is that *mpower*(b, j, m) = b^j **mod** m for all integers $0 \leq j < k$ whenever b is a positive integer, m is an integer with $m \geq 2$, and $b < m$.

When k is even, we have *mpower*(b, k, m) = *mpower*($b, k/2, m$)^2 **mod** m = $(b^{k/2}$ **mod** $m)^2$ **mod** $m = b^k$ **mod** m, where we have used the inductive hypothesis to replace *mpower*($b, k/2, m$) by $b^{k/2}$ **mod** m.

When k is odd, we have *mpower*(b, k, m) = $((mpower(b, \lfloor k/2 \rfloor, m))^2$ **mod** $m \cdot b$ **mod** m) **mod** m = $((b^{\lfloor k/2 \rfloor}$ **mod** $m)^2$ **mod** $m \cdot b$ **mod** m) **mod** $m = b^{2\lfloor k/2 \rfloor + 1}$ **mod** m = b^k **mod** m, using Exercise 23 in Section 3.1, because $2\lfloor k/2 \rfloor + 1 = 2(k - 1)/2 + 1 = k$

when k is odd. Here we have used the inductive hypothesis to replace $mpower(b, \lfloor k/2 \rfloor, m)$ by $b^{\lfloor k/2 \rfloor} \bmod m$. This completes the inductive step and shows that Algorithm 2 is correct. ◀

Next we give a recursive algorithm for finding greatest common divisors.

EXAMPLE 4   Give a recursive algorithm for computing the greatest common divisor of two nonnegative integers a and b with $a < b$.

Solution: We can base a recursive algorithm on the reduction $\gcd(a, b) = \gcd(b \bmod a, a)$ and the condition $\gcd(0, b) = b$ when $b > 0$. This produces the procedure in Algorithm 3. ◀

ALGORITHM 3 A Recursive Algorithm for Computing $gcd(a, b)$.

procedure $gcd(a, b$: nonnegative integers with $a < b$)
if $a = 0$ **then** $gcd(a, b) := b$
else $gcd(a, b) := gcd(b \bmod a, a)$

We will now give recursive versions of searching algorithms which were introduced in Section 2.1.

EXAMPLE 5   Express the linear search algorithm as a recursive procedure.

Solution: To *search* for x in the search sequence $a_1, a_2, \ldots, a_n$, at the ith step of the algorithm x and a_i are compared. If x equals a_i then i is the location of x. Otherwise, the search for x is reduced to a search in a sequence with one fewer element, namely, the sequence $a_{i+1}, \ldots, a_n$. We can now give a recursive procedure, which is displayed as pseudocode in Algorithm 4.

Let $search(i, j, x)$ be the procedure that searches for x in the sequence $a_i, a_{i+1}, \ldots, a_j$. The input to the procedure consists of the triple $(1, n, x)$. The procedure terminates at a step if the first term of the remaining sequence is x or if there is only one term of the sequence and this is not x. If x is not the first term and there are additional terms, the same procedure is carried out but with a search sequence of one fewer term, obtained by deleting the first term of the search sequence. ◀

ALGORITHM 4 A Recursive Linear Search Algorithm.

procedure $search(i, j, x)$
if $a_i = x$ **then**
    $location := i$
else if $i = j$ **then**
    $location := 0$
else
    $search(i + 1, j, x)$

EXAMPLE 6 Construct a recursive version of a binary search algorithm.

Solution: Suppose we want to locate x in the sequence $a_1, a_2, \ldots, a_n$. To perform a binary search, we begin by comparing x with the middle term, $a_{\lfloor (n+1)/2 \rfloor}$. Our algorithm will terminate if x equals this term. Otherwise, we reduce the search to a smaller search sequence, namely, the first half of the sequence if x is smaller than the middle term of the original sequence, and the second half otherwise. We have reduced the solution of the search problem to the solution of the same problem with a sequence approximately half as long. We express this recursive version of a binary search algorithm as Algorithm 5. ◀

ALGORITHM 5 A Recursive Binary Search Algorithm.

procedure *binary search*(x, i, j)
$m := \lfloor (i + j)/2 \rfloor$
if $x = a_m$ **then**
    location $:= m$
else if $(x < a_m$ and $i < m)$ **then**
    binary search$(x, i, m - 1)$
else if $(x > a_m$ and $j > m)$ **then**
    binary search$(x, m + 1, j)$
else *location* $:= 0$

RECURSION AND ITERATION

A recursive definition expresses the value of a function at a positive integer in terms of the values of the function at smaller integers. This means that we can devise a recursive algorithm to evaluate a recursively defined function at a positive integer.

EXAMPLE 7 The recursive procedure in Algorithm 6 gives the value of $n!$ when the input is a positive integer n. ◀

ALGORITHM 6 A Recursive Procedure for Factorials.

procedure *factorial*$(n$: positive integer$)$
if $n = 1$ **then**
    factorial$(n) := 1$
else
    factorial$(n) := n \cdot$ *factorial*$(n - 1)$

There is another way to evaluate the factorial function at an integer from its recursive definition. Instead of successively reducing the computation to the evaluation of the function at smaller integers, we can start with the value of the function at 1 and successively apply the recursive definition to find the values of the function at successive larger integers. Such a procedure is called **iterative.** In other words, to find $n!$ using an iterative procedure, we start with 1, the value of the factorial function at 1, and multiply successively by each positive integer less than or equal to n. This procedure is shown in Algorithm 7.

ALGORITHM 7 An Iterative Procedure for Factorials.

procedure *iterative factorial*(n: positive integer)
$x := 1$
for $i := 1$ **to** n
$\quad x := i \cdot x$
$\{x \text{ is } n!\}$

After this code has been executed, the value of the variable x is $n!$. For instance, going through the loop six times gives $6! = 1 \cdot 2 \cdot 3 \cdot 4 \cdot 5 \cdot 6 = 720$.

Often an iterative approach for the evaluation of a recursively defined sequence requires much less computation than a procedure using recursion (unless special-purpose recursive machines are used). This is illustrated by the iterative and recursive procedures for finding the nth Fibonacci number. The recursive procedure is given first.

ALGORITHM 8 A Recursive Algorithm for Fibonacci Numbers.

procedure *fibonacci*(n: nonnegative integer)
if $n = 0$ **then** *fibonacci*(0) := 0
else if $n = 1$ **then** *fibonacci*(1) := 1
else *fibonacci*(n) := *fibonacci*($n - 1$) + *fibonacci*($n - 2$)

When we use a recursive procedure to find f_n, we first express f_n as $f_{n-1} + f_{n-2}$. Then we replace both of these Fibonacci numbers by the sum of two previous Fibonacci numbers, and so on. When f_1 or f_0 arises, it is replaced by its value.

Note that at each stage of the recursion, until f_1 or f_0 is obtained, the number of Fibonacci numbers to be evaluated has doubled. For instance, when we find f_4 using this recursive algorithm, we must carry out all the computations illustrated in the tree diagram in Figure 1. This tree consists of a root labeled with f_4, and branches from the root to vertices labeled with the two Fibonacci numbers f_3 and f_2 that occur in the reduction of the computation of f_4. Each subsequent reduction produces two branches in the tree. This branching ends when f_0 and f_1 are reached. The reader can verify that this algorithm requires $f_{n+1} - 1$ additions to find f_n.

Now consider the amount of computation required to find f_n using the iterative approach in Algorithm 9.

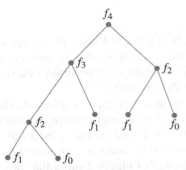

FIGURE 1   Evaluating f_4 Recursively.

ALGORITHM 9 **An Iterative Algorithm for Computing Fibonacci Numbers.**

---

procedure *iterative fibonacci*(n: nonnegative integer)
if $n = 0$ **then** $y := 0$
else
begin
    $x := 0$
    $y := 1$
    for $i := 1$ to $n - 1$
    begin
        $z := x + y$
        $x := y$
        $y := z$
    end
end
{y is the nth Fibonacci number}

This procedure initializes x as $f_0 = 0$ and y as $f_1 = 1$. When the loop is traversed, the sum of x and y is assigned to the auxiliary variable z. Then x is assigned the value of y and y is assigned the value of the auxiliary variable z. Therefore, after going through the loop the first time, it follows that x equals f_1 and y equals $f_0 + f_1 = f_2$. Furthermore, after going through the loop $n - 1$ times, x equals f_{n-1} and y equals f_n (the reader should verify this statement). Only $n - 1$ additions have been used to find f_n with this iterative approach when $n > 1$. Consequently, this algorithm requires far less computation than does the recursive algorithm.

We have shown that a recursive algorithm may require far more computation than an iterative one when a recursively defined function is evaluated. It is sometimes preferable to use a recursive procedure even if it is less efficient than the iterative procedure. In particular, this is true when the recursive approach is easily implemented and the iterative approach is not. (Also, machines designed to handle recursion may be available that eliminate the advantage of using iteration.)

Demo

Links

THE MERGE SORT

We now describe a recursive sorting algorithm called the **merge sort** algorithm. We will demonstrate how the merge sort algorithm works with an example before describing it in generality.

EXAMPLE 8   We will sort the list 8, 2, 4, 6, 9, 7, 10, 1, 5, 3 using the merge sort. A merge sort begins by splitting the list into individual elements by successively splitting lists in two. The progression of sublists for this example is represented with the balanced binary tree of height 4 shown in the upper half of Figure 2.

Sorting is done by successively merging pairs of lists. At the first stage, pairs of individual elements are merged into lists of length two in increasing order. Then successive merges of pairs of lists are performed until the entire list is put into increasing order. The succession of merged lists in increasing order is represented by the balanced binary tree of height 4 shown in the lower half of Figure 2 (note that this tree is displayed "upside down"). ◀

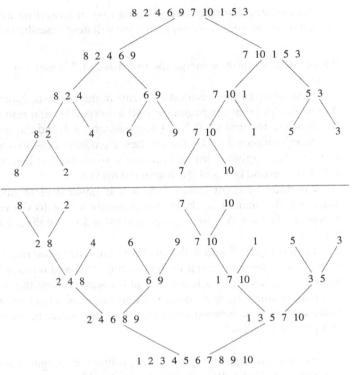

FIGURE 2   **The Merge Sort of 8, 2, 4, 6, 9, 7, 10, 1, 5, 3.**

In general, a merge sort proceeds by iteratively splitting lists into two sublists of equal length (or where one sublist has one more element than the other) until each sublist contains one element. This succession of sublists can be represented by a balanced binary tree. The procedure continues by successively merging pairs of lists, where both lists are in increasing order, into a larger list with elements in increasing order, until the original list is put into increasing order. The succession of merged lists can be represented by a balanced binary tree.

We can also describe the merge sort recursively. To do a merge sort, we split a list into two sublists of equal, or approximately equal, size, sorting each sublist using the merge sort algorithm, and then merging the two lists. The recursive version of the merge sort is given in Algorithm 10. This algorithm uses the subroutine *merge*, which is described in Algorithm 11.

ALGORITHM 10 A Recursive Merge Sort.

---

procedure *mergesort*($L = a_1, \ldots, a_n$)
if $n > 1$ **then**
    $m := \lfloor n/2 \rfloor$
    $L_1 := a_1, a_2, \ldots, a_m$
    $L_2 := a_{m+1}, a_{m+2}, \ldots, a_n$
    $L := merge(mergesort(L_1), \ mergesort(L_2))$
{L is now sorted into elements in nondecreasing order}

An efficient algorithm for merging two ordered lists into a larger ordered list is needed to implement the merge sort. We will now describe such a procedure.

EXAMPLE 9   We will describe how to merge the two lists 2, 3, 5, 6 and 1, 4. Table 1 illustrates the steps we use.

First, compare the smallest elements in the two lists, 2 and 1, respectively. Since 1 is the smaller, put it at the beginning of the merged list and remove it from the second list. At this stage, the first list is 2, 3, 5, 6, the second is 4, and the combined list is 1.

Next, compare 2 and 4, the smallest elements of the two lists. Since 2 is the smaller, add it to the combined list and remove it from the first list. At this stage the first list is 3, 5, 6, the second is 4, and the combined list is 1, 2.

Continue by comparing 3 and 4, the smallest elements of their respective lists. Since 3 is the smaller of these two elements, add it to the combined list and remove it from the first list. At this stage the first list is 5, 6, and the second is 4. The combined list is 1, 2, 3.

Then compare 5 and 4, the smallest elements in the two lists. Since 4 is the smaller of these two elements, add it to the combined list and remove it from the second list. At this stage the first list is 5, 6, the second list is empty, and the combined list is 1, 2, 3, 4.

Finally, since the second list is empty, all elements of the first list can be appended to the end of the combined list in the order they occur in the first list. This produces the ordered list 1, 2, 3, 4, 5, 6.   ◀

We will now consider the general problem of merging two ordered lists L_1 and L_2, into an ordered list L. We will describe an algorithm for solving this problem. Start with an empty list L. Compare the smallest elements of the two lists. Put the smaller of these two elements at the left end of L, and remove it from the list it was in. Next, if one of L_1 and L_2 is empty, append the other (nonempty) list to L, which completes the merging. If neither L_1 nor L_2 is empty, repeat this process. Algorithm 11 gives a pseudocode description of this procedure.

We will need estimates for the number of comparisons used to merge two ordered lists in the analysis of the merge sort. We can easily obtain such an estimate for Algorithm 11. Each time a comparison of an element from L_1 and an element from L_2 is made, an additional element is added to the merged list L. However, when either L_1 or L_2 is empty, no more comparisons are needed. Hence, Algorithm 11 is least efficient when $m + n - 2$ comparisons are carried out, where m and n are the number of elements in L_1 and L_2, respectively, leaving one element in each of L_1 and L_2. The next comparison will be the last one needed, because it will make one of these lists empty. Hence, Algorithm 11 uses no more than $m + n - 1$ comparisons. Lemma 1 summarizes this estimate.

TABLE 1 **Merging the Two Sorted Lists 2, 3, 5, 6 and 1, 4.**			
First List	*Second List*	*Merged List*	*Comparison*
2 3 5 6	1 4		1 < 2
2 3 5 6	4	1	2 < 4
3 5 6	4	1 2	3 < 4
5 6	4	1 2 3	4 < 5
5 6		1 2 3 4	
		1 2 3 4 5 6	

ALGORITHM 11 Merging Two Lists.

---

procedure *merge*(L_1, L_2: lists)
L := empty list
while L_1 and L_2 are both nonempty
begin
    remove smaller of first element of L_1 and L_2 from the list it is
        in and put it at the left end of L
    if removal of this element makes one list empty **then** remove
        all elements from the other list and append them to L
end {L is the merged list with elements in increasing order}

LEMMA 1 Two sorted lists with m elements and n elements can be merged into a sorted list using no more than $m + n - 1$ comparisons.

Sometimes two sorted lists of length m and n can be merged using far fewer than $m + n - 1$ comparisons. For instance, when $m = 1$, a binary search procedure can be applied to put the one element in the first list into the second list. This requires only $\lceil \log n \rceil$ comparisons, which is much smaller than $m + n - 1 = n$, for $m = 1$. On the other hand, for some values of m and n, Lemma 1 gives the best possible bound. That is, there are lists with m and n elements that cannot be merged using fewer than $m + n - 1$ comparisons. (See Exercise 35 at the end of this section.)

We can now analyze the complexity of the merge sort. Instead of studying the general problem, we will assume that n, the number of elements in the list, is a power of 2, say 2^m. This will make the analysis less complicated, but when this is not the case, various modifications can be applied that will yield the same estimate.

At the first stage of the splitting procedure, the list is split into two sublists, of 2^{m-1} elements each, at level 1 of the tree generated by the splitting. This process continues, splitting the two sublists with 2^{m-1} elements into four sublists of 2^{m-2} elements each at level 2, and so on. In general, there are 2^{k-1} lists at level $k - 1$, each with 2^{m-k+1} elements. These lists at level $k - 1$ are split into 2^k lists at level k, each with 2^{m-k} elements. At the end of this process, we have 2^m lists each with one element at level m.

We start merging by combining pairs of the 2^m lists of one element into 2^{m-1} lists, at level $m - 1$, each with two elements. To do this, 2^{m-1} pairs of lists with one element each are merged. The merger of each pair requires exactly one comparison.

The procedure continues, so that at level k ($k = m, m - 1, m - 2, \ldots, 3, 2, 1$), 2^k lists each with 2^{m-k} elements are merged into 2^{k-1} lists, each with 2^{m-k+1} elements, at level $k - 1$. To do this a total of 2^{k-1} mergers of two lists, each with 2^{m-k} elements, are needed. But, by Lemma 1, each of these mergers can be carried out using at most $2^{m-k} + 2^{m-k} - 1 = 2^{m-k+1} - 1$ comparisons. Hence, going from level k to $k - 1$ can be accomplished using at most $2^{k-1}(2^{m-k+1} - 1)$ comparisons. Summing all these estimates shows that the number of comparisons required for the merge sort is at most

$$\sum_{k=1}^{m} 2^{k-1}(2^{m-k+1} - 1) = \sum_{k=1}^{m} 2^m - \sum_{k=1}^{m} 2^{k-1} = m2^m - (2^m - 1) = n \log n - n + 1,$$

since $m = \log n$ and $n = 2^m$. (We evaluated $\sum_{k=1}^{m} 2^m$ by noting that it is the sum of m identical terms, each equal to 2^m. We evaluated $\sum_{k=1}^{m} 2^{k-1}$ using the formula for the sum of the terms of a geometric progression from Theorem 1 of Section 3.2.)

This analysis shows that the merge sort achieves the best possible big-O estimate for the number of comparisons needed by sorting algorithms, as stated in the following theorem.

THEOREM 1   The number of comparisons needed to merge sort a list with n elements is $O(n \log n)$.

We describe another efficient algorithm, the quick sort, in the exercises.

Exercises

1. Give a recursive algorithm for computing nx whenever n is a positive integer and x is an integer.

2. Give a recursive algorithm for finding the sum of the first n positive integers.

3. Give a recursive algorithm for finding the sum of the first n odd positive integers.

4. Give a recursive algorithm for finding the maximum of a finite set of integers.

5. Give a recursive algorithm for finding the minimum of a finite set of integers.

6. Devise a recursive algorithm for finding $x^n \bmod m$ whenever n, x, and m are positive integers based on the fact that $x^n \bmod m = (x^{n-1} \bmod m \cdot x \bmod m) \bmod m$.

7. Give a recursive algorithm for finding $n! \bmod m$ whenever n and m are positive integers.

8. Give a recursive algorithm for finding a **mode** of a list of integers. (A **mode** is an element in the list that occurs at least as often as every other element.)

9. Devise a recursive algorithm for computing the greatest common divisor of two nonnegative integers a and b with $a < b$ if $\gcd(a, b) = \gcd(a, b - a)$.

10. Prove that the recursive algorithm for finding the sum of the first n positive integers you found in Exercise 2 is correct.

11. Describe a recursive algorithm for multiplying two nonnegative integers x and y based on the fact that $xy = 2(x \cdot (y/2))$ when y is even and $xy = 2(x \cdot \lfloor y/2 \rfloor) + x$ when y is odd, together with the initial condition $xy = 0$ when $y = 0$.

12. Prove that the algorithm you devised in Exercise 11 is correct.

13. Prove that the recursive algorithm that you found in Exercise 1 is correct.

14. Prove that the recursive algorithm that you found in Exercise 4 is correct.

15. Prove that Algorithm 1 is correct.

16. Devise a recursive algorithm to find a^{2^n} where a is a real number and n is a positive integer. [*Hint:* Use the equality $a^{2^{n+1}} = (a^{2^n})^2$.]

17. How does the number of multiplications used by the algorithm in Exercise 16 compare to the number of multiplications used by Algorithm 1 to evaluate a^{2^n}?

*18. Use the algorithm in Exercise 16 to devise an algorithm for evaluating a^n when n is a nonnegative integer. (*Hint:* Use the binary expansion of n.)

*19. How does the number of multiplications used by the algorithm in Exercise 18 compare to the number of multiplications used by Algorithm 1 to evaluate a^n?

20. How many additions are used by the recursive and iterative algorithms given in Algorithms 8 and 9, respectively, to find the Fibonacci number f_7?

21. Devise a recursive algorithm to find the nth term of the sequence defined by $a_0 = 1$, $a_1 = 2$, and $a_n = a_{n-1} \cdot a_{n-2}$, for $n = 2, 3, 4, \ldots$.

22. Devise an iterative algorithm to find the nth term of the sequence defined in Exercise 21.

23. Is the recursive or the iterative algorithm for finding the sequence in Exercise 21 more efficient?

24. Devise a recursive algorithm to find the nth term of the sequence defined by $a_0 = 1$, $a_1 = 2$, $a_2 = 3$, and $a_n = a_{n-1} + a_{n-2} + a_{n-3}$, for $n = 3, 4, 5, \ldots$.

25. Devise an iterative algorithm to find the nth term of the sequence defined in Exercise 24.

26. Is the recursive or the iterative algorithm for finding the sequence in Exercise 24 more efficient?

27. Give iterative and recursive algorithms for finding the nth term of the sequence defined by $a_0 = 1$, $a_1 = 3$, $a_2 = 5$, and $a_n = a_{n-1} \cdot a_{n-2}^2 \cdot a_{n-3}^3$. Which is more efficient?

28. Give a recursive algorithm to find the number of partitions of a positive integer based on the recursive definition given in Exercise 47 in Section 3.4.

29. Give a recursive algorithm for finding the reversal of a bit string. (See the definition of the reversal of a bit string in the preamble of Exercise 34 in Section 3.4.)

30. Give a recursive algorithm for finding the string w^i, the concatenation of i copies of w, when w is a bit string.

31. Give a recursive algorithm for computing values of the Ackermann function. (*Hint:* See the preamble to Exercise 48 in Section 3.4.)

32. Use a merge sort to sort 4, 3, 2, 5, 1, 8, 7, 6. Show all the steps used by the algorithm.

33. Use a merge sort to sort $b, d, a, f, g, h, z, p, o, k$. Show all the steps used by the algorithm.

34. How many comparisons are required to merge these pairs of lists using Algorithm 11?

   a) 1, 3, 5, 7, 9; 2, 4, 6, 8, 10
   b) 1, 2, 3, 4, 5; 6, 7, 8, 9, 10
   c) 1, 5, 6, 7, 8; 2, 3, 4, 9, 10

35. Show that there are lists with m elements and n elements such that they cannot be merged into one sorted list using Algorithm 11 with fewer than $m + n - 1$ comparisons.

*36. What is the least number of comparisons needed to merge any two lists in increasing order into one list in increasing order when the number of elements in the two lists are

   a) 1, 4?   **b)** 2, 4?   **c)** 3, 4?   **d)** 4, 4?

*37. Prove that the merge sort algorithm is correct.

The **quick sort** is an efficient algorithm. To sort $a_1, a_2, \ldots, a_n$, this algorithm begins by taking the first element a_1 and forming two sublists, the first containing those elements that are less than a_1, in the order they arise, and the second containing those elements greater than a_1, in the order they arise. Then a_1 is put at the end of the first sublist. This procedure is repeated recursively for each sublist, until all sublists contain one item. The ordered list of n items is obtained by combining the sublists of one item in the order they occur.

38. Sort 3, 5, 7, 8, 1, 9, 2, 4, 6 using the quick sort.

39. Let $a_1, a_2, \ldots, a_n$ be a list of n distinct real numbers. How many comparisons are needed to form two sublists from this list, the first containing elements less than a_1 and the second containing elements greater than a_1?

40. Describe the quick sort algorithm using pseudocode.

41. What is the largest number of comparisons needed to order a list of four elements using the quick sort algorithm?

42. What is the least number of comparisons needed to order a list of four elements using the quick sort algorithm?

43. Determine the worst-case complexity of the quick sort algorithm in terms of the number of comparisons used.

*44. Show that $\log n!$ is greater than $(n \log n)/4$ for $n > 4$. [*Hint:* Begin with the inequality $n! > n(n-1)(n-2) \cdots \lceil n/2 \rceil$.]

3.6   Program Correctness

INTRODUCTION

Suppose that we have designed an algorithm to solve a problem and have written a program to implement it. How can we be sure that the program always produces the correct answer? After all the bugs have been removed so that the syntax is correct, we can test the program with sample input. It is not correct if an incorrect result is produced for any sample input. But even if the program gives the correct answer for all sample input, it may not always produce the correct answer (unless all possible input has been tested). We need a proof to show that the program *always* gives the correct output.

    Program verification, the proof of correctness of programs, uses the rules of inference and proof techniques described in this chapter, including mathematical induction. Since an incorrect program can lead to disastrous effects, a large amount of methodology has been constructed for verifying programs. Efforts have been devoted to automating program verification so that it can be carried out using a computer. However, only limited progress has been made toward this goal. Indeed, some mathematicians and theoretical computer scientists argue that it will never be realistic to mechanize the proof of correctness of complex programs.

Some of the concepts and methods used to prove that programs are correct will be introduced in this section. However, a complete methodology for program verification will not be developed in this book. This section is meant to be a brief introduction to the area of program verification, which ties together the rules of logic, proof techniques, and the concept of an algorithm.

PROGRAM VERIFICATION

A program is said to be **correct** if it produces the correct output for every possible input. A proof that a program is correct consists of two parts. The first part shows that the correct answer is obtained if the program terminates. This part of the proof establishes the **partial correctness** of the program. The second part of the proof shows that the program always terminates.

To specify what it means for a program to produce the correct output, two propositions are used. The first is the **initial assertion,** which gives the properties that the input values must have. The second is the **final assertion,** which gives the properties that the output of the program should have, if the program did what was intended. The appropriate initial and final assertions must be provided when a program is checked.

DEFINITION 1

A program, or program segment, S is said to be *partially correct with respect to* the initial assertion p and the final assertion q if whenever p is true for the input values of S and S terminates, then q is true for the output values of S. The notation $p\{S\}q$ indicates that the program, or program segment, S is partially correct with respect to the initial assertion p and the final assertion q.

Note: The notation $p\{S\}q$ is known as a *Hoare triple* after Tony Hoare, who introduced the concept of partial correctness.

Note that the notion of partial correctness has nothing to do with whether a program terminates; it focuses only on whether the program does what it is expected to do if it terminates.

A simple example illustrates the concepts of initial and final assertions.

EXAMPLE 1

Show that the program segment

$$y := 2$$
$$z := x + y$$

is correct with respect to the initial assertion p: $x = 1$ and the final assertion q: $z = 3$.

Solution: Suppose that p is true, so that $x = 1$ as the program begins. Then y is assigned the value 2, and z is assigned the sum of the values of x and y, which is 3. Hence, S is correct with respect to the initial assertion p and the final assertion q. Thus, $p\{S\}q$ is true. ◀

RULES OF INFERENCE

A useful rule of inference proves that a program is correct by splitting the program into a series of subprograms and then showing that each subprogram is correct.

Suppose that the program S is split into subprograms S_1 and S_2. Write $S = S_1; S_2$ to indicate that S is made up of S_1 followed by S_2. Suppose that the correctness of S_1 with respect to the initial assertion p and final assertion q, and the correctness of S_2 with respect to the initial assertion q and the final assertion r, have been established. It follows that if p is true and S_1 is executed and terminates, then q is true; and if q is true, and S_2 executes and terminates, then r is true. Thus, if p is true and $S = S_1; S_2$ is executed and terminates, then r is true. This rule of inference, called the **composition rule,** can be stated as

$$p\{S_1\}q$$
$$q\{S_2\}r$$
$$\therefore\ p\{S_1; S_2\}r.$$

This rule of inference will be used later in this section.

Next, some rules of inference for program segments involving conditional statements and loops will be given. Since programs can be split into segments for proofs of correctness, this will let us verify many different programs.

CONDITIONAL STATEMENTS

First, rules of inference for conditional statements will be given. Suppose that a program segment has the form

> **if** *condition* **then**
> S

where S is a block of statements. Then S is executed if *condition* is true, and it is not executed when *condition* is false. To verify that this segment is correct with respect to the initial assertion p and final assertion q, two things must be done. First, it must be shown that when p is true and *condition* is also true, then q is true after S terminates. Second, it must be shown that when p is true and *condition* is false, then q is true (since in this case S does not execute).

This leads to the following rule of inference:

$$(p \wedge condition)\{S\}q$$
$$(p \wedge \neg condition) \rightarrow q$$
$$\therefore\ p\{\textbf{if } condition \textbf{ then } S\}q.$$

Example 2 illustrates how this rule of inference is used.

C. ANTHONY R. HOARE (BORN 1934) Tony Hoare is currently Professor of Computer Science at Oxford University, England, and is a Fellow of the Royal Society. Hoare has made many important contributions to the theory of programming languages and to programming methodology. He was the first person to define a programming language based on how programs could be proved to be correct with respect to their specifications. Hoare is also the creator of the quick sort, one of the most commonly used and studied sorting algorithms (see the exercise set in Section 3.5). Hoare is a noted writer in the technical and social aspects of computer science.

EXAMPLE 2   Verify that the program segment

> **if** $x > y$ **then**
> $\quad y := x$

is correct with respect to the initial assertion **T** and the final assertion $y \geq x$.

Solution: When the initial assertion is true and $x > y$, the assignment $y := x$ is carried out. Hence, the final assertion, which asserts that $y \geq x$, is true in this case. Moreover, when the initial assertion is true and $x > y$ is false, so that $x \leq y$, the final assertion is again true. Hence, using the rule of inference for program segments of this type, this program is correct with respect to the given initial and final assertions.   ◀

Similarly, suppose that a program has a statement of the form

> **if** *condition* **then**
> $\quad S_1$
> **else**
> $\quad S_2$

If *condition* is true, then S_1 executes; if *condition* is false, then S_2 executes. To verify that this program segment is correct with respect to the initial assertion p and the final assertion q, two things must be done. First, it must be shown that when p is true and *condition* is true, then q is true after S_1 terminates. Second, it must be shown that when p is true and *condition* is false, then q is true after S_2 terminates. This leads to the following rule of inference:

$$(p \wedge condition)\{S_1\}q$$
$$\underline{(p \wedge \neg condition)\{S_2\}q}$$
$$\therefore p\{\textbf{if } condition \textbf{ then } S_1 \textbf{ else } S_2\}q.$$

The following example illustrates how this rule of inference is used.

EXAMPLE 3   Verify that the program segment

> **if** $x < 0$ **then**
> $\quad abs := -x$
> **else**
> $\quad abs := x$

is correct with respect to the initial assertion **T** and the final assertion $abs = |x|$.

Solution: Two things must be demonstrated. First, it must be shown that if the initial assertion is true and $x < 0$, then $abs = |x|$. This is correct, since when $x < 0$ the assignment statement $abs := -x$ sets $abs = -x$, which is $|x|$ by definition when $x < 0$. Second, it must be shown that if the initial assertion is true and $x < 0$ is false, so that $x \geq 0$, then $abs = |x|$.

This is also correct, since in this case the program uses the assignment statement $abs := x$, and x is $|x|$ by definition when $x \geq 0$, so that $abs := x$. Hence, using the rule of inference for program segments of this type, this segment is correct with respect to the given initial and final assertions. ◀

LOOP INVARIANTS

Next, proofs of correctness of **while** loops will be described. To develop a rule of inference for program segments of the type

> **while** *condition*
>   *S*

note that S is repeatedly executed until *condition* becomes false. An assertion that remains true each time S is executed must be chosen. Such an assertion is called a **loop invariant.** In other words, p is a loop invariant if $(p \wedge condition)\{S\}p$ is true.

Suppose that p is a loop invariant. It follows that if p is true before the program segment is executed, p and $\neg condition$ are true after termination, if it occurs. This rule of inference is

$$\frac{(p \wedge condition)\{S\}p}{\therefore \; p\{\textbf{while } condition \;\; S\}(\neg condition \wedge p).}$$

The use of a loop invariant is illustrated in Example 4.

EXAMPLE 4   A loop invariant is needed to verify that the program segment

> $i := 1$
> $factorial := 1$
> **while** $i < n$
> **begin**
> $i := i + 1$
> $factorial := factorial \cdot i$
> **end**

terminates with $factorial = n!$ when n is a positive integer.

Let p be the assertion "*factorial* $= i!$ and $i \leq n$." We first prove that p is a loop invariant. Suppose that, at the beginning of one execution of the **while** loop, p is true and the condition of the **while** loop holds; in other words, assume that $factorial = i!$ and that $i < n$. The new values i_{new} and $factorial_{new}$ of i and $factorial$ are $i_{new} = i + 1$ and $factorial_{new} = factorial \cdot (i + 1) = (i + 1)! = i_{new}!$. Since $i < n$, we also have $i_{new} = i + 1 \leq n$. Thus p is true at the end of the execution of the loop. This shows that p is a loop invariant.

Now we consider the program segment. Just before entering the loop, $i = 1 \leq n$ and $factorial = 1 = 1! = i!$ both hold, so p is true. Since p is a loop invariant, the rule of inference just introduced implied that if the **while** loop terminates, it terminates with p true and with $i < n$ false. In this case, at the end, $factorial = i!$ and $i \leq n$ are true, but $i < n$ is false; in other words, $i = n$ and $factorial = i! = n!$, as desired.

Finally, we need to check that the **while** loop actually terminates. At the beginning of the program i is assigned the value 1, so after $n - 1$ traversals of the loop, the new value of i will be n, and the loop terminates at that point. ◄

A final example will be given to show how the various rules of inference can be used to verify the correctness of a longer program.

EXAMPLE 5   We will outline how to verify the correctness of the program S for computing the product of two integers.

procedure *multiply*(m, n: integers)

$S_1 \begin{cases} \textbf{if } n < 0 \textbf{ then } a := -n \\ \textbf{else } a := n \end{cases}$

$S_2 \begin{cases} k := 0 \\ x := 0 \end{cases}$

$S_3 \begin{cases} \textbf{while } k < a \\ \textbf{begin} \\ \quad x := x + m \\ \quad k := k + 1 \\ \textbf{end} \end{cases}$

$S_4 \begin{cases} \textbf{if } n < 0 \textbf{ then } product := -x \\ \textbf{else } product := x \end{cases}$

The goal is to prove that after S is executed, *product* has the value mn. The proof of correctness can be carried out by splitting S into four segments, with $S = S_1; S_2; S_3; S_4$, as shown in the listing of S. The rule of composition can be used to build the correctness proof. Here is how the argument proceeds. The details will be left as an exercise for the reader.

Let p be the initial assertion that m and n are integers. Then, it can be shown that $p\{S_1\}q$ is true, when q is the proposition $p \wedge (a = |n|)$. Next, let r be the proposition $q \wedge (k = 0) \wedge (x = 0)$. It is easily verified that $q\{S_2\}r$ is true. It can be shown that "$x = mk$ and $k \leq a$" is an invariant for the loop in S_3. Furthermore, it is easy to see that the loop terminates after a iterations, with $k = a$, so that $x = ma$ at this point. Since r implies that $x = m \cdot 0$ and $0 \leq a$, the loop invariant is true before the loop is entered. Since the loop terminates with $k = a$, it follows that $r\{S_3\}s$ is true where s is the proposition "$x = ma$ and $a = |n|$." Finally, it can be shown that S_4 is correct with respect to the initial assertion s and final assertion t, where t is the proposition "$product = mn$."

Putting all this together, since $p\{S_1\}q$, $q\{S_2\}r$, $r\{S_3\}s$, and $s\{S_4\}t$ are all true, it follows from the rule of composition that $p\{S\}t$ is true. Furthermore, since all four segments terminate, S does terminate. This verifies the correctness of the program. ◄

Exercises

1. Prove that the program segment

   $y := 1$
   $z := x + y$

   is correct with respect to the initial assertion $x = 0$ and the final assertion $z = 1$.

2. Verify that the program segment

   if $x < 0$ **then** $x := 0$

   is correct with respect to the initial assertion **T** and the final assertion $x \geq 0$.

3. Verify that the program segment

   $x := 2$
   $z := x + y$
   if $y > 0$ **then**
   $\quad z := z + 1$
   else
   $\quad z := 0$

   is correct with respect to the initial assertion $y = 3$ and the final assertion $z = 6$.

4. Verify that the program segment

   if $x < y$ **then**
   $\quad min := x$
   else
   $\quad min := y$

   is correct with respect to the initial assertion **T** and the final assertion
   $(x \leq y \wedge min = x) \vee (x > y \wedge min = y)$.

*5. Devise a rule of inference for verification of partial correctness of statements of the form

   if *condition* 1 **then**
   $\quad S_1$
   else if *condition* 2 **then**
   $\quad S_2$
   $\quad \vdots$
   else
   $\quad S_n$

   where $S_1, S_2, \ldots, S_n$ are blocks.

6. Use the rule of inference developed in Exercise 5 to verify that the program

   if $x < 0$ **then**
   $\quad y := -2|x|/x$
   else if $x > 0$ **then**

   $\quad y := 2|x|/x$
   else if $x = 0$ **then**
   $\quad y := 2$

   is correct with respect to the initial assertion **T** and the final assertion $y = 2$.

7. Use a loop invariant to prove that the following program segment for computing the nth power, where n is a positive integer, of a real number x is correct.

   $power := 1$
   $i := 1$
   while $i \leq n$
   begin
   $\quad power := power * x$
   $\quad i := i + 1$
   end

*8. Prove that the iterative program for finding f_n given in Section 3.5 is correct.

9. Provide all the details in the proof of correctness given in Example 5.

10. Suppose that both the implication $p_0 \rightarrow p_1$ and the program assertion $p_1\{S\}q$ are true. Show that $p_0\{S\}q$ also must be true.

11. Suppose that both the program assertion $p\{S\}q_0$ and the implication $q_0 \rightarrow q_1$ are true. Show that $p\{S\}q_1$ also must be true.

12. This program computes quotients and remainders.

   $r := a$
   $q := 0$
   while $r \geq d$
   begin
   $\quad r := r - d$
   $\quad q := q + 1$
   end

   Verify that it is partially correct with respect to the initial assertion "a and d are positive integers" and the final assertion "q and r are integers such that $a = dq + r$ and $0 \leq r < d$."

13. Use a loop invariant to verify that the Euclidean algorithm (Algorithm 6 in Section 2.5) is partially correct with respect to the initial assertion "a and b are positive integers" and the final assertion "$x = \gcd(a, b)$."

Key Terms and Results

TERMS

sequence: a function with domain that is a subset of the set of integers

geometric progression: a sequence of the form $a, ar, ar^2, \ldots$ where a and r are real numbers

arithmetic progression: a sequence of the form $a, a + d, a + 2d, \ldots$ where a and d are real numbers

string: a finite sequence

empty string: a string of length zero

$\sum_{i=1}^{n}$: the sum $a_1 + a_2 + \cdots + a_n$

$\prod_{i=1}^{n}$: the product $a_1 a_2 \cdots a_n$

countable set: a set that is either finite or can be placed in one-to-one correspondence with the set of positive integers

uncountable set: a set that is not countable

Cantor diagonalization argument: a proof technique that can be used to show that the set of rational numbers is countable

the principle of mathematical induction: the statement $\forall n\, P(n)$ is true if $P(1)$ is true and $\forall k[P(k) \rightarrow P(k+1)]$ is true.

basis step: the proof of $P(1)$ in a proof by mathematical induction of $\forall n\, P(n)$

inductive step: the proof of $P(k) \rightarrow P(k+1)$ in a proof by mathematical induction of $\forall n\, P(n)$

strong induction: The statement $\forall n\, P(n)$ is true if $P(1)$ is true and $\forall k[(P(1) \wedge \cdots \wedge P(k)) \rightarrow P(k+1)]$ is true.

well-ordering property: Every nonempty set of nonnegative integers has a least element.

recursive definition of a function: a definition of a function that specifies an initial set of values and a rule for obtaining values of this function at integers from its values at smaller integers

recursive definition of a set: a definition of a set that specifies an initial set of elements in the set and a rule for obtaining other elements from those in the set

structural induction: a technique for proving results about recursively defined sets

recursive algorithm: an algorithm that proceeds by reducing a problem to the same problem with smaller input

merge sort: a sorting algorithm that sorts a list by splitting it in two, sorting each of the two resulting lists, and merging the results into a sorted list

iteration: a procedure based on the repeated use of operations in a loop

program correctness: verification that a procedure always produces the correct result

loop invariant: a property that remains true during every traversal of a loop

initial assertion: the statement specifying the properties of the input values of a program

final assertion: the statement specifying the properties the output values should have if the program worked correctly

RESULTS

halting problem: No procedure exists that, when given a program and input to this program, determines whether the program terminates when given this input.

the sum of terms of a geometric series: $\sum_{j=0}^{n} ar^j = (ar^{n+1} - a)/(r - 1)$ if $r \neq 1$.

The set of rational numbers is countable.

The set of real numbers is uncountable.

Review Questions

1. Describe the process of formulating and resolving conjecture and demonstrate this process with the example of finding primes of the form $a^n - 1$ where a and n are positive integers.

2. Show that the set of odd integers is countable.

3. Give an example of an uncountable set.

4. **a)** Can you use the principle of mathematical induction to find a formula for the sum of the first n terms of a sequence?

   b) Can you use the principle of mathematical induction to determine whether a given formula for the sum of the first n terms of a sequence is correct?

   c) Find a formula for the sum of the first n even positive integers, and prove it using mathematical induction.

5. **a)** For which positive integers n is it true that $11n + 17 \leq 2^n$?

   b) Prove the conjecture you made in part (a) using mathematical induction.

6. **a)** Which amounts of postage can be formed using only 5-cent and 9-cent stamps?

   b) Prove the conjecture you made using mathematical induction.

   c) Prove the conjecture you made using the second principle of mathematical induction.

   d) Find a proof of your conjecture different from the ones you gave in (b) and (c).

7. Give two different examples of proofs that use strong induction.

8. **a)** State the well-ordering property for the set of positive integers.

   b) Use this property to show that every positive integer can be written as the product of primes.

9. **a)** Explain why a function is well-defined if it is defined recursively by specifying $f(1)$ and a rule for finding $f(n)$ from $f(n - 1)$.

   b) Provide a recursive definition of the function $f(n) = (n + 1)!$.

10. **a)** Give a recursive definition of the Fibonacci numbers.

b) Show that $f_n > \alpha^{n-2}$ whenever $n \geq 3$ where f_n is the nth term of the Fibonacci sequence and $\alpha = (1 + \sqrt{5})/2$.

11. a) Explain why a sequence a_n is well-defined if it is defined recursively by specifying a_1 and a_2 and a rule for finding a_n from $a_1, a_2, \ldots, a_{n-1}$ for $n = 3, 4, 5, \ldots$.

b) Find the value of a_n if $a_1 = 1$, $a_2 = 2$, and $a_n = a_{n-1} + a_{n-2} + \cdots + a_1$, for $n = 3, 4, 5, \ldots$.

12. Give two examples of how well-formed formulae are defined recursively for different sets of elements and operators.

13. a) Give a recursive definition of the length of a string.

b) Use the recursive definition from part (a) and structural induction to prove that $l(xy) = l(x) + l(y)$.

14. a) What is a recursive algorithm?

b) Describe a recursive algorithm for computing the sum of n numbers in a sequence.

15. Describe a recursive algorithm for computing the greatest common divisor of two positive integers.

16. a) Describe the merge sort algorithm.

b) Use the merge sort algorithm to put the list 4, 10, 1, 5, 3, 8, 7, 2, 6, 9 in increasing order.

c) Give a big-O estimate for the number of comparisons used by the merge sort.

17. a) Does testing a computer program to see whether it produces the correct output for certain input values verify that the program always produces the correct output?

b) Does showing that a computer program is partially correct with respect to an initial assertion and a final assertion verify that the program always produces the correct output? If not, what else is needed?

18. What techniques can you use to show that a long computer program is partially correct with respect to an initial assertion and a final assertion?

19. What is a loop invariant? How is a loop invariant used?

Supplementary Exercises

1. Prove that $2^{2^5} + 1$ is composite.

2. a) Formulate a conjecture concerning which integers of the form $a^n + 1$, where $a \in \mathbf{Z}^+$ and $n \in \mathbf{Z}^+$, are necessarily composite.

b) Prove your conjecture.

3. Prove that $\sqrt[3]{7}$ is irrational.

4. Prove that $\sqrt{5}$ is irrational.

5. Show that there are no integer solutions of $x^4 + y^4 = 1000$.

6. Prove that $n^4 - 1$ is divisible by 5 when n is not divisible by 5. Use a proof by cases, with four different cases—one for each of the nonzero remainders that an integer not divisible by 5 can have when you divide it by 5.

7. Prove or disprove that $|x - y| \geq |x| - |y|$ whenever x and y are real numbers.

***8.** We define the **Ulam numbers** by setting $u_1 = 1$ and $u_2 = 2$. Furthermore, after determining whether the integers less than n are Ulam numbers, we set n equal to the next Ulam number if it can be written uniquely as the sum of two different Ulam numbers. Note that $u_3 = 3, u_4 = 4, u_5 = 6$, and $u_6 = 8$.

a) Find the first 20 Ulam numbers.

b) Prove that there are infinitely many Ulam numbers.

9. Give a constructive proof that there is a polynomial $P(x)$ such that $P(x_1) = y_1, P(x_2) = y_2, \ldots, P(x_n) = y_n$, where $x_1, \ldots, x_n, y_1, \ldots, y_n$ are real numbers and the

x_i are distinct. [*Hint:* Let

$$P(x) = \sum_{i=1}^{n} \left(\prod_{i \neq j} \frac{x - x_j}{x_i - x_j} \right) y_i.]$$

10. Show that $1^3 + 3^3 + 5^3 + \cdots + (2n + 1)^3 = (n + 1)^2 (2n^2 + 4n + 1)$ whenever n is a positive integer.

11. Show that $1 \cdot 2^0 + 2 \cdot 2^1 + 3 \cdot 2^2 + \cdots + n \cdot 2^{n-1} = (n - 1) \cdot 2^n + 1$ whenever n is a positive integer.

12. Show that
$$\frac{1}{1 \cdot 3} + \frac{1}{3 \cdot 5} + \cdots + \frac{1}{(2n - 1)(2n + 1)} = \frac{n}{2n + 1}$$
whenever n is a positive integer.

13. Show that
$$\frac{1}{1 \cdot 4} + \frac{1}{4 \cdot 7} + \cdots + \frac{1}{(3n - 2)(3n + 1)} = \frac{n}{3n + 1}$$
whenever n is a positive integer.

14. Use mathematical induction to show that $2^n > n^2 + n$ whenever n is an integer greater than 4.

15. Use mathematical induction to show that $2^n > n^3$ whenever n is an integer greater than 9.

16. Find an integer N such that $2^n > n^4$ whenever n is greater than N. Prove that your result is correct using mathematical induction.

17. Use mathematical induction to prove that $a - b$ is a factor of $a^n - b^n$ whenever n is a positive integer.

18. Use mathematical induction to prove that 9 divides $n^3 + (n + 1)^3 + (n + 2)^3$ whenever n is a nonnegative integer.

19. Use mathematical induction to prove this formula for the sum of the terms of an arithmetic progression.

$$a + (a + d) + \cdots + (a + nd) = (n + 1)(2a + nd)/2$$

20. Suppose that $a_j \equiv b_j \pmod{m}$ for $j = 1, 2, \ldots, n$. Use mathematical induction to prove that

 a) $\displaystyle\sum_{j=1}^{n} a_j \equiv \sum_{j=1}^{n} b_j \pmod{m}$.

 b) $\displaystyle\prod_{j=1}^{n} a_j \equiv \prod_{j=1}^{n} b_j \pmod{m}$.

21. Show that if n is a positive integer, then

$$\sum_{k=1}^{n} \frac{k+4}{k(k+1)(k+2)} = \frac{n(3n+7)}{2(n+1)(n+2)}.$$

22. For which positive integers n is $n + 6 < (n^2 - 8n)/16$? Prove your answer using mathematical induction.

23. (Requires calculus) Suppose that $f(x) = e^x$ and $g(x) = xe^x$. Use mathematical induction together with the product rule and the fact that $f'(x) = e^x$ to prove that $g^{(n)}(x) = (x + n)e^x$ whenever n is a positive integer.

24. (Requires calculus) Suppose that $f(x) = e^x$ and $g(x) = e^{cx}$, where c is a constant. Use mathematical induction together with the chain rule and the fact that $f'(x) = e^x$ to prove that $g^{(n)} = c^n e^{cx}$ whenever n is a positive integer.

*25. Determine which Fibonacci numbers are even, and use a form of mathematical induction to prove your conjecture.

*26. Determine which Fibonacci numbers are divisible by 3. Use a form of mathematical induction to prove your conjecture.

*27. Prove that $f_k f_n + f_{k+1} f_{n+1} = f_{n+k+1}$ for all nonnegative integers n, where k is a nonnegative integer and f_i denotes the ith Fibonacci number.

The sequence of **Lucas numbers** is defined by $l_0 = 2$, $l_1 = 1$, and $l_n = l_{n-1} + l_{n-2}$ for $n = 2, 3, 4, \ldots$.

28. Show that $f_n + f_{n+2} = l_{n+1}$ whenever n is a positive integer, where f_i and l_i are the ith Fibonacci number and ith Lucas number, respectively.

29. Show that $l_0^2 + l_1^2 + \cdots + l_n^2 = l_n l_{n+1} + 2$ whenever n is a nonnegative integer and l_i is the ith Lucas number.

*30. Use mathematical induction to show that the product of any n consecutive positive integers is divisible by $n!$. [*Hint:* Use the identity $m(m + 1) \cdots (m + n - 1)/n! = (m - 1)m(m + 1) \cdots (m + n - 2)/n! + m(m + 1) \cdots (m + n - 2)/(n - 1)!$.]

31. Use mathematical induction to show that $(\cos x + i \sin x)^n = \cos nx + i \sin nx$ whenever n is a positive integer. [*Hint:* Use the identities $\cos(a + b) = \cos a \cos b - \sin a \sin b$ and $\sin(a + b) = \sin a \cos b + \cos a \sin b$.]

*32. Use mathematical induction to show that $\sum_{j=1}^{n} \cos jx = \cos[(n + 1)x/2] \sin(nx/2)/\sin(x/2)$ whenever n is a positive integer and $\sin(x/2) \neq 0$.

33. Use mathematical induction to prove that $\sum_{j=1}^{n} j^2 2^j = n^2 2^{n+1} - n2^{n+2} + 3 \cdot 2^{n+1} - 6$ for every positive integer n.

34. (Requires calculus) Suppose that the sequence $x_1, x_2, \ldots, x_n, \ldots$ is recursively defined by $x_1 = 0$ and $x_{n+1} = \sqrt{x_n + 6}$.

 a) Use mathematical induction to show that $x_1 < x_2 < \cdots < x_n < \cdots$, that is, the sequence $\{x_n\}$ is monotonically increasing.

 b) Use mathematical induction to prove that $x_n < 3$ for $n = 1, 2, \ldots$.

 c) Show that $\lim_{n\to\infty} x_n = 3$.

35. Use mathematical induction to prove that if n people stand in a line, where n is a positive integer, and if the first person in the line is a woman and the last person in line is a man, then somewhere in the line there is a woman directly in front of a man.

*36. Suppose that in a country there is a direct one-way road connecting every pair of cities. Use mathematical induction to show that there is a city that can be reached from every other city either directly or via exactly one other city.

37. Use mathematical induction to show that when n circles divide the plane into regions, these regions can be colored with two different colors such that no regions with a common boundary are colored the same.

*38. Suppose that among a group of cars on a circular track there is enough fuel for one car to complete a lap. Use mathematical induction to show that there is a car in the group that can complete a lap by obtaining gas from other cars as it travels around the track.

39. Show that if n is a positive integer, then

$$\sum_{j=1}^{n}(2j - 1)\left(\sum_{k=j}^{n} 1/k\right) = n(n + 1)/2.$$

40. A **unit** or **Egyptian fraction** is a fraction of the form $1/n$, where n is a positive integer. In this exercise, we will use strong induction to show that a greedy algorithm can be used to express every rational number p/q with $0 < p/q < 1$ as the sum of distinct unit fractions. At each step of the algorithm, we find the smallest positive integer n such that $1/n$ can be added to the sum without exceeding p/q. For example, to express $5/7$ we first start the sum with $1/2$. Since $5/7 - 1/2 = 3/14$ we add $1/5$ to the sum since 5 is the smallest positive integer k such that $1/k < 3/14$. Since $3/14 - 1/5 = 1/70$, the algorithm terminates, showing that $5/7 = 1/2 + 1/5 + 1/70$. Let $T(p)$ be the statement that this algorithm terminates for all rational numbers p/q with $0 < p/q < 1$. We will prove that the algorithm always terminates by showing that $T(p)$ holds for all positive integers p.

 a) Show that the basis step $T(1)$ holds.

 b) Suppose that $T(k)$ holds for positive integers k with $k < p$. That is, assume that the algorithm terminates for all rational numbers k/r, where $1 \le k < p$. Show that if we start with p/q and the fraction $1/n$ is selected in the first step of the algorithm, then $p/q = p'/q' + 1/n$, where $p' = np - q$ and $q' = nq$. After considering the case where $p/q = 1/n$, use the induction hypothesis to show that the greedy algorithm terminates when it begins with p'/q' and complete the inductive step.

The **McCarthy 91 function** (defined by John McCarthy, one of the founders of artificial intelligence) is defined using the rule

$$M(n) = \begin{cases} n - 10 & \text{if } n > 100 \\ M(M(n + 11)) & \text{if } n \le 100 \end{cases}$$

for all positive integers n.

41. By successively using the defining rule for $M(n)$, find

a) $M(102)$.   b) $M(101)$.   c) $M(99)$.
d) $M(97)$.   e) $M(87)$.   f) $M(76)$.

**42. Show that the function $M(n)$ is a well-defined function from the set of positive integers to the set of positive integers. [*Hint:* Prove that $M(n) = 91$ for all positive integers n with $n \le 101$.]

43. Is this proof that

$$\frac{1}{1 \cdot 2} + \frac{1}{2 \cdot 3} + \cdots + \frac{1}{(n - 1)n} = \frac{3}{2} - \frac{1}{n},$$

whenever n is a positive integer, correct? Justify your answer.

Basis step: The result is true when $n = 1$ since

$$\frac{1}{1 \cdot 2} = \frac{3}{2} - \frac{1}{1}.$$

Inductive step: Assume that the result is true for n. Then

$$\frac{1}{1 \cdot 2} + \frac{1}{2 \cdot 3} + \cdots + \frac{1}{(n - 1)n} + \frac{1}{n(n + 1)}$$
$$= \frac{3}{2} - \frac{1}{n} + \left(\frac{1}{n} - \frac{1}{n + 1} \right)$$
$$= \frac{3}{2} - \frac{1}{n + 1}.$$

Hence, the result is true for $n + 1$ if it is true for n. This completes the proof.

*44. A jigsaw puzzle is put together by successively joining pieces that fit together into blocks. A move is made each time a piece is added to a block, or when two blocks are joined. Use the second form of mathematical induction to prove that no matter how the moves are carried out, exactly $n - 1$ moves are required to assemble a puzzle with n pieces.

*45. Show that n circles divide the plane into $n^2 - n + 2$ regions if every two circles intersect in exactly two points and no three circles contain a common point.

*46. Show that n planes divide three-dimensional space into $(n^3 + 5n + 6)/6$ regions if any three of these planes have a point in common and no four contain a common point.

*47. Use the well-ordering property to show that $\sqrt{2}$ is irrational. (*Hint:* Assume that $\sqrt{2}$ is rational. Show that the set of positive integers of the form $b\sqrt{2}$ has a least element a. Then show that $a\sqrt{2} - a$ is a smaller positive integer of this form.)

JOHN McCARTHY (BORN 1927) John McCarthy was born in Boston. He grew up in Boston and in Los Angeles. He studied mathematics both as an undergraduate and a graduate student, receiving his B.S. in 1948 from the California Institute of Technology and his Ph.D. in 1951 from Princeton. After graduating from Princeton, McCarthy held positions at Princeton, Stanford, Dartmouth, and M.I.T. He held a position at Stanford from 1962 until 1994, and is now an emeritus professor there. At Stanford, he was the director of the Artificial Intelligence Laboratory, held a named chair in the School of Engineering, and was a senior fellow in the Hoover Institution.

McCarthy was a pioneer in the study of artificial intelligence, a term he coined in 1955. He worked on problems related to the reasoning and information needs required for intelligent computer behavior. McCarthy was among the first computer scientists to design time-sharing computer systems. He developed LISP, a programming language for computing using symbolic expressions. He played an important role in using logic to verify the correctness of computer programs. McCarthy has also worked on the social implications of computer technology. He is currently working on the problem of how people and computers make conjectures through assumptions that complications are absent from situations. McCarthy is an advocate of the sustainability of human progress and is an optimist about the future of humanity. He has also begun writing science fiction stories. Some of his recent writing explores the possibility that the world is a computer program written by some higher force.

Among the awards McCarthy has won are the Turing Award from the Association for Computing Machinery, the Research Excellence Award of the International Conference on Artificial Intelligence, the Kyoto Prize, and the National Medal of Science.

48. A set is **well-ordered** if every nonempty subset of this set has a least element. Determine whether each of the following sets is well-ordered.

  a) the set of integers
  b) the set of integers greater than -100
  c) the set of positive rationals
  d) the set of positive rationals with denominator less than 100

*49. Show that the well-ordering property can be proved when the principle of mathematical induction is taken as an axiom.

*50. Show that the principle of mathematical induction and strong induction are equivalent; that is, each can be shown to be valid from the other.

51. a) Show that if $a_1, a_2, \ldots, a_n$ are positive integers, then $\gcd(a_1, a_2, \ldots, a_{n-1}, a_n) = \gcd(a_1, a_2, \ldots, a_{n-2}, \gcd(a_{n-1}, a_n))$.

  b) Use part (a), together with the Euclidean algorithm, to develop a recursive algorithm for computing the greatest common divisor of a set of n positive integers.

*52. Describe a recursive algorithm for writing the greatest common divisor of n positive integers as a linear combination of these integers.

53. Find an explicit formula for $f(n)$ if $f(1) = 1$ and $f(n) = f(n-1) + 2n - 1$ for $n \geq 2$. Prove your result using mathematical induction.

**54. Give a recursive definition of the set of bit strings that contain twice as many 0s as 1s.

55. Let S be the set of bit strings defined recursively by $\lambda \in S$ and $0x \in S$, $x1 \in S$ if $x \in S$, where λ is the empty string.

  a) Find all strings in S of length not exceeding five.
  b) Give an explicit description of the elements of S.

56. Let S be the set of strings defined recursively by $abc \in S$, $bac \in S$, $acb \in S$, and $abcx \in S$; $abxc \in S$, $axbc \in S$, $xabc \in S$ if $x \in S$.

  a) Find all elements of S of length eight or less.
  b) Show that every element of S has a length divisible by three.

The set B of all **balanced strings of parentheses** is defined recursively by $\lambda \in B$, where λ is the empty string; $(x) \in B$, $xy \in B$ if $x, y \in B$.

57. Show that $(()())$ is a balanced string of parentheses and $(())$ is not a balanced string of parentheses.

58. Find all balanced strings of parentheses with exactly six symbols.

59. Find all balanced strings of parentheses with four or fewer symbols.

60. Use induction to show that if x is a balanced string of parentheses, then the number of left parentheses equals the number of right parentheses in x.

Define the function N on the set of strings of parentheses by

$$N(\lambda) = 0, N\big((\big) = 1, N\big( ) \big) = -1,$$
$$N(uv) = N(u) + N(v),$$

where λ is the empty string, and u and v are strings. It can be shown that N is well-defined.

61. Find

  a) $N\big(()\big)$.   **b)** $N\big()))()((\big)$.
  c) $N\big((()(()\big)$.   **d)** $N\big(()((()))(())\big)$.

**62. Show that a string w of parentheses is balanced if and only if $N(w) = 0$ and $N(u) \geq 0$ whenever u is a prefix of w, that is, $w = uv$.

*63. Give a recursive algorithm for finding all balanced strings of parentheses containing n or fewer symbols.

64. Give a recursive algorithm for finding $\gcd(a, b)$, where a and b are nonnegative integers, based on these facts: $\gcd(a, b) = \gcd(b, a)$ if $a > b$, $\gcd(0, b) = b$, $\gcd(a, b) = 2\gcd(a/2, b/2)$ if a and b are even, $\gcd(a, b) = \gcd(a/2, b)$ if a is even and b is odd, and $\gcd(a, b) = \gcd(a, b - a)$.

65. Verify the program segment

  if $x > y$ **then**
    $x := y$

with respect to the initial assertion **T** and the final assertion $x \leq y$.

*66. Develop a rule of inference for verifying recursive programs and use it to verify the recursive program for computing factorials given in Section 3.5.

67. Devise a recursive algorithm that counts the number of times the integer 0 occurs in a list of integers.

Exercises 68–75 deal with some unusual sequences, informally called **self-generating sequences**, produced by simple recurrence relations or rules. In particular, Exercises 68–75 deal with the sequence $\{a(n)\}$ defined by $a(n) = n - a(a(n-1))$ for $n \geq 1$ and $a(0) = 0$. (This sequence, as well as those in Exercises 72 and 73, are defined in Douglas Hofstader's fascinating book *Gödel, Escher, Bach* ([Ho99]).

68. Find the first 10 terms of the sequence $\{a(n)\}$ defined in the preamble to this exercise.

*69. Prove that this sequence is well defined. That is, show that $a(n)$ is uniquely defined for all nonnegative integers n.

**70. Prove that $a(n) = \lfloor (n+1)\mu \rfloor$ where $\mu = (-1 + \sqrt{5})/2$. [*Hint:* First show for all $n > 0$ that $(\mu n - \lfloor \mu n \rfloor) + (\mu^2 n - \lfloor \mu^2 n \rfloor) = 1$. Then show for all real numbers α with $0 \leq \alpha < 1$ and $\alpha \neq 1 - \mu$ that $\lfloor (1+\mu)(1-\alpha) \rfloor + \lfloor \alpha + \mu \rfloor = 1$, considering the cases $0 \leq \alpha < 1 - \mu$ and $1 - \mu < \alpha < 1$ separately.]

*71. Use the formula from Exercise 70 to show that $a(n) = a(n-1)$ if $\mu n - \lfloor \mu n \rfloor < 1 - \mu$ and $a(n) = a(n-1) + 1$ otherwise.

296 3 / Mathematical Reasoning, Induction, and Recursion   *3–84*

72. Find the first 10 terms of each of the following self-generating sequences:

a) $a(n) = n - a(a(a(n - 1)))$ for $n \geq 1$ with $a(0) = 0$.

b) $a(n) = n - a(a(a(a(n - 1))))$ for $n \geq 1$ with $a(0) = 0$.

c) $a(n) = a(n - a(n - 1)) + a(n - a(n - 2))$ for $n \geq 3$ with $a(1) = 1$ and $a(2) = 1$.

73. Find the first 10 terms of both the sequences $m(n)$ and $f(n)$ defined by the following pair of interwoven recurrence relations: $m(n) = n - f(m(n - 1))$, $f(n) = n - m(f(n - 1))$ for $n \geq 1$ with $f(0) = 1$ and $m(0) = 0$.

Golomb's self-generating sequence is the unique nondecreasing sequence of positive integers $a_1, a_2, a_3, \ldots$, which has the property that it contains exactly a_k occurrences of k for each positive integer k.

74. Find the first 20 terms of Golomb's self-generating sequence.

*75. Show that if $f(n)$ is the largest integer m such that $a_m = n$, where a_m is the mth term of Golomb's self-generating sequence, then $f(n) = \sum_{k=1}^{n} a_k$ and $f(f(n)) = \sum_{k=1}^{n} k a_k$.

The set $\mathcal{L}$ of **logarithmico-exponential functions,** introduced by the famous British mathematician G. H. Hardy, is the smallest set of functions such that:

- the function $f(n) = \alpha$ belongs to $\mathcal{L}$, whenever α is a real number;
- the function $f(n) = n$ belongs to $\mathcal{L}$;
- if the functions $f(n)$ and $g(n)$ belong to $\mathcal{L}$, then $f(n) - g(n)$ belongs to $\mathcal{L}$;
- if the function $f(n)$ belongs to $\mathcal{L}$, then $e^{f(n)}$ belongs to $\mathcal{L}$;

GODFREY HAROLD HARDY (1877–1947) Hardy, born in Cranleigh, Surrey, England, was the older of two children of Isaac Hardy and Sophia Hall Hardy. His father was the geography and drawing master at the Cranleigh School and also gave singing lessons and played soccer. His mother gave piano lessons and helped run a boardinghouse for young students. Hardy's parents were devoted to their children's education. Hardy demonstrated his numerical ability at the early age of two when he began writing down numbers into the millions. He had a private mathematics tutor rather than attending regular classes at the Cranleigh School. He moved to Winchester College, a private high school, when he was 13 and was awarded a scholarship. He excelled in his studies and demonstrated a strong interest in mathematics. He entered Trinity College, Cambridge, in 1896 on a scholarship and won several prizes during his time there, graduating in 1899.

Hardy held the position of lecturer in mathematics at Trinity College at Cambridge University from 1906 to 1919, when he was appointed to the Sullivan chair of geometry at Oxford. He had become unhappy at Cambridge with the dismissal of the famous philosopher and mathematician Bertrand Russell from Trinity for antiwar activities and did not like a heavy load of administrative duties. In 1931 he returned to Cambridge as the Sadleirian professor of pure mathematics, where he remained until his retirement in 1942. He was a pure mathematician and held an elitist view of mathematics, hoping his research could never be applied. Ironically, he is perhaps best known as one of the developers of the Hardy–Weinberg law, which predicts patterns of inheritance. His work in this area appeared as a letter to the journal *Science* in which he used simple algebraic ideas to demonstrate errors in an article on genetics. Hardy worked primarily in number theory and function theory, working on such topics as the Riemann zeta function, Fourier series, and the distribution of primes. He made many important contributions to many important problems, such as Waring's problem about representing positive integers as the sum of kth powers and the problem of representing odd integers as the sum of three primes. Hardy is also remembered for his collaborations with John E. Littlewood, a colleague at Cambridge, with whom he wrote more than 100 papers and the famous Indian mathematical prodigy Srinivasa Ramanujan. His collaboration with Littlewood led to the joke that there were only three important English mathematicians at that time, Hardy, Littlewood, and Hardy–Littlewood, although some people thought that Hardy had invented a fictitious person, Littlewood, since Littlewood was seldom seen outside Cambridge. Hardy had the wisdom of recognizing Ramanujan's genius from unconventional but extremely creative writings Ramanujan sent him, while other mathematicians failed to see the genius. Hardy brought Ramanujan to Cambridge and collaborated on important joint papers, establishing new results on the number of partitions of an integer. Hardy was interested in mathematics education, and his book *A Course in Pure Mathematics* had a profound effect on undergraduate instruction in mathematics in the first half of the twentieth century. Hardy also wrote *A Mathematician's Apology* in which he gives his answer to the question whether it is worthwhile to devote one's life to the study of mathematics. It presents Hardy's view of what mathematics is and what a mathematician does.

Hardy had a strong interest in sports. He was an avid cricket fan and followed scores closely. One peculiar trait he had was that he did not like his picture taken (only five snapshots are known) and disliked mirrors, covering them with towels immediately on entering a hotel room.

■ if $f(n)$ belongs to $\mathcal{L}$ and there exists an integer N such that $f(n) > 0$ for $n \geq N$ (this means that f is called **eventually positive**), then $\ln f(n)$ belongs to $\mathcal{L}$, where $\ln x$ denotes the natural logarithm of x, as usual.

Hardy showed for every logarithmico-exponential function not identically zero that $f(n)$ is either eventually positive or eventually negative. He proved that if $f(n)$ and $g(n)$ belong to $\mathcal{L}$, then either $f(n)$ is $o(g(n))$, $g(n)$ is $o(f(n))$, or $f(n)$ and $g(n)$ are of the same order.

76. Show that if $f(n)$ and $g(n)$ belong to $\mathcal{L}$, then $f(n) + g(n)$ belongs to $\mathcal{L}$.

*77. Show that if $f(n)$ and $g(n)$ belong to $\mathcal{L}$ and are eventually positive, then $f(n)g(n)$ and $f(n)/g(n)$ belong to $\mathcal{L}$, and that this implies, using the fact that every logarithmico-exponential function is eventually positive, eventually negative, or identically zero, that the product and quotient of any two functions, not identically zero, in $\mathcal{L}$ are in $\mathcal{L}$.

78. Use Exercises 76 and 77 to show that every polynomial $f(n) = a_m n^m + a_{m-1} n^{m-1} + \cdots + a_0$ with real coefficients belongs to $\mathcal{L}$.

79. Show that if $f(n)$ belongs to $\mathcal{L}$ and is eventually positive, then $\sqrt{f(n)}$ belongs to $\mathcal{L}$.

80. Show that the function $e^{\sqrt{n}\sqrt{\ln n \ln \ln n}}$ belongs to $\mathcal{L}$.

SRINIVASA RAMANUJAN (1887–1920) The famous mathematical prodigy Ramanujan was born and raised in southern India near the city of Madras. His father was a clerk in a cloth shop. His mother contributed to the family income by singing at a local temple. Ramanujan studied at the local English language school, displaying his talent and interest for mathematics. At 13 he mastered a textbook used by college students. When he was 15, a university student lent him a copy of *Synopsis of Pure Mathematics*. Ramanujan decided to work out the over 6000 results in this book, stated without proof or explanation, writing on sheets later collected to form notebooks. He graduated from high school in 1904, winning a scholarship to the University of Madras. Enrolling in a fine arts curriculum, he neglected his subjects other than mathematics and lost his scholarship. He failed to pass examinations at the university four times from 1904 to 1907, doing well only in mathematics. During this time he filled his notebooks with original writings, sometimes rediscovering already published work and at other times making new discoveries.

Without a university degree, it was difficult for Ramanujan to find a decent job. To survive, he had to depend on the goodwill of his friends. He tutored students in mathematics, but his unconventional ways of thinking and failure to stick to the syllabus caused problems. He was married in 1909 in an arranged marriage to a young woman nine years his junior. Needing to support himself and his wife, he moved to Madras and sought a job. He showed his notebooks of mathematical writings to his potential employers, but the books bewildered them. However, a professor at the Presidency College recognized his genius and supported him for a while, and in 1912 he found work as an accounts clerk, earning a small salary.

Ramanujan continued his mathematical work during this time and published his first paper in 1910 in an Indian journal. He realized that his work was beyond that of Indian mathematicians and decided to write to leading English mathematicians. The first mathematicians he wrote to turned down his request for help. But in January 1913 he wrote to G. H. Hardy, who was inclined to turn Ramanujan down, but the mathematical statements in the letter, although stated without proof, puzzled Hardy. He decided to examine them closely with the help of his colleague and collaborator J. E. Littlewood. They decided, after careful study, that Ramanujan was probably a genius, since his statements "could only be written down by a mathematician of the highest class; they must be true, because if they were not true, no one would have the imagination to invent them."

Hardy arranged a scholarship for Ramanujan, bringing him to England in 1914. Hardy personally tutored him in mathematical analysis, and they collaborated for five years, proving significant theorems about the number of partitions of integers. During this time, Ramanujan made important contributions to number theory and also worked on continued fractions, infinite series, and elliptic functions. Ramanujan had amazing insight involving certain types of functions and series, but his purported theorems on prime numbers were often wrong, illustrating his vague idea of what constitutes a correct proof. He was one of the youngest members ever appointed a Fellow of the Royal Society. Unfortunately, in 1917 Ramanujan became extremely ill. At the time, it was thought that he had trouble with the English climate and had contracted tuberculosis. It is now thought that he suffered from a vitamin deficiency, brought on by Ramanujan's strict vegetarianism and shortages in wartime England. He returned to India in 1919, continuing to do mathematics even when confined to his bed. He was religious and thought his mathematical talent came from his family deity, Namagiri. He considered mathematics and religion to be linked. He said that "an equation for me has no meaning unless it expresses a thought of God." His short life came to an end in April 1920, when he was 32 years old. Ramanujan left several notebooks of unpublished results. The writings in these notebooks illustrate Ramanujan's insights but are quite sketchy. Several mathematicians have devoted many years of study to explaining and justifying the results in these notebooks.

Computer Projects

WRITE PROGRAMS WITH THESE INPUT AND OUTPUT.

1. Given the terms of a sequence $a_1, a_2, \ldots, a_n$, find $\sum_{j=1}^{n} a_j$ and $\prod_{j=1}^{n} a_j$.

2. Given a geometric progression $a, ar, ar^2, \ldots, ar^n$, find the sum of its terms.

3. Given a nonnegative integer n, find the sum of the n smallest positive integers.

** 4. Given a $2^n \times 2^n$ chessboard with one square missing, construct a tiling of this chessboard using L-shaped pieces.

** 5. Generate all well-formed formulae for expressions involving the variables x, y, and z and the operators $\{+, *, /, -\}$ with n or fewer symbols.

** 6. Generate all well-formed formulae for propositions with n or fewer symbols where each symbol is **T**, **F**, one of the propositional variables p and q, or an operator from $\{\neg, \vee, \wedge, \rightarrow, \leftrightarrow\}$.

7. Given a string, find its reversal.

8. Given a real number a and a nonnegative integer n, find a^n using recursion.

9. Given a real number a and a nonnegative integer n, find a^{2^n} using recursion.

*10. Given a real number a and a nonnegative integer n, find a^n using the binary expansion of n and a recursive algorithm for computing a^{2^k}.

11. Given two integers not both zero, find their greatest common divisor using recursion.

12. Given a list of integers and an element x, locate x in this list using a recursive implementation of a linear search.

13. Given a list of integers and an element x, locate x in this list using a recursive implementation of a binary search.

14. Given a nonnegative integer n, find the nth Fibonacci number using iteration.

15. Given a nonnegative integer n, find the nth Fibonacci number using recursion.

16. Given a positive integer, find the number of partitions of this integer. (See Exercise 47 of Section 3.4.)

17. Given positive integers m and n, find $A(m, n)$, the value of Ackermann's function at the pair (m, n). (See the preamble to Exercise 48 of Section 3.4.)

18. Given a list of n integers, sort these integers using the merge sort.

Computations and Explorations

USE A COMPUTATIONAL PROGRAM OR PROGRAMS YOU HAVE WRITTEN TO DO THESE EXERCISES.

1. Verify Goldbach's conjecture, which states that every even positive integer n is the sum of two primes, for $n \le 10,000$.

2. Find the smallest prime factor of $n! + 1$ for all positive integers n with $n \le 20$.

3. Find the smallest set of n consecutive composite integers for each positive integer n with $n \le 10$.

4. Find as many twin primes as you can.

5. Verify the $3x + 1$ conjecture for as many positive integers as possible.

6. What are the largest values of n for which $n!$ has fewer than 100 decimal digits and fewer than 1000 decimal digits?

7. Determine which Fibonacci numbers are divisible by 5, which are divisible by 7, and which are divisible by 11. Prove that your conjectures are correct.

8. Construct tilings using L-shaped pieces of various 16×16, 32×32, and 64×64 chessboards with one square missing.

9. Explore which $m \times n$ chessboards can be completely covered by L-shaped pieces. Can you make a conjecture that answers this question?

10. Which values of Ackermann's function are small enough that you are able to compute them?

11. Compare either the number of operations or the time needed to compute Fibonacci numbers recursively versus that needed to compute them iteratively.

Writing Projects

RESPOND TO THESE WITH ESSAYS USING OUTSIDE SOURCES.

1. Provide a brief explanation of the types of methods used to prove what is currently known about Goldbach's conjecture.

2. Describe the conjectures that have been made about the number of twin primes not exceeding a real number x. On what basis were these conjectures made?

3. Describe some open questions in number theory other than the ones mentioned in Section 3.1.

4. Explain the different ways in which the *Encyclopedia of Integer Sequences* has been found useful. Also, describe a few of the more unusual sequences in this encyclopedia and how they arise.

5. Define the recently invented EKG sequence and describe some of its properties and open questions about it.

6. Look up the definition of a transcendental number. Explain how to show that such numbers exist and how such numbers can be constructed. Which famous numbers can be shown to be transcendental and for which famous numbers is it still unknown whether they are transcendental?

7. Describe the origins of mathematical induction. Who were the first people to use it and to which problems did they apply it?

8. In the past 25 years, several important theorems have been proved based on extensive computer computations. Discuss the validity of such proofs and describe the controversy surrounding proofs based on computer calculations.

9. The L-shaped pieces used in the exercises of Section 3.3 are examples of *polyominoes*, introduced by Golomb in 1954. Describe some of the problems and associated results concerning tiling chessboards with polyominoes.

10. Discuss the uses of Ackermann's function both in the theory of recursive definitions and in the analysis of the complexity of algorithms for set unions.

11. Discuss some of the various methodologies used to establish the correctness of programs and compare them to Hoare's methods described in Section 3.6.

12. Explain how the ideas and concepts of program correctness can be extended to prove that operating systems are secure.

CHAPTER 3

SECTION 3.1

1. Since every second integer is divisible by 2, the product is divisible by 2. Since every third integer is divisible by 3, the product is divisible by 3. Therefore the product has both 2 and 3 in its prime factorization and is therefore divisible by $3 \cdot 2 = 6$.   **3.** $n^4 - 1 = (2k+1)^4 - 1 = 16k^4 + 32k^3 + 24k^2 + 8k = 8k(k+1)(2k^2 + 2k + 1)$. One of k or $k+1$ is even, so 16 divides $n^4 - 1$.   **5.** Since $5^4 = 625$, both x and y must be less than 5. Then $x^4 + y^4 \le 4^4 + 4^4 = 512 < 625$.   **7.** If $3x^2 - 1 = 8y$, then $3x^2 \equiv 1 \pmod 8$. If x is an odd integer, then by Exercise 2, $x^2 \equiv 1 \pmod 8$, so $3x^2 \equiv 3 \pmod 8$. If x is even, then $x^2 \equiv 0$ or $4 \pmod 8$, so $3x^2 \equiv 0$ or $4 \pmod 8$. This contradiction implies that there are no integer solutions to the given equation.   **9.** If $x^4 - 3 = 16y^4$, then $x^4 \equiv 3 \pmod{16}$. By Exercise 3, the fourth power of an odd integer is congruent to 1 modulo 16. The fourth power of an even integer is congruent to 0 modulo 16. Thus x^4 cannot be congruent to 3 modulo 16, and the equation has no solutions.   **11.** The harmonic mean of distinct positive real numbers a and b is always less than their geometric mean. To prove $2ab/(a+b) < \sqrt{ab}$, multiply both sides by $(a+b)/(2\sqrt{ab})$ to obtain the equivalent inequality $\sqrt{ab} < (a+b)/2$, which is proved in Example 1.   **13.** The parity (oddness or evenness) of the sum of the numbers written on the board never changes, since $j + k$ and $|j - k|$ have the same parity (and at each step we reduce the sum by $j + k$ but increase it by $|j - k|$). Therefore the integer at the end of the process must have the same parity as $1 + 2 + \cdots + (2n) = n(2n + 1)$, which is odd since n is odd. **15.** $n = 1601$ is a counterexample. **17.** Suppose that $3^{1/3} = a/b$ where $a, b \in \mathbf{Z}, b \neq 0$, and $\gcd(a, b) = 1$. Then $3 = a^3/b^3$, so that $3b^3 = a^3$. Hence $3 \mid a^3$, which can happen only if $3 \mid a$. Let $a = 3m$. Then $3b^3 = 27m^3$, or $b^3 = 9m^3$. Thus $3 \mid b^3$, which shows that $3 \mid b$. This is a contradiction of the assumption that $\gcd(a, b) = 1$. **19.** By the rational root test from high school algebra, any rational number that satisfies this polynomial with integer coefficients is of the form p/q, where p is a factor of the constant term (1), and q is a factor of the leading coefficient (1). So the only possible rational roots are ± 1; since neither of them is a root, there are no rational roots. **21.** $a^2 \equiv b^2 \pmod{p}$ if and only if $p \mid (a^2 - b^2) = (a+b)(a-b)$. By the uniqueness of prime factorization, this is equivalent to $p \mid (a - b)$ or $p \mid (a + b)$, which is the same as $a \equiv b \pmod{p}$ or $a \equiv -b \pmod{p}$. **23.** Both sides are nonnegative integers less than m, congruent to ab modulo m, so they must be equal. **25.** 3, 5, and 7 are primes of the desired form. **27.** The integer $p_1 p_2 \cdots p_n p_{n+1}$, where p_j is the jth prime, is divisible by $n + 1$ distinct primes. **29.** If not, then suppose that $q_1, q_2, \ldots, q_n$ are all the primes of the form $6k + 5$. Let $Q = 6q_1 q_2 \cdots q_n - 1$. Note that Q is of the form $6k+5$, where $k = q_1 q_2 \cdots q_n - 1$. Let $Q = p_1 p_2 \cdots p_t$ be the prime factorization of Q. No p_i is $2, 3,$ or any q_j, because the remainder when Q is divided by 2 is 1, by 3 is 2, and by q_j is $q_j - 1$. All odd primes other than 3 are of the form $6k + 1$ or $6k + 5$, and the product of primes of the form $6k + 1$ is also of this form. Therefore at least one of the p_i's must be of the form $6k+5$, a contradiction. **31.** We prove this by considering the three cases of $n = 3k, n = 3k + 1$, and $n = 3k + 2$ for some integer k. If n is a multiple of 3, then the left-hand side is $\lfloor \frac{x}{3} \rfloor + \lfloor \frac{x+n}{3} \rfloor + \lfloor \frac{x+2n}{3} \rfloor = \lfloor \frac{x}{3} \rfloor + \lfloor \frac{x}{3} \rfloor + \frac{n}{3} + \lfloor \frac{x}{3} \rfloor + \frac{2n}{3} = 3 \lfloor \frac{x}{3} \rfloor + n$, and the right-hand side of the desired equality is also $3 \lfloor \frac{x}{3} \rfloor + n$. If $n = 3k + 1$, then the left-hand side is $\lfloor \frac{x}{3} \rfloor + \lfloor \frac{x+3k+1}{3} \rfloor + \lfloor \frac{x+6k+2}{3} \rfloor = \lfloor \frac{x}{3} \rfloor + \lfloor \frac{x+1}{3} \rfloor + k + \lfloor \frac{x+2}{3} \rfloor + 2k = \lfloor \frac{x}{3} \rfloor + \lfloor \frac{x+1}{3} \rfloor + \lfloor \frac{x+2}{3} \rfloor + n - 1$, and the right-hand side is $\lfloor x \rfloor + n - 1$. By Exercise 68 in Section 1.8, these are equal. The third case is similar. **33. a)** Without loss of generality, assume that the x sequence is already sorted into nondecreasing order, since we can relabel the indices. There are only a finite number of possible orderings for the y sequence, so if we can show that we can increase the sum (or at least keep it the same) whenever we find y_i and y_j that are out of order (i.e., $i < j$ but $y_i > y_j$) by switching them, then we will have shown that the sum is largest when the y sequence is in nondecreasing order. Indeed, if we perform the swap, then we have added $x_i y_j + x_j y_i$ to the sum and subtracted $x_i y_i + x_j y_j$. The net effect is to have added $x_i y_j + x_j y_i - x_i y_i - x_j y_j = (x_j - x_i)(y_i - y_j)$, which is nonnegative by our ordering assumptions. **b)** similar to part (a). **35.** Let $x = n + (r/m) + \epsilon$, where n is an integer, r is a nonnegative integer less than m, and ϵ is

a real number with $0 \leq \epsilon < 1/m$. The left-hand side is $\lfloor nm + r + m\epsilon \rfloor = nm + r$. On the right-hand side, the terms $\lfloor x \rfloor$ through $\lfloor x + (m + r - 1)/m \rfloor$ are all just n and the terms from $\lfloor x + (m - r)/m \rfloor$ on are all $n + 1$. Therefore, the right-hand side is $(m - r)n + r(n + 1) = nm + r$, as well. **37.** Recall that a nonconstant polynomial can take on the same value only a finite number of times. Thus f can take on the values 0 and ± 1 only finitely many times, so if there is not some y such that $f(y)$ is composite, then there must be some x_0 such that $\pm f(x_0)$ is prime, say p. Look at $f(x_0 + kp)$. When we plug $x_0 + kp$ in for x in the polynomial and multiply it out, every term will contain a factor of p except for the terms that form $f(x_0)$. Therefore $f(x_0 + kp) = f(x_0) + mp = (m + 1)p$ for some integer m. As k varies, this value can be $0, p,$ or $-p$ only finitely many times; therefore it must be a composite number for some values of k. **39.** Assume that every even integer greater than 2 is the sum of two primes, and let n be an integer greater than 5. If n is odd, write $n = 3 + (n - 3)$ and decompose $n - 3 = p + q$ into the sum of two primes; if n is even, then write $n = 2 + (n - 2)$ and decompose $n - 2 = p + q$ into the sum of two primes. For the converse, assume that every integer greater than 5 is the sum of three primes, and let n be an even integer greater than 2. Write $n + 2$ as the sum of three primes, one of which is necessarily 2, so $n + 2 = 2 + p + q$, whence $n = p + q$. **41. a)** $6 \to 3 \to 10 \to 5 \to 16 \to 8 \to 4 \to 2 \to 1$ **b)** $7 \to 22 \to 11 \to 34 \to 17 \to 52 \to 26 \to 13 \to 40 \to 20 \to 10 \to 5 \to 16 \to 8 \to 4 \to 2 \to 1$ **c)** $17 \to 52 \to 26 \to 13 \to 40 \to 20 \to 10 \to 5 \to 16 \to 8 \to 4 \to 2 \to 1$ **d)** $21 \to 64 \to 32 \to 16 \to 8 \to 4 \to 2 \to 1$ **43.** $1 + 2 + 3 = 6; 1 + 2 + 4 + 7 + 14 = 28; 1 + 2 + 4 + 8 + 16 + 31 + 62 + 124 + 248 = 496$ **45.** The sum of the proper divisors is $(1+2+4+8+\cdots+2^{p-1})+(2^p - 1)(1+2+4+8+\cdots+2^{p-2}) = 2^p - 1 + (2^p - 1)(2^{p-1} - 1) = (2^p - 1)(1 + 2^{p-1} - 1) = (2^p - 1)2^{p-1}$. **47.** $(3, 5, 0) \to (3, 2, 3) \to (6, 2, 0) \to (6, 0, 2) \to (1, 5, 2) \to (1, 4, 3)$ **49.** Suppose we had a program S that could tell whether a program with its given input ever prints the digit 1. Here is an algorithm for solving the halting problem: Given a program P and its input I, construct a program P', which is just like P but never prints anything (even if P did print something) except that if and when it is about to halt, it prints a 1 and halts. Then P halts on an input if and only if P' ever prints a 1 on that same input. Feed P' and I to S, and that will tell us whether or not P halts on input I. Since we know that the halting problem is in fact not solvable, we have a contradiction. Therefore no such program S exists. **51.** Run the two programs concurrently and wait for one to halt.

SECTION 3.2

1. a) 3 **b)** -1 **c)** 787 **d)** 2639 **3. a)** $a_0 = 2, a_1 = 3, a_2 = 5, a_3 = 9$ **b)** $a_0 = 1, a_1 = 4, a_2 = 27, a_3 = 256$

c) $a_0 = 0$, $a_1 = 0$, $a_2 = 1$, $a_3 = 1$ **d)** $a_0 = 0$, $a_1 = 1$, $a_2 = 2$, $a_3 = 3$ **5. a)** 2, 5, 8, 11, 14, 17, 20, 23, 26, 29 **b)** 1, 1, 1, 2, 2, 2, 3, 3, 3, 4   **c)** 1, 1, 3, 3, 5, 5, 7, 7, 9, 9 **d)** -1, -2, -2, 8, 88, 656, 4912, 40064, 362368, 3627776   **e)** 3, 6, 12, 24, 48, 96, 192, 384, 768, 1536 **f)** 1, 1, 2, 3, 5, 8, 13, 21, 34, 55   **g)** 1, 2, 2, 3, 3, 3, 3, 4, 4, 4 **h)** 3, 3, 5, 4, 4, 3, 5, 5, 4, 3   **7.** Each term could be twice the previous term; the nth term could be obtained from the previous term by adding $n - 1$; the terms could be the positive integers that are not multiples of 3; there are infinitely many other possibilities.   **9. a)** One 1 and one 0, followed by two 1s and two 0s, followed by three 1s and three 0s, and so on   **b)** The positive integers are listed in increasing order with each even positive integer listed twice.   **c)** The terms in odd-numbered locations are the successive powers of 2; the terms in even-numbered locations are all 0.   **d)** $a_n = 3 \cdot 2^{n-1}$ **e)** $a_n = 15 - 7(n - 1) = 22 - 7n$ **f)** $a_n = (n^2 + n + 4)/2$ **g)** $a_n = 2n^3$ **h)** $a_n = n! + 1$ **11.** Among the integers $1, 2, \ldots, a_n$, where a_n is the nth positive integer not a perfect square, the nonsquares are $a_1, a_2, \ldots, a_n$ and the squares are $1^2, 2^2, \ldots, k^2$, where k is the integer with $k^2 < n+k < (k+1)^2$. Consequently, $a_n = n+k$, where $k^2 < a_n < (k+1)^2$. To find k, first note that $k^2 < n+k < (k+1)^2$, so $k^2 + 1 \le n + k \le (k+1)^2 - 1$. Hence $(k - \frac{1}{2})^2 + \frac{3}{4} = k^2 - k + 1 \le n \le k^2 + k = (k + \frac{1}{2})^2 - \frac{1}{4}$. It follows that $k - \frac{1}{2} < \sqrt{n} < k + \frac{1}{2}$, so $k = \{\sqrt{n}\}$ and $a_n = n + k = n + \{\sqrt{n}\}$. **13. a)** 20   **b)** 11   **c)** 30   **d)** 511   **15. a)** 1533   **b)** 510 **c)** 4923   **d)** 9842   **17.   a)** 21   **b)** 78   **c)** 18   **d)** 18 **19.** $\sum_{j=1}^{n}(a_j - a_{j-1}) = a_n - a_0$ **21. a)** n^2 **b)** $n(n+1)/2$ **23.** 15150   **25.** $\frac{n(n+1)(2n+1)}{3} + \frac{n(n+1)}{2} + (n+1)(m-(n+1)^2+1)$, where $n = \lfloor \sqrt{m} \rfloor - 1$ **27. a)** 0   **b)** 1680   **c)** 1   **d)** 1024 **29.** 34   **31. a)** Countable, $-1, -2, -3, -4, \ldots$ **b)** Countable, $0, 2, -2, 4, -4, \ldots$ **c)** Uncountable **d)** Countable, $0, 7, -7, 14, -14, \ldots$ **33.** Assume that $A - B$ is countable. Then, since $A = (A - B) \cup B$, the elements of A can be listed in a sequence by alternating elements of $A - B$ and elements of B. This contradicts the uncountability of A.   **35.** Assume that B is countable. Then the elements of B can be listed as b_1, b_2, b_3, ... Since A is a subset of B, taking the subsequence of $\{b_n\}$ that contains the terms that are in A gives a listing of the elements of A. Since A is uncountable, this is impossible. **37.** Suppose that $A_1, A_2, A_3, \ldots$ are countable sets. Since A_i is countable, we can list its elements in a sequence as $a_{i1}, a_{i2}, a_{i3}, \ldots$. The elements of the set $\bigcup_{i=1}^{n} A_i$ can be listed by listing all terms a_{ij} with $i + j = 2$, then all terms a_{ij} with $i + j = 3$, then all terms a_{ij} with $i + j = 4$, and so on.   **39.** There are a finite number, namely, 2^m, bit strings of length m. The set of all bit strings is the union of the bit strings of lengths m over $m = 0, 1, 2, \ldots$. Since the union of a countable number of countable sets is countable, there are a countable number of bit strings.   **41.** For any finite alphabet there are a finite number of strings of length n, whenever n is a positive integer. It follows by the result of

Exercise 37 that there are only a finite number of strings from any given finite alphabet. Since the set of all computer programs in a particular language is a subset of the set of all strings of a finite alphabet, which is a countable set, by the result of Exercise 34, it is itself a countable set. **43.** Exercise 41 shows that there are only a countable number of computer programs. Consequently, there are only a countable number of computable functions. Since, as Exercise 42 shows, there are an uncountable number of functions, not all functions are computable.   **45.** Given a positive integer x, we show that there is exactly one positive rational number m/n (in lowest terms) such that $K(m/n) = x$. From the prime factorization of x, read off the m and n such that $K(m/n) = x$. The primes that occur to even powers are the primes that occur in the prime factorization of m, with the exponents being half the corresponding exponents in x; and the primes that occur to odd powers are the primes that occur in the prime factorization of n, with the exponents being half of one more than the exponents in x.

SECTION 3.3

1. $n(n+1)$ **3.** Let $P(n)$ be "$\sum_{j=0}^{n} 3 \cdot 5^j = 3(5^{n+1} - 1)/4$." *Basis step:* $P(0)$ is true since $\sum_{j=0}^{0} 3 \cdot 5^j = 3 = 3(5^1 - 1)/4$. *Inductive step:* Assume that $\sum_{j=0}^{k} 3 \cdot 5^j = 3(5^{k+1} - 1)/4$. Then $\sum_{j=0}^{k+1} 3 \cdot 5^j = (\sum_{j=0}^{k} 3 \cdot 5^j) + 3 \cdot 5^{k+1} = 3(5^{k+1}-1)/4 + 3 \cdot 5^{k+1} = 3(5^{k+1} + 4 \cdot 5^{k+1} - 1)/4 = 3(5^{k+2} - 1)/4$.   **5.** By examining small values of n we make the conjecture that $P(n)$ is true where $P(n)$ is the statement "$\sum_{j=1}^{n} 1/2^j = (2^n - 1)/2^n$." *Basis step:* $P(1)$ is true since $\frac{1}{2} = (2^1 - 1)/2^1$. *Inductive step:* Assume that $\sum_{j=1}^{k} 1/2^j = (2^k - 1)/2^k$. Then $\sum_{j=1}^{k+1} \frac{1}{2^j} = (\sum_{j=1}^{k} \frac{1}{2^j}) + \frac{1}{2^{k+1}} = \frac{2^k - 1}{2^k} + \frac{1}{2^{k+1}} = \frac{2^{k+1} - 2 + 1}{2^{k+1}} = \frac{2^{k+1} - 1}{2^{k+1}}$.   **7.** Let $P(n)$ be "$\sum_{j=1}^{n} j^2 = n(n+1)(2n+1)/6$." *Basis step:* $P(1)$ is true since $\sum_{1}^{1} j^2 = 1 = 1(1+1)(2 \cdot 1 + 1)/6$. *Inductive step:* Assume that $\sum_{j=1}^{k} j^2 = k(k+1)(2k+1)/6$. Then $\sum_{j=1}^{k+1} j^2 = (\sum_{j=1}^{k} j^2) + (k+1)^2 = k(k+1)(2k+1)/6 + (k+1)^2 = (k+1)[2k^2 + k + 6k + 6]/6 = (k+1)(k+2) \cdot (2k+3)/6 = (k+1)((k+1)+1)(2(k+1)+1)/6$. **9.** Let $P(n)$ be "$1^2 + 3^2 + \cdots + (2n+1)^2 = (n+1)(2n+1)(2n+3)/3$." *Basis step:* $P(0)$ is true since $1^2 = 1 = (0+1)(2 \cdot 0 + 1)(2 \cdot 0 + 3)/3$. *Inductive step:* Assume that $P(k)$ is true. Then $1^2 + 3^2 + \cdots + (2k+1)^2 + (2(k+1)+1)^2 = (k+1)(2k+1)(2k+3)/3 + (2k+3)^2 = (2k+3)[(k+1)(2k+1)/3 + (2k+3)] = (2k+3)(2k^2 + 9k + 10)/3 = (2k+3)(2k+5)(k+2)/3 = ((k+1)+1)(2(k+1)+1) \cdot (2(k+1)+3)/3$.   **11.** Let $P(n)$ be "$1 + nh \le (1 + h)^n, h > -1$." *Basis step:* $P(0)$ is true since $1 + 0 \cdot h = 1 \le 1 = (1 + h)^0$. *Inductive step:* Assume $1 + kh \le (1 + h)^k$. Then since $(1+h) > 0$, $(1+h)^{k+1} = (1+h)(1+h)^k \ge (1+h)(1+kh) = 1 + (k+1)h + kh^2 \ge 1 + (k+1)h$.   **13.** Let $P(n)$ be "$2^n > n^2$." *Basis step:* $P(5)$ is true since $2^5 = 32 > 25 = 5^2$. *Inductive step:* Assume that $P(k)$ is true, that is, $2^k > k^2$.

Then $2^{k+1} = 2 \cdot 2^k > k^2 + k^2 > k^2 + 4k \geq k^2 + 2k + 1 = (k+1)^2$ since $k > 4$.   **15.** Let $P(n)$ be "$1 \cdot 2 + 2 \cdot 3 + \cdots + n(n+1) = n(n+1)(n+2)/3$." *Basis step:* $P(1)$ is true since $1 \cdot 2 = 2 = 1(1+1)(1+2)/3$. *Inductive step:* Assume that $P(k)$ is true. Then $1 \cdot 2 + 2 \cdot 3 + \cdots + k(k+1) + (k+1)(k+2) = [k(k+1)(k+2)/3] + (k+1)(k+2) = (k+1)(k+2)[(k/3)+1] = (k+1)(k+2)(k+3)/3$.   **17.** Let $P(n)$ be "$1^2 - 2^2 + 3^2 - \cdots + (-1)^{n-1}n^2 = (-1)^{n-1}n(n+1)/2$." *Basis step:* $P(1)$ is true since $1^2 = 1 = (-1)^0 1^2$. *Inductive step:* Assume that $P(k)$ is true. Then $1^2 - 2^2 + 3^2 - \cdots + (-1)^{k-1}k^2 + (-1)^k(k+1)^2 = (-1)^{k-1}k(k+1)/2 + (-1)^k(k+1)^2 = (-1)^k(k+1)[-k/2 + (k+1)] = (-1)^k(k+1)[(k/2)+1] = (-1)^k(k+1)(k+2)/2$.
19. Let $P(n)$ be "a postage of n cents can be formed using 3-cent and 5-cent stamps." *Basis step:* $P(8)$ is true since 8 cents postage can be formed with one 3-cent and one 5-cent stamp. *Inductive step:* Assume that $P(k)$ is true, that is, postage of k cents can be formed. We will show how to form postage of $k+1$ cents. By the inductive hypothesis postage of k cents can be formed. If this included a 5-cent stamp, replace this with two 3-cent stamps to obtain $k+1$ cents postage. Otherwise, only 3-cent stamps were used and $k \geq 9$. Remove three of these 3-cent stamps and replace them with two 5-cent stamps to obtain $k+1$ cents postage.
21. Let $P(n)$ be "$n^5 - n$ is divisible by 5." *Basis step:* $P(0)$ is true since $0^5 - 0 = 0$ is divisible by 5. *Inductive step:* Assume that $P(k)$ is true, that is, $k^5 - 5$ is divisible by 5. Then $(k+1)^5 - (k+1) = (k^5 + 5k^4 + 10k^3 + 10k^2 + 5k + 1) - (k+1) = (k^5 - k) + 5(k^4 + 2k^3 + 2k^2 + k)$ is also divisible by 5, since both terms in this sum are divisible by 5.   **23.** Let $P(n)$ be the proposition that $(2n-1)^2 - 1$ is divisible by 8. The basis case $P(1)$ is true since $8 \mid 0$. Now assume that $P(k)$ is true. Since $((2(k+1) - 1)^2 - 1) = ((2k-1)^2 - 1) + 8k$, $P(k+1)$ is true since both terms on the right-hand side are divisible by 8. This shows that $P(n)$ is true for all positive integers so that $m^2 - 1$ is divisible by 8 whenever m is an odd positive integer.   **25.** Let $P(n)$ be the statement that a set with n elements has $n(n-1)/2$ two-element subsets. $P(2)$, the basis case, is true, since a set with two elements has one subset with two elements—namely, itself—and $2(2-1)/2 = 1$. Now assume that $P(k)$ is true. Let S be a set with $k+1$ elements. Choose an element a in S and let $T = S - \{a\}$. A two-element subset of S either contains a or it does not. Those subsets not containing a are the subsets of two elements of T; by the inductive hypothesis there are $k(k-1)/2$ of these. There are k subsets of two elements of S that contain a, since such a subset contains a and one of the k elements in T. Hence there are $k(k-1)/2 + k = (k+1)k/2$ two-element subsets of S. This completes the inductive proof.   **27.** Let $P(n)$ be the statement that $1^4 + 2^4 + 3^4 + \cdots + n^4 = n(n+1)(2n+1)(3n^2 + 3n - 1)/30$. $P(1)$ is true since $1 \cdot 2 \cdot 3 \cdot 5/30 = 1$. Assume that $P(k)$ is true. Then $(1^4 + 2^4 + 3^4 + \cdots + k^4) + (k+1)^4 = k(k+1)(2k+1)(3k^2 + 3k - 1)/30 + (k+1)^4 = ((k+1)/30)(k(2k+1)(3k^2 + 3k - 1) + 30(k+1)^3) = ((k+1)/30)(6k^4 + 39k^3 + 91k^2 + 89k + 30) = ((k+1)/30)(k+2)(2k+3)(3(k+1)^2 + 3(k+1) - 1)$. This

demonstrates that $P(k+1)$ is true.   **29.** By inspection we find that the inequality $2n + 3 \leq 2^n$ does not hold for $n = 0, 1, 2, 3$. Let $P(n)$ be the proposition that this inequality holds for the positive integer n. $P(4)$, the basis case, is true since $2 \cdot 4 + 3 = 11 \leq 16 = 2^4$. For the inductive step assume that $P(k)$ is true. Then, by the inductive hypothesis, $2(k+1) + 3 = (2k+3) + 2 < 2^k + 2$. But since $k \geq 1, 2^k + 2 \leq 2^k + 2^k = 2^{k+1}$. This shows that $P(k+1)$ is true.   **31. a)** The postages that can be formed using 5-cent and 6-cent stamps are 5 cents, 6 cents, 10 cents, 11 cents, 12 cents, 15 cents, 16 cents, 17 cents, 18 cents, and all postages of 20 cents or more.   **b)** We will prove that all postages of 20 cents or more can be formed using 5-cent and 6-cent stamps. Let $P(n)$ be the statement that postage of n cents can be formed. $P(20)$ is true since postage of 20 cents can be formed using four 5-cent stamps. Now assume that $P(k)$ is true. If a 5-cent stamp was used to form postage of n cents, then replace it by a 6-cent stamp to form postage of $k+1$ cents. Otherwise, if only 6-cent stamps were used, since $k \geq 20$ at least four 6-cent stamps were used. Replace four 6-cent stamps by five 5-cent stamps to get postage of $k+1$ cents. Hence $P(k+1)$ is true. This completes the proof by mathematical induction.   **c)** Let $P(n)$ be as in (b). The basis cases are $P(20)$, $P(21)$, $P(22)$, $P(23)$, and $P(24)$. These are true since postage of 20 cents, 21 cents, 22 cents, 23 cents, and 24 cents can be formed using four 5-cent stamps, three 5-cent stamps and one 6-cent stamp, two 5-cent stamps and two 6-cent stamps, one 5-cent and three 6-cent stamps, and four 6-cent stamps, respectively. Now assume that $P(j)$ is true for $20 \leq j \leq k$, where $k \geq 24$. Since $k + 1 \geq 25$, it follows that $k - 4 \geq 20$, so that by the inductive hypothesis postage of $k - 4$ can be formed. Add a 5-cent stamp to obtain postage of $k+1$ cents, showing that $P(k+1)$ is true. This completes the proof by strong induction.   **33.** All multiples of \$10 greater than or equal to \$40 can be formed as well as \$20. Let $P(n)$ be the statement that $10n$ dollars can be formed. $P(4)$ is true since \$40 can be formed using two \$20s. Now assume that $P(k)$ is true with $k \geq 4$. If a \$50 bill is used to form $10k$ dollars, replace it by three \$20 bills to obtain $10(k+1)$ dollars. Otherwise, at least two \$20 bills were used since $10k$ is at least \$40. Replace two \$20 bills with a \$50 bill to obtain \$$10(k+1)$. This shows that $P(k+1)$ is true.   **35.** *Basis step:* There are four base cases. If $n = 1 = 4 \cdot 0 + 1$, then clearly the second player wins. If there are two, three, or four matches ($n = 4 \cdot 0 + 2$, $n = 4 \cdot 0 + 3$, or $n = 4 \cdot 1$), then the first player can win by removing all but one match. *Inductive step:* Assume the strong inductive hypothesis, that in games with k or fewer matches, the first player can win if $k \equiv 0$, 2 or 3 (mod 4) and the second player can win if $k \equiv 1$ (mod 4). Suppose we have a game with $k + 1$ matches, with $k \geq 4$. If $k + 1 \equiv 0$ (mod 4), then the first player can remove three matches, leaving $k - 2$ matches for the other player. Since $k - 2 \equiv 1$ (mod 4), by the inductive hypothesis, this is a game that the second player at that point (who is the first player in our game) can win. Similarly, if $k + 1 \equiv 2$ (mod 4), then the first player can remove one match; and if $k + 1 \equiv 3$ (mod 4), then the first player can remove two matches. Finally, if $k + 1 \equiv 1$ (mod 4), then the first player must leave $k, k - 1$, or $k - 2$ matches for the other player. Since $k \equiv 0$ (mod 4), $k - 1 \equiv 3$ (mod 4), and $k - 2 \equiv 2$ (mod 4), by the inductive hypothesis, this is a game that the first player at that point (who is the second player in our game) can win. **37.** *Basis step:* For $n = 1$, the left-hand side is just $\frac{1}{1}$ which is 1. For $n = 2$, there are three nonempty subsets $\{1\}, \{2\},$ and $\{1, 2\}$, so the left-hand side is $\frac{1}{1} + \frac{1}{2} + \frac{1}{1 \cdot 2} = 2$. *Inductive step:* Assume that the statement is true for k. The set of the first $k + 1$ positive integers has many nonempty subsets, but they fall into three categories: a nonempty subset of the first k positive integers together with $k + 1$, a nonempty subset of the first k positive integers, or just $\{k + 1\}$. By the inductive hypothesis, the sum of the first category is k. For the second category, we can factor out $1/(k + 1)$ from each term of the sum and what remains is just k by the inductive hypothesis, so this part of the sum is $k/(k + 1)$. Finally, the third category simply yields $1/(k + 1)$. Hence, the entire summation is $k + k/(k + 1) + 1/(k + 1) = k + 1$. **39.** We use the notation (i, j) to mean the square in row i and column j and use induction on $i + j$ to show that every square can be reached by the knight. *Basis step:* There are six base cases, for the cases when $i + j \leq 2$. The knight is already at $(0, 0)$ to start, so the empty sequence of moves reaches that square. To reach $(1, 0)$, the knight moves $(0, 0) \to (2, 1) \to (0, 2) \to (1, 0)$. Similarly, to reach $(0, 1)$, the knight moves $(0, 0) \to (1, 2) \to (2, 0) \to (0, 1)$. Note that the knight has reached $(2, 0)$ and $(0, 2)$ in the process. For the last basis step there is $(0, 0) \to (1, 2) \to (2, 0) \to (0, 1) \to (2, 2) \to (0, 3) \to (1, 1)$. *Inductive step:* Assume the inductive hypothesis, that the knight can reach any square (i, j) for which $i + j = k$, where k is an integer greater than 1. We must show how the knight can reach each square (i, j) when $i + j = k + 1$. Since $k + 1 \geq 3$, at least one of i and j is at least 2. If $i \geq 2$, then by the inductive hypothesis, there is a sequence of moves ending at $(i - 2, j + 1)$, since $i - 2 + j + 1 = i + j - 1 = k$; from there it is just one step to (i, j); similarly, if $j \geq 2$. **41.** *Basis step:* The base cases $n = 0$ and $n = 1$ are true since the derivative of x^0 is 0 and the derivative $x^1 = x$ is 1. *Inductive step:* Using the product rule, the inductive hypothesis, and the base case shows that $\frac{d}{dx} x^{k+1} = \frac{d}{dx}(x \cdot x^k) = x \cdot \frac{d}{dx} x^k + x^k \frac{d}{dx} x = x \cdot kx^{k-1} + x^k \cdot 1 = kx^k + x^k = (k+1)x^k$. **43.** Let $P(n)$ be the statement that $\mathbf{AB}^n = \mathbf{B}^n \mathbf{A}$. $P(1)$ is true since $\mathbf{AB} = \mathbf{BA}$. Now assume that $P(n)$ is true. Then $\mathbf{AB}^{n+1} = \mathbf{AB}^n \mathbf{B} = \mathbf{B}^n \mathbf{AB} = \mathbf{B}^n \mathbf{BA} = \mathbf{B}^{n+1} \mathbf{A}$. It follows that $P(n + 1)$ is true. **45.** Let $P(n)$ be "$(A_1 \cup A_2 \cup \cdots \cup A_n) \cap B = (A_1 \cap B) \cup (A_2 \cap B) \cup \cdots \cup (A_n \cap B)$." *Basis step:* $P(1)$ is trivially true. *Inductive step:* Assume that $P(k)$ is true. Then $(A_1 \cup A_2 \cup \cdots \cup A_k \cup A_{k+1}) \cap B = [(A_1 \cup A_2 \cup \cdots \cup$

$A_k) \cup A_{k+1}] \cap B = [(A_1 \cup A_2 \cup \cdots \cup A_k) \cap B] \cup (A_{k+1} \cap B) = [(A_1 \cap B) \cup (A_2 \cap B) \cup \cdots \cup (A_k \cap B)] \cup (A_{k+1} \cap B) = (A_1 \cap B) \cup (A_2 \cap B) \cup \cdots \cup (A_k \cap B) \cup (A_{k+1} \cap B)$. **47.** Let $P(n)$ be "$\overline{\bigcup_{k=1}^{n} A_k} = \bigcap_{k=1}^{n} \overline{A_k}$." *Basis step:* $P(1)$ is trivially true. *Inductive step:* Assume that $P(k)$ is true. Then $\overline{\bigcup_{j=1}^{k+1} A_j} = \overline{\left(\bigcup_{j=1}^{k} A_j\right) \cup A_{k+1}} = \overline{\left(\bigcup_{j=1}^{k} A_j\right)} \cap \overline{A_{k+1}} = \left(\bigcap_{j=1}^{k} \overline{A_j}\right) \cap \overline{A_{k+1}} = \bigcap_{j=1}^{k+1} \overline{A_j}$. **49.** Let $P(n)$ be "$[(p_1 \to p_2) \wedge (p_2 \to p_3) \wedge \cdots \wedge (p_{n-1} \to p_n)] \to [(p_1 \wedge \cdots \wedge p_{n-1}) \to p_n]$." *Basis step:* $P(2)$ is true since $(p_1 \to p_2) \to (p_1 \to p_2)$ is a tautology. *Inductive step:* Assume $P(k)$ is true. To show $[(p_1 \to p_2) \wedge \cdots \wedge (p_{k-1} \to p_k) \wedge (p_k \to p_{k+1})] \to [(p_1 \wedge \cdots \wedge p_{k-1} \wedge p_k) \to p_{k+1}]$ is a tautology, assume the hypothesis of this implication is true. Since both the hypothesis and $P(k)$ are true, it follows that $(p_1 \wedge \cdots \wedge p_{k-1}) \to p_k$ is true. Since this is true, and since $p_k \to p_{k+1}$ is true (it is part of the assumption) it follows by hypothetical syllogism that $(p_1 \wedge \cdots \wedge p_{k-1}) \to p_{k+1}$ is true. The weaker statement $(p_1 \wedge \cdots \wedge p_{k-1} \wedge p_k) \to p_{k+1}$ follows from this. **51.** The two sets do not overlap if $n + 1 = 2$. In fact, the implication $P(1) \to P(2)$ is false. **53.** The error is in going from the base case $n = 0$ to the next case, $n = 1$; we cannot write 1 as the sum of two smaller natural numbers. **55.** Assume that the well-ordering property holds. Suppose that $P(1)$ is true and that the implication $(P(1) \wedge P(2) \wedge \cdots \wedge P(n)) \to P(n + 1)$ is true for every positive integer $n \geq 1$. Let S be the set of integers n for which $P(n)$ is false. We will show $S = \emptyset$. Assume that $S \neq \emptyset$. Then by the well-ordering property there is a least integer m in S. We know that m cannot be 1 because $P(1)$ is true. Since $n = m$ is the least integer such that $P(n)$ is false, $P(1), P(2), \ldots, P(m - 1)$ are true, and $m - 1 \geq 1$. Since $(P(1) \wedge P(2) \wedge \cdots \wedge P(m-1)) \to P(m)$ is true, it follows that $P(m)$ must also be true, which is a contradiction. Hence $S = \emptyset$. **57.** Let $P(n)$ be "$H_{2^n} \leq 1 + n$." *Basis step:* $P(0)$ is true since $H_{2^0} = H_1 = 1 \leq 1 + 0$. *Inductive step:* Assume that $H_{2^k} \leq 1 + k$. Then $H_{2^{k+1}} = H_{2^k} + \sum_{j=2^k+1}^{2^{k+1}} \frac{1}{j} \leq 1 + k + 2^k \left(\frac{1}{2^{k+1}}\right) < 1 + k + 1 = 1 + (k + 1)$. **59.** Let $P(n)$ be "$1/\sqrt{1} + 1/\sqrt{2} + 1/\sqrt{3} + \cdots + 1/\sqrt{n} > 2 \left(\sqrt{n + 1} - 1\right)$." *Basis step:* $P(1)$ is true since $1 > 2 \left(\sqrt{2} - 1\right)$. *Inductive step:* Assume that $P(k)$ is true. Then $1 + 1/\sqrt{2} + \cdots + 1/\sqrt{k} + 1/\sqrt{k+1} > 2 \left(\sqrt{k+1} - 1\right) + 1/\sqrt{k+1}$. If we show that $2 \left(\sqrt{k+1} - 1\right) + 1/\sqrt{k+1} > 2 \left(\sqrt{k+2} - 1\right)$, it follows that $P(k + 1)$ is true. This inequality is equivalent to $2 \left(\sqrt{k+2} - \sqrt{k+1}\right) < 1/\sqrt{k+1}$, which is equivalent to $2 \left(\sqrt{k+2} - \sqrt{k+1}\right) \left(\sqrt{k+2} + \sqrt{k+1}\right) < \sqrt{k+1}/\sqrt{k+1} + \sqrt{k+2}/\sqrt{k+1}$. This is equivalent to $2 < 1 + \sqrt{k+2}/\sqrt{k+1}$, which is clearly true. **61.** We will first prove the result when n is a power of 2, that is, if $n = 2^k$, $k = 1, 2, \ldots$. Let $P(k)$ be the statement $A \geq G$, where A and G are the arithmetic and geometric means of a set of $n = 2^k$ positive real numbers. *Basis* *step:* $k = 1$ and $n = 2^1 = 2$. Note that $(\sqrt{a_1} - \sqrt{a_2})^2 \geq 0$. Expanding this shows that $a_1 - 2\sqrt{a_1 a_2} + a_2 \geq 0$, that is, $(a_1 + a_2)/2 \geq (a_1 a_2)^{1/2}$. *Inductive step:* Assume that $P(k)$ is true, with $n = 2^k$. We will show that $P(k + 1)$ is true. We have $2^{k+1} = 2n$. Now $(a_1 + a_2 + \cdots + a_{2n})/(2n) = ((a_1 + a_2 + \cdots + a_n)/n + (a_{n+1} + a_{n+2} + \cdots + a_{2n})/n)/2$ and similarly $(a_1 a_2 \cdots a_{2n})^{1/(2n)} = [(a_1 \cdots a_n)^{1/n}(a_{n+1} \cdots a_{2n})^{1/n}]^{1/2}$. To simplify the notation, let $A(x, y, \ldots)$ and $G(x, y, \ldots)$ denote the arithmetic mean and geometric mean of $x, y, \ldots$, respectively. Also, if $x \leq x'$, $y \leq y'$, and so on, then $A(x, y, \ldots) \leq A(x', y', \ldots)$ and $G(x, y, \ldots) \leq G(x', y', \ldots)$. Hence $A(a_1, \ldots, a_{2n}) = A(A(a_1, \ldots, a_n), A(a_{n+1}, \ldots, a_{2n})) \geq A(G(a_1, \ldots, a_n), G(a_{n+1}, \ldots, a_{2n})) \geq G(G(a_1, \ldots, a_n), G(a_{n+1}, \ldots, a_{2n})) = G(a_1, \ldots, a_{2n})$. This finishes the proof for powers of 2. Now if n is not a power of 2, let m be the next higher power of 2, and let $a_{n+1}, \ldots, a_m$ all equal $A(a_1, \ldots, a_n) = \bar{a}$. Then we have $((a_1 a_2 \cdots a_n)\bar{a}^{m-n})^{1/m} \leq A(a_1, \ldots, a_m)$, since m is a power of 2. Since $A(a_1, \ldots, a_m) = \bar{a}$, it follows that $(a_1 \cdots a_n)^{1/m}\bar{a}^{1-n/m} \leq \bar{a}^{n/m}$. Raising both sides to the (m/n)th power gives $G(a_1, \ldots, a_n) \leq A(a_1, \ldots, a_n)$. **63.** There is nothing to prove for the basis case when $n = 1$. Now assume the inductive hypothesis. Suppose that $p \mid a_1 a_2 \cdots a_k a_{k+1}$. Note that $\gcd(p, a_1, a_2, \ldots, a_k) = 1$ or p. If it is 1, by Lemma 1 in Section 2.6, $p \mid a_{k+1}$. If it is p, then $p \mid a_1 a_2 \cdots a_k$, so that by the inductive hypothesis, $p \mid a_i$ for some $i \leq k$. This completes the proof.   **65.** Following the hint, we first want to show that if $w^2 + x^2 + y^2 + z^2 = 2wxyz$, then all the variables must be even. Clearly either none, two, or all must be even, since the right-hand side is even. Suppose all the variables were odd. Then the left-hand side is $1 + 1 + 1 + 1 \equiv 0 \pmod{4}$ (see Exercise 2 in Section 3.1). But the right-hand side is congruent to 2 modulo 4 in this case, a contradiction. Next suppose that two of the variables were odd and two were even. Then the left-hand side is 2 modulo 4 while the right-hand side is 0 modulo 4, another contradiction. So we conclude that all the variables are even, and we make the substitution $w = 2a, x = 2b, y = 2c, z = 2d$ and simplify to obtain $a^2 + b^2 + c^2 + d^2 = 8abcd$. We repeat the argument modulo 8 to conclude $a = 2e, b = 2f, c = 2g, d = 2h$, whence $e^2 + f^2 + g^2 + h^2 = 32efgh$, and so on forever. Thus each of our original variables must have arbitrarily large powers of 2 as factors, an impossibility.   **67.** Let $P(n)$ be the statement that if $x_1, x_2, \ldots, x_n$ are n distinct real numbers, then $n - 1$ multiplications are used to find the product of these numbers no matter how parentheses are inserted in the product. We will prove that $P(n)$ is true using the second principle of mathematical induction. The basis case $P(1)$ is true since $1 - 1 = 0$ multiplications are required to find the product of x_1, a product with only one factor. Suppose that $P(k)$ is true for $1 \leq k \leq n$. The last multiplication used to find the product of the $n + 1$ distinct real numbers $x_1, x_2, \ldots, x_n, x_{n+1}$ is a multiplication of

the product of the first k of these numbers for some k and the product of the last $n + 1 - k$ of them. By the inductive hypothesis, $k - 1$ multiplications are used to find the product of k of the numbers, no matter how parentheses were inserted in the product of these numbers, and $n - k$ multiplications are used to find the product of the other $n + 1 - k$ of them, no matter how parentheses were inserted in the product of these numbers. Since one more multiplication is required to find the product of all $n + 1$ numbers, the total number of multiplications used equals $(k - 1) + (n - k) + 1 = n$. Hence $P(n + 1)$ is true. The proof is complete.

69.

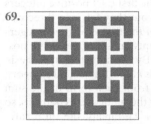

71. Let $P(n)$ be the statement that every $2^n \times 2^n \times 2^n$ chessboard with a $1 \times 1 \times 1$ cube removed can be covered by tiles that are $2 \times 2 \times 2$ cubes each with a $1 \times 1 \times 1$ cube removed. The basis step, $P(1)$, holds since one tile coincides with the solid to be tiled. Now assume that $P(k)$ holds. Now consider a $2^{k+1} \times 2^{k+1} \times 2^{k+1}$ cube with a $1 \times 1 \times 1$ cube removed. Split this object into eight pieces using planes parallel to its faces and running through its center. The missing $1 \times 1 \times 1$ piece occurs in one of these eight pieces. Now position one tile with its center at the center of the large object so that the missing $1 \times 1 \times 1$ cube lies in the octant in which the large object is missing a $1 \times 1 \times 1$ cube. This creates eight $2^k \times 2^k \times 2^k$ cubes, each missing a $1 \times 1 \times 1$ cube. By the inductive hypothesis we can fill each of these eight objects with tiles. Putting these tilings together produces the desired tiling.

73.

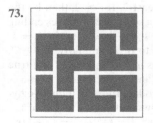

75. Assume that $a = dq + r = dq' + r'$ such that $0 \leq r < d$ and $0 \leq r' < d$. Then $d(q - q') = r' - r$. It follows that d divides $r' - r$. Since $-d < r' - r < d$, we have $r' - r = 0$. Hence $r' = r$. It follows that $q = q'$.   **77.** This is a paradox caused by self-reference. The answer is clearly "no." There are a finite number of English words, so only a finite number of strings of 15 words or less; therefore only a finite number of positive integers can be so described, not all of them.

SECTION 3.4

1. **a)** $f(1) = 3$, $f(2) = 5$, $f(3) = 7$, $f(4) = 9$ **b)** $f(1) = 3, f(2) = 9, f(3) = 27, f(4) = 81$ **c)** $f(1) = 2$, $f(2) = 4$, $f(3) = 16$, $f(4) = 65{,}536$ **d)** $f(1) = 3$, $f(2) = 13, f(3) = 183, f(4) = 33{,}673$ **3. a)** $f(2) = -1$, $f(3) = 5, f(4) = 2, f(5) = 17$ **b)** $f(2) = -4, f(3) = 32$, $f(4) = -4096$, $f(5) = 536{,}870{,}912$ **c)** $f(2) = 8$, $f(3) = 176$, $f(4) = 92{,}672$, $f(5) = 25{,}764{,}174{,}848$ **d)** $f(2) = -\frac{1}{2}$, $f(3) = -4$, $f(4) = \frac{1}{8}$, $f(5) = -32$ **5. a)** Not valid **b)** $f(n) = 1 - n$. *Basis step:* $f(0) = 1 = 1 - 0$. *Inductive step:* if $f(k) = 1 - k$, then $f(k + 1) = f(k) - 1 = 1 - k - 1 = 1 - (k + 1)$. **c)** $f(n) = 4 - n$ if $n > 0$, and $f(0) = 2$. *Basis step:* $f(0) = 2$ and $f(1) = 3 = 4 - 1$. *Inductive step* (with $k \geq 1$): $f(k + 1) = f(k) - 1 = (4 - k) - 1 = 4 - (k + 1)$. **d)** $f(n) = 2^{\lfloor (n+1)/2 \rfloor}$. *Basis step:* $f(0) = 1 = 2^{\lfloor (0+1)/2 \rfloor}$ and $f(1) = 2 = 2^{\lfloor (1+1)/2 \rfloor}$. *Inductive step* (with $k \geq 1$): $f(k + 1) = 2f(k - 1) = 2 \cdot 2^{\lfloor k/2 \rfloor} = 2^{\lfloor k/2 \rfloor + 1} = 2^{\lfloor ((k+1)+1)/2 \rfloor}$. **e)** $f(n) = 3^n$. *Basis step:* Trivial. *Inductive step:* For odd n, $f(n) = 3f(n - 1) = 3 \cdot 3^{n-1} = 3^n$; and for even $n > 1$, $f(n) = 9f(n - 2) = 9 \cdot 3^{n-2} = 3^n$. **7.** There are many possible correct answers. We will supply relatively simple ones. **a)** $a_{n+1} = a_n + 6$ for $n \geq 1$ and $a_1 = 6$ **b)** $a_{n+1} = a_n + 2$ for $n \geq 1$ and $a_1 = 3$ **c)** $a_{n+1} = 10a_n$ for $n \geq 1$ and $a_1 = 10$ **d)** $a_{n+1} = a_n$ for $n \geq 1$ and $a_1 = 5$ **9.** $F(0) = 0, F(n) = F(n - 1) + n$ for $n \geq 1$ **11.** $P_m(0) = 0, P_m(n + 1) = P_m(n) + m$ **13.** Let $P(n)$ be "$f_1 + f_3 + \cdots + f_{2n-1} = f_{2n}$." *Basis step:* $P(1)$ is true since $f_1 = 1 = f_2$. *Inductive step:* Assume that $P(k)$ is true. Then $f_1 + f_3 + \cdots + f_{2k-1} + f_{2k+1} = f_{2k} + f_{2k+1} = f_{2k+2} = f_{2(k+1)}$. **15.** *Basis step:* $f_0 f_1 + f_1 f_2 = 0 \cdot 1 + 1 \cdot 1 = 1^2 = f_2^2$. *Inductive step:* Assume that $f_0 f_1 + f_1 f_2 + \cdots + f_{2k-1} f_{2k} = f_{2k}^2$. Then $f_0 f_1 + f_1 f_2 + \cdots + f_{2k-1} f_{2k} + f_{2k} f_{2k+1} + f_{2k+1} f_{2k+2} = f_{2k}^2 + f_{2k} f_{2k+1} + f_{2k+1} f_{2k+2} = f_{2k}(f_{2k} + f_{2k+1}) + f_{2k+1} f_{2k+2} = f_{2k} f_{2k+2} + f_{2k+1} f_{2k+2} = (f_{2k} + f_{2k+1}) f_{2k+2} = f_{2k+2}^2$. **17.** The number of divisions used by the Euclidean algorithm to find $\gcd(f_{n+1}, f_n)$ is 0 for $n = 0$, 1 for $n = 1$, and $n - 1$ for $n \geq 2$. To prove this result for $n \geq 2$ we use mathematical induction. For $n = 2$, one division shows that $\gcd(f_3, f_2) = \gcd(2, 1) = \gcd(1, 0) = 1$. Now assume that $k - 1$ divisions are used to find $\gcd(f_{k+1}, f_k)$. To find $\gcd(f_{k+2}, f_{k+1})$, first divide f_{k+2} by f_{k+1} to obtain $f_{k+2} = 1 \cdot f_{k+1} + f_k$. After one division we have $\gcd(f_{k+2}, f_{k+1}) = \gcd(f_{k+1}, f_k)$. By the inductive hypothesis it follows that exactly $k - 1$ more divisions are required. This shows that k divisions are required to find $\gcd(f_{k+2}, f_{k+1})$, finishing the inductive proof. **19.** $|A| = -1$. Hence $|A^n| = (-1)^n$. It follows that $f_{n+1} f_{n-1} - f_n^2 = (-1)^n$. **21. a)** Proof by induction. *Basis step:* For $n = 1$, $\max(-a_1) = -a_1 = -\min(a_1)$. For $n = 2$, there are two

cases. If $a_2 \geq a_1$ then $-a_1 \geq -a_2$, so $\max(-a_1, -a_2) = -a_1 = -\min(a_1, a_2)$. If $a_2 < a_1$, then $-a_1 < -a_2$, so $\max(-a_1, -a_2) = -a_2 = -\min(a_1, a_2)$. *Inductive step:* Assume true for k with $k \geq 2$. Then $\max(-a_1, -a_2, \ldots, -a_k, -a_{k+1}) = \max(\max(-a_1, \ldots, -a_k), -a_{k+1}) = \max(-\min(a_1, \ldots, a_k), -a_{k+1}) = -\min(\min(a_1, \ldots, a_k), a_{k+1}) = -\min(a_1, \ldots, a_{k+1})$. **b)** Proof by mathematical induction. *Basis step:* For $n = 1$, the result is the identity $a_1 + b_1 = a_1 + b_1$. For $n = 2$, first consider the case in which $a_1 + b_1 \geq a_2 + b_2$. Then $\max(a_1 + b_1, a_2 + b_2) = a_1 + b_1$. Also note that $a_1 \leq \max(a_1, a_2)$ and $b_1 \leq \max(b_1, b_2)$, so that $a_1 + b_1 \leq \max(a_1, a_2) + \max(b_1, b_2)$. Therefore $\max(a_1 + b_1, a_2 + b_2) = a_1 + b_1 \leq \max(a_1, a_2) + \max(b_1, b_2)$. The case with $a_1 + b_1 < a_2 + b_2$ is similar. *Inductive step:* Assume that the result is true for k. Then $\max(a_1 + b_1, a_2 + b_2, \ldots, a_k + b_k, a_{k+1} + b_{k+1}) = \max(\max(a_1 + b_1, a_2 + b_2, \ldots, a_k + b_k), a_{k+1} + b_{k+1}) \leq \max(\max(a_1, a_2, \ldots, a_k) + \max(b_1, b_2, \ldots, b_k), a_{k+1} + b_{k+1}) \leq \max(\max(a_1, a_2, \ldots, a_k), a_{k+1}) + \max(\max(b_1, b_2, \ldots, b_k), b_{k+1}) = \max(a_1, a_2, \ldots, a_k, a_{k+1}) + \max(b_1, b_2, \ldots, b_k, b_{k+1})$. **c)** Same as (b), but replace every occurrence of "max" by "min" and invert each inequality. **23.** $5 \in S$, and $x + y \in S$ if $x, y \in S$. **25. a)** $0 \in S$, and if $x \in S$, then $x + 2 \in S$ and $x - 2 \in S$. **b)** $2 \in S$, and if $x \in S$, then $x + 3 \in S$. **c)** $1 \in S, 2 \in S, 3 \in S, 4 \in S$, and if $x \in S$, then $x + 5 \in S$. **27. a)** $(0, 1)$, $(1, 1)$, $(2, 1)$; $(0, 2)$, $(1, 2)$, $(2, 2)$, $(3, 2)$, $(4, 2)$; $(0, 3)$, $(1, 3)$, $(2, 3)$, $(3, 3)$, $(4, 3)$, $(5, 3)$, $(6, 3)$; $(0, 4)$, $(1, 4)$, $(2, 4)$, $(3, 4)$, $(4, 4)$, $(5, 4)$, $(6, 4)$, $(7, 4)$, $(8, 4)$ **b)** Let $P(n)$ be the statement that $a \leq 2b$ whenever $(a, b) \in S$ is obtained by n applications of the recursive step. *Basis step:* $P(0)$ is true, since the only element of S obtained with no applications of the recursive step is $(0, 0)$, and indeed $0 \leq 2 \cdot 0$. *Inductive step:* Assume that $a \leq 2b$ whenever $(a, b) \in S$ is obtained by k or fewer applications of the recursive step, and consider an element obtained with $k + 1$ applications of the recursive step. Since the final application of the recursive step to an element (a, b) must be applied to an element obtained with fewer applications of the recursive step, we know that $a \leq 2b$. Add $0 \leq 2$, $1 \leq 2$, and $2 \leq 2$, respectively, to obtain $a \leq 2(b + 1)$, $a + 1 \leq 2(b + 1)$, and $a + 2 \leq 2(b + 1)$, as desired. **c)** This holds for the basis step, since $0 \leq 0$. If this holds for (a, b), then it also holds for the elements obtained from (a, b) in the recursive step, since adding $0 \leq 2$, $1 \leq 2$, and $2 \leq 2$, respectively, to $a \leq 2b$ yields $a \leq 2(b + 1)$, $a + 1 \leq 2(b + 1)$, and $a + 2 \leq 2(b + 1)$. **29. a)** Define S by $(1, 1) \in S$, and if $(a, b) \in S$, then $(a + 2, b) \in S$, $(a, b + 2) \in S$, and $(a + 1, b + 1) \in S$. All elements put in S satisfy the condition, because $(1, 1)$ has an even sum of coordinates, and if (a, b) has an even sum of coordinates, then so do $(a + 2, b)$, $(a, b + 2)$, and $(a + 1, b + 1)$. Conversely, we show by induction on the sum of the coordinates that if $a + b$ is even, then $(a, b) \in S$. If the sum is 2, then $(a, b) = (1, 1)$, and the basis step put (a, b) into S. Otherwise the sum is at least 4, and at least one of $(a-2, b)$, $(a, b-2)$, and $(a-1, b-1)$ must have positive integer coordinates whose sum is an even number smaller than $a + b$, and therefore must be in S. Then one application of the recursive step shows that $(a, b) \in S$. **b)** Define S by $(1, 1)$, $(1, 2)$, and $(2, 1)$ are in S, and if $(a, b) \in S$, then $(a+2, b)$ and $(a, b+2)$ are in S. To prove that our definition works, we note first that $(1, 1)$, $(1, 2)$, and $(2, 1)$ all have an odd coordinate, and if (a, b) has an odd coordinate, then so do $(a + 2, b)$ and $(a, b + 2)$. Conversely, we show by induction on the sum of the coordinates that if (a, b) has at least one odd coordinate, then $(a, b) \in S$. If $(a, b) = (1, 1)$ or $(a, b) = (1, 2)$ or $(a, b) = (2, 1)$, then the basis step put (a, b) into S. Otherwise either a or b is at least 3, so at least one of $(a - 2, b)$ and $(a, b - 2)$ must have positive integer coordinates whose sum is smaller than $a + b$, and therefore must be in S. Then one application of the recursive step shows that $(a, b) \in S$. **c)** $(1, 6) \in S$ and $(2, 3) \in S$, and if $(a, b) \in S$, then $(a + 2, b) \in S$ and $(a, b + 6) \in S$. To prove that our definition works, we note first that $(1, 6)$ and $(2, 3)$ satisfy the condition, and if (a, b) satisfies the condition, then so do $(a + 2, b)$ and $(a, b + 6)$. Conversely we show by induction on the sum of the coordinates that if (a, b) satisfies the condition, then $(a, b) \in S$. For sums 5 and 7, the only points are $(1, 6)$, which the basis step put into S, $(2, 3)$, which the basis step put into S, and $(4, 3) = (2+2, 3)$, which is in S by one application of the recursive definition. For a sum greater than 7, either $a \geq 3$, or $a \leq 2$ and $b \geq 9$, in which case either $(a - 2, b)$ or $(a, b - 6)$ must have positive integer coordinates whose sum is smaller than $a + b$ and satisfy the condition for being in S. Then one application of the recursive step shows that $(a, b) \in S$. **31.** If x is a set or a variable representing a set, then x is a well-formed formula. If x and y are well-formed formulae, then so are $\overline{x}$, $(x \cup y)$, $(x \cap y)$, and $(x - y)$. **33. a)** If $x \in D = \{0, 1, 2, 3, 4, 5, 6, 7, 8, 9\}$, then $m(x) = x$; if $s = tx$, where $t \in D^*$ and $x \in D$, then $m(s) = \min(m(s), x)$. **b)** Let $t = wx$, where $w \in D^*$ and $x \in D$. If $w = \lambda$, then $m(st) = m(sx) = \min(m(s), x) = \min(m(s), m(x))$ by the recursive step and the basis step of the definition of m. Otherwise, $m(st) = m((sw)x) = \min(m(sw), x)$ by the definition of m. Now $m(sw) = \min(m(s), m(w))$ by the inductive hypothesis of the structural induction, so $m(st) = \min(\min(m(s), m(w)), x) = \min(m(s), \min(m(w), x))$ by the meaning of min. But $\min(m(w), x) = m(wx) = m(t)$ by the recursive step of the definition of m. Thus $m(st) = \min(m(s), m(t))$. **35.** $\lambda^R = \lambda$ and $(ux)^R = xu^R$ for $x \in \Sigma, u \in \Sigma^*$. **37.** $w^0 = \lambda$ and $w^{n+1} = ww^n$. **39.** When the string consists of n 0s followed by n 1s for some nonnegative integer n **41.** Let $P(i)$ be "$l(w^i) = i \cdot l(w)$." $P(0)$ is true since $l(w^0) = 0 = 0 \cdot l(w)$. Assume $P(i)$ is true. Then $l(w^{i+1}) = l(ww^i) = l(w) + l(w^i) = l(w) + i \cdot l(w) = (i + 1) \cdot l(w)$. **43.** *Basis step:* For

the full binary tree consisting of just a root the result is true since $n(T) = 1$ and $h(T) = 0$, and $1 \geq 2 \cdot 0 + 1$. *Inductive step:* Assume that $n(T_1) \geq 2h(T_1) + 1$ and $n(T_2) \geq 2h(T_2) + 1$. By the recursive definitions of $n(T)$ and $h(T)$, we have $n(T) = 1 + n(T_1) + n(T_2)$ and $h(T) = 1 + \max(h(T_1), h(T_2))$. Therefore $n(T) = 1 + n(T_1) + n(T_2) \geq 1 + 2h(T_1) + 1 + 2h(T_2) + 1 \geq 1 + 2 \cdot \max(h(T_1), h(T_2)) + 2 = 1 + 2(\max(h(T_1), h(T_2)) + 1) = 1 + 2h(T)$. **45.** *Basis step:* $a_{0,0} = 0 = 0 + 0$. *Inductive step:* Assume that $a_{m',n'} = m' + n'$ whenever (m', n') is less than (m, n) in the lexicographic ordering of $\mathbf{N} \times \mathbf{N}$. If $n = 0$ then $a_{m,n} = a_{m-1,n} + 1 = m - 1 + n + 1 = m + n$. If $n > 0$, then $a_{m,n} = a_{m,n-1} + 1 = m + n - 1 + 1 = m + n$. **47. a)** $P_{m,m} = P_m$ since a number exceeding m cannot be used in a partition of m. **b)** Since there is only one way to partition 1, namely, $1 = 1$, it follows that $P_{1,n} = 1$. Since there is only one way to partition m into 1s, $P_{m,1} = 1$. When $n > m$ it follows that $P_{m,n} = P_{m,m}$ since a number exceeding m cannot be used. $P_{m,m} = 1 + P_{m,m-1}$ since one extra partition, namely, $m = m$, arises when m is allowed in the partition. $P_{m,n} = P_{m,n-1} + P_{m-n,n}$ if $m > n$ since a partition of m into integers not exceeding n either does not use any ns and hence is counted in $P_{m,n-1}$ or else uses an n and a partition of $m - n$, and hence is counted in $P_{m-n,n}$. **c)** $P_5 = 7, P_6 = 11$ **49.** Let $P(n)$ be "$A(n, 2) = 4$." *Basis step:* $P(1)$ is true since $A(1, 2) = A(0, A(1, 1)) = A(0, 2) = 2 \cdot 2 = 4$. *Inductive step:* Assume that $P(n)$ is true, that is, $A(n, 2) = 4$. Then $A(n + 1, 2) = A(n, A(n + 1, 1)) = A(n, 2) = 4$. **51. a)** 16 **b)** 65,536 **53.** Use a double induction argument to prove the stronger statement: $A(m, k) > A(m, l)$ when $k > l$. *Basis step:* When $m = 0$ the statement is true since $k > l$ implies that $A(0, k) = 2k > 2l = A(0, l)$. *Inductive step:* Assume that $A(m, x) > A(m, y)$ for all nonnegative integers x and y with $x > y$. We will show that this implies that $A(m + 1, k) > A(m + 1, l)$ if $k > l$. *Basis steps:* When $l = 0$ and $k > 0$, $A(m + 1, l) = 0$ and either $A(m + 1, k) = 2$ or $A(m + 1, k) = A(m, A(m + 1, k - 1))$. If $m = 0$, this is $2A(1, k - 1) = 2^k$. If $m > 0$ this is greater than 0 by the inductive hypothesis. In all cases $A(m + 1, k) > 0$, and in fact, $A(m + 1, k) \geq 2$. If $l = 1$ and $k > 1$ then $A(m + 1, l) = 2$ and $A(m + 1, k) = A(m, A(m + 1, k - 1))$, with $A(m + 1, k - 1) \geq 2$. Hence by the inductive hypothesis, $A(m, A(m + 1, k - 1)) \geq A(m, 2) > A(m, 1) = 2$. *Inductive step:* Assume that $A(m + 1, r) > A(m + 1, s)$ for all $r > s, s = 0, 1, \ldots, l$. Then if $k + 1 > l + 1$ it follows that $A(m + 1, k + 1) = A(m, A(m + 1, k)) > A(m, A(m + 1, k)) = A(m + 1, l + 1)$. **55.** From Exercise 54 it follows that $A(i, j) \geq A(i - 1, j) \geq \cdots \geq A(0, j) = 2j \geq j$. **57.** Let $P(n)$ be "$F(n)$ is well-defined." Then $P(0)$ is true since $F(0)$ is specified. Assume that $P(k)$ is true for all $k < n$. Then $F(n)$ is well-defined at n since $F(n)$ is given in terms of $F(0), F(1), \ldots, F(n - 1)$. So $P(n)$ is true for all integers n. **59. a)** The value of $F(1)$ is ambigu-

ous.   **b)** $F(2)$ is not defined, since $F(0)$ is not defined.
c) $F(3)$ is ambiguous and $F(4)$ is not defined since $F(\frac{4}{3})$ makes no sense.   **d)** The definition of $F(1)$ is ambiguous since both the second and third clause seem to apply.
e) $F(2)$ cannot be computed since trying to compute $F(2)$ gives $F(2) = 1 + F(F(1)) = 1 + F(2)$.   **61. a)** 1
b) 2   **c)** 3   **d)** 3   **e)** 4   **f)** 4   **g)** 5   **63.** $f_0^*(n) = \lceil n/a \rceil$
65. $f_2^*(n) = \lceil \log \log n \rceil$ for $n \geq 2$, $f_2^*(1) = 0$

SECTION 3.5

1. procedure *mult*(*n*: positive integer, *x*: integer)
   if $n = 1$ **then** $mult(n, x) := x$
   else $mult(n, x) := x + mult(n - 1, x)$
3. procedure *sum of odds* (*n*: positive integer)
   if $n = 1$ **then** *sum of odds* (*n*) := 1
   else *sum of odds*(*n*) :=*sum of odds* (*n* − 1) + 2*n* − 1
5. procedure *smallest*($a_1, \ldots, a_n$: integers)
   if $n = 1$ **then** *smallest*($a_1, \ldots, a_n$) = a_1
   else *smallest*($a_1, \ldots, a_n$) :=
     min(*smallest*($a_1, \ldots, a_{n-1}$), a_n)
7. procedure *modfactorial*(*n, m*: positive integers)
   if $n = 1$ **then** *modfactorial*(*n, m*) := 1
   else *modfactorial*(*n, m*) :=
     $(n \cdot modfactorial(n - 1, m))$ **mod** *m*
9. procedure gcd(*a, b*: nonnegative integers)
   {$a < b$ assumed to hold}
   if $a = 0$ **then** gcd(*a, b*) := *b*
   else if $a = b - a$ **then** gcd(*a, b*) := *a*
   else if $a < b - a$ **then** gcd(*a, b*) := gcd(*a, b* − *a*)
   else gcd(*a, b*) := gcd(*b* − *a, a*)
11. procedure *multiply*(*x, y* : nonnegative integers)
   if $y = 0$ **then** *multiply*(*x, y*) := 0
   else if *y* is even **then**
     multiply(*x, y*) := $2x \cdot multiply(x, y/2)$
   else *multiply*(*x, y*) := $2x \cdot multiply(x, (y - 1)/2) + x$
13. If $n = 1$, then $nx = x$, and the algorithm correctly returns x. Assume that the algorithm correctly computes kx. To compute $(k + 1)x$ it recursively computes the product of $k + 1 - 1 = k$ and x, and then adds x. By the inductive hypothesis, it computes that product correctly, so the answer returned is $kx + x = (k + 1)x$, which is correct.
15. If $n = 0$, then the first line of the program correctly returns the function value 1. Assume that the program works correctly for $n = k$. If $n = k + 1$, then the **else** clause is executed, and the value *a* times *power*(*a, k*) is returned. Since the latter is a^k by the inductive hypothesis, this equals $a \cdot a^k = a^{k+1}$, which is correct.   **17.** *n* multiplications versus 2^n **19.** $O(\log n)$ versus *n*
21. procedure *a*(*n*: nonnegative integer)
   if $n = 0$ **then** $a(n) := 1$
   else if $n = 1$ **then** $a(n) := 2$
   else $a(n) := a(n - 1) * a(n - 2)$

23. Iterative
25. procedure *iterative*(*n*: nonnegative integer)
   if $n = 0$ **then** $z := 1$
   else if $n = 1$ **then** $z := 2$
   else
   begin
     $x := 1$
     $y := 2$
     $z := 3$
     for $i := 1$ **to** $n - 2$
     begin
       $w := x + y + z$
       $x := y$
       $y := z$
       $z := w$
     end
   end
   {*z* is the *n*th term of the sequence}
27. We first give a recursive procedure and then an iterative procedure.
procedure *r*(*n*: nonnegative integer)
if $n < 3$ **then** $r(n) := 2n + 1$
else $r(n) = r(n - 1) \cdot (r(n - 2))^2 \cdot (r(n - 3))^3$

procedure *i*(*n* : nonnegative integer)
if $n = 0$ **then** $z := 1$
else if $n = 1$ **then** $z := 3$
else
begin
   $x := 1$
   $y := 3$
   $z := 5$
   for $i := 1$ **to** $n - 2$
   begin
     $w := z * y^2 * x^3$
     $x := y$
     $y := z$
     $z := w$
   end
end
{*z* is the *n*th term of the sequence}
The iterative version is more efficient.
29. procedure *reverse* (*w*: bit string)
   $n := \text{length}(w)$
   if $n \leq 1$ **then** *reverse*(*w*) := *w*
   else *reverse*(*w*) :=
     substr(*w, n, n*)*reverse*(*substr*(*w*, 1, *n* − 1))
   {*substr*(*w, a, b*) is the substring of *w* consisting of
     the symbols in the *a*th through *b*th positions}
31. procedure *A*(*m, n*: nonnegative integers)
   if $m = 0$ **then** $A(m, n) := 2n$
   else if $n = 0$ **then** $A(m, n) := 0$
   else if $n = 1$ **then** $A(m, n) := 2$
   else $A(m, n) := A(m - 1, A(m, n - 1))$

33.

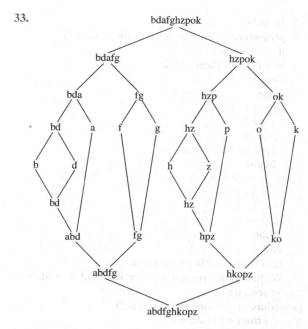

35. Let the two lists be $1, 2, \ldots, m - 1, m + n - 1$ and m, $m + 1, \ldots, m + n - 2, m + n$, respectively.   **37.** If $n = 1$, then the algorithm does nothing, which is correct, since a list with one element is already sorted. Assume that the algorithm works correctly for $n = 1$ through $n = k$. If $n = k + 1$, then the list is split into two lists, L_1 and L_2. By the inductive hypothesis, *mergesort* correctly sorts each of these sublists; furthermore *merge* correctly merges two sorted lists into one, since with each comparison, the smallest element in $L_1 \cup L_2$ not yet put into L is put there.   **39.** $O(n)$ **41.** 6   **43.** $O(n^2)$

SECTION 3.6

1. Suppose that $x = 0$. The program segment first assigns the value 1 to y and then assigns the value $x + y = 0 + 1 = 1$ to z.   **3.** Suppose that $y = 3$. The program segment assigns the value 2 to x and then assigns the value $x + y = 2 + 3 = 5$ to z. Since $y = 3 > 0$ it then assigns the value $z + 1 = 5 + 1 = 6$ to z.

5. $(p \wedge condition1)\{S_1\}q$
    $(p \wedge \neg condition1 \wedge condition2)\{S_2\}q$

        .
        .
        .

    $(p \wedge \neg condition1 \wedge \neg condition2$
                $\cdots \wedge \neg condition(n - 1)\{S_n\}q$

$\therefore$ $p\{$**if** $condition1$ **then** S_1;
    else if $condition2$ **then** $S_2; \ldots;$ **else** $S_n\}q$

7. We will show that p : "$power = x^{i-1}$ and $i \leq n + 1$" is a loop invariant. Note that p is true initially, since before

the loop starts, $i = 1$ and $power = 1 = x^0 = x^{1-1}$. Next, we must show that if p is true and $i \leq n$ after an execution of the loop, then p remains true after one more execution. The loop increments i by 1. Hence, since $i \leq n$ before this pass, $i \leq n + 1$ after this pass. Also the loop assigns $power \cdot x$ to $power$. By the inductive hypothesis we see that $power$ is assigned the value $x^{i-1} \cdot x = x^i$. Hence p remains true. Furthermore, the loop terminates after n traversals of the loop with $i = n + 1$ since i is assigned the value 1 prior to entering the loop, is incremented by 1 on each pass, and the loop terminates when $i > n$. Consequently, at termination $power = x^n$, as desired.   **9.** Suppose that p is "m and n are integers." Then if the condition $n < 0$ is true, $a = -n = |n|$ after S_1 is executed. If the condition $n < 0$ is false, then $a = n = |n|$ after S_1 is executed. Hence $p\{S_1\}q$ is true where q is $p \wedge (a = |n|)$. Since S_2 assigns the value 0 to both k and x, it is clear that $q\{S_2\}r$ is true where r is $q \wedge (k = 0) \wedge (x = 0)$. Suppose that r is true. Let $P(k)$ be "$x = mk$ and $k \leq a$." We can show that $P(k)$ is a loop invariant for the loop in S_3. $P(0)$ is true, since before the loop is entered $x = 0 = m \cdot 0$ and $0 \leq a$. Now assume $P(k)$ is true and $k < a$. Then $P(k + 1)$ is true since x is assigned the value $x + m = mk + m = m(k + 1)$. The loop terminates when $k = a$, and at that point $x = ma$. Hence $r\{S_3\}s$ is true where s is "$a = |n|$ and $x = ma$." Now assume that s is true. Then if $n < 0$ it follows that $a = -n$, so $x = -mn$. In this case S_4 assigns $-x = mn$ to $product$. If $n > 0$ then $x = ma = mn$, so S_4 assigns mn to $product$. Hence $s\{S_4\}t$ is true.   **11.** Suppose that the initial assertion p is true. Then since $p\{S\}q_0$ is true, q_0 is true after the segment S is executed. Since $q_0 \rightarrow q_1$ is true, it also follows that q_1 is true after S is executed. Hence $p\{S\}q_1$ is true.   **13.** We will use the proposition p, "$\gcd(a, b) = \gcd(x, y)$ and $y \geq 0$," as the loop invariant. Note that p is true before the loop is entered, since at that point $x = a$, $y = b$, and y is a positive integer, using the initial assertion. Now assume that p is true and $y > 0$; then the loop will be executed again. Inside the loop, x and y are replaced by y and x **mod** y, respectively. By Lemma 1 of Section 2.5, $\gcd(x, y) = \gcd(y, x \bmod y)$. Therefore, after execution of the loop, the value of $\gcd(x, y)$ is the same as it was before. Moreover, since y is the remainder, it is at least 0. Hence p remains true, so that it is a loop invariant. Furthermore, if the loop terminates, then $y = 0$. In this case, we have $\gcd(x, y) = x$, the final assertion. Therefore the program, which gives x as its output, has correctly computed $\gcd(a, b)$. Finally, we can prove the loop must terminate, since each iteration causes the value of y to decrease by at least 1. Therefore, the loop can be iterated at most b times.

SUPPLEMENTARY EXERCISES

1. $2^{2^5} + 1 = 4294967297 = 641 \cdot 6700417$ **3.** Proof by contradiction: Suppose that $\sqrt[3]{7} = p/q$, where p and q are positive integers with no common factor. Then $p^3 = 7q^3$. Therefore 7 is a factor of p^3, and hence a factor of p (if it were not, then the prime factorization of p^3 could not contain any 7s). Write $p = 7k$ for some positive integer k. This gives $49k^3 = q^3$. Hence 7 is a factor of q (by the same reasoning as before). But this contradicts the fact that p and q had no nontrivial common factors. Therefore $\sqrt[3]{7}$ is not a rational number.   **5.** The only possible summands are $1^4 = 1, 2^4 = 16, 3^4 = 81, 4^4 = 256$, and $5^4 = 625$. Clearly no two of these sum to 1000.   **7.** Let $z = x - y$, so that $x = y + z$. Then the inequality we are trying to prove becomes $|z| \geq |y + z| - |y|$, which is equivalent to $|y| + |z| \geq |y + z|$. But this is the triangle inequality proved as Exercise 35 of Section 1.5.   **9.** Let $P(x)$ be as in the hint. Then $P(x)$ is a polynomial (of degree $n - 1$, in fact); and if $x = x_m$, then $\prod_{i \neq j}(x - x_j)/(x_i - x_j) = 0$ unless $i = m$. Thus $P(x_m) = \prod_{j \neq m} y_m(x_m - x_j)/(x_m - x_j) = 1 \cdot y_m = y_m$.   **11.** Let $P(n)$ be "$1 \cdot 1 + 2 \cdot 2 + \cdots + n \cdot 2^{n-1} = (n-1)2^n + 1$." *Basis step:* $P(1)$ is true since $1 \cdot 1 = 1 = (1-1)2^1 + 1$. *Inductive step:* Assume that $P(k)$ is true. Then $1 \cdot 1 + 2 \cdot 2 + \cdots + k \cdot 2^{k-1} + (k+1) \cdot 2^k = (k-1)2^k + 1 + (k+1)2^k = 2k \cdot 2^k + 1 = ((k+1)-1)2^{k+1} + 1$.   **13.** Let $P(n)$ be "$1/1 \cdot 4 + \cdots + 1/[(3n-2)(3n+1)] = n/(3n+1)$." *Basis step:* $P(1)$ is true since $1/1 \cdot 4 = 1/4$. *Inductive step:* Assume $P(k)$ is true. Then $1/1 \cdot 4 + \cdots + 1/[(3k-2)(3k+1)] + 1/[(3k+1)(3k+4)] = k/(3k+1) + 1/[(3k+1)(3k+4)] = [k(3k+4)+1]/[(3k+1)(3k+4)] = [(3k+1)(k+1)]/[(3k+1)(3k+4)] = (k+1)/(3k+4)$.   **15.** Let $P(n)$ be "$2^n > n^3$." *Basis step:* $P(10)$ is true since $1024 > 1000$. *Inductive step:* Assume $P(k)$ is true. Then $(k+1)^3 = k^3 + 3k^2 + 3k + 1 \leq k^3 + 9k^2 \leq k^3 + k^3 = 2k^3 < 2 \cdot 2^k = 2^{k+1}$.   **17.** Let $P(n)$ be "$a - b$ is a factor of $a^n - b^n$." *Basis step:* $P(1)$ is trivially true. Assume $P(k)$ is true. Then $a^{k+1} - b^{k+1} = a^{k+1} - ab^k + ab^k - b^{k+1} = a(a^k - b^k) + b^k(a - b)$. Then since $a - b$ is a factor of $a^k - b^k$ and $a - b$ is a factor of $a - b$, it follows that $a - b$ is a factor of $a^{k+1} - b^{k+1}$.   **19.** Let $P(n)$ be "$a + (a+d) + \cdots + (a+nd) = (n+1)(2a+nd)/2$." *Basis step:* $P(1)$ is true since $a + (a + d) = 2a + d = 2(2a+d)/2$. *Inductive step:* Assume that $P(k)$ is true. Then $a + (a+d) + \cdots + (a+kd) + (a+(k+1)d) = (k+1)(2a+kd)/2 + a + (k+1)d = \frac{1}{2}[2ak + 2a + k^2d + kd + 2a + 2kd + 2d] = \frac{1}{2}[2ak + 4a + k^2d + 3kd + 2d] = \frac{1}{2}(k+2)(2a+(k+1)d)$.   **21.** *Basis step:* This is true for $n = 1$, since $5/6 = 10/12$. *Inductive step:* Assume that the equation holds for $n = k$, and consider $n = k + 1$. Then $\sum_{i=1}^{k+1} \frac{i+4}{i(i+1)(i+2)} = \sum_{i=1}^{k} \frac{i+4}{i(i+1)(i+2)} + \frac{k+5}{(k+1)(k+2)(k+3)} = \frac{k(3k+7)}{2(k+1)(k+2)} + \frac{k+5}{(k+1)(k+2)(k+3)}$ (by the inductive hypothesis) $= \frac{1}{(k+1)(k+2)} \cdot (\frac{k(3k+7)}{2} + \frac{k+5}{k+3}) = \frac{1}{2(k+1)(k+2)(k+3)} \cdot (k(3k+7)(k+3) + 2(k+5)) = \frac{1}{2(k+1)(k+2)(k+3)} \cdot (3k^3 + 16k^2 + 23k + 10) = \frac{1}{2(k+1)(k+2)(k+3)} \cdot (3k+10)(k+1)^2 = \frac{1}{2(k+2)(k+3)} \cdot (3k+10)(k+1) = \frac{(k+1)(3(k+1)+7)}{2((k+1)+1)((k+1)+2)}$, as desired.   **23.** *Basis step:* The statement is true for $n = 1$, since the derivative of $g(x) = xe^x$ is $x \cdot e^x + e^x = (x+1)e^x$ by the product rule. *Inductive step:* Assume that the statement is true for $n = k$, i.e., the kth derivative is given by $g^{(k)} = (x+k)e^x$. Differen-

tiating by the product rule gives the $(k+1)$st derivative: $g^{(k+1)} = (x+k)e^x + e^x = (x+(k+1))e^x$, as desired.   **25.** We will use strong induction to show that f_n is even if $n \equiv 0 \pmod 3$ and is odd otherwise. *Basis step:* This follows since $f_0 = 0$ is even and $f_1 = 1$ is odd. *Inductive step:* Assume that if $j \leq k$, then f_j is even if $j \equiv 0 \pmod 3$ and is odd otherwise. Now suppose $k + 1 \equiv 0 \pmod 3$. Then $f_{k+1} = f_k + f_{k-1}$ is even since f_k and f_{k-1} are both odd. If $k + 1 \equiv 1 \pmod 3$, then $f_{k+1} = f_k + f_{k-1}$ is odd since f_k is even and f_{k-1} is odd. Finally, if $k + 1 \equiv 2 \pmod 3$, then $f_{k+1} = f_k + f_{k-1}$ is odd, since f_k is odd and f_{k-1} is even. This completes the inductive proof.   **27.** Let $P(n)$ be the statement that $f_k f_n + f_{k+1} f_{n+1} = f_{n+k+1}$ for every nonnegative integer k. *Basis step:* This consists of showing that $P(0)$ and $P(1)$ both hold. $P(0)$ is true since $f_k f_0 + f_{k+1} f_1 = f_{k+1} \cdot 0 + f_{k+1} \cdot 1 = f_1$. Since $f_k f_1 + f_{k+1} f_2 = f_k + f_{k+1} = f_{k+2}$, it follows that $P(1)$ is true. *Inductive step:* Now assume that $P(j)$ holds. Then, by the inductive hypothesis and the recursive definition of the Fibonacci numbers, it follows that $f_{k+1} f_{j+1} + f_{k+2} f_{j+2} = f_k(f_{j-1} + f_j) + f_{k+1}(f_j + f_{j+1}) = (f_k f_{j-1} + f_{k+1} f_j) + (f_k f_j + f_{k+1} f_{j+1}) = f_{j-1+k+1} + f_{j+k+1} = f_{j+k+2}$. This shows that $P(j+1)$ is true and completes the proof.   **29.** Let $P(n)$ be the statement $l_0^2 + l_1^2 + \cdots + l_n^2 = l_n l_{n+1} + 2$. *Basis step:* $P(0)$ and $P(1)$ both hold since $l_0^2 = 2^2 = 2 \cdot 1 + 2 = l_0 l_1 + 2$ and $l_0^2 + l_1^2 = 2^2 + 1^2 = 1 \cdot 3 + 2 = l_1 l_3 + 2$. *Inductive step:* Assume that $P(k)$ holds. Then by the inductive hypothesis $l_0^2 + l_1^2 + \cdots + l_k^2 + l_{k+1}^2 = l_k l_{k+1} + 2 + l_{k+1}^2 = l_{k+1}(l_k + l_{k+1}) + 2 = l_{k+1} l_{k+2} + 2$. This shows that $P(k+1)$ holds and completes the proof.   **31.** Let $P(n)$ be the statement that the identity holds for the integer n. *Basis step:* $P(1)$ is obviously true. *Inductive step:* Assume that $P(k)$ is true. Then $\cos(k+1)x + i \sin(k+1)x = \cos(kx+x) + i \sin(kx+x) = \cos kx \cos x - \sin kx \sin x + i(\sin kx \cos x + \cos kx \sin x) = \cos x(\cos kx + i \sin kx)(\cos x + i \sin x) = (\cos x + i \sin x)^k(\cos x + i \sin x) = (\cos x + i \sin x)^{k+1}$. It follows that $P(k+1)$ is true, completing the proof.   **33.** Rewrite the right-hand side as $2^{n+1}(n^2 - 2n + 3) - 6$. For $n = 1$ we have $2 = 4 \cdot 2 - 6$. Assume that the equation holds for $n = k$, and consider $n = k + 1$. Then $\sum_{j=1}^{k+1} j^2 2^j = \sum_{j=1}^{k} j^2 2^j + (k+1)^2 2^{k+1} = 2^{k+1}(k^2 - 2k + 3) - 6 + (k^2 + 2k + 1)2^{k+1}$ (by the inductive hypothesis) $= 2^{k+1}(2k^2 + 4) - 6 = 2^{k+2}(k^2 + 2) - 6 = 2^{k+2}((k+1)^2 - 2(k+1) + 3) - 6$.   **35.** When $n = 1$ the statement is vacuously true. Assume that the statement is true for $n = k$, and consider $k + 1$ people standing in a line, with a woman first and a man last. If the kth person is a woman, then we have that woman standing in front of the man at the end. If the kth person is a man, then the first k people in line satisfy the conditions of the inductive hypothesis for the first k people in line, so again we can conclude that there is a woman directly in front of a man somewhere in the line.   **37.** *Basis step:* When $n = 1$ there is one circle, and we can color the inside blue and the outside red to satisfy the conditions. *Inductive step:* Assume the inductive hypothesis that if there are k circles, then the regions can be 2-colored such that no regions with a common boundary have the same color, and consider a situation with $k + 1$ circles. Remove one of the circles, producing a picture with k circles, and invoke the inductive hypothesis to color it in the prescribed manner. Then replace the removed circle and change the color of every region inside this circle. The resulting figure satisfies the condition, since if two regions have a common boundary, then either that boundary involved the new circle, in which case the regions on either side used to be the same region and now the inside portion is different from the outside, or else the boundary did not involve the new circle, in which case the regions are colored differently because they were colored differently before the new circle was restored. **39.** If $n = 1$ then the equation reads $1 \cdot 1 = 1 \cdot 2/2$, which is true. Assume that the equation is true for n and consider it for $n + 1$. Then $\sum_{j=1}^{n+1}(2j-1)\left(\sum_{k=j}^{n+1}\frac{1}{k}\right) = \sum_{j=1}^{n}(2j-1)\left(\sum_{k=j}^{n+1}\frac{1}{k}\right) +$ $(2(n+1)-1)\cdot\frac{1}{n+1} = \sum_{j=1}^{n}(2j-1)\left(\frac{1}{n+1}+\sum_{k=j}^{n}\frac{1}{k}\right) + \frac{2n+1}{n+1} =$ $\left(\frac{1}{n+1}\sum_{j=1}^{n}(2j-1)\right) + \left(\sum_{j=1}^{n}(2j-1)\sum_{k=j}^{n}\frac{1}{k}\right) + \frac{2n+1}{n+1} =$ $\left(\frac{1}{n+1}\cdot n^2\right) + \frac{n(n+1)}{2} + \frac{2n+1}{n+1}$ (by the inductive hypothesis) $=$ $\frac{2n^2+n(n+1)^2+(4n+2)}{2(n+1)} = \frac{2(n+1)^2+n(n+1)^2}{2(n+1)} = \frac{(n+1)(n+2)}{2}$. **41. a)** 92 **b)** 91 **c)** 91 **d)** 91 **e)** 91 **f)** 91 **43.** The basis step is incorrect since $n \neq 1$ for the sum shown. **45.** Let $P(n)$ be "the plane is divided into $n^2 - n + 2$ regions by n circles if every two of these circles have two common points but no three have a common point." *Basis step:* $P(1)$ is true since a circle divides the plane into $2 = 1^2 - 1 + 2$ regions. *Inductive step:* Assume that $P(k)$ is true, that is, k circles with the specified properties divide the plane into $k^2 - k + 2$ regions. Suppose that a $(k + 1)$st circle is added. This circle intersects each of the other k circles in two points so that these points of intersection form $2k$ new arcs, each of which splits an old region. Hence there are $2k$ regions split, which shows that there are $2k$ more regions than there were previously. Hence $k+1$ circles satisfying the specified properties divide the plane into $k^2 - k + 2 + 2k = (k^2 + 2k + 1) - (k + 1) + 2 = (k + 1)^2 - (k + 1) + 2$ regions. **47.** Suppose $\sqrt{2}$ were rational. Then $\sqrt{2} = a/b$, where a and b are positive integers. It follows that the set $S = \{n\sqrt{2} \mid n \in \mathbf{N}\} \cap \mathbf{N}$ is a nonempty set of positive integers, since $b\sqrt{2} = a$ belongs to S. Let t be the least element of S, which exists by the well-ordering property. Then $t = s\sqrt{2}$ for some integer s. We have $t - s = s\sqrt{2} - s = s(\sqrt{2}-1)$, so that $t - s$ is a positive integer since $\sqrt{2} > 1$. Hence $t - s$ belongs to S. This is a contradiction since $t - s = s\sqrt{2} - s < s$. Hence $\sqrt{2}$ is irrational. **49.** Suppose that the well-ordering property were false. Let S be a nonempty set of nonnegative integers that has no least element. Let $P(n)$ be the statement "$i \notin S, i = 0, 1, \ldots, n$." $P(0)$ is true because if $0 \in S$ then S has a least element, namely, 0. Now suppose that $P(n)$ is true. Thus $0 \notin S, 1 \notin S, \ldots, n \notin S$. Clearly $n + 1$ cannot be in S, for if it were, it would be

its least element. Thus $P(n + 1)$ is true. So by the principle of mathematical induction, $n \notin S$ for all nonnegative integers n. Thus $S = \emptyset$, a contradiction. **51. a)** Let $d = \gcd(a_1, a_2, \ldots, a_n)$. Then d is a divisor of each a_i and so must be a divisor of $\gcd(a_{n-1}, a_n)$. Hence d is a common divisor of $a_1, a_2, \ldots, a_{n-2}$, and $\gcd(a_{n-1}, a_n)$. To show it is the greatest common divisor of these numbers, suppose that c is a common divisor of them. Then c is a divisor of a_i for $i = 1, 2, \ldots, n - 2$ and a divisor of $\gcd(a_{n-1}, a_n)$, so that it is a divisor of a_{n-1} and a_n. Hence c is a common divisor of $a_1, a_2, \ldots, a_{n-1}, a_n$. Hence it is a divisor of d, the greatest common divisor of $a_1, a_2, \ldots, a_n$. It follows that d is the greatest common divisor, as claimed. **b)** If $n = 2$, apply the Euclidean algorithm. Otherwise, apply the Euclidean algorithm to a_{n-1} and a_n, obtaining $d = \gcd(a_{n-1}, a_n)$, and then apply the algorithm recursively to $a_1, a_2, \ldots, a_{n-2}, d$. **53.** $f(n) = n^2$. Let $P(n)$ be "$f(n) = n^2$." *Basis step:* $P(1)$ is true since $f(1) = 1 = 1^2$, which follows from the definition of f. *Inductive step:* Assume $f(n) = n^2$. Then $f(n+1) = f((n+1)-1)+2(n+1) -1 = f(n)+2n+1 = n^2+2n+1 = (n+1)^2$. **55. a)** $\lambda, 0,$ $1, 00, 01, 11, 000, 001, 011, 111, 0000, 0001, 0011, 0111, 1111,$ $00000, 00001, 00011, 00111, 01111, 11111$ **b)** $S = \{\alpha\beta \mid \alpha$ is a string of m 0s and β is a string of n 1s, $m \geq 0, n \geq 0\}$ **57.** Apply the first recursive step to λ to get $() \in B$. Apply the second recursive step to this string to get $()() \in B$. Apply the first recursive step to this string to get $(()()) \in B$. By Exercise 60, $(())$ is not in B because the number of left parentheses does not equal the number of right parentheses. **59.** $\lambda, (), (()), ()()$ **61. a)** 0 **b)** -2 **c)** 2 **d)** 0 **63.** **procedure** *generate(n*: nonnegative integer)

if n is odd **then**
begin
$\quad S := S(n - 1); T := T(n - 1)$
end
else if $n = 0$ **then**
begin
$\quad S := \emptyset; T := \{\lambda\}$
end
else
begin
$\quad T_1 := T(n - 2); S_1 := S(n - 2)$
$\quad T := T_1 \cup \{(x) \mid x \in T_1 \cup S_1 \text{ and } l(x) = n - 2\}$
$\quad S := S_1 \cup \{xy \mid x \in T_1 \text{ and } y \in T_1 \cup S_1$
$\qquad$ and $l(xy) = n\}$
end $\{T \cup S$ is the set of balanced strings of length at most $n\}$

65. If $x \leq y$ initially, $x := y$ is not executed, so $x \leq y$ is a true final assertion. If $x > y$ initially, then $x := y$ is executed, so $x \leq y$ is again a true final assertion.

67. **procedure** *zerocount($a_1, a_2, \ldots, a_n$*: list of integers)
if $n = 1$ **then**
$\quad$ **if** $a_1 = 0$ **then** $zerocount(a_1, a_2, \ldots, a_n) := 1$
$\quad$ **else** $zerocount(a_1, a_2, \ldots, a_n) := 0$
else

if $a_n = 0$ **then** *zerocount*$(a_1, a_2, \ldots, a_n) :=$
  zerocount$(a_1, a_2, \ldots, a_{n-1}) + 1$
else *zerocount*$(a_1, a_2, \ldots, a_n) :=$
  zerocount$(a_1, a_2, \ldots, a_{n-1})$

69. We will prove that $a(n)$ is a natural number and $a(n) \le n$. This is true for the base case $n = 0$, since $a(0) = 0$. Now assume that $a(n-1)$ is a natural number and $a(n-1) \le n-1$. Then $a(a(n-1))$ is a applied to a natural number less than or equal to $n-1$. Hence $a(a(n-1))$ is also a natural number less than or equal to $n-1$. Therefore $n - a(a(n-1))$ is n less some natural number less than or equal to $n-1$, which is a natural number less than or equal to n.   **71.** From Exercise 70, $a(n) = \lfloor (n+1)\mu \rfloor$ and $a(n-1) = \lfloor n\mu \rfloor$. Since $\mu < 1$, these two values are equal or they differ by 1. First suppose that $\mu n - \lfloor \mu n \rfloor < 1 - \mu$. This is equivalent to $\mu(n+1) < 1 + \lfloor \mu n \rfloor$. If this is true, then $\lfloor \mu(n+1) \rfloor = \lfloor \mu n \rfloor$. On the other hand, if $\mu n - \lfloor \mu n \rfloor \ge 1 - \mu$, then $\mu(n+1) \ge 1 + \lfloor \mu n \rfloor$, so $\lfloor \mu(n+1) \rfloor = \lfloor \mu n \rfloor + 1$, as desired.   **73.** $f(0) = 1, m(0) = 0; f(1) = 1, m(1) = 0; f(2) = 2, m(2) = 1; f(3) = 2, m(3) = 2; f(4) = 3, m(4) = 2; f(5) = 3, m(5) = 3; f(6) = 4, m(6) = 4; f(7) = 5, m(7) = 4; f(8) = 5, m(8) = 5; f(9) = 6, m(9) = 6$ **75.** The last occurrence of n is in the position for which the total number of 1s, 2s, $\ldots$, n's all together is that position number. But since a_k is the number of occurrences of k, this is just $\sum_{k=1}^{n} a_k$, as desired. Since $f(n)$ is the sum of the first n terms of the sequence, $f(f(n))$ is the sum of the first $f(n)$ terms of the sequence. But since $f(n)$ is the last term whose value is n, this means that the sum is the sum of all terms of the sequence whose value is at most n. Since there are a_k terms of the sequence whose value is k, this sum is $\sum_{k=1}^{n} k \cdot a_k$, as desired.   **77.** Suppose that $f(n)$ and $g(n)$ are both in $\mathcal{L}$ and eventually positive. Then $\ln f(n)$ and $\ln g(n)$ are in $\mathcal{L}$, so by Exercise 76, $\ln f(n) + \ln g(n) = \ln(f(n)g(n)) \in \mathcal{L}$. Therefore, $e^{\ln(f(n)g(n))} = f(n)g(n) \in \mathcal{L}$. Similarly, $\ln f(n) - \ln g(n) = \ln(f(n)/g(n)) \in \mathcal{L}$, so $e^{\ln(f(n)/g(n))} = f(n)/g(n) \in \mathcal{L}$.

Now suppose that $f(n)$ and $g(n)$ are both in $\mathcal{L}$ and neither is identically zero. If $f(n)$ and $g(n)$ are both eventually negative, then $-f(n)$ and $-g(n)$ are both eventually positive and also in $\mathcal{L}$, so $f(n)g(n) = (-f(n))(-g(n))$ and $f(n)/g(n) = (-f(n))/(-g(n))$ are in $\mathcal{L}$. If one of the functions, say, $f(n)$, is eventually positive and the other eventually negative, then $f(n)g(n) = -(f(n))(-g(n)) \in \mathcal{L}$ and similarly for the quotient.   **79.** If $f(n) \in \mathcal{L}$ and is eventually positive, then $\ln f(n) \in \mathcal{L}$, so by the result of Exercise 77, $\frac{1}{2} \ln f(n) = \ln(\sqrt{f(n)}) \in \mathcal{L}$. Hence $\sqrt{f(n)} = e^{\ln \sqrt{f(n)}} \in \mathcal{L}$.

CHAPTER

4

Counting

Combinatorics, the study of arrangements of objects, is an important part of discrete mathematics. This subject was studied as long ago as the seventeenth century, when combinatorial questions arose in the study of gambling games. Enumeration, the counting of objects with certain properties, is an important part of combinatorics. We must count objects to solve many different types of problems. For instance, counting is used to determine the complexity of algorithms. Counting is also required to determine whether there are enough telephone numbers or Internet protocol addresses to meet demand. Furthermore, counting techniques are used extensively when probabilities of events are computed.

The basic rules of counting, which we will study in Section 4.1, can solve a tremendous variety of problems. For instance, we can use these rules to enumerate the different phone numbers possible in the United States, the allowable passwords on a computer system, and the different orders in which the runners in a race can finish. Another important combinatorial tool is the pigeonhole principle, which we will study in Section 4.2. This states that when objects are placed in boxes and there are more objects than boxes, then there is a box containing at least two objects. For instance, we can use this principle to show that among a set of 15 or more students, at least 3 were born on the same day of the week.

We can phrase many counting problems in terms of ordered or unordered arrangements of the objects of a set. These arrangements, called permutations and combinations, are used in many counting problems. For instance, suppose the 100 top finishers on a competitive exam taken by 2000 students are invited to a banquet. We can enumerate the possible sets of 100 students that will be invited, as well as the ways the top 10 prizes can be awarded.

Another problem in combinatorics involves generating all the arrangements of a specified kind. This is often important in computer simulations. We will devise algorithms to generate arrangements of various types.

4.1 The Basics of Counting

INTRODUCTION

A password on a computer system consists of six, seven, or eight characters. Each of these characters must be a digit or a letter of the alphabet. Each password must contain at least one digit. How many such passwords are there? The techniques needed to answer this question and a wide variety of other counting problems will be introduced in this section.

Counting problems arise throughout mathematics and computer science. For example, we must count the successful outcomes of experiments and all the possible outcomes of these experiments to determine probabilities of discrete events. We need to count the number of operations used by an algorithm to study its time complexity.

We will introduce the basic techniques of counting in this section. These methods serve as the foundation for almost all counting techniques.

BASIC COUNTING PRINCIPLES

Assessment

We will present two basic counting principles, the **product rule** and the **sum rule.** Then we will show how they can be used to solve many different counting problems.

The product rule applies when a procedure is made up of separate tasks.

> **THE PRODUCT RULE** Suppose that a procedure can be broken down into a sequence of two tasks. If there are n_1 ways to do the first task and n_2 ways to do the second task after the first task has been done, then there are $n_1 n_2$ ways to do the procedure.

Extra Examples

Examples 1–9 show how the product rule is used.

EXAMPLE 1   The chairs of an auditorium are to be labeled with a letter and a positive integer not exceeding 100. What is the largest number of chairs that can be labeled differently?

Solution: The procedure of labeling a chair consists of two tasks, namely, assigning one of the 26 letters and then assigning one of the 100 possible integers to the seat. The product rule shows that there are $26 \cdot 100 = 2600$ different ways that a chair can be labeled. Therefore, the largest number of chairs that can be labeled differently is 2600.   ◀

EXAMPLE 2   There are 32 microcomputers in a computer center. Each microcomputer has 24 ports. How many different ports to a microcomputer in the center are there?

Solution: The procedure of choosing a port consists of two tasks, first picking a microcomputer and then picking a port on this microcomputer. Since there are 32 ways to choose the microcomputer and 24 ways to choose the port no matter which microcomputer has been selected, the product rule shows that there are $32 \cdot 24 = 768$ ports.   ◀

An extended version of the product rule is often useful. Suppose that a procedure is carried out by performing the tasks $T_1, T_2, \ldots, T_m$ in sequence. If task T_i can be done in n_i ways after tasks $T_1, T_2, \ldots,$ and T_{i-1} have been done, then there are $n_1 \cdot n_2 \cdot \cdots \cdot n_m$ ways to carry out the procedure. This version of the product rule can be proved by mathematical induction from the product rule for two tasks (see Exercise 56 at the end of the section).

EXAMPLE 3   How many different bit strings are there of length seven?

Solution: Each of the seven bits can be chosen in two ways, since each bit is either 0 or 1. Therefore, the product rule shows there are a total of $2^7 = 128$ different bit strings of length seven.   ◀

2 choices for each bit

EXAMPLE 4   How many different license plates are available if each plate contains a sequence of three letters followed by three digits (and no sequences of letters are prohibited, even if they are obscene)?

26 choices   10 choices
for each   for each
letter   digit

Solution: There are 26 choices for each of the three letters and ten choices for each of the three digits. Hence, by the product rule there are a total of $26 \cdot 26 \cdot 26 \cdot 10 \cdot 10 \cdot 10 = 17{,}576{,}000$ possible license plates.   ◄

EXAMPLE 5   **Counting Functions** How many functions are there from a set with m elements to one with n elements?

Solution: A function corresponds to a choice of one of the n elements in the codomain for each of the m elements in the domain. Hence, by the product rule there are $n \cdot n \cdot \cdots \cdot n = n^m$ functions from a set with m elements to one with n elements. For example, there are 5^3 different functions from a set with three elements to a set with five elements.   ◄

EXAMPLE 6   **Counting One-to-One Functions** How many one-to-one functions are there from a set with m elements to one with n elements?

Solution: First note when $m > n$ there are no one-to-one functions from a set with m elements to a set with n elements. Now let $m \leq n$. Suppose the elements in the domain are $a_1, a_2, \ldots, a_m$. There are n ways to choose the value of the function at a_1. Since the function is one-to-one, the value of the function at a_2 can be picked in $n - 1$ ways (since the value used for a_1 cannot be used again). In general, the value of the function at a_k can be chosen in $n - k + 1$ ways. By the product rule, there are $n(n - 1)(n - 2) \cdots (n - m + 1)$ one-to-one functions from a set with m elements to one with n elements. For example, there are $5 \cdot 4 \cdot 3 = 60$ one-to-one functions from a set with three elements to a set with five elements.   ◄

EXAMPLE 7   **The Telephone Numbering Plan** The format of telephone numbers in North America is specified by a *numbering plan*. A telephone number consists of ten digits, which are split into a three-digit area code, a three-digit office code, and a four-digit station code. Because of signaling considerations, there are certain restrictions on some of these digits. To specify the allowable format, let X denote a digit that can take any of the values 0 through 9, let N denote a digit that can take any of the values 2 through 9, and let Y denote a digit that must be a 0 or a 1. Two numbering plans, which will be called the old plan and the new plan, will be discussed. (The old plan, in use in the 1960s, has been replaced by the new plan, but the recent rapid growth in demand for new numbers will make even this new plan obsolete.) As will be shown, the new plan allows the use of more numbers.

Links

In the old plan, the formats of the area code, office code, and station code are *NYX, NNX,* and *XXXX*, respectively, so that telephone numbers had the form *NYX-NNX-XXXX*. In the new plan, the formats of these codes are *NXX, NXX,* and *XXXX*, respectively, so that telephone numbers have the form *NXX-NXX-XXXX*. How many different North American telephone numbers are possible under the old plan and under the new plan?

Solution: By the product rule, there are $8 \cdot 2 \cdot 10 = 160$ area codes with format *NYX* and $8 \cdot 10 \cdot 10 = 800$ area codes with format *NXX*. Similarly, by the product rule, there are $8 \cdot 8 \cdot 10 = 640$ office codes with format *NNX*. The product rule also shows that there are $10 \cdot 10 \cdot 10 \cdot 10 = 10,000$ station codes with format *XXXX*.

Consequently, applying the product rule again, it follows that under the old plan there are

$$160 \cdot 640 \cdot 10,000 = 1,024,000,000$$

different numbers available in North America. Under the new plan there are

$$800 \cdot 800 \cdot 10,000 = 6,400,000,000$$

different numbers available. ◄

EXAMPLE 8   What is the value of k after the following code has been executed?

```
k := 0
for i₁ := 1 to n₁
    for i₂ := 1 to n₂
        .
        .
        .
        for iₘ := 1 to nₘ
            k := k + 1
```

Solution: The initial value of k is zero. Each time the nested loop is traversed, 1 is added to k. Let T_i be the task of traversing the ith loop. Then the number of times the loop is traversed is the number of ways to do the tasks $T_1, T_2, \ldots, T_m$. The number of ways to carry out the task T_j, $j = 1, 2, \ldots, m$, is n_j, since the jth loop is traversed once for each integer i_j with $1 \le i_j \le n_j$. By the product rule, it follows that the nested loop is traversed $n_1 n_2 \cdots n_m$ times. Hence, the final value of k is $n_1 n_2 \cdots n_m$. ◄

EXAMPLE 9   **Counting Subsets of a Finite Set**   Use the product rule to show that the number of different subsets of a finite set S is $2^{|S|}$.

Solution: Let S be a finite set. List the elements of S in arbitrary order. Recall that there is a one-to-one correspondence between subsets of S and bit strings of length $|S|$. Namely, a subset of S is associated with the bit string with a 1 in the ith position if the ith element in the list is in the subset, and a 0 in this position otherwise. By the product rule, there are $2^{|S|}$ bit strings of length $|S|$. Hence, $|P(S)| = 2^{|S|}$. ◄

The product rule is often phrased in terms of sets in this way: If $A_1, A_2, \ldots, A_m$ are finite sets, then the number of elements in the Cartesian product of these sets is the product of the number of elements in each set. To relate this to the product rule, note that the task of choosing an element in the Cartesian product $A_1 \times A_2 \times \cdots \times A_m$ is done by choosing an element in A_1, an element in A_2, $\ldots$, and an element in A_m. By the product rule it follows that

$$|A_1 \times A_2 \times \cdots \times A_m| = |A_1| \cdot |A_2| \cdot \cdots \cdot |A_m|.$$

We now introduce the sum rule.

THE SUM RULE If a first task can be done in n_1 ways and a second task in n_2 ways, and if these tasks cannot be done at the same time, then there are $n_1 + n_2$ ways to do one of these tasks.

Example 10 illustrates how the sum rule is used.

EXAMPLE 10   Suppose that either a member of the mathematics faculty or a student who is a mathematics major is chosen as a representative to a university committee. How many different choices are there for this representative if there are 37 members of the mathematics faculty and 83 mathematics majors?

Solution: The first task, choosing a member of the mathematics faculty, can be done in 37 ways. The second task, choosing a mathematics major, can be done in 83 ways. From the sum rule it follows that there are $37 + 83 = 120$ possible ways to pick this representative. ◄

We can extend the sum rule to more than two tasks. Suppose that the tasks T_1, $T_2, \ldots, T_m$ can be done in $n_1, n_2, \ldots, n_m$ ways, respectively, and no two of these tasks can be done at the same time. Then the number of ways to do one of these tasks is $n_1 + n_2 + \cdots + n_m$. This extended version of the sum rule is often useful in counting problems, as Examples 11 and 12 show. This version of the sum rule can be proved using mathematical induction from the sum rule for two sets. (This is Exercise 55 at the end of the section.)

EXAMPLE 11   A student can choose a computer project from one of three lists. The three lists contain 23, 15, and 19 possible projects, respectively. How many possible projects are there to choose from?

Solution: The student can choose a project from the first list in 23 ways, from the second list in 15 ways, and from the third list in 19 ways. Hence, there are $23 + 15 + 19 = 57$ projects to choose from. ◄

EXAMPLE 12   What is the value of k after the following code has been executed?

```
k := 0
for i₁ := 1 to n₁
    k := k + 1
for i₂ := 1 to n₂
    k := k + 1
        .
        .
        .
for iₘ := 1 to nₘ
    k := k + 1
```

Solution: The initial value of k is zero. This block of code is made up of m different loops. Each time a loop is traversed, 1 is added to k. Let T_i be the task of traversing the ith loop. The task T_i can be done in n_i ways, since the ith loop is traversed n_i times. Since no two of these tasks can be done at the same time, the sum rule shows that the final value of k, which is the number of ways to do one of the tasks $T_i, i = 1, 2, \ldots, m$, is $n_1 + n_2 + \cdots + n_m$. ◀

The sum rule can be phrased in terms of sets as: If $A_1, A_2, \ldots, A_m$ are disjoint sets, then the number of elements in the union of these sets is the sum of the numbers of elements in them. To relate this to our statement of the sum rule, let T_i be the task of choosing an element from A_i for $i = 1, 2, \ldots, m$. There are $|A_i|$ ways to do T_i. From the sum rule, since no two of the tasks can be done at the same time, the number of ways to choose an element from one of the sets, which is the number of elements in the union, is

$$|A_1 \cup A_2 \cup \cdots \cup A_m| = |A_1| + |A_2| + \cdots + |A_m|.$$

This equality applies only when the sets in question are disjoint. The situation is much more complicated when these sets have elements in common. That situation will be briefly discussed later in this section and discussed in more depth in Chapter 6.

MORE COMPLEX COUNTING PROBLEMS

Many counting problems cannot be solved using just the sum rule or just the product rule. However, many complicated counting problems can be solved using both of these rules.

EXAMPLE 13

Extra Examples

In a version of the computer language BASIC, the name of a variable is a string of one or two alphanumeric characters, where uppercase and lowercase letters are not distinguished. (An *alphanumeric* character is either one of the 26 English letters or one of the 10 digits.) Moreover, a variable name must begin with a letter and must be different from the five strings of two characters that are reserved for programming use. How many different variable names are there in this version of BASIC?

Solution: Let V equal the number of different variable names in this version of BASIC. Let V_1 be the number of these that are one character long and V_2 be the number of these that are two characters long. Then by the sum rule, $V = V_1 + V_2$. Note that $V_1 = 26$, since a one-character variable name must be a letter. Furthermore, by the product rule there are $26 \cdot 36$ strings of length two that begin with a letter and end with an alphanumeric character. However, five of these are excluded, so that $V_2 = 26 \cdot 36 - 5 = 931$. Hence, there are $V = V_1 + V_2 = 26 + 931 = 957$ different names for variables in this version of BASIC. ◀

EXAMPLE 14

Each user on a computer system has a password, which is six to eight characters long, where each character is an uppercase letter or a digit. Each password must contain at least one digit. How many possible passwords are there?

Solution: Let P be the total number of possible passwords, and let $P_6, P_7,$ and P_8 denote the number of possible passwords of length 6, 7, and 8, respectively. By the sum rule, $P = P_6 + P_7 + P_8$. We will now find $P_6, P_7,$ and P_8. Finding P_6 directly is difficult. To find P_6 it is easier to find the number of strings of uppercase letters and digits that are six characters long, including those with no digits, and subtract from this the number of strings with no digits. By the product rule, the number of strings of six characters is 36^6, and the number of strings with no digits is 26^6. Hence,

$$P_6 = 36^6 - 26^6 = 2{,}176{,}782{,}336 - 308{,}915{,}776 = 1{,}867{,}866{,}560.$$

Similarly, it can be shown that

$$P_7 = 36^7 - 26^7 = 78{,}364{,}164{,}096 - 8{,}031{,}810{,}176 = 70{,}332{,}353{,}920$$

and

$$P_8 = 36^8 - 26^8 = 2{,}821{,}109{,}907{,}456 - 208{,}827{,}064{,}576$$
$$= 2{,}612{,}282{,}842{,}880.$$

Consequently,

$$P = P_6 + P_7 + P_8 = 2{,}684{,}483{,}063{,}360.$$ ◀

EXAMPLE 15   **Counting Internet Addresses** In the Internet, which is made up of interconnected physical networks of computers, each computer (or more precisely, each network connection of a computer) is assigned an *Internet address*. In Version 4 of the Internet Protocol (IPv4), now in use, an address is a string of 32 bits. It begins with a *network number* (*netid*). The netid is followed by a *host number* (*hostid*), which identifies a computer as a member of a particular network.

Three forms of addresses are used, with different numbers of bits used for netids and hostids. **Class A addresses,** used for the largest networks, consist of 0, followed by a 7-bit netid and a 24-bit hostid. **Class B addresses,** used for medium-sized networks, consist of 10, followed by a 14-bit netid and a 16-bit hostid. **Class C addresses,** used for the smallest networks, consist of 110, followed by a 21-bit netid and an 8-bit hostid. There are several restrictions on addresses because of special uses: 1111111 is not available as the netid of a Class A network, and the hostids consisting of all 0s and all 1s are not available for use in any network. A computer on the Internet has either a Class A, a Class B, or a Class C address. (Besides Class A, B, and C addresses, there are also Class D addresses, reserved for use in multicasting when multiple computers are addressed at a single time, consisting of 1110 followed by 28 bits, and Class E addresses, reserved for future use, consisting of 11110 followed by 27 bits. Neither Class D nor Class E addresses are assigned as the IP address of a computer on the Internet.) Figure 1 illustrates IPv4 addressing. (Limitations on the number of Class A and Class B netids have made IPv4 addressing inadequate; IPv6, which will replace IPv4, uses 128-bit addresses to solve this problem.)

How many different IPv4 addresses are available for computers on the Internet?

Bit Number	0	1	2	3	4	8	16	24	31
Class A	0	netid					hostid		
Class B	1	0	netid					hostid	
Class C	1	1	0	netid					hostid
Class D	1	1	1	0	Multicast Address				
Class E	1	1	1	1	0	Address			

FIGURE 1   Internet Addresses (IPv4).

Solution: Let x be the number of available addresses for computers on the Internet, and let $x_A, x_B,$ and x_C denote the number of Class A, Class B, and Class C addresses available, respectively. By the sum rule, $x = x_A + x_B + x_C$.

To find x_A, note that there are $2^7 - 1 = 127$ Class A netids, recalling that the netid 1111111 is unavailable. For each netid, there are $2^{24} - 2 = 16,777,214$ hostids, recalling that the hostids consisting of all 0s and all 1s are unavailable. Consequently, $x_A = 127 \cdot 16,777,214 = 2,130,706,178$.

To find x_B and x_C, note that there are $2^{14} = 16,384$ Class B netids and $2^{21} = 2,097,152$ Class C netids. For each Class B netid, there are $2^{16} - 2 = 65,534$ hostids, and for each Class C netid, there are $2^8 - 2 = 254$ hostids, recalling that in each network the hostids consisting of all 0s and all 1s are unavailable. Consequently, $x_B = 1,073,709,056$ and $x_C = 532,676,608$.

We conclude that the total number of IPv4 addresses available is $x = x_A + x_B + x_C = 2,130,706,178 + 1,073,709,056 + 532,676,608 = 3,737,091,842.$ ◀

THE INCLUSION–EXCLUSION PRINCIPLE

When two tasks can be done at the same time, we cannot use the sum rule to count the number of ways to do one of the two tasks. Adding the number of ways to do each task leads to an overcount, since the ways to do both tasks are counted twice. To correctly count the number of ways to do one of the two tasks, we add the number of ways to do each of the two tasks and then subtract the number of ways to do both tasks. This technique is called the **principle of inclusion–exclusion.** Example 16 illustrates how we can solve counting problems using this principle.

EXAMPLE 16   How many bit strings of length eight either start with a 1 bit or end with the two bits 00?

Extra
Examples

Solution: The first task, constructing a bit string of length eight beginning with a 1 bit, can be done in $2^7 = 128$ ways. This follows by the product rule, since the first bit can be chosen in only one way and each of the other seven bits can be chosen in two ways.

The second task, constructing a bit string of length eight ending with the two bits 00, can be done in $2^6 = 64$ ways. This follows by the product rule, since each of the first six bits can be chosen in two ways and the last two bits can be chosen in only one way.

Both tasks, constructing a bit string of length eight that begins with a 1 and ends with 00, can be done in $2^5 = 32$ ways. This follows by the product rule, since the first bit can be chosen in only one way, each of the second through the sixth bits can be chosen in two ways, and the last two bits can be chosen in one way. Consequently, the number of bit strings of length eight that begin with a 1 or end with a 00, which equals the number of ways to do either the first task or the second task, equals $128 + 64 - 32 = 160$. ◀

We can phrase this counting principle in terms of sets. Let A_1 and A_2 be sets and let T_1 be the task of choosing an element from A_1 and T_2 the task of choosing an element from A_2. There are $|A_1|$ ways to do T_1 and $|A_2|$ ways to do T_2. The number of ways to do either T_1 or T_2 is the sum of the number of ways to do T_1 and the number of ways to do T_2, minus the number of ways to do both T_1 and T_2. Since there are $|A_1 \cup A_2|$ ways to do either T_1 or T_2 and $|A_1 \cap A_2|$ ways to do both T_1 and T_2, we have

$$|A_1 \cup A_2| = |A_1| + |A_2| - |A_1 \cap A_2|.$$

This is the formula given in Section 1.7 for the number of elements in the union of two sets.

The principle of inclusion–exclusion can be generalized to find the number of ways to do one of n different tasks or, equivalently, to find the number of elements in the union of n sets, whenever n is a positive integer. We will study the inclusion–exclusion principle and some of its many applications in Chapter 6.

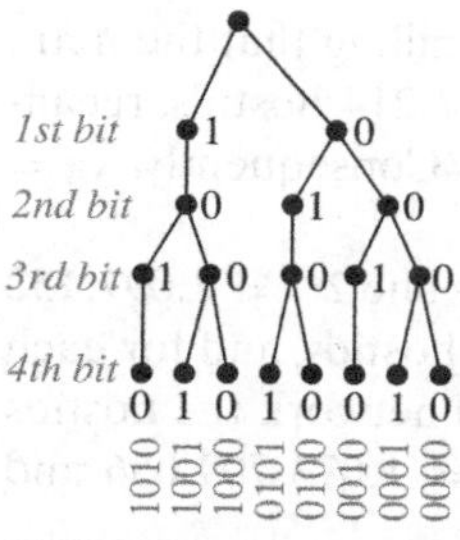

TREE DIAGRAMS

Counting problems can be solved using **tree diagrams.** A tree consists of a root, a number of branches leaving the root, and possible additional branches leaving the endpoints of other branches. (We will study trees in detail in Chapter 9.) To use trees in counting, we use a branch to represent each possible choice. We represent the possible outcomes by the leaves, which are the endpoints of branches not having other branches starting at them.

Note that when a tree diagram is used to solve a counting problem, the number of choices required to reach a leaf can vary (see Example 18, for example).

FIGURE 2
Bit Strings of Length Four without Consecutive 1s.

EXAMPLE 17 How many bit strings of length four do not have two consecutive 1s?

Solution: The tree diagram in Figure 2 displays all bit strings of length four without two consecutive 1s. We see that there are eight bit strings of length four without two consecutive 1s. ◄

EXAMPLE 18 A playoff between two teams consists of at most five games. The first team that wins three games wins the playoff. In how many different ways can the playoff occur?

Solution: The tree diagram in Figure 3 displays all the ways the playoff can proceed, with the winner of each game shown. We see that there are 20 different ways for the playoff to occur. ◄

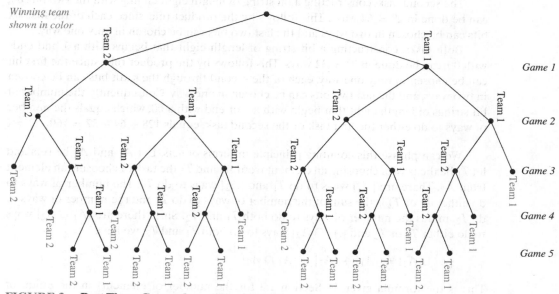

FIGURE 3 **Best Three Games Out of Five Playoffs.**

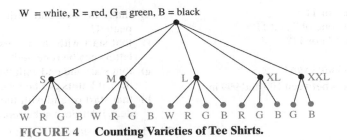

W = white, R = red, G = green, B = black

FIGURE 4   Counting Varieties of Tee Shirts.

EXAMPLE 19   Suppose that "I Love New Jersey" tee shirts come in five different sizes: S, M, L, XL, and XXL. Further suppose that each size comes in four colors, white, red, green, and black, except for XL, which comes only in red, green, and black, and XXL, which comes only in green and black. How many different shirts does a souvenir shop have to stock to have at least one of each available size and color of the tee shirt?

Solution: The tree diagram in Figure 4 displays all possible size and color pairs. It follows that the souvenir shop owner needs to stock 17 different tee shirts.   ◀

Exercises

1. There are 18 mathematics majors and 325 computer science majors at a college.

   a) How many ways are there to pick two representatives, so that one is a mathematics major and the other is a computer science major?

   b) How many ways are there to pick one representative who is either a mathematics major or a computer science major?

2. An office building contains 27 floors and has 37 offices on each floor. How many offices are in the building?

3. A multiple-choice test contains ten questions. There are four possible answers for each question.

   a) How many ways can a student answer the questions on the test if every question is answered?

   b) How many ways can a student answer the questions on the test if the student can leave answers blank?

4. A particular brand of shirt comes in 12 colors, has a male version and a female version, and comes in three sizes for each sex. How many different types of this shirt are made?

5. There are six different airlines that fly from New York to Denver and seven that fly from Denver to San Francisco. How many different possibilities are there for a trip from New York to San Francisco via Denver, when an airline is picked for the flight to Denver and an airline is picked for the continuation flight to San Francisco?

6. There are four major auto routes from Boston to Detroit and six from Detroit to Los Angeles. How many major auto routes are there from Boston to Los Angeles via Detroit?

7. How many different three-letter initials can people have?

8. How many different three-letter initials with none of the letters repeated can people have?

9. How many different three-letter initials are there that begin with an *A*?

10. How many bit strings are there of length eight?

11. How many bit strings of length ten begin and end with a 1?

12. How many bit strings are there of length six or less?

13. How many bit strings with length not exceeding *n*, where *n* is a positive integer, consist entirely of 1s?

14. How many bit strings of length *n*, where *n* is a positive integer, start and end with 1s?

15. How many strings are there of lowercase letters of length four or less?

16. How many strings are there of four lowercase letters that have the letter *x* in them?

17. How many strings of five ASCII characters contain the character @ (at sign) at least once? (*Note:* There are 128 different ASCII characters.)

18. How many positive integers less than 1000

   a) are divisible by 7?

   b) are divisible by 7 but not by 11?

   c) are divisible by both 7 and 11?

   d) are divisible by either 7 or 11?

   e) are divisible by exactly one of 7 and 11?

   f) are divisible by neither 7 nor 11?

   g) have distinct digits?

   h) have distinct digits and are even?

19. How many positive integers between 100 and 999 inclusive

   a) are divisible by 7?

   b) are odd?

   c) have the same three decimal digits?

   d) are not divisible by 4?

   e) are divisible by 3 or 4?

   f) are not divisible by either 3 or 4?

   g) are divisible by 3 but not by 4?

   h) are divisible by 3 and 4?

20. How many positive integers between 1000 and 9999 inclusive

   a) are divisible by 9?

   b) are even?

   c) have distinct digits?

   d) are not divisible by 3?

   e) are divisible by 5 or 7?

   f) are not divisible by either 5 or 7?

   g) are divisible by 5 but not by 7?

   h) are divisible by 5 and 7?

21. How many strings of three decimal digits

   a) do not contain the same digit three times?

   b) begin with an odd digit?

   c) have exactly two digits that are 4s?

22. How many strings of four decimal digits

   a) do not contain the same digit twice?

   b) end with an even digit?

   c) have exactly three digits that are 9s?

23. A committee is formed containing either the governor or one of the two senators of each of the 50 states. How many ways are there to form this committee?

24. How many license plates can be made using either three digits followed by three letters or three letters followed by three digits?

25. How many license plates can be made using either two letters followed by four digits or two digits followed by four letters?

26. How many license plates can be made using either three letters followed by three digits or four letters followed by two digits?

27. How many license plates can be made using either two or three letters followed by either two or three digits?

28. How many strings of eight English letters are there

   a) if letters can be repeated?

   b) if no letter can be repeated?

   c) that start with X, if letters can be repeated?

   d) that start with X, if no letter can be repeated?

   e) that start and end with X, if letters can be repeated?

   f) that start with the letters BO (in that order), if letters can be repeated?

   g) that start and end with the letters BO (in that order), if letters can be repeated?

   h) that start or end with the letters BO (in that order), if letters can be repeated?

29. How many strings of eight English letters are there

   a) that contain no vowels, if letters can be repeated?

   b) that contain no vowels, if letters cannot be repeated?

   c) that start with a vowel, if letters can be repeated?

   d) that start with a vowel, if letters cannot be repeated?

   e) that contain at least one vowel, if letters can be repeated?

   f) that contain exactly one vowel, if letters can be repeated?

   g) that start with X and contain at least one vowel, if letters can be repeated?

   h) that start and end with X and contain at least one vowel, if letters can be repeated?

30. How many different functions are there from a set with 10 elements to sets with the following numbers of elements?

   a) 2   **b)** 3   **c)** 4   **d)** 5

31. How many one-to-one functions are there from a set with five elements to sets with the following number of elements?

   a) 4   **b)** 5   **c)** 6   **d)** 7

32. How many functions are there from the set $\{1, 2, \ldots, n\}$, where n is a positive integer, to the set $\{0, 1\}$?

33. How many functions are there from the set $\{1, 2, \ldots, n\}$, where n is a positive integer, to the set $\{0, 1\}$

   a) that are one-to-one?

   b) that assign 0 to both 1 and n?

   c) that assign 1 to exactly one of the positive integers less than n?

34. How many partial functions (see the exercises in Section 1.8) are there from a set with five elements to sets with each of these number of elements?

   a) 1   **b)** 2   **c)** 5   **d)** 9

35. How many partial functions (see the exercises in Section 1.8) are there from a set with m elements to a set with n elements, where m and n are positive integers?

36. How many subsets of a set with 100 elements have more than one element?

37. A **palindrome** is a string whose reversal is identical to the string. How many bit strings of length n are palindromes?

38. In how many ways can a photographer at a wedding arrange 6 people in a row from a group of 10 people, where the bride and the groom are among these 10 people, if

    a) the bride must be in the picture?

    b) both the bride and groom must be in the picture?

    c) exactly one of the bride and the groom is in the picture?

39. In how many ways can a photographer at a wedding arrange six people in a row, including the bride and groom, if

    a) the bride must be next to the groom?

    b) the bride is not next to the groom?

    c) the bride is positioned somewhere to the left of the groom?

40. How many bit strings of length seven either begin with two 0s or end with three 1s?

41. How many bit strings of length 10 either begin with three 0s or end with two 0s?

*42. How many bit strings of length 10 contain either five consecutive 0s or five consecutive 1s?

**43. How many bit strings of length eight contain either three consecutive 0s or four consecutive 1s?

44. Every student in a discrete mathematics class is either a computer science or a mathematics major or is a joint major in these two subjects. How many students are in the class if there are 38 computer science majors (including joint majors), 23 mathematics majors (including joint majors), and 7 joint majors?

45. How many positive integers not exceeding 100 are divisible either by 4 or by 6?

46. The name of a variable in the C programming language is a string that can contain uppercase letters, lowercase letters, digits, or underscores. Further, the first character in the string must be a letter, either uppercase or lowercase, or an underscore. If the name of a variable is determined by its first eight characters, how many different variables can be named in C? (Note that the name of a variable may contain fewer than eight characters.)

47. Suppose that at some future time every telephone in the world is assigned a number that contains a country code 1 to 3 digits long, that is, of the form X, XX, or XXX, followed by a ten-digit telephone number of the form NXX-NXX-XXXX (as described in Example 7). How many different telephone numbers would be available worldwide under this numbering plan?

48. Use a tree diagram to find the number of bit strings of length four with no three consecutive 0s.

49. How many ways are there to arrange the letters a, b, c, and d such that a is not followed immediately by b?

50. Use a tree diagram to find the number of ways that the World Series can occur, where the first team that wins four games out of seven wins the series.

51. Use a tree diagram to determine the number of subsets of $\{3, 7, 9, 11, 24\}$ with the property that the sum of the elements in the subset is less than 28.

52. a) Suppose that a store sells six varieties of soft drinks: cola, ginger ale, orange, root beer, lemonade, and cream soda. Use a tree diagram to determine the number of different types of bottles the store must stock to have all varieties available in all size bottles if all varieties are available in 12-ounce bottles, all but lemonade are available in 20-ounce bottles, only cola and ginger ale are available in 32-ounce bottles, and all but lemonade and cream soda are available in 64-ounce bottles?

    b) Answer the question in part (a) using counting rules.

53. a) Suppose that a popular style of running shoe is available for both men and women. The woman's shoe comes in sizes 6, 7, 8, and 9, and the man's shoe comes in sizes 8, 9, 10, 11, and 12. The man's shoe comes in white and black, while the woman's shoe comes in white, red, and black. Use a tree diagram to determine the number of different shoes that a store has to stock to have at least one pair of this type of running shoe for all available sizes and colors for both men and women.

    b) Answer the question in part (a) using counting rules.

*54. Use the product rule to show that there are 2^{2^n} different truth tables for propositions in n variables.

55. Use mathematical induction to prove the sum rule for m tasks from the sum rule for two tasks.

56. Use mathematical induction to prove the product rule for m tasks from the product rule for two tasks.

57. How many diagonals does a convex polygon with n sides have? (A polygon is convex if every line segment connecting two points in the interior or boundary of the polygon lies entirely within this set.)

58. Data are transmitted over the Internet in **datagrams,** which are structured blocks of bits. Each datagram contains header information organized into a maximum of 14 different fields (specifying many things, including the source and destination addresses) and a data area that contains the actual data that are transmitted. One of the 14 header fields is the **header length field** (denoted by HLEN), which is specified by the protocol to be 4 bits long and that specifies the header length in terms of 32-bit blocks of bits. For example, if HLEN = 0110, the header is made up of six 32-bit blocks. Another of the 14 header fields is the 16-bit-long **total length field** (denoted by TOTAL LENGTH), which specifies the length in bits of the entire datagram, including both the header fields and the data area. The length of the data area is the total length of the datagram minus the length of the header.

a) The largest possible value of TOTAL LENGTH (which is 16 bits long) determines the maximum total length in octets (blocks of 8 bits) of an Internet datagram. What is this value?

b) The largest possible value of HLEN (which is 4 bits long) determines the maximum total header length in 32-bit blocks. What is this value? What is the maximum total header length in octets?

c) The minimum (and most common) header length is 20 octets. What is the maximum total length in octets of the data area of an Internet datagram?

d) How many different strings of octets in the data area can be transmitted if the header length is 20 octets and the total length is as long as possible?

4.2 The Pigeonhole Principle

INTRODUCTION

Suppose that a flock of pigeons flies into a set of pigeonholes to roost. The **pigeonhole principle** states that if there are more pigeons than pigeonholes, then there must be at least one pigeonhole with at least two pigeons in it (see Figure 1). Of course, this principle applies to other objects besides pigeons and pigeonholes.

THEOREM 1   **THE PIGEONHOLE PRINCIPLE**   If $k + 1$ or more objects are placed into k boxes, then there is at least one box containing two or more of the objects.

Proof: Suppose that none of the k boxes contains more than one object. Then the total number of objects would be at most k. This is a contradiction, since there are at least $k + 1$ objects.   ◁

The pigeonhole principle is also called the **Dirichlet drawer principle,** after the nineteenth-century German mathematician Dirichlet, who often used this principle in his work. The following examples show how the pigeonhole principle is used.

EXAMPLE 1   Among any group of 367 people, there must be at least two with the same birthday, because there are only 366 possible birthdays.   ◀

EXAMPLE 2   In any group of 27 English words, there must be at least two that begin with the same letter, since there are 26 letters in the English alphabet.   ◀

EXAMPLE 3   How many students must be in a class to guarantee that at least two students receive the same score on the final exam, if the exam is graded on a scale from 0 to 100 points?

G. LEJEUNE DIRICHLET (1805–1859)   G. Lejeune Dirichlet was born into a French family living near Cologne, Germany. He studied at the University of Paris and held positions at the University of Breslau and the University of Berlin. In 1855 he was chosen to succeed Gauss at the University of Göttingen. Dirichlet is said to be the first person to master Gauss's *Disquisitiones Arithmeticae*, which appeared 20 years earlier. He is said to have kept a copy at his side even when he traveled. Dirichlet made many important discoveries in number theory, including the theorem that there are infinitely many primes in arithmetical progressions $an + b$ when a and b are relatively prime. He proved the $n = 5$ case of Fermat's Last Theorem, that there are no nontrivial solutions in integers to $x^5 + y^5 = z^5$. Dirichlet also made many contributions to analysis.

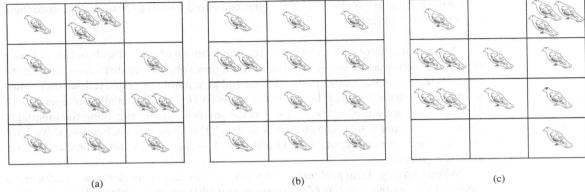

(a)   (b)   (c)

FIGURE 1   There Are More Pigeons Than Pigeonholes.

Solution: There are 101 possible scores on the final. The pigeonhole principle shows that among any 102 students there must be at least 2 students with the same score.   ◄

The pigeonhole principle is a useful tool in many proofs, including proofs of surprising results such as that given in Example 4.

EXAMPLE 4   Show that for every integer n there is a multiple of n that has only 0s and 1s in its decimal expansion.

Extra
Examples

Solution: Let n be a positive integer. Consider the n integers $1, 11, 111, \ldots, 11 \cdots 1$ (where the last integer in this list is the integer with $n + 1$ 1s in its decimal expansion). Note that there are n possible remainders when an integer is divided by n. Since there are $n + 1$ integers in this list, by the pigeonhole principle there must be two with the same remainder when divided by n. The difference of these two integers has a decimal expansion consisting entirely of 0s and 1s and is divisible by n.   ◄

THE GENERALIZED PIGEONHOLE PRINCIPLE

The pigeonhole principle states that there must be at least two objects in the same box when there are more objects than boxes. However, even more can be said when the number of objects exceeds a multiple of the number of boxes. For instance, among any set of 21 decimal digits there must be 3 that are the same. This follows because when 21 objects are distributed into 10 boxes, one box must have more than 2 objects.

THEOREM 2   **THE GENERALIZED PIGEONHOLE PRINCIPLE**   If N objects are placed into k boxes, then there is at least one box containing at least $\lceil N/k \rceil$ objects.

Proof: Suppose that none of the boxes contains more than $\lceil N/k \rceil - 1$ objects. Then, the total number of objects is at most

$$k \left(\left\lceil \frac{N}{k} \right\rceil - 1 \right) < k \left(\left(\frac{N}{k} + 1 \right) - 1 \right) = N,$$

where the inequality $\lceil N/k \rceil < (N/k) + 1$ has been used. This is a contradiction since there are a total of N objects. ◁

A common type of problem asks for the minimum number of objects so that at least r of these objects must be in one of k boxes when these objects are distributed among the boxes. When we have N objects, the generalized pigeonhole principle tells us there must be at least r objects in one of the boxes as long as $\lceil N/k \rceil \geq r$. The smallest integer N with $N/k > r - 1$, namely, $N = k(r-1) + 1$, is the smallest integer satisfying the inequality $\lceil N/k \rceil \geq r$. Could a smaller value of N suffice? The answer is no, because if we have $k(r-1)$ objects, we could put $r - 1$ of them in each of the k boxes and no box would have at least r objects.

When thinking about problems of this type, it is useful to consider how you can avoid having at least r objects in one of the boxes as you add successive objects. To avoid adding a rth object to any box, you eventually end up with $r - 1$ objects in each box. There is no way to add the next object without putting a rth object in that box.

Examples 5–8 illustrate how the generalized pigeonhole principle is applied.

EXAMPLE 5 Among 100 people there are at least $\lceil 100/12 \rceil = 9$ who were born in the same month. ◀

EXAMPLE 6 What is the minimum number of students required in a discrete mathematics class to be sure that at least six will receive the same grade, if there are five possible grades, A, B, C, D, and F?

Extra Examples

Solution: The minimum number of students needed to ensure that at least six students receive the same grade is the smallest integer N such that $\lceil N/5 \rceil = 6$. The smallest such integer is $N = 5 \cdot 5 + 1 = 26$. If you have only 25 students, it is possible for there to be five who have received each grade so that no six students have received the same grade. Thus, 26 is the minimum number of students needed to ensure that at least six students will receive the same grade. ◀

EXAMPLE 7 **a)** How many cards must be selected from a standard deck of 52 cards to guarantee that at least three cards of the same suit are chosen?
b) How many must be selected to guarantee that at least three hearts are selected?

Solution:

a) Suppose there are four boxes, and as cards are selected they are placed in the box reserved for cards of that suit. Using the generalized pigeonhole principle, we see that if N cards are selected, there is at least one box containing at least $\lceil N/4 \rceil$ cards. Consequently, we know that at least three cards of one suit are selected if $\lceil N/4 \rceil \geq 3$. The smallest integer N such that $\lceil N/4 \rceil \geq 3$ is $N = 2 \cdot 4 + 1 = 9$, so nine cards suffice. Note that if eight cards are selected, it is possible to have two cards of each suit, so that more than eight cards are needed. Consequently, nine cards must be selected to guarantee that at least three cards of one suit are chosen. One good way to think about this is to note that after the eighth card is chosen, there is no way to avoid having a third card of some suit.
b) We do not use the generalized pigeonhole principle to answer this question, since we want to make sure that there are three hearts, not just three cards of one suit. Note that in the worst case, we can select all the clubs, diamonds, and spades, 39 cards in all, before we select a single heart. The next three cards will be all hearts, so we may need to select 42 cards to get three hearts. ◀

EXAMPLE 8 What is the least number of area codes needed to guarantee that the 25 million phones in a state have distinct ten-digit telephone numbers? (Assume that telephone numbers are of the form NXX-NXX-XXXX, where the first three digits form the area code, N represents a digit from 2 to 9 inclusive, and X represents any digit.)

Solution: There are eight million different phone numbers of the form NXX-XXXX (as shown in Example 7 of Section 4.1). Hence, by the generalized pigeonhole principle, among 25 million telephones, at least $\lceil 25{,}000{,}000/8{,}000{,}000 \rceil$ of them must have identical phone numbers. Hence, at least four area codes are required to ensure that all ten-digit numbers are different. ◀

Example 9, although not an application of the generalized pigeonhole principle, makes use of similar principles.

EXAMPLE 9   Suppose that a computer science laboratory has 15 workstations and ten servers. A cable can be used to directly connect a workstation to a server. Only one direct connection to a server can be active at any time. We want to guarantee that at any time any set of ten or fewer workstations can simultaneously access different servers via direct connections. Although we could do this by connecting every workstation directly to every server (using 150 connections), what is the minimum number of direct connections needed to achieve this goal?

Solution: Suppose that we label the workstations $W_1, W_2, \ldots, W_{15}$ and the servers $S_1, S_2, \ldots, S_{10}$. Furthermore, suppose that we connect W_k to S_k for $k = 1, 2, \ldots, 10$ and each of $W_{11}, W_{12}, W_{13}, W_{14}$, and W_{15} to all ten servers. We have a total of 60 direct connections. Clearly any set of ten or fewer workstations can simultaneously access different servers. We see this by noting that if workstation W_j is included with $1 \leq j \leq 10$, it can access server S_j, and for each workstation W_k with $k \geq 11$ included, there must be a corresponding workstation W_j with $1 \leq j \leq 10$ not included, so that W_k can access server S_j. (This follows since there are at least as many available servers S_j as there are workstations W_j with $1 \leq j \leq 10$ not included.)

Now suppose there are fewer than 60 direct connections between workstations and servers. Then some server would be connected to at most $\lfloor 59/10 \rfloor = 5$ workstations. (If all servers were connected to at least six workstations, there would be at least $6 \cdot 10 = 60$ direct connections.) This means that the remaining nine servers are not enough to allow the other ten workstations to simultaneously access different servers. Consequently, at least 60 direct connections are needed. It follows that 60 is the answer. ◀

SOME ELEGANT APPLICATIONS OF THE PIGEONHOLE PRINCIPLE

In many interesting applications of the pigeonhole principle, the objects to be placed in boxes must be chosen in a clever way. A few such applications will be described here.

EXAMPLE 10   During a month with 30 days a baseball team plays at least one game a day, but no more than 45 games. Show that there must be a period of some number of consecutive days during which the team must play exactly 14 games.

Solution: Let a_j be the number of games played on or before the jth day of the month. Then $a_1, a_2, \ldots, a_{30}$ is an increasing sequence of distinct positive integers, with $1 \leq a_j \leq 45$. Moreover, $a_1 + 14, a_2 + 14, \ldots, a_{30} + 14$ is also an increasing sequence of distinct positive integers, with $15 \leq a_j + 14 \leq 59$.

The 60 positive integers $a_1, a_2, \ldots, a_{30}, a_1 + 14, a_2 + 14, \ldots, a_{30} + 14$ are all less than or equal to 59. Hence, by the pigeonhole principle two of these integers are equal. Since the integers $a_j, j = 1, 2, \ldots, 30$ are all distinct and the integers $a_j + 14, j = 1, 2, \ldots, 30$ are all distinct, there must be indices i and j with $a_i = a_j + 14$. This means that exactly 14 games were played from day $j + 1$ to day i.   ◄

EXAMPLE 11   Show that among any $n + 1$ positive integers not exceeding $2n$ there must be an integer that divides one of the other integers.

Solution: Write each of the $n + 1$ integers $a_1, a_2, \ldots, a_{n+1}$ as a power of 2 times an odd integer. In other words, let $a_j = 2^{k_j} q_j$ for $j = 1, 2, \ldots, n + 1$, where k_j is a nonnegative integer and q_j is odd. The integers $q_1, q_2, \ldots, q_{n+1}$ are all odd positive integers less than $2n$. Since there are only n odd positive integers less than $2n$, it follows from the pigeonhole principle that two of the integers $q_1, q_2, \ldots, q_{n+1}$ must be equal. Therefore, there are integers i and j such that $q_i = q_j$. Let q be the common value of q_i and q_j. Then, $a_i = 2^{k_i} q$ and $a_j = 2^{k_j} q$. It follows that if $k_i < k_j$, then a_i divides a_j; while if $k_i > k_j$, then a_j divides a_i.   ◄

A clever application of the pigeonhole principle shows the existence of an increasing or a decreasing subsequence of a certain length in a sequence of distinct integers. Some definitions will be reviewed before this application is presented. Suppose that $a_1, a_2, \ldots, a_N$ is a sequence of real numbers. A **subsequence** of this sequence is a sequence of the form $a_{i_1}, a_{i_2}, \ldots, a_{i_m}$, where $1 \leq i_1 < i_2 < \cdots < i_m \leq N$. Hence, a subsequence is a sequence obtained from the original sequence by including some of the terms of the original sequence in their original order, and perhaps not including other terms. A sequence is called **strictly increasing** if each term is larger than the one that precedes it, and it is called **strictly decreasing** if each term is smaller than the one that precedes it.

THEOREM 3   Every sequence of $n^2 + 1$ distinct real numbers contains a subsequence of length $n + 1$ that is either strictly increasing or strictly decreasing.

We give an example before presenting the proof of Theorem 3.

EXAMPLE 12   The sequence $8, 11, 9, 1, 4, 6, 12, 10, 5, 7$ contains ten terms. Note that $10 = 3^2 + 1$. There are four increasing subsequences of length four, namely, $1, 4, 6, 12; 1, 4, 6, 7; 1, 4, 6, 10$; and $1, 4, 5, 7$. There is also a decreasing subsequence of length four, namely, $11, 9, 6, 5$.   ◄

The proof of the theorem will now be given.

Proof: Let $a_1, a_2, \ldots, a_{n^2+1}$ be a sequence of $n^2 + 1$ distinct real numbers. Associate an ordered pair with each term of the sequence, namely, associate (i_k, d_k) to the term a_k, where i_k is the length of the longest increasing subsequence starting at a_k, and d_k is the length of the longest decreasing subsequence starting at a_k.

Suppose that there are no increasing or decreasing subsequences of length $n + 1$. Then i_k and d_k are both positive integers less than or equal to n, for $k = 1, 2, \ldots, n^2 + 1$. Hence, by the product rule there are n^2 possible ordered pairs for (i_k, d_k). By the pigeonhole principle, two of these $n^2 + 1$ ordered pairs are equal. In other words, there exist terms a_s and a_t, with $s < t$ such that $i_s = i_t$ and $d_s = d_t$. We will show that this is impossible. Because the terms of the sequence are distinct, either $a_s < a_t$ or $a_s > a_t$. If $a_s < a_t$, then, since $i_s = i_t$, an increasing subsequence of length $i_t + 1$ can be built starting at a_s, by taking a_s followed by an increasing subsequence of length i_t beginning at a_t. This is a contradiction. Similarly, if $a_s > a_t$, it can be shown that d_s must be greater than d_t, which is a contradiction.   ◁

The final example shows how the generalized pigeonhole principle can be applied to an important part of combinatorics called **Ramsey theory,** after the English mathematician F. P. Ramsey. In general, Ramsey theory deals with the distribution of subsets of elements of sets.

EXAMPLE 13 Assume that in a group of six people, each pair of individuals consists of two friends or two enemies. Show that there are either three mutual friends or three mutual enemies in the group.

Solution: Let A be one of the six people. Of the five other people in the group, there are either three or more who are friends of A, or three or more who are enemies of A. This follows from the generalized pigeonhole principle, since when five objects are divided into two sets, one of the sets has at least $\lceil 5/2 \rceil = 3$ elements. In the former case, suppose that B, C, and D are friends of A. If any two of these three individuals are friends, then these two and A form a group of three mutual friends. Otherwise, B, C, and D form a set of three mutual enemies. The proof in the latter case, when there are three or more enemies of A, proceeds in a similar manner.   ◀

The **Ramsey number** $R(m, n)$, where m and n are positive integers greater than or equal to 2, denotes the minimum number of people at a party so that there are either m mutual friends or n mutual enemies, assuming that every pair of people at the party are friends or enemies. Example 13 shows that $R(3, 3) \leq 6$. We conclude that $R(3, 3) = 6$ since in a group of five people where every two people are friends or enemies, there may not be three mutual friends or three mutual enemies (see Exercise 24).

It is possible to prove some useful properties about Ramsey numbers, but for the most part it is difficult to find their exact values. Note that by symmetry it can be shown that $R(m, n) = R(n, m)$ (see Exercise 28). We also have $R(2, n) = n$ for every positive integer $n \geq 2$ (see Exercise 27). The exact values of only nine Ramsey numbers $R(m, n)$ with $3 \leq m \leq n$ are known, including $R(4, 4) = 18$. Only bounds are known for many other Ramsey numbers, including $R(5, 5)$, which is known to satisfy $43 \leq R(5, 5) \leq 49$. The reader interested in learning more about Ramsey numbers should consult [MiRo91] or [GrRoSp90].

FRANK PLUMPTON RAMSEY (1903–1930) Frank Plumpton Ramsey, son of the president of Magdalene College, Cambridge, was educated at Winchester and Trinity Colleges. After graduating in 1923, he was elected a fellow of King's College, Cambridge, where he spent the remainder of his life. Ramsey made important contributions to mathematical logic. What we now call Ramsey theory began with his clever combinatorial arguments, published in the paper "On a Problem of Formal Logic." Ramsey also made contributions to the mathematical theory of economics. He was noted as an excellent lecturer on the foundations of mathematics. His death at the age of 26 deprived the mathematical community and Cambridge University of a brilliant young scholar.

Exercises

1. Show that in any set of six classes there must be two that meet on the same day, assuming that no classes are held on weekends.

2. Show that if there are 30 students in a class, then at least two have last names that begin with the same letter.

3. A drawer contains a dozen brown socks and a dozen black socks, all unmatched. A man takes socks out at random in the dark.
   a) How many socks must he take out to be sure that he has at least two socks of the same color?
   b) How many socks must he take out to be sure that he has at least two black socks?

4. A bowl contains ten red balls and ten blue balls. A woman selects balls at random without looking at them.
   a) How many balls must she select to be sure of having at least three balls of the same color?
   b) How many balls must she select to be sure of having at least three blue balls?

5. Show that among any group of five (not necessarily consecutive) integers, there are two with the same remainder when divided by 4.

6. Let d be a positive integer. Show that among any group of $d + 1$ (not necessarily consecutive) integers there are two with exactly the same remainder when they are divided by d.

7. Let n be a positive integer. Show that in any set of n consecutive integers there is exactly one divisible by n.

8. Show that if f is a function from S to T where S and T are finite sets with $|S| > |T|$, then there are elements s_1 and s_2 in S such that $f(s_1) = f(s_2)$, or in other words, f is not one-to-one.

9. What is the minimum number of students, each of whom comes from one of the 50 states, enrolled in a university to guarantee that there are at least 100 who come from the same state?

*10. Let (x_i, y_i), $i = 1, 2, 3, 4, 5$, be a set of five distinct points with integer coordinates in the xy plane. Show that the midpoint of the line joining at least one pair of these points has integer coordinates.

*11. Let (x_i, y_i, z_i), $i = 1, 2, 3, 4, 5, 6, 7, 8, 9$, be a set of nine distinct points with integer coordinates in xyz space. Show that the midpoint of at least one pair of these points has integer coordinates.

12. How many ordered pairs of integers (a, b) are needed to guarantee that there are two ordered pairs (a_1, b_1) and (a_2, b_2) such that $a_1 \bmod 5 = a_2 \bmod 5$ and $b_1 \bmod 5 = b_2 \bmod 5$?

13. a) Show that if five integers are selected from the first eight positive integers, there must be a pair of these integers with a sum equal to 9.

   b) Is the conclusion in part (a) true if four integers are selected rather than five?

14. a) Show that if seven integers are selected from the first 10 positive integers, there must be at least two pairs of these integers with the sum 11.
   b) Is the conclusion in part (a) true if six integers are selected rather than seven?

15. How many numbers must be selected from the set $\{1, 2, 3, 4, 5, 6\}$ to guarantee that at least one pair of these numbers add up to 7?

16. How many numbers must be selected from the set $\{1, 3, 5, 7, 9, 11, 13, 15\}$ to guarantee that at least one pair of these numbers add up to 16?

17. A company stores products in a warehouse. Storage bins in this warehouse are specified by their aisle, location in the aisle, and shelf. There are 50 aisles, 85 horizontal locations in each aisle, and 5 shelves throughout the warehouse. What is the least number of products the company can have so that at least two products must be stored in the same bin?

18. Suppose that there are nine students in a discrete mathematics class at a small college.
   a) Show that the class must have at least five male students or at least five female students.
   b) Show that the class must have at least three male students or at least seven female students.

19. Suppose that every student in a discrete mathematics class of 25 students is a freshman, a sophomore, or a junior.
   a) Show that there are at least nine freshmen, at least nine sophomores, or at least nine juniors in the class.
   b) Show that there are either at least three freshmen, at least 19 sophomores, or at least five juniors in the class.

20. Find an increasing subsequence of maximal length and a decreasing subsequence of maximal length in the sequence 22, 5, 7, 2, 23, 10, 15, 21, 3, 17.

21. Construct a sequence of 16 positive integers that has no increasing or decreasing subsequence of five terms.

22. Show that if there are 101 people of different heights standing in a line, it is possible to find 11 people in the order they are standing in the line with heights that are either increasing or decreasing.

*23. Describe an algorithm in pseudocode for producing the largest increasing or decreasing subsequence of a sequence of distinct integers.

24. Show that in a group of five people (where any two people are either friends or enemies), there are not necessarily three mutual friends or three mutual enemies.

25. Show that in a group of ten people (where any two people are either friends or enemies), there are either three mutual friends or four mutual enemies, and there are either three mutual enemies or four mutual friends.

26. Use Exercise 25 to show that among any group of 20 people (where any two people are either friends or enemies), there are either four mutual friends or four mutual enemies.

27. Show that if n is a positive integer with $n \geq 2$, then the Ramsey number $R(2, n)$ equals n.

28. Show that if m and n are positive integers with $m \geq 2$ and $n \geq 2$, then the Ramsey numbers $R(m, n)$ and $R(n, m)$ are equal.

29. Show that there are at least six people in California (population: 34 million) with the same three initials who were born on the same day of the year (but not necessarily in the same year).

30. Show that if there are 100,000,000 wage earners in the United States who earn less than 1,000,000 dollars, then there are two who earned exactly the same amount of money, to the penny, last year.

31. There are 38 different time periods during which classes at a university can be scheduled. If there are 677 different classes, how many different rooms will be needed?

32. A computer network consists of six computers. Each computer is directly connected to at least one of the other computers. Show that there are at least two computers in the network that are directly connected to the same number of other computers.

33. A computer network consists of six computers. Each computer is directly connected to zero or more of the other computers. Show that there are at least two computers in the network that are directly connected to the same number of other computers.

34. Find the least number of cables required to connect eight computers to four printers to guarantee that four computers can directly access four different printers. Justify your answer.

35. Find the least number of cables required to connect 100 computers to 20 printers to guarantee that 20 computers can directly access 20 different printers. Justify your answer.

*36. Prove that at a party where there are at least two people, there are two people who know the same number of other people there.

37. An arm wrestler is the champion for a period of 75 hours. The arm wrestler had at least one match an hour, but no more than 125 total matches. Show that there is a period of consecutive hours during which the arm wrestler had exactly 24 matches.

*38. Is the statement in Exercise 37 true if 24 is replaced by

a) 2?   b) 23?   c) 25?   d) 30?

39. Show that if f is a function from S to T where S and T are finite sets and $m = \lceil |S|/|T| \rceil$, then there are at least m elements of S mapped to the same value of T. That is, show that there are elements $s_1, s_2, \ldots, s_m$ of S such that $f(s_1) = f(s_2) = \cdots = f(s_m)$.

40. There are 51 houses on a street. Each house has an address between 1000 and 1099, inclusive. Show that at least two houses have addresses that are consecutive integers.

*41. Let x be an irrational number. Show that for some positive integer j not exceeding n, the absolute value of the difference between jx and the nearest integer to jx is less than $1/n$.

42. Let $n_1, n_2, \ldots, n_t$ be positive integers. Show that if $n_1 + n_2 + \cdots + n_t - t + 1$ objects are placed into t boxes, then for some $i, i = 1, 2, \ldots, t$, the ith box contains at least n_i objects.

*43. A proof of Theorem 3 based on the generalized pigeonhole principle is outlined in this problem. The notation used is the same as that used in the proof in the text.

a) Assume that $i_k \leq n$ for $k = 1, 2, \ldots, n^2 + 1$. Use the generalized pigeonhole principle to show that there are $n + 1$ terms $a_{k_1}, a_{k_2}, \ldots, a_{k_{n+1}}$ with $i_{k_1} = i_{k_2} = \cdots = i_{k_{n+1}}$, where $1 \leq k_1 < k_2 < \cdots < k_{n+1}$.

b) Show that $a_{k_j} > a_{k_{j+1}}$ for $j = 1, 2, \ldots, n$. (*Hint:* Assume that $a_{k_j} < a_{k_{j+1}}$, and show that this implies that $i_{k_j} > i_{k_{j+1}}$, which is a contradiction.)

c) Use parts (a) and (b) to show that if there is no increasing subsequence of length $n + 1$, then there must be a decreasing subsequence of this length.

4.3   Permutations and Combinations

INTRODUCTION

Suppose that a tennis team has ten members. The coach has to select five players to make the trip to a match at another school. In addition, the coach has to prepare an ordered list of four players to play the four singles matches. In this section, methods will be developed to count the different unordered collections of the five players that are selected to make the trip and the different lists of four players to play the four singles matches. More generally, techniques will be introduced for counting the unordered selections of distinct objects and the ordered arrangements of objects of a finite set.

PERMUTATIONS

A **permutation** of a set of distinct objects is an ordered arrangement of these objects. We also are interested in ordered arrangements of some of the elements of a set. An ordered arrangement of r elements of a set is called an **r-permutation.**

EXAMPLE 1 Let $S = \{1, 2, 3\}$. The arrangement 3, 1, 2 is a permutation of S. The arrangement 3, 2 is a 2-permutation of S. ◀

The number of r-permutations of a set with n elements is denoted by $P(n, r)$. We can find $P(n, r)$ using the product rule.

THEOREM 1

The number of r-permutations of a set with n distinct elements is

$$P(n, r) = n(n - 1)(n - 2) \cdots (n - r + 1).$$

Proof: The first element of the permutation can be chosen in n ways, since there are n elements in the set. There are $n - 1$ ways to choose the second element of the permutation, since there are $n - 1$ elements left in the set after using the element picked for the first position. Similarly, there are $n - 2$ ways to choose the third element, and so on, until there are exactly $n - (r - 1) = n - r + 1$ ways to choose the rth element. Consequently, by the product rule, there are

$$n(n - 1)(n - 2) \cdots (n - r + 1)$$

r-permutations of the set. ◁

From Theorem 1 it follows that

$$P(n, r) = n(n - 1)(n - 2) \cdots (n - r + 1) = \frac{n!}{(n - r)!}$$

In particular, note that $P(n, n) = n!$. We will illustrate this result with some examples.

EXAMPLE 2 How many ways are there to select a first-prize winner, a second-prize winner, and a third-prize winner from 100 different people who have entered a contest?

Solution: Because it matters which person wins which prize, the number of ways to pick the three prize winners is the number of ordered selections of three elements from a set of 100 elements, that is, the number of 3-permutations of a set of 100 elements. Consequently, the answer is

$$P(100, 3) = 100 \cdot 99 \cdot 98 = 970,200.$$ ◀

EXAMPLE 3 Suppose that there are eight runners in a race. The winner receives a gold medal the second-place finisher receives a silver medal, and the third-place finisher receives a bronze medal. How many different ways are there to award these medals, if all possible outcomes of the race can occur and there are no ties?

Solution: The number of different ways to award the medals is the number of 3-permutations of a set with eight elements. Hence, there are $P(8, 3) = 8 \cdot 7 \cdot 6 = 336$ possible ways to award the medals. ◀

EXAMPLE 4   Suppose that a saleswoman has to visit eight different cities. She must begin her trip in a specified city, but she can visit the other seven cities in any order she wishes. How many possible orders can the saleswoman use when visiting these cities?

Solution: The number of possible paths between the cities is the number of permutations of seven elements, since the first city is determined, but the remaining seven can be ordered arbitrarily. Consequently, there are $7! = 7 \cdot 6 \cdot 5 \cdot 4 \cdot 3 \cdot 2 \cdot 1 = 5040$ ways for the saleswoman to choose her tour. If, for instance, the saleswoman wishes to find the path between the cities with minimum distance, and she computes the total distance for each possible path, she must consider a total of 5040 paths! ◀

EXAMPLE 5   How many permutations of the letters *ABCDEFGH* contain the string *ABC*?

Solution: Because the letters *ABC* must occur as a block, we can find the answer by finding the number of permutations of six objects, namely, the block *ABC* and the individual letters *D*, *E*, *F*, *G*, and *H*. Because these six objects can occur in any order, there are $6! = 720$ permutations of the letters *ABCDEFGH* in which *ABC* occurs as a block. ◀

COMBINATIONS

An *r*-**combination** of elements of a set is an unordered selection of *r* elements from the set. Thus, an *r*-combination is simply a subset of the set with *r* elements.

EXAMPLE 6   Let *S* be the set $\{1, 2, 3, 4\}$. Then $\{1, 3, 4\}$ is a 3-combination from *S*. ◀

The number of *r*-combinations of a set with *n* distinct elements is denoted by $C(n, r)$. Note that $C(n, r)$ is also denoted by $\binom{n}{r}$ and is called a **binomial coefficient.** We will learn where this terminology arises in Section 4.4.

EXAMPLE 7   We see that $C(4, 2) = 6$, since the 2-combinations of $\{a, b, c, d\}$ are the six subsets $\{a, b\}$, $\{a, c\}$, $\{a, d\}$, $\{b, c\}$, $\{b, d\}$, and $\{c, d\}$. ◀

We can determine the number of *r*-combinations of a set with *n* elements using the formula for the number of *r*-permutations of a set. To do this, note that the *r*-permutations of a set can be obtained by first forming *r*-combinations and then ordering the elements in these combinations. The proof of the following theorem, which gives the value of $C(n, r)$, is based on this observation.

THEOREM 2   The number of *r*-combinations of a set with *n* elements, where *n* is a nonnegative integer and *r* is an integer with $0 \leq r \leq n$, equals

$$C(n, r) = \frac{n!}{r! \, (n - r)!}.$$

Proof: The r-permutations of the set can be obtained by forming the $C(n, r)$ r-combinations of the set, and then ordering the elements in each r-combination, which can be done in $P(r, r)$ ways. Consequently,

$$P(n, r) = C(n, r) \cdot P(r, r).$$

This implies that

$$C(n, r) = \frac{P(n, r)}{P(r, r)} = \frac{n!/(n - r)!}{r!/(r - r)!} = \frac{n!}{r!\,(n - r)!}. \qquad \triangleleft$$

Remark: The formula in Theorem 2, although explicit, is not helpful when $C(n, r)$ is computed for large values of n and r. The reasons are that it is practical to compute exact values of factorials exactly only for small integer values, and when floating point arithmetic is used, the formula in Theorem 2 may produce a value that is not an integer. In practice, to compute $C(n, r)$ you cancel out all the terms in the larger factorial in the denominator from the numerator and denominator, multiply all the terms that do not cancel in the numerator and then divide by the smaller factorial in the denominator. Many calculators have a built-in function for $C(n, r)$.

Corollary 1 displays a useful identity for the number of r-combinations of a set.

COROLLARY 1   Let n and r be nonnegative integers with $r \leq n$. Then $C(n, r) = C(n, n - r)$.

Proof: From Theorem 2 it follows that

$$C(n, r) = \frac{n!}{r!\,(n - r)!}$$

and

$$C(n, n - r) = \frac{n!}{(n - r)!\,[n - (n - r)]!} = \frac{n!}{(n - r)!\,r!}.$$

Hence, $C(n, r) = C(n, n - r)$. $\triangleleft$

We can also prove Corollary 1 using a proof that shows that both sides of the equation in Corollary 1 count the same objects using different reasoning. We describe this important type of proof in Definition 1.

DEFINITION 1   A *combinatorial proof* is a proof that uses counting arguments to prove a theorem, rather than some other method such as algebraic techniques.

Many identities involving binomial coefficients can be proved using combinatorial proofs. An identity can be proved using a combinatorial proof if it can be shown that the two sides of the identity count the same elements, but in different ways. We now provide a combinatorial proof of Corollary 1.

Proof: Suppose that S is a set with n elements. Every subset A of S with r elements corresponds to a subset of S with $n - r$ elements, namely $\overline{A}$. Consequently, $C(n, r) = C(n, n - r)$. ◁

EXAMPLE 8

Extra
Examples

How many ways are there to select five players from a 10-member tennis team to make a trip to a match at another school?

Solution: The answer is given by the number of 5-combinations of a set with ten elements. By Theorem 2, the number of such combinations is

$$C(10, 5) = \frac{10!}{5! \, 5!} = 252.$$ ◄

EXAMPLE 9

A group of 30 people have been trained as astronauts to go on the first mission to Mars. How many ways are there to select a crew of six people to go on this mission (assuming that all crew members have the same job)?

Solution: The number of ways to select a crew of six from the pool of 30 people is the number of 6-combinations of a set with 30 elements, because the order in which these people are chosen does not matter. By Theorem 2, the number of such combinations is

$$C(30, 6) = \frac{30!}{6! \, 24!} = \frac{30 \cdot 29 \cdot 28 \cdot 27 \cdot 26 \cdot 25}{6 \cdot 5 \cdot 4 \cdot 3 \cdot 2 \cdot 1} = 593{,}775.$$ ◄

EXAMPLE 10

How many bit strings of length n contain exactly r 1s?

Solution: The positions of r 1s in a bit string of length n form an r-combination of the set $\{1, 2, 3, \ldots, n\}$. Hence, there are $C(n, r)$ bit strings of length n that contain exactly r 1s. ◄

EXAMPLE 11

How many ways are there to select a committee to develop a discrete mathematics course at a school if the committee is to consist of three faculty members from the mathematics department and four from the computer science department, if there are nine faculty members of the mathematics department and 11 of the computer science department?

Solution: By the product rule, the answer is the product of the number of 3-combinations of a set with nine elements and the number of 4-combinations of a set with 11 elements. By Theorem 2, the number of ways to select the committee is

$$C(9, 3) \cdot C(11, 4) = \frac{9!}{3! 6!} \cdot \frac{11!}{4! 7!} = 84 \cdot 330 = 27{,}720.$$ ◄

Exercises

1. List all the permutations of $\{a, b, c\}$.

2. How many permutations are there of the set $\{a, b, c, d, e, f, g\}$?

3. How many permutations of $\{a, b, c, d, e, f, g\}$ end with a?

4. Let $S = \{1, 2, 3, 4, 5\}$.

   a) List all the 3-permutations of S.

   b) List all the 3-combinations of S.

5. Find the value of each of these quantities.

   a) $P(6, 3)$ **b)** $P(6, 5)$ **c)** $P(8, 1)$

   d) $P(8, 5)$ **e)** $P(8, 8)$ **f)** $P(10, 9)$

6. Find the value of each of these quantities.

   a) $C(5, 1)$ **b)** $C(5, 3)$ **c)** $C(8, 4)$

   d) $C(8, 8)$ **e)** $C(8, 0)$ **f)** $C(12, 6)$

7. Find the number of 5-permutations of a set with nine elements.

8. In how many different orders can five runners finish a race if no ties are allowed?

9. How many possibilities are there for the win, place, and show (first, second, and third) positions in a horse race with 12 horses if all orders of finish are possible?

10. There are six different candidates for governor of a state. In how many different orders can the names of the candidates be printed on a ballot?

11. How many bit strings of length ten contain

   a) exactly four 1s?
   b) at most four 1s?
   c) at least four 1s?
   d) an equal number of 0s and 1s?

12. How many bit strings of length 12 contain

   a) exactly three 1s?
   b) at most three 1s?
   c) at least three 1s?
   d) an equal number of 0s and 1s?

13. A group contains n men and n women. How many ways are there to arrange these people in a row if the men and women alternate?

14. In how many ways can a set of two positive integers less than 100 be chosen?

15. In how many ways can a set of five letters be selected from the English alphabet?

16. How many subsets with an odd number of elements does a set with ten elements have?

17. How many subsets with more than two elements does a set with 100 elements have?

18. A coin is flipped eight times where each flip comes up either heads or tails. How many possible outcomes

   a) are there in total?
   b) contain exactly three heads?
   c) contain at least three heads?
   d) contain the same number of heads and tails?

19. A coin is flipped ten times where each flip comes up either heads or tails. How many possible outcomes

   a) are there in total?
   b) contain exactly two heads?
   c) contain at most three tails?
   d) contain the same number of heads and tails?

20. How many bit strings of length ten have

   a) exactly three 0s?
   b) more 0s than 1s?
   c) at least seven 1s?
   d) at least three 1s?

21. How many permutations of the letters $ABCDEFG$ contain

   a) the string BCD?

   b) the string $CFGA$?
   c) the strings BA and GF?
   d) the strings ABC and DE?
   e) the strings ABC and CDE?
   f) the strings CBA and BED?

22. How many permutations of the letters $ABCDEFGH$ contain

   a) the string ED?
   b) the string CDE?
   c) the strings BA and FGH?
   d) the strings AB, DE, and GH?
   e) the strings CAB and BED?
   f) the strings BCA and ABF?

23. How many ways are there for eight men and five women to stand in a line so that no two women stand next to each other? (*Hint:* First position the men and then consider possible positions for the women.)

24. How many ways are there for ten women and six men to stand in a line so that no two men stand next to each other? (*Hint:* First position the women and then consider possible positions for the men.)

25. One hundred tickets, numbered 1, 2, 3, . . . , 100, are sold to 100 different people for a drawing. Four different prizes are awarded, including a grand prize (a trip to Tahiti). How many ways are there to award the prizes if

   a) there are no restrictions?
   b) the person holding ticket 47 wins the grand prize?
   c) the person holding ticket 47 wins one of the prizes?
   d) the person holding ticket 47 does not win a prize?
   e) the people holding tickets 19 and 47 both win prizes?
   f) the people holding tickets 19, 47, and 73 all win prizes?
   g) the people holding tickets 19, 47, 73, and 97 all win prizes?
   h) none of the people holding tickets 19, 47, 73, and 97 wins a prize?
   i) the grand prize winner is a person holding ticket 19, 47, 73, or 97?
   j) the people holding tickets 19 and 47 win prizes, but the people holding tickets 73 and 97 do not win prizes?

26. Thirteen people on a softball team show up for a game.

   a) How many ways are there to choose ten players to take the field?
   b) How many ways are there to assign the ten positions by selecting players from the 13 people who show up?
   c) Of the 13 people who show up, three are women. How many ways are there to choose ten players

to take the field if at least one of these players must be a woman?

27. A club has 25 members.

    a) How many ways are there to choose four members of the club to serve on an executive committee?

    b) How many ways are there to choose a president, vice president, secretary, and treasurer of the club?

28. A professor writes 40 discrete mathematics true/false questions. Of the statements in these questions, 17 are true. If the questions can be positioned in any order, how many different answer keys are possible?

29. How many 4-permutations of the positive integers not exceeding 100 contain three consecutive integers in the correct order

    a) where consecutive means in the usual order of the integers and where these consecutive integers can perhaps be separated by other integers in the permutation?

    b) where consecutive means both that the numbers be consecutive integers and that they be in consecutive positions in the permutation?

30. Seven women and nine men are on the faculty in the mathematics department at a school.

    a) How many ways are there to select a committee of five members of the department if at least one woman must be on the committee?

    b) How many ways are there to select a committee of five members of the department if at least one woman and at least one man must be on the committee?

31. The English alphabet contains 21 consonants and five vowels. How many strings of six lowercase letters of the English alphabet contain

    a) exactly one vowel?   **b)** exactly two vowels?
    c) at least one vowel?   **d)** at least two vowels?

32. How many strings of six lowercase letters from the English alphabet contain

    a) the letter a?

    b) the letters a and b?

    c) the letters a and b in consecutive positions with a preceding b, with all the letters distinct?

    d) the letters a and b, where a is somewhere to the left of b in the string, with all the letters distinct?

33. Suppose that a department contains ten men and 15 women. How many ways are there to form a committee with six members if it must have the same number of men and women?

34. Suppose that a department contains ten men and 15 women. How many ways are there to form a committee with six members if it must have more women than men?

35. How many bit strings contain exactly eight 0s and ten 1s if every 0 must be immediately followed by a 1?

36. How many bit strings contain exactly five 0s and 14 1s if every 0 must be immediately followed by two 1s?

37. How many bit strings of length ten contain at least three 1s and at least three 0s?

38. How many ways are there to select 12 countries in the United Nations to serve on a council if 3 are selected from a block of 45, 4 are selected from a block of 57, and the others are selected from the remaining 69 countries?

39. How many license plates consisting of three letters followed by three digits contain no letter or digit twice?

40. How many ways are there to seat six people around a circular table, where seatings are considered to be the same if they can be obtained from each other by rotating the table?

41. How many ways are there for a horse race with three horses to finish if ties are possible? (*Note:* Two or three horses may tie.)

*42. How many ways are there for a horse race with four horses to finish if ties are possible? (*Note:* Any number of the four horses may tie.)

*43. There are six runners in the 100-yard dash. How many ways are there for three medals to be awarded if ties are possible? (The runner or runners who finish with the fastest time receive gold medals, the runner or runners who finish with exactly one runner ahead receive silver medals, and the runner or runners who finish with exactly two runners ahead receive bronze medals.)

*44. This procedure is used to break ties in games in the championship round of the World Cup soccer tournament. Each team selects five players in a prescribed order. Each of these players takes a penalty kick, with a player from the first team followed by a player from the second team and so on, following the order of players specified. If the score is still tied at the end of the ten penalty kicks, this procedure is repeated. If the score is till tied after 20 penalty kicks, a sudden-death shootout occurs, with the first team scoring an unanswered goal victorious.

    a) How many different scoring scenarios are possible if the game is settled in the first round of ten penalty kicks, where the round ends once it is impossible for a team to equal the number of goals scored by the other team?

    b) How many different scoring scenarios for the first and second groups of penalty kicks are possible if the game is settled in the second round of ten penalty kicks?

    c) How many scoring scenarios are possible for the full set of penalty kicks if the game is settled with no more than ten total additional kicks after the two rounds of five kicks for each team?

4.4   Binomial Coefficients

As we remarked in Section 4.3, the number of r-combinations from a set with n elements is often denoted by $\binom{n}{r}$. This number is also called a **binomial coefficient** because these numbers occur as coefficients in the expansion of powers of binomial expressions such as $(a + b)^n$. We will discuss the **Binomial Theorem,** which gives a power of a binomial expression as a sum of terms involving binomial coefficients. We will prove this theorem using a combinatorial proof. We will also show how combinatorial proofs can be used to establish some of the many different identities that express relationships among binomial coefficients.

THE BINOMIAL THEOREM

Links

The binomial theorem gives the coefficients of the expansion of powers of binomial expressions. A **binomial** expression is simply the sum of two terms, such as $x + y$. (The terms can be products of constants and variables, but that does not concern us here.) Example 1 illustrates why this theorem holds.

EXAMPLE 1   The expansion of $(x + y)^3$ can be found using combinatorial reasoning instead of multiplying the three terms out. When $(x + y)^3 = (x + y)(x + y)(x + y)$ is expanded, all products of a term in the first sum, a term in the second sum, and a term in the third sum are added. Terms of the form x^3, x^2y, xy^2, and y^3 arise. To obtain a term of the form x^3, an x must be chosen in each of the sums, and this can be done in only one way. Thus, the x^3 term in the product has a coefficient of 1. To obtain a term of the form x^2y, an x must be chosen in two of the three sums (and consequently a y in the other sum). Hence, the number of such terms is the number of 2-combinations of three objects, namely $\binom{3}{2}$. Similarly, the number of terms of the form xy^2 is the number of ways to pick one of the three sums to obtain an x (and consequently take a y from each of the other two sums). This can be done in $\binom{3}{1}$ ways. Finally, the only way to obtain a y^3 term is to choose the y for each of the three sums in the product, and this can be done in exactly one way. Consequently, it follows that

$$(x + y)^3 = (x + y)(x + y)(x + y) = (xx + xy + yx + yy)(x + y)$$
$$= xxx + xxy + xyx + xyy + yxx + yxy + yyx + yyy$$
$$= x^3 + 3x^2y + 3xy^2 + y^3.$$

◀

The Binomial Theorem will now be stated.

THEOREM 1   **THE BINOMIAL THEOREM**   Let x and y be variables, and let n be a nonnegative integer. Then

$$(x + y)^n = \sum_{j=0}^{n} \binom{n}{j} x^{n-j} y^j$$

$$= \binom{n}{0} x^n + \binom{n}{1} x^{n-1}y + \binom{n}{2} x^{n-2}y^2 + \cdots + \binom{n}{n-1} xy^{n-1} + \binom{n}{n} y^n.$$

Proof: A combinatorial proof of the theorem will be given. The terms in the product when it is expanded are of the form $x^{n-j}y^j$ for $j = 0, 1, 2, \ldots, n$. To count the number of terms of the form $x^{n-j}y^j$, note that to obtain such a term it is necessary to choose $n - j$ xs from the n sums (so that the other j terms in the product are ys). Therefore, the coefficient of $x^{n-j}y^j$ is $\binom{n}{n-j}$, which is equal to $\binom{n}{j}$. This proves the theorem.   ◁

The use of the Binomial Theorem is illustrated by Examples 2–4.

EXAMPLE 2   What is the expansion of $(x + y)^4$?

Extra
Examples

Solution: From the Binomial Theorem it follows that

$$(x + y)^4 = \sum_{j=0}^{4} \binom{4}{j} x^{4-j} y^j$$

$$= \binom{4}{0} x^4 + \binom{4}{1} x^3 y + \binom{4}{2} x^2 y^2 + \binom{4}{3} xy^3 + \binom{4}{4} y^4$$

$$= x^4 + 4x^3 y + 6x^2 y^2 + 4xy^3 + y^4.$$ ◀

EXAMPLE 3   What is the coefficient of $x^{12} y^{13}$ in the expansion of $(x + y)^{25}$?

Solution: From the Binomial Theorem it follows that this coefficient is

$$\binom{25}{13} = \frac{25!}{13! \, 12!} = 5,200,300.$$ ◀

EXAMPLE 4   What is the coefficient of $x^{12} y^{13}$ in the expansion of $(2x - 3y)^{25}$?

Solution: First, note that this expression equals $(2x + (-3y))^{25}$. By the Binomial Theorem, we have

$$(2x + (-3y))^{25} = \sum_{j=0}^{25} \binom{25}{j} (2x)^{25-j} (-3y)^j.$$

Consequently, the coefficient of $x^{12} y^{13}$ in the expansion is obtained when $j = 13$, namely,

$$\binom{25}{13} 2^{12} (-3)^{13} = -\frac{25!}{13! \, 12!} 2^{12} 3^{13}.$$ ◀

We can prove some useful identities using the Binomial Theorem, as Corollaries 1, 2, and 3 demonstrate.

COROLLARY 1   Let n be a nonnegative integer. Then

$$\sum_{k=0}^{n} \binom{n}{k} = 2^n.$$

Proof: Using the Binomial Theorem with $x = 1$ and $y = 1$, we see that

$$2^n = (1 + 1)^n = \sum_{k=0}^{n} \binom{n}{k} 1^k 1^{n-k} = \sum_{k=0}^{n} \binom{n}{k}.$$

This is the desired result. ◁

There is also a nice combinatorial proof of Corollary 1, which we now present.

Proof: A set with n elements has a total of 2^n different subsets. Each subset has zero elements, one element, two elements, ..., or n elements in it. There are $\binom{n}{0}$ subsets with zero elements, $\binom{n}{1}$ subsets with one element, $\binom{n}{2}$ subsets with two elements, ..., and $\binom{n}{n}$ subsets with n elements. Therefore,

$$\sum_{k=0}^{n} \binom{n}{k}$$

counts the total number of subsets of a set with n elements. This shows that

$$\sum_{k=0}^{n} \binom{n}{k} = 2^n.$$ ◁

COROLLARY 2	Let n be a positive integer. Then $$\sum_{k=0}^{n} (-1)^k \binom{n}{k} = 0.$$

Proof: By the Binomial Theorem it follows that

$$0 = 0^n = ((-1) + 1)^n = \sum_{k=0}^{n} \binom{n}{k} (-1)^k 1^{n-k} = \sum_{k=0}^{n} \binom{n}{k} (-1)^k.$$

This proves the corollary. ◁

Remark: Corollary 2 implies that

$$\binom{n}{0} + \binom{n}{2} + \binom{n}{4} + \cdots = \binom{n}{1} + \binom{n}{3} + \binom{n}{5} + \cdots.$$

COROLLARY 3	Let n be a nonnegative integer. Then $$\sum_{k=0}^{n} 2^k \binom{n}{k} = 3^n.$$

Proof: We recognize that the left-hand side of this formula is the expansion of $(1 + 2)^n$ provided by the Binomial Theorem. Therefore, by the Binomial Theorem, we see that

$$(1 + 2)^n = \sum_{k=0}^{n} \binom{n}{k} 1^{n-k} 2^k = \sum_{k=0}^{n} \binom{n}{k} 2^k.$$

Hence

$$\sum_{k=0}^{n} 2^k \binom{n}{k} = 3^n. \qquad \triangleleft$$

PASCAL'S IDENTITY AND TRIANGLE

The binomial coefficients satisfy many different identities. We introduce one of the most important of these now.

THEOREM 2

PASCAL'S IDENTITY Let n and k be positive integers with $n \geq k$. Then

$$\binom{n+1}{k} = \binom{n}{k-1} + \binom{n}{k}.$$

Proof: Suppose that T is a set containing $n + 1$ elements. Let a be an element in T, and let $S = T - \{a\}$. Note that there are $\binom{n+1}{k}$ subsets of T containing k elements. However, a subset of T with k elements either contains a together with $k - 1$ elements of S, or contains k elements of S and does not contain a. Since there are $\binom{n}{k-1}$ subsets of $k - 1$ elements of S, there are $\binom{n}{k-1}$ subsets of k elements of T that contain a. And there are $\binom{n}{k}$ subsets of k elements of T that do not contain a, since there are $\binom{n}{k}$ subsets of k elements of S. Consequently,

$$\binom{n+1}{k} = \binom{n}{k-1} + \binom{n}{k}. \qquad \triangleleft$$

Remark: A combinatorial proof of Pascal's Identity has been given. It is also possible to prove this identity by algebraic manipulation from the formula for $\binom{n}{r}$ (see Exercise 19 at the end of this section).

Remark: Pascal's Identity, together with the initial conditions $\binom{n}{0} = \binom{n}{n} = 1$ for all integers n, can be used to recursively define binomial coefficients. This recursive definition

Links

BLAISE PASCAL (1623–1662) Blaise Pascal exhibited his talents at an early age, although his father, who had made discoveries in analytic geometry, kept mathematics books away from him to encourage other interests. At 16 Pascal discovered an important result concerning conic sections. At 18 he designed a calculating machine, which he built and sold. Pascal, along with Fermat, laid the foundations for the modern theory of probability. In this work he made new discoveries concerning what is now called Pascal's triangle. In 1654, Pascal abandoned his mathematical pursuits to devote himself to theology. After this, he returned to mathematics only once. One night, distracted by a severe toothache, he sought comfort by studying the mathematical properties of the cycloid. Miraculously, his pain subsided, which he took as a sign of divine approval of the study of mathematics.

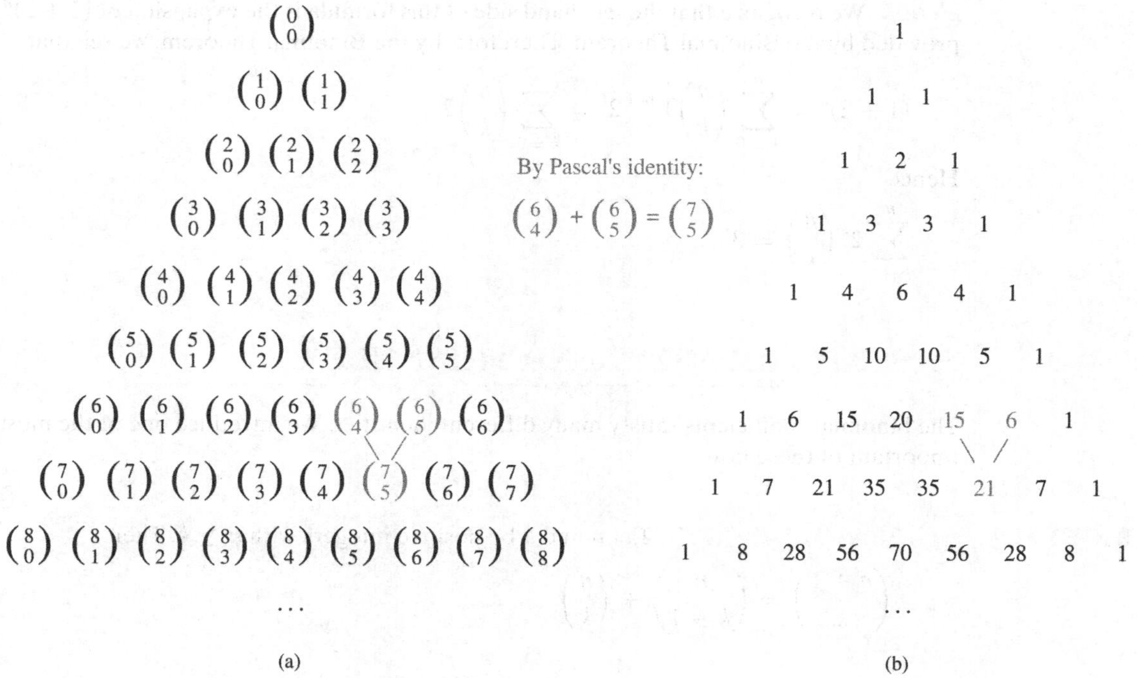

$$\binom{0}{0}$$

$$\binom{1}{0}\ \binom{1}{1}$$

$$\binom{2}{0}\ \binom{2}{1}\ \binom{2}{2}$$

By Pascal's identity:

$$\binom{3}{0}\ \binom{3}{1}\ \binom{3}{2}\ \binom{3}{3}$$

$$\binom{6}{4} + \binom{6}{5} = \binom{7}{5}$$

$$\binom{4}{0}\ \binom{4}{1}\ \binom{4}{2}\ \binom{4}{3}\ \binom{4}{4}$$

$$\binom{5}{0}\ \binom{5}{1}\ \binom{5}{2}\ \binom{5}{3}\ \binom{5}{4}\ \binom{5}{5}$$

$$\binom{6}{0}\ \binom{6}{1}\ \binom{6}{2}\ \binom{6}{3}\ \binom{6}{4}\ \binom{6}{5}\ \binom{6}{6}$$

$$\binom{7}{0}\ \binom{7}{1}\ \binom{7}{2}\ \binom{7}{3}\ \binom{7}{4}\ \binom{7}{5}\ \binom{7}{6}\ \binom{7}{7}$$

$$\binom{8}{0}\ \binom{8}{1}\ \binom{8}{2}\ \binom{8}{3}\ \binom{8}{4}\ \binom{8}{5}\ \binom{8}{6}\ \binom{8}{7}\ \binom{8}{8}$$

...

								1								
							1		1							
						1		2		1						
					1		3		3		1					
				1		4		6		4		1				
			1		5		10		10		5		1			
		1		6		15		20		15		6		1		
	1		7		21		35		35		21		7		1	
1		8		28		56		70		56		28		8		1

...

(a)   (b)

FIGURE 1   Pascal's Triangle.

is useful in the computation of binomial coefficients since only the addition of integers is needed to use this recursive definition.

Pascal's Identity is the basis for a geometric arrangement of the binomial coefficients in a triangle, as shown in Figure 1.

The nth row in the triangle consists of the binomial coefficients

$$\binom{n}{k},\ k = 0, 1, \dots, n.$$

This triangle is known as **Pascal's triangle.** Pascal's Identity shows that when two adjacent binomial coefficients in this triangle are added, the binomial coefficient in the next row between these two coefficients is produced.

SOME OTHER IDENTITIES OF THE BINOMIAL COEFFICIENTS

We conclude this section with combinatorial proofs of two of the many identities enjoyed by the binomial coefficients.

THEOREM 3

VANDERMONDE'S IDENTITY   Let $m, n,$ and r be nonnegative integers with r not exceeding either m or n. Then

$$\binom{m+n}{r} = \sum_{k=0}^{r} \binom{m}{r-k}\binom{n}{k}.$$

Remark: This identity was discovered by mathematician Alexandre-Théophile Vandermonde in the eighteenth century.

Proof: Suppose that there are m items in one set and n items in a second set. Then the total number of ways to pick r elements from the union of these sets is $\binom{m+n}{r}$. Another way to pick r elements from the union is to pick k elements from the first set and then $r - k$ elements from the second set, where k is an integer with $0 \leq k \leq r$. This can be done in $\binom{m}{k}\binom{n}{r-k}$ ways, using the product rule. Hence, the total number of ways to pick r elements from the union also equals

$$\binom{m+n}{r} = \sum_{k=0}^{r} \binom{m}{r-k}\binom{n}{k}.$$

This proves Vandermonde's Identity.   ◁

Corollary 4 follows from Vandermonde's Identity.

COROLLARY 4   If n is a nonnegative integer, then

$$\binom{2n}{n} = \sum_{k=0}^{n} \binom{n}{k}^2$$

Proof: We use Vandermonde's Identity with $m = r = n$ to obtain

$$\binom{2n}{n} = \sum_{k=0}^{n} \binom{n}{n-k}\binom{n}{k} = \sum_{k=0}^{n} \binom{n}{k}^2.$$

The last equality was obtained using the identity $\binom{n}{k} = \binom{n}{n-k}$.   ◁

We can prove combinatorial identities by counting bit strings with different properties, as the proof of Theorem 4 will demonstrate.

THEOREM 4   Let n and r be nonnegative integers with $r \leq n$. Then

$$\binom{n+1}{r+1} = \sum_{j=r}^{n} \binom{j}{r}.$$

Proof: We use a combinatorial proof. By Example 10 in Section 4.3, the left-hand side, $\binom{n+1}{r+1}$, counts the bit strings of length $n + 1$ containing $r + 1$ ones.

ALEXANDRE-THÉOPHILE VANDERMONDE (1735–1796)   Because Alexandre-Théophile Vandermonde was a sickly child, his physician father directed him to a career in music. However, he later developed an interest in mathematics. His complete mathematical work consists of four papers published in 1771–1772. These papers include fundamental contributions on the roots of equations, on the theory of determinants, and on the knight's tour problem (introduced in the exercises in Section 8.5). Vandermonde's interest in mathematics lasted for only 2 years. Afterward, he published papers on harmony, experiments with cold, and the manufacture of steel. He also became interested in politics, joining the cause of the French revolution and holding several different positions in government.

We show that the right-hand side counts the same objects by considering the cases corresponding to the possible locations of the final 1 in a string with $r + 1$ ones. This final one must occur at position $r + 1, r + 2, \ldots,$ or $n + 1$. Furthermore, if the last one is the kth bit there must be r ones among the first $k - 1$ positions. Consequently, by Example 10 in Section 4.3, there are $\binom{k-1}{r}$ such bit strings. Summing over k with $r + 1 \leq k \leq n + 1$, we find that there are

$$\sum_{k=r+1}^{n+1} \binom{k-1}{r} = \sum_{j=r}^{n} \binom{j}{r}$$

bit strings of length n containing exactly $r + 1$ ones. (Note that the last step follows from the change of variables $j = k - 1$.) Since the left-hand side and the right-hand side count the same objects, they are equal. This completes the proof. ◁

Exercises

1. Find the expansion of $(x + y)^4$
   a) using combinatorial reasoning, as in Example 1.
   b) using the Binomial Theorem.
2. Find the expansion of $(x + y)^5$
   a) using combinatorial reasoning, as in Example 1.
   b) using the Binomial Theorem.
3. Find the expansion of $(x + y)^6$.
4. Find the coefficient of $x^5 y^8$ in $(x + y)^{13}$.
5. How many terms are there in the expansion of $(x + y)^{100}$?
6. What is the coefficient of x^7 in $(1 + x)^{11}$?
7. What is the coefficient of x^9 in $(2 - x)^{19}$?
8. What is the coefficient of $x^8 y^9$ in the expansion of $(3x + 2y)^{17}$?
9. What is the coefficient of $x^{101} y^{99}$ in the expansion of $(2x - 3y)^{200}$?
*10. Give a formula for the coefficient of x^k in the expansion of $(x + 1/x)^{100}$, where k is an integer.
*11. Give a formula for the coefficient of x^k in the expansion of $(x^2 - 1/x)^{100}$, where k is an integer.
12. The row of Pascal's triangle containing the binomial coefficients $\binom{10}{k}, 0 \leq k \leq 10$, is:

    1 10 45 120 210 252 210 120 45 10 1

    Use Pascal's identity to produce the row immediately following this row in Pascal's triangle.
13. What is the row of Pascal's triangle containing the binomial coefficients $\binom{9}{k}, 0 \leq k \leq 9$?
14. Show that if n is a positive integer, then $1 = \binom{n}{0} < \binom{n}{1} < \cdots < \binom{n}{\lfloor n/2 \rfloor} = \binom{n}{\lceil n/2 \rceil} > \cdots > \binom{n}{n-1} > \binom{n}{n} = 1$.
15. Show that $\binom{n}{k} \leq 2^n$ for all positive integers n and k with $0 \leq k \leq n$.
16. a) Use Exercise 14 and Corollary 1 to show that if n is an integer greater than 1, then $\binom{n}{\lfloor n/2 \rfloor} \geq 2^n/n$.
    b) Conclude from part (a) that if n is a positive integer, then $\binom{2n}{n} \geq 4^n/2n$.
☞17. Show that if n and k are integers with $1 \leq k \leq n$, then $\binom{n}{k} \leq n^k/2^{k-1}$.
18. Suppose that b is an integer with $b \geq 7$. Use the Binomial Theorem and the appropriate row of Pascal's triangle to find the base-b expansion of $(11)_b^4$ [that is, the fourth power of the number $(11)_b$ in base-b notation].
19. Prove Pascal's Identity, using the formula for $\binom{n}{r}$.
20. Suppose that k and n are integers with $1 \leq k < n$. Prove the **hexagon identity**

$$\binom{n-1}{k-1}\binom{n}{k+1}\binom{n+1}{k} = \binom{n-1}{k}\binom{n}{k-1}\binom{n+1}{k+1},$$

which relates terms in Pascal's triangle that form a hexagon.
21. Prove that if n and k are integers with $1 \leq k \leq n$, then $k\binom{n}{k} = n\binom{n-1}{k-1}$
    a) using a combinatorial proof. (*Hint:* Show that the two sides of the identity count the number of ways to select a subset with k elements from a set with n elements and then an element of this subset.)
    b) using an algebraic proof based on the formula for $\binom{n}{r}$ given in Theorem 2 in Section 4.3.
22. Prove the identity $\binom{n}{r}\binom{r}{k} = \binom{n}{k}\binom{n-k}{r-k}$, whenever $n, r,$ and k are nonnegative integers with $r \leq n$ and $k \leq r$,
    a) using a combinatorial argument.
    b) using an argument based on the formula for the number of r-combinations of a set with n elements.
23. Show that if n and k are positive integers, then

$$\binom{n+1}{k} = (n+1)\binom{n}{k-1} / k.$$

Use this identity to construct an inductive definition of the binomial coefficients.

24. Show that if p is a prime and k is an integer such that $1 \leq k \leq p-1$, then p divides $\binom{p}{k}$.

25. Let n be a positive integer. Show that $\binom{2n}{n+1} + \binom{2n}{n} = \binom{2n+2}{n+1}/2$.

*26. Let n and k be integers with $1 \leq k \leq n$. Show that $\sum_{k=1}^{n} \binom{n}{k} \binom{n}{k-1} = \binom{2n+2}{n+1}/2 - \binom{2n}{n}$.

*27. Prove that

$$\sum_{k=0}^{r} \binom{n+k}{k} = \binom{n+r+1}{r}$$

whenever n and r are positive integers,

a) using a combinatorial argument.

b) using Pascal's identity.

28. Show that if n is a positive integer, then $\binom{2n}{2} = 2\binom{n}{2} + n^2$

a) using a combinatorial argument.

b) by algebraic manipulation.

*29. Give a combinatorial proof that $\sum_{k=1}^{n} k\binom{n}{k} = n2^{n-1}$. (*Hint:* Count in two ways the number of ways to select a committee and to then select a leader of the committee.)

*30. Give a combinatorial proof that $\sum_{k=1}^{n} k\binom{n}{k}^2 = n\binom{2n-1}{n-1}$. (*Hint:* Count in two ways the number of ways to select a committee, with n members from a group of n mathematics professors and n computer science professors, such that the chairperson of the committee is a mathematics professor.)

31. Show that a nonempty set has the same number of subsets with an odd number of elements as it does subsets with an even number of elements.

*32. Prove the Binomial Theorem using mathematical induction.

33. In this exercise we will count the number of paths in the xy plane between the origin $(0, 0)$ and point (m, n) such that each path is made up of a series of steps, where each step is a move one unit to the right or a move one unit upward. (No moves to the left or downward are allowed.) Two such paths from $(0, 0)$ to $(5, 3)$ are illustrated here.

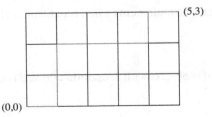

a) Show that each path of the type described can be represented by a bit string consisting of m 0s and n 1s, where a 0 represents a move one unit to the right and a 1 represents a move one unit upward.

b) Conclude from part (a) that there are $\binom{m+n}{n}$ paths of the desired type.

34. Use Exercise 33 to prove that $\binom{n}{k} = \binom{n}{n-k}$ whenever k is an integer with $0 \leq k \leq n$. [*Hint:* Consider the number of paths of the type described in Exercise 33 from $(0, 0)$ to $(n-k, k)$ and from $(0, 0)$ to $(k, n-k)$.]

35. Use Exercise 33 to prove Theorem 4. [*Hint:* Count the number of paths with n steps of the type described in Exercise 33. Every such path must end at one of the points $(n-k, k)$ for $k = 0, 1, 2, \ldots, n$.]

36. Use Exercise 33 to prove Pascal's Identity. [*Hint:* Show that a path of the type described in Exercise 33 from $(0, 0)$ to $(n+1-k, k)$ passes through either $(n+1-k, k-1)$ or $(n-k, k)$, but not through both.]

37. Prove the identity in Exercise 27 using Exercise 33. [*Hint:* First, note that the number of paths from $(0, 0)$ to $(n+1, r)$ equals $\binom{n+1+r}{r}$. Second, count the number of paths by summing the number of these paths that start by going k units upward for $k = 0, 1, 2, \ldots, r$.]

38. Give a combinatorial proof that if n is a positive integer then $\sum_{k=0}^{n} k^2 \binom{n}{k} = n(n+1)2^{n-2}$. [*Hint:* Show that both sides count the ways to select a subset of a set of n elements together with two not necessarily distinct elements from this subset. Furthermore, express the right-hand side as $n(n-1)2^{n-2} + n2^{n-1}$.]

*39. Determine a formula involving binomial coefficients for the nth term of a sequence if its initial terms are those listed. [*Hint:* Looking at Pascal's triangle will be helpful. Although infinitely many sequences start with a specified set of terms, each of the following lists is the start of a sequence of the type desired.]

a) $1, 3, 6, 10, 15, 21, 28, 36, 45, 55, 66, \ldots$

b) $1, 4, 10, 20, 35, 56, 84, 120, 165, 220, \ldots$

c) $1, 2, 6, 20, 70, 252, 924, 3432, 12870, 48620, \ldots$

d) $1, 1, 2, 3, 6, 10, 20, 35, 70, 126, \ldots$

e) $1, 1, 1, 3, 1, 5, 15, 35, 1, 9, \ldots$

f) $1, 3, 15, 84, 495, 3003, 18564, 116280, 735471, 4686825, \ldots$

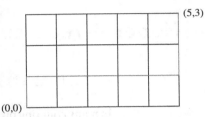

4.5 Generalized Permutations and Combinations

INTRODUCTION

In many counting problems, elements may be used repeatedly. For instance, a letter or digit may be used more than once on a license plate. When a dozen donuts are selected, each variety can be chosen repeatedly. This contrasts with the counting problems discussed earlier in the chapter where we only considered permutations and combinations in which each item could be used at most once. In this section we will show how to solve counting problems where elements may be used more than once.

Also, some counting problems involve indistinguishable elements. For instance, to count the number of ways the letters of the word *SUCCESS* can be rearranged, the placement of identical letters must be considered. This contrasts with the counting problems discussed earlier where all elements were considered distinguishable. In this section we will describe how to solve counting problems in which some elements are indistinguishable.

Moreover, in this section we will explain how to solve another important class of counting problems, problems involving counting the ways to place distinguishable elements in boxes. An example of this type of problem is the number of different ways poker hands can be dealt to four players.

Taken together, the methods described earlier in this chapter and the methods introduced in this section form a useful toolbox for solving a wide range of counting problems. When the additional methods discussed in Chapter 6 are added to this arsenal, you will be able to solve a large percentage of the counting problems that arise in a wide range of areas of study.

PERMUTATIONS WITH REPETITION

Counting permutations when repetition of elements is allowed can easily be done using the product rule, as Example 1 shows.

EXAMPLE 1 How many strings of length n can be formed from the English alphabet?

Solution: By the product rule, since there are 26 letters, and since each letter can be used repeatedly, we see that there are 26^n strings of length n. ◀

The number of r-permutations of a set with n elements when repetition is allowed is given in Theorem 1.

THEOREM 1 The number of r-permutations of a set of n objects with repetition allowed is n^r.

Proof: There are n ways to select an element of the set for each of the r positions in the r-permutation when repetition is allowed, since for each choice all n objects are available. Hence, by the product rule there are n^r r-permutations when repetition is allowed. ◁

COMBINATIONS WITH REPETITION

Consider these examples of combinations with repetition of elements allowed.

EXAMPLE 2   How many ways are there to select four pieces of fruit from a bowl containing apples, oranges, and pears if the order in which the pieces are selected does not matter, only the type of fruit and not the individual piece matters, and there are at least four pieces of each type of fruit in the bowl?

Solution: To solve this problem we list all the ways possible to select the fruit. There are 15 ways:

4 apples	4 oranges	4 pears
3 apples, 1 orange	3 apples, 1 pear	3 oranges, 1 apple
3 oranges, 1 pear	3 pears, 1 apple	3 pears, 1 orange
2 apples, 2 oranges	2 apples, 2 pears	2 oranges, 2 pears
2 apples, 1 orange, 1 pear	2 oranges, 1 apple, 1 pear	2 pears, 1 apple, 1 orange

The solution is the number of 4-combinations with repetition allowed from a three-element set, {*apple, orange, pear*}.   ◄

To solve more complex counting problems of this type, we need a general method for counting the *r*-combinations of an *n*-element set. In Example 3 we will illustrate such a method.

EXAMPLE 3   How many ways are there to select five bills from a cash box containing $1 bills, $2 bills, $5 bills, $10 bills, $20 bills, $50 bills, and $100 bills? Assume that the order in which the bills are chosen does not matter, that the bills of each denomination are indistinguishable, and that there are at least five bills of each type.

Solution: Since the order in which the bills are selected does not matter and seven different types of bills can be selected as many as five times, this problem involves counting 5-combinations with repetition allowed from a set with seven elements. Listing all possibilities would be tedious, since there are a large number of solutions. Instead, we will illustrate the use of a technique for counting combinations with repetition allowed.

Suppose that a cash box has seven compartments, one to hold each type of bill, as illustrated in Figure 1. These bins are separated by six dividers, as shown in the picture. The choice of five bills corresponds to placing five markers in the compartments holding different types of bills. Figure 2 illustrates this correspondence for three different ways to select five bills, where the six dividers are represented by bars and the five bills by stars.

The number of ways to select five bills corresponds to the number of ways to arrange six bars and five stars. Consequently, the number of ways to select the five bills is the number of ways to select the positions of the five stars, from 11 possible positions. This corresponds to the number of unordered selections of 5 objects from a set of 11 objects, which can be done in $C(11, 5)$ ways. Consequently, there are

$$C(11, 5) = \frac{11!}{5!\,6!} = 462$$

ways to choose five bills from the cash box with seven types of bills.   ◄

Theorem 2 generalizes this discussion.

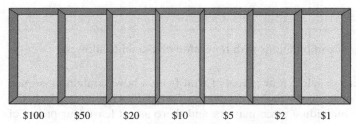

FIGURE 1   Cash Box with Seven Types of Bills.

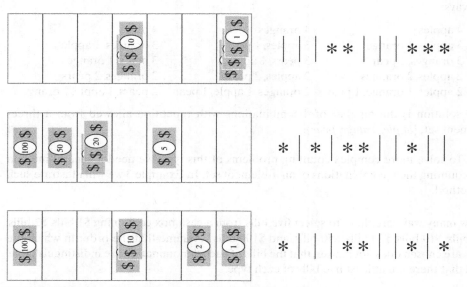

FIGURE 2   Examples of Ways to Select Five Bills.

THEOREM 2   There are $C(n + r - 1, r)$ r-combinations from a set with n elements when repetition of elements is allowed.

Proof: Each r-combination of a set with n elements when repetition is allowed can be represented by a list of $n - 1$ bars and r stars. The $n - 1$ bars are used to mark off n different cells, with the ith cell containing a star for each time the ith element of the set occurs in the combination. For instance, a 6-combination of a set with four elements is represented with three bars and six stars. Here

$$** | * | | ***$$

represents the combination containing exactly two of the first element, one of the second element, none of the third element, and three of the fourth element of the set.

As we have seen, each different list containing $n - 1$ bars and r stars corresponds to an r-combination of the set with n elements, when repetition is allowed. The number of such lists is $C(n - 1 + r, r)$, since each list corresponds to a choice of the r positions to place the r stars from the $n - 1 + r$ positions that contain r stars and $n - 1$ bars.   ◁

Examples 4–7 show how Theorem 2 is applied.

EXAMPLE 4   Suppose that a cookie shop has four different kinds of cookies. How many different ways can six cookies be chosen? Assume that only the type of cookie, and not the individual cookies or the order in which they are chosen, matters.

Extra Examples

Solution: The number of ways to choose six cookies is the number of 6-combinations of a set with four elements. From Theorem 2 this equals $C(4 + 6 - 1, 6) = C(9, 6)$. Since

$$C(9, 6) = C(9, 3) = \frac{9 \cdot 8 \cdot 7}{1 \cdot 2 \cdot 3} = 84,$$

there are 84 different ways to choose the six cookies.   ◀

Theorem 2 can also be used to find the number of solutions of certain linear equations where the variables are integers subject to constraints. This is illustrated by Example 5.

EXAMPLE 5   How many solutions does the equation

$$x_1 + x_2 + x_3 = 11$$

have, where $x_1, x_2,$ and x_3 are nonnegative integers?

Solution: To count the number of solutions, we note that a solution corresponds to a way of selecting 11 items from a set with three elements, so that x_1 items of type one, x_2 items of type two, and x_3 items of type three are chosen. Hence, the number of solutions is equal to the number of 11-combinations with repetition allowed from a set with three elements. From Theorem 2 it follows that there are

$$C(3 + 11 - 1, 11) = C(13, 11) = C(13, 2) = \frac{13 \cdot 12}{1 \cdot 2} = 78$$

solutions.

The number of solutions of this equation can also be found when the variables are subject to constraints. For instance, we can find the number of solutions where the variables are integers with $x_1 \geq 1, x_2 \geq 2,$ and $x_3 \geq 3$. A solution to the equation subject to these constraints corresponds to a selection of 11 items with x_1 items of type one, x_2 items of type two, and x_3 items of type three, where, in addition, there is at least one item of type one, two items of type two, and three items of type three. So, choose one item of type one, two of type two, and three of type three. Then select five additional items. By Theorem 2 this can be done in

$$C(3 + 5 - 1, 5) = C(7, 5) = C(7, 2) = \frac{7 \cdot 6}{1 \cdot 2} = 21$$

ways. Thus, there are 21 solutions of the equation subject to the given constraints.   ◀

There is a one-to-one correspondence between r-combinations from a set with n elements when repetition is allowed and the ways to place r indistinguishable balls into n distinguishable bins. To set up this correspondence, we put a ball in the ith bin each time the ith element of the set is included in the r-combination.

EXAMPLE 6   How many ways are there to place ten indistinguishable balls into eight distinguishable bins?

Solution: The number of ways to place ten indistinguishable balls into eight bins equals the number of 10-combinations from a set with eight elements when repetition is allowed. Consequently, there are

$$C(8 + 10 - 1, 10) = C(17, 10) = \frac{17!}{10!7!} = 19{,}448.$$ ◀

Example 7 shows how counting the number of combinations with repetition allowed arises in determining the value of a variable that is incremented each time a certain type of nested loop is traversed.

EXAMPLE 7   What is the value of k after the following pseudocode has been executed?

```
k := 0
for i₁ := 1 to n
    for i₂ := 1 to i₁
            .
            .
            .
            for iₘ := 1 to iₘ₋₁
                k := k + 1
```

Solution: Note that the initial value of k is 0 and that 1 is added to k each time the nested loop is traversed with a sequence of integers $i_1, i_2, \ldots, i_m$ such that

$$1 \le i_m \le i_{m-1} \le \cdots \le i_1 \le n.$$

The number of such sequences of integers is the number of ways to choose m integers from $\{1, 2, \ldots, n\}$, with repetition allowed. (To see this, note that once such a sequence has been selected, if we order the integers in the sequence in nondecreasing order, this uniquely defines an assignment of $i_m, i_{m-1}, \ldots, i_1$. Conversely, every such assignment corresponds to a unique unordered set.) Hence, from Theorem 2, it follows that $k = C(n + m - 1, m)$ after this code has been executed. ◀

The formulae for the numbers of ordered and unordered selections of r elements, chosen with and without repetition allowed from a set with n elements, are shown in Table 1.

PERMUTATIONS WITH INDISTINGUISHABLE OBJECTS

Some elements may be indistinguishable in counting problems. When this is the case, care must be taken to avoid counting things more than once. Consider Example 8.

EXAMPLE 8   How many different strings can be made by reordering the letters of the word

Extra
Examples

SUCCESS?

Solution: Because some of the letters of *SUCCESS* are the same, the answer is *not* given by the number of permutations of seven letters. This word contains three Ss, two Cs,

TABLE 1 Combinations and Permutations with and without Repetition.		
Type	*Repetition Allowed?*	*Formula*
r-permutations	No	$\dfrac{n!}{(n-r)!}$
r-combinations	No	$\dfrac{n!}{r!\,(n-r)!}$
r-permutations	Yes	n^r
r-combinations	Yes	$\dfrac{(n+r-1)!}{r!\,(n-1)!}$

one U, and one E. To determine the number of different strings that can be made by reordering the letters, first note that the three Ss can be placed among the seven positions in $C(7, 3)$ different ways, leaving four positions free. Then the two Cs can be placed in $C(4, 2)$ ways, leaving two free positions. The U can be placed in $C(2, 1)$ ways, leaving just one position free. Hence E can be placed in $C(1, 1)$ way. Consequently, from the product rule, the number of different strings that can be made is

$$C(7, 3)C(4, 2)C(2, 1)C(1, 1) = \frac{7!}{3!\,4!} \cdot \frac{4!}{2!\,2!} \cdot \frac{2!}{1!\,1!} \cdot \frac{1!}{1!\,0!}$$

$$= \frac{7!}{3!\,2!\,1!\,1!}$$

$$= 420 .$$ ◄

We can prove Theorem 3 using the same sort of reasoning as in Example 8.

THEOREM 3   The number of different permutations of n objects, where there are n_1 indistinguishable objects of type 1, n_2 indistinguishable objects of type 2, ..., and n_k indistinguishable objects of type k, is

$$\frac{n!}{n_1!\,n_2!\cdots n_k!}.$$

Proof: To determine the number of permutations, first note that the n_1 objects of type one can be placed among the n positions in $C(n, n_1)$ ways, leaving $n - n_1$ positions free. Then the objects of type two can be placed in $C(n - n_1, n_2)$ ways, leaving $n - n_1 - n_2$ positions free. Continue placing the objects of type three, ..., type $k - 1$, until at the last stage n_k objects of type k can be placed in $C(n - n_1 - n_2 - \cdots - n_{k-1}, n_k)$ ways. Hence, by the product rule, the total number of different permutations is

$$C(n, n_1)C(n - n_1, n_2) \cdots C(n - n_1 - \cdots - n_{k-1}, n_k)$$

$$= \frac{n!}{n_1!\,(n-n_1)!} \frac{(n-n_1)!}{n_2!\,(n-n_1-n_2)!} \cdots \frac{(n-n_1-\cdots-n_{k-1})!}{n_k!\,0!}$$

$$= \frac{n!}{n_1!\,n_2!\cdots n_k!}.$$ ◁

DISTRIBUTING OBJECTS INTO BOXES

Some counting problems can be solved by enumerating the ways distinguishable objects can be placed into distinguishable boxes. Consider the following example in which the objects are cards and the "boxes" are hands of players.

EXAMPLE 9   How many ways are there to distribute hands of 5 cards to each of four players from the standard deck of 52 cards?

Solution: We will use the product rule to solve this problem. To begin, note that the first player can be dealt 5 cards in $C(52, 5)$ ways. The second player can be dealt 5 cards in $C(47, 5)$ ways, since only 47 cards are left. The third player can be dealt 5 cards in $C(42, 5)$ ways. Finally, the fourth player can be dealt 5 cards in $C(37, 5)$ ways. Hence, the total number of ways to deal four players 5 cards each is

$$C(52, 5)C(47, 5)C(42, 5)C(37, 5) = \frac{52!}{47!\,5!} \cdot \frac{47!}{42!\,5!} \cdot \frac{42!}{37!\,5!} \cdot \frac{37!}{32!\,5!}$$

$$= \frac{52!}{5!\,5!\,5!\,5!\,32!}.$$
◀

Remark: The solution to Example 9 equals the number of permutations of 52 objects, with 5 indistinguishable objects of each of four different types, and 32 objects of a fifth type. This equality can be seen by defining a one-to-one correspondence between permutations of this type and distributions of cards to the players. To define this correspondence, first order the cards from 1 to 52. Then cards dealt to the first player correspond to the cards in the positions assigned to objects of the first type in the permutation. Similarly, cards dealt to the second, third, and fourth players, respectively, correspond to cards in the positions assigned to objects of the second, third, and fourth type, respectively. The cards not dealt to any player correspond to cards in the positions assigned to objects of the fifth type. The reader should verify that this is a one-to-one correspondence.

Example 9 is a typical problem that involves distributing distinguishable objects into distinguishable boxes. The distinguishable objects are the 52 cards, and the five distinguishable boxes are the hands of the four players and the rest of the deck. Counting problems that involve distributing distinguishable objects into boxes can be solved using the following theorem.

THEOREM 4   The number of ways to distribute n distinguishable objects into k distinguishable boxes so that n_i objects are placed into box $i, i = 1, 2, \ldots, k$, equals

$$\frac{n!}{n_1!\,n_2!\cdots n_k!}.$$

Theorem 4 can be proved using the product rule. We leave the details as Exercise 47. It can also be proved (see Exercise 48) by setting up a one-to-one correspondence between the permutations counted by Theorem 3 and the ways to distribute objects counted by Theorem 4.

Exercises

1. In how many different ways can five elements be selected in order from a set with three elements when repetition is allowed?

2. In how many different ways can five elements be selected in order from a set with five elements when repetition is allowed?

3. How many strings of six letters are there?

4. Every day a student randomly chooses a sandwich for lunch from a pile of wrapped sandwiches. If there are six kinds of sandwiches, how many different ways are there for the student to choose sandwiches for the seven days of a week if the order in which the sandwiches are chosen matters?

5. How many ways are there to assign three jobs to five employees if each employee can be given more than one job?

6. How many ways are there to select five unordered elements from a set with three elements when repetition is allowed?

7. How many ways are there to select three unordered elements from a set with five elements when repetition is allowed?

8. How many different ways are there to choose a dozen donuts from the 21 varieties at a donut shop?

9. A bagel shop has onion bagels, poppy seed bagels, egg bagels, salty bagels, pumpernickel bagels, sesame seed bagels, raisin bagels, and plain bagels. How many ways are there to choose

   a) six bagels?
   b) a dozen bagels?
   c) two dozen bagels?
   d) a dozen bagels with at least one of each kind?
   e) a dozen bagels with at least three egg bagels and no more than two salty bagels?

10. A croissant shop has plain croissants, cherry croissants, chocolate croissants, almond croissants, apple croissants, and broccoli croissants. How many ways are there to choose

    a) a dozen croissants?
    b) three dozen croissants?
    c) two dozen croissants with at least two of each kind?
    d) two dozen croissants with no more than two broccoli croissants?
    e) two dozen croissants with at least five chocolate croissants and at least three almond croissants?
    f) two dozen croissants with at least one plain croissant, at least two cherry croissants, at least three chocolate croissants, at least one almond croissant, at least two apple croissants, and no more than three broccoli croissants?

11. How many ways are there to choose eight coins from a piggy bank containing 100 identical pennies and 80 identical nickels?

12. How many different combinations of pennies, nickels, dimes, quarters, and half dollars can a piggy bank contain if it has 20 coins in it?

13. A book publisher has 3000 copies of a discrete mathematics book. How many ways are there to store these books in their three warehouses if the copies of the book are indistinguishable?

14. How many solutions are there to the equation

    $$x_1 + x_2 + x_3 + x_4 = 17,$$

    where $x_1, x_2, x_3,$ and x_4 are nonnegative integers?

15. How many solutions are there to the equation

    $$x_1 + x_2 + x_3 + x_4 + x_5 = 21,$$

    where $x_i, i = 1, 2, 3, 4, 5,$ is a nonnegative integer such that

    a) $x_1 \geq 1$?
    b) $x_i \geq 2$ for $i = 1, 2, 3, 4, 5$?
    c) $0 \leq x_1 \leq 10$?
    d) $0 \leq x_1 \leq 3, 1 \leq x_2 < 4,$ and $x_3 \geq 15$?

16. How many solutions are there to the equation

    $$x_1 + x_2 + x_3 + x_4 + x_5 + x_6 = 29,$$

    where $x_i, i = 1, 2, 3, 4, 5, 6,$ is a nonnegative integer such that

    a) $x_i > 1$ for $i = 1, 2, 3, 4, 5, 6$?
    b) $x_1 \geq 1, x_2 \geq 2, x_3 \geq 3, x_4 \geq 4, x_5 > 5,$ and $x_6 \geq 6$?
    c) $x_1 \leq 5$?
    d) $x_1 < 8$ and $x_2 > 8$?

17. How many strings of 10 ternary digits (0, 1, or 2) are there that contain exactly two 0s, three 1s, and five 2s?

18. How many strings of 20 decimal digits are there that contain two 0s, four 1s, three 2s, one 3, two 4s, three 5s, two 7s, and three 9s?

19. Suppose that a large family has 14 children, including two sets of identical triplets, three sets of identical twins, and two individual children. How many ways are there to seat these children in a row of chairs if the identical triplets or twins cannot be distinguished from one another?

20. How many solutions are there to the inequality

    $$x_1 + x_2 + x_3 \leq 11,$$

    where $x_1, x_2,$ and x_3 are nonnegative integers? (*Hint:* Introduce an auxiliary variable x_4 so that $x_1 + x_2 + x_3 + x_4 = 11$.)

21. How many ways are there to distribute six indistinguishable balls into nine distinguishable bins?

22. How many ways are there to distribute 12 indistinguishable balls into six distinguishable bins?

23. How many ways are there to distribute 12 distinguishable objects into six distinguishable boxes so that two objects are placed in each box?

24. How many ways are there to distribute 15 distinguishable objects into five distinguishable boxes so that the boxes have one, two, three, four, and five objects in them, respectively.

25. How many positive integers less than 1,000,000 have the sum of their digits equal to 19?

26. How many positive integers less than 1,000,000 have exactly one digit equal to 9 and have a sum of digits equal to 13?

27. There are 10 questions on a discrete mathematics final exam. How many ways are there to assign scores to the problems if the sum of the scores is 100 and each question is worth at least 5 points?

28. Show that there are $C(n + r - q_1 - q_2 - \cdots - q_r - 1, n - q_1 - q_2 - \cdots - q_r)$ different unordered selections of n objects of r different types that include at least q_1 objects of type one, q_2 objects of type two, ..., and q_r objects of type r.

29. How many different bit strings can be transmitted if the string must begin with a 1 bit, must include three additional 1 bits (so that a total of four 1 bits is sent), must include a total of twelve 0 bits, and must have at least two 0 bits following each 1 bit?

30. How many different strings can be made from the letters in *MISSISSIPPI*, using all the letters?

31. How many different strings can be made from the letters in *ABRACADABRA*, using all the letters?

32. How many different strings can be made from the letters in *AARDVARK*, using all the letters, if all three As must be consecutive?

33. How many different strings can be made from the letters in *ORONO*, using some or all of the letters?

34. How many strings with five or more characters can be formed from the letters in *SEERESS*?

35. How many strings with seven or more characters can be formed from the letters in *EVERGREEN*?

36. How many different bit strings can be formed using six 1s and eight 0s?

37. A student has three mangos, two papayas, and two kiwi fruits. If the student eats one piece of fruit each day, and only the type of fruit matters, in how many different ways can these fruits be consumed?

38. A professor packs her collection of 40 issues of a mathematics journal in four boxes with 10 issues per box. How many ways can she distribute the journals if

a) each box is numbered, so that they are distinguishable?

b) the boxes are identical, so that they cannot be distinguished?

39. How many ways are there to travel in xyz space from the origin $(0, 0, 0)$ to the point $(4, 3, 5)$ by taking steps one unit in the positive x direction, one unit in the positive y direction, or one unit in the positive z direction? (Moving in the negative x, y, or z direction is prohibited, so that no backtracking is allowed.)

40. How many ways are there to travel in $xyzw$ space from the origin $(0, 0, 0, 0)$ to the point $(4, 3, 5, 4)$ by taking steps one unit in the positive x, positive y, positive z, or positive w direction?

41. How many ways are there to deal hands of seven cards to each of five players from a standard deck of 52 cards?

42. In bridge, the 52 cards of a standard deck are dealt to four players. How many different ways are there to deal bridge hands to four players?

43. What is the probability that each player has a hand containing an ace when the 52 cards of a standard deck are dealt to four players?

44. In how many ways can a dozen books be placed on four distinguishable shelves

a) if the books are indistinguishable copies of the same title?

b) if no two books are the same, and the positions of the books on the shelves matter? (*Hint:* Break this into 12 tasks, placing each book separately. Start with the sequence 1, 2, 3, 4 to represent the shelves. Represent the books by b_i, $i = 1, 2, \ldots, 12$. Place b_1 to the right of one of the terms in 1, 2, 3, 4. Then successively place $b_2, b_3, \ldots,$ and b_{12}.)

45. How many ways can n books be placed on k distinguishable shelves

a) if the books are indistinguishable copies of the same title?

b) if no two books are the same, and the positions of the books on the shelves matter?

46. A shelf holds 12 books in a row. How many ways are there to choose five books so that no two adjacent books are chosen? (*Hint:* Represent the books that are chosen by bars and the books not chosen by stars. Count the number of sequences of five bars and seven stars so that no two bars are adjacent.)

*47. Use the product rule to prove Theorem 4, by first placing objects in the first box, then placing objects in the second box, and so on.

*48. Prove Theorem 4 by first setting up a one-to-one correspondence between permutations of n objects with n_i indistinguishable objects of type i, $i = 1, 2, 3, \ldots, k$, and the distributions of n objects in k boxes such that n_i objects are placed in box i, $i = 1, 2, 3, \ldots, k$ and then applying Theorem 3.

*49. In this exercise we will prove Theorem 2 by setting up a one-to-one correspondence between the set of r-combinations with repetition allowed of $S = \{1, 2, 3, \ldots, n\}$ and the set of r-combinations of the set $T = \{1, 2, 3, \ldots, n + r - 1\}$.

a) Arrange the elements in an r-combination, with repetition allowed, of S into an increasing sequence $x_1 \le x_2 \le \cdots \le x_r$. Show that the sequence formed by adding $k - 1$ to the kth term is strictly increasing. Conclude that this sequence is made up of r distinct elements from T.

b) Show that the procedure described in (a) defines a one-to-one correspondence between the set of r-combinations, with repetition allowed, of S and the r-combinations of T. (*Hint:* Show the correspondence can be reversed by associating to the r-combination $\{x_1, x_2, \ldots, x_r\}$ of T, with $1 \le x_1 < x_2 < \cdots < x_r \le n + r - 1$, the r-combination with repetition allowed from S, formed by subtracting $k - 1$ from the kth element.)

c) Conclude that there are $C(n + r - 1, r)$ r-combinations with repetition allowed from a set with n elements.

50. How many ways are there to distribute five distin-

guishable objects into three indistinguishable boxes?

51. How many ways are there to distribute five indistinguishable objects into three indistinguishable boxes?

52. How many different terms are there in the expansion of $(x_1 + x_2 + \cdots + x_m)^n$ after all terms with identical sets of exponents are added?

*53. Prove the **Multinomial Theorem:** If n is a positive integer, then

$$(x_1 + x_2 + \cdots + x_m)^n$$
$$= \sum_{n_1 + n_2 + \cdots + n_m = n} C(n; n_1, n_2, \ldots, n_m) x_1^{n_1} x_2^{n_2} \cdots x_n^{n_m},$$

where

$$C(n; n_1, n_2, \ldots, n_m) = \frac{n!}{n_1! \, n_2! \cdots n_m!}$$

is a **multinomial coefficient.**

54. Find the expansion of $(x + y + z)^4$.

55. Find the coefficient of $x^3 y^2 z^5$ in $(x + y + z)^{10}$.

56. How many terms are there in the expansion of $(x + y + z)^{100}$?

4.6   Generating Permutations and Combinations

INTRODUCTION

Methods for counting various types of permutations and combinations were described in the previous sections of this chapter, but sometimes permutations or combinations need to be generated, not just counted. Consider the following three problems. First, suppose that a salesman must visit six different cities. In which order should these cities be visited to minimize total travel time? One way to determine the best order is to determine the travel time for each of the $6! = 720$ different orders in which the cities can be visited and choose the one with the smallest travel time. Second, suppose some numbers from a set of six numbers have 100 as their sum. One way to find these numbers is to generate all the $2^6 = 64$ subsets and check the sum of their terms. Third, suppose a laboratory has 95 employees. A group of 12 of these employees with a particular set of 25 skills is needed for a project. (Each employee can have one or more of these skills.) One way to find such a set of employees is to generate all sets of 12 of these employees and check whether they have the desired skills. These examples show that it is often necessary to generate permutations and combinations to solve problems.

GENERATING PERMUTATIONS

Links

Any set with n elements can be placed in one-to-one correspondence with the set $\{1, 2, 3, \ldots, n\}$. We can list the permutations of any set of n elements by generating the permutations of the n smallest positive integers and then replacing these integers with the corresponding elements. Many different algorithms have been developed to generate the $n!$ permutations of this set. We will describe one of these that is based on the **lexicographic ordering** of the set of permutations of $\{1, 2, 3, \ldots, n\}$. In this ordering, the permutation $a_1a_2 \cdots a_n$ precedes the permutation of $b_1b_2 \cdots b_n$, if for some k, with $1 \le k \le n$, $a_1 = b_1, a_2 = b_2, \ldots, a_{k-1} = b_{k-1}$, and $a_k < b_k$. In other words, a permutation of the set of the n smallest positive integers precedes (in lexicographic order) a second permutation if the number in this permutation in the first position where the two permutations disagree is smaller than the number in that position in the second permutation.

EXAMPLE 1   The permutation 23415 of the set $\{1, 2, 3, 4, 5\}$ precedes the permutation 23514, since these permutations agree in the first two positions, but the number in the third position in the first permutation, 4, is smaller than the number in the third position in the second permutation, 5. Similarly, the permutation 41532 precedes 52143.   ◀

An algorithm for generating the permutations of $\{1, 2, \ldots, n\}$ can be based on a procedure that constructs the next permutation in lexicographic order following a given permutation $a_1a_2 \cdots a_n$. We will show how this can be done. First, suppose that $a_{n-1} < a_n$. Interchange a_{n-1} and a_n to obtain a larger permutation. No other permutation is both larger than the original permutation and smaller than the permutation obtained by interchanging a_{n-1} and a_n. For instance, the next largest permutation after 234156 is 234165. On the other hand, if $a_{n-1} > a_n$, then a larger permutation cannot be obtained by interchanging these last two terms in the permutation. Look at the last three integers in the permutation. If $a_{n-2} < a_{n-1}$, then the last three integers in the permutation can be rearranged to obtain the next largest permutation. Put the smaller of the two integers a_{n-1} and a_n that is greater than a_{n-2} in position $n - 2$. Then, place the remaining integer and a_{n-2} into the last two positions in increasing order. For instance, the next largest permutation after 234165 is 234516.

On the other hand, if $a_{n-2} > a_{n-1}$ (and $a_{n-1} > a_n$), then a larger permutation cannot be obtained by permuting the last three terms in the permutation. Based on these observations, a general method can be described for producing the next largest permutation in increasing order following a given permutation $a_1a_2 \cdots a_n$. First, find the integers a_j and a_{j+1} with $a_j < a_{j+1}$ and

$$a_{j+1} > a_{j+2} > \cdots > a_n,$$

that is, the last pair of adjacent integers in the permutation where the first integer in the pair is smaller than the second. Then, the next largest permutation in lexicographic order is obtained by putting in the jth position the least integer among $a_{j+1}, a_{j+2}, \ldots,$ and a_n that is greater than a_j and listing in increasing order the rest of the integers $a_j, a_{j+1}, \ldots, a_n$ in positions $j + 1$ to n. It is easy to see that there is no other permutation larger than the permutation $a_1a_2 \cdots a_n$ but smaller than the new permutation produced. (The verification of this fact is left as an exercise for the reader.)

EXAMPLE 2   What is the next largest permutation in lexicographic order after 362541?

Extra
Examples

Solution: The last pair of integers a_j and a_{j+1} where $a_j < a_{j+1}$ is $a_3 = 2$ and $a_4 = 5$. The least integer to the right of 2 that is greater than 2 in the permutation is $a_5 = 4$. Hence, 4 is placed in the third position. Then the integers 2, 5, and 1 are placed in order in the last three positions, giving 125 as the last three positions of the permutation. Hence, the next permutation is 364125.   ◀

To produce the $n!$ permutations of the integers $1, 2, 3, \ldots, n$, begin with the smallest permutation in lexicographic order, namely, $123 \cdots n$, and successively apply the procedure described for producing the next largest permutation of $n! - 1$ times. This yields all the permutations of the n smallest integers in lexicographic order.

EXAMPLE 3 Generate the permutations of the integers 1, 2, 3 in lexicographic order.

Solution: Begin with 123. The next permutation is obtained by interchanging 3 and 2 to obtain 132. Next, since $3 > 2$ and $1 < 3$, permute the three integers in 132. Put the smaller of 3 and 2 in the first position, and then put 1 and 3 in increasing order in positions 2 and 3 to obtain 213. This is followed by 231, obtained by interchanging 1 and 3, since $1 < 3$. The next largest permutation has 3 in the first position, followed by 1 and 2 in increasing order, namely, 312. Finally, interchange 1 and 2 to obtain the last permutation, 321. ◄

Algorithm 1 displays the procedure for finding the next largest permutation in lexicographic order after a permutation that is not $n\ n-1\ n-2\ \cdots\ 2\ 1$, which is the largest permutation.

ALGORITHM 1 Generating the Next Largest Permutation in Lexicographic Order.

---

procedure *next permutation*($a_1 a_2 \cdots a_n$: permutation of
$\qquad \{1, 2, \ldots, n\}$ not equal to $n\ n-1\ \cdots\ 2\ 1$)
$j := n - 1$
while $a_j > a_{j+1}$
$\quad j := j - 1$
$\{j$ is the largest subscript with $a_j < a_{j+1}\}$
$k := n$
while $a_j > a_k$
$\quad k := k - 1$
$\{a_k$ is the smallest integer greater than a_j to the right of $a_j\}$
interchange a_j and a_k
$r := n$
$s := j + 1$
while $r > s$
begin
$\quad$ interchange a_r and a_s
$\quad r := r - 1$
$\quad s := s + 1$
end
$\{$this puts the tail end of the permutation after the jth position in
$\quad$ increasing order$\}$

GENERATING COMBINATIONS

How can we generate all the combinations of the elements of a finite set? Since a combination is just a subset, we can use the correspondence between subsets of $\{a_1, a_2, \ldots, a_n\}$ and bit strings of length n.

Recall that the bit string corresponding to a subset has a 1 in position k if a_k is in the subset, and has a 0 in this position if a_k is not in the subset. If all the bit strings of length n can be listed, then by the correspondence between subsets and bit strings, a list of all the subsets is obtained.

Recall that a bit string of length n is also the binary expansion of an integer between 0 and $2^n - 1$. The 2^n bit strings can be listed in order of their increasing size as integers in their binary expansions. To produce all binary expansions of length n, start with the bit string $000\ldots00$, with n zeros. Then, successively find the next largest expansion until the bit string $111\ldots11$ is obtained. At each stage the next largest binary expansion is found by locating the first position from the right that is not a 1, then changing all the 1s to the right of this position to 0s and making this first 0 (from the right) a 1.

EXAMPLE 4   Find the next largest bit string after 10 0010 0111.

Solution: The first bit from the right that is not a 1 is the fourth bit from the right. Change this bit to a 1 and change all the following bits to 0s. This produces the next largest bit string, 10 0010 1000.   ◄

The procedure for producing the next largest bit string after $b_{n-1}b_{n-2}\ldots b_1b_0$ is given as Algorithm 2.

ALGORITHM 2 Generating the Next Largest Bit String.

---

procedure *next bit string*($b_{n-1}\, b_{n-2}\, \ldots\, b_1 b_0$: bit string not equal to 11 $\ldots$ 11)
$i := 0$
while $b_i = 1$
begin
    $b_i := 0$
    $i := i + 1$
end
$b_i := 1$

Next, an algorithm for generating the r-combinations of the set $\{1, 2, 3, \ldots, n\}$ will be given. An r-combination can be represented by a sequence containing the elements in the subset in increasing order. The r-combinations can be listed using lexicographic order on these sequences. The next combinations after $a_1a_2\cdots a_r$ can be obtained in the following way: First, locate the last element a_i in the sequence such that $a_i \neq n - r + i$. Then, replace a_i with $a_i + 1$ and a_j with $a_i + j - i + 1$, for $j = i + 1, i + 2, \ldots, r$. It is left for the reader to show that this produces the next largest combination in lexicographic order. This procedure is illustrated with the following example.

EXAMPLE 5   Find the next largest 4-combination of the set $\{1, 2, 3, 4, 5, 6\}$ after $\{1, 2, 5, 6\}$.

Solution: The last term among the terms a_i with $a_1 = 1, a_2 = 2, a_3 = 5$, and $a_4 = 6$ such that $a_i \neq 6 - 4 + i$ is $a_2 = 2$. To obtain the next largest 4-combination, increment a_2 by 1 to obtain $a_2 = 3$. Then set $a_3 = 3 + 1 = 4$ and $a_4 = 3 + 2 = 5$. Hence the next largest 4-combination is $\{1, 3, 4, 5\}$.   ◄

Algorithm 3 displays pseudocode for this procedure.

ALGORITHM 3 **Generating the Next *r*-Combination in Lexicographic Order.**

---

procedure *next r-combination*($\{a_1, a_2, \ldots, a_r\}$: proper subset of
$\{1, 2, \ldots, n\}$ not equal to $\{n - r + 1, \ldots, n\}$ with
$a_1 < a_2 < \cdots < a_r$)
$i := r$
while $a_i = n - r + i$
$\quad i := i - 1$
$a_i := a_i + 1$
for $j := i + 1$ **to** r
$\quad a_j := a_i + j - i$

Exercises

1. Find the next largest permutation in lexicographic order after each of these permutations.

   a) 1432   **b)** 54123
   c) 12453   **d)** 45231
   e) 6714235   **f)** 31528764

2. Find the next largest permutation in lexicographic order after each of these permutations.

   a) 1342   **b)** 45321
   c) 13245   **d)** 612345
   e) 1623547   **f)** 23587416

3. Place these permutations of $\{1, 2, 3, 4, 5\}$ in lexicographic order: 43521, 15432, 45321, 23451, 23514, 14532, 21345, 45213, 31452, 31542.

4. Place these permutations of $\{1,2,3,4,5,6\}$ in lexicographic order: 234561, 231456, 165432, 156423, 543216, 541236, 231465, 314562, 432561, 654321, 654312, 435612.

5. Use Algorithm 1 to generate the 24 permutations of the first four positive integers in lexicographic order.

6. Use Algorithm 2 to list all the subsets of the set $\{1, 2, 3, 4\}$.

7. Use Algorithm 3 to list all the 3-combinations of $\{1, 2, 3, 4, 5\}$.

8. Show that Algorithm 1 produces the next largest permutation in lexicographic order.

9. Show that Algorithm 3 produces the next largest *r*-combination in lexicographic order after a given *r*-combination.

10. Develop an algorithm for generating the *r*-permutations of a set of *n* elements.

11. List all 3-permutations of $\{1, 2, 3, 4, 5\}$.

The remaining exercises in this section develop another algorithm for generating the permutations of $\{1, 2, 3, \ldots, n\}$. This algorithm is based on Cantor expansions of integers. Every nonnegative integer less than $n!$ has a unique Cantor expansion

$$a_1 1! + a_2 2! + \cdots + a_{n-1}(n-1)!$$

where a_i is a nonnegative integer not exceeding i, for $i = 1, 2, \ldots, n-1$. The integers $a_1, a_2, \ldots, a_{n-1}$ are called the **Cantor digits** of this integer.

Given a permutation of $\{1, 2, \ldots, n\}$, let $a_{k-1}, k = 2, 3, \ldots, n$, be the number of integers less than k that follow k in the permutation. For instance, in the permutation 43215, a_1 is the number of integers less than 2 that follow 2, so that $a_1 = 1$. Similarly, for this example $a_2 = 2$, $a_3 = 3$, and $a_4 = 0$. Consider the function from the set of permutations $\{1, 2, 3, \ldots, n\}$ to the set of nonnegative integers less than $n!$ that sends a permutation to the integer that has $a_1, a_2, \ldots, a_{n-1}$, defined in this way, as its Cantor digits.

12. Find the integers that correspond to these permutations.

   a) 246531   **b)** 12345   **c)** 654321

*13. Show that the correspondence described here is a bijection between the set of permutations of $\{1, 2, 3, \ldots, n\}$ and the nonnegative integers less than $n!$.

14. Find the permutations of $\{1, 2, 3, 4, 5\}$ that correspond to these integers with respect to the correspondence between Cantor expansions and permutations as described in the preamble to Exercise 12.

   a) 3   **b)** 89   **c)** 111

15. Develop an algorithm for producing all permutations of a set of n elements based on the correspondence described in the preamble to Exercise 12.

*16. The following method can be used to generate a random permutation of a sequence of n terms. First, interchange the nth term and the $r(n)$th term where $r(n)$ is a randomly selected integer with $1 \le r(n) \le n$. Next, interchange the $(n-1)$th term of the resulting sequence with its $r(n-1)$th term where $r(n-1)$ is a randomly selected integer with $1 \le r(n-1) \le n-1$.

Continue this process until $j = n$, where at the jth step you interchange the $(n-j+1)$th term of the resulting sequence with its $r(n-j+1)$th term, where $r(n-j+1)$ is a randomly selected integer with $1 \le r(n-j+1) \le n-j+1$. Show that when this method is followed each of the $n!$ different permutations of the terms of the sequence is equally likely to be generated. [*Hint:* Use mathematical induction, assuming that the probability that each of the permutations of $n-1$ terms produced by this procedure for a sequence of $n-1$ terms is $1/(n-1)!$.]

Key Terms and Results

TERMS

combinatorics: the study of arrangements of objects

enumeration: the counting of arrangements of objects

tree diagram: a diagram made up of a root, branches leaving the root, and other branches leaving some of the endpoints of branches

permutation: an ordered arrangement of the elements of a set

r-permutation: an ordered arrangement of r elements of a set

$P(n, r)$: the number of r-permutations of a set with n elements

r-combination: an unordered selection of r elements of a set

$C(n, r)$: the number of r-combinations of a set with n elements

$\binom{n}{r}$ (binomial coefficient): also the number of r-combinations of a set with n elements

combinatorial proof: a proof based on counting arguments

Pascal's triangle: a representation of the binomial coefficients where the ith row of the triangle contains $\binom{i}{j}$ for $j = 0, 1, 2, \ldots, i$

RESULTS

the product rule: a basic counting technique, which states that the number of ways to do a procedure that consists of two subtasks is the product of the number of ways to do the first task and the number of ways to do the second task after the first task has been done

the sum rule: a basic counting technique, which states that the number of ways to do a task in one of two ways is the sum of the number of ways to do these tasks if they cannot be done simultaneously

the pigeonhole principle: When more than k objects are placed in k boxes, there must be a box containing more than one object.

the generalized pigeonhole principle: When N objects are placed in k boxes, there must be a box containing at least $\lceil N/k \rceil$ objects.

$$P(n, r) = \frac{n!}{(n-r)!}$$

$$C(n, r) = \binom{n}{r} = \frac{n!}{r!(n-r)!}$$

Pascal's Identity: $\binom{n+1}{k} = \binom{n}{k-1} + \binom{n}{k}$

the Binomial Theorem: $(x + y)^n = \sum_{k=0}^{n} \binom{n}{k} x^{n-k} y^k$

There are n^r r-permutations of a set with n elements when repetition is allowed.

There are $C(n + r - 1, r)$ r-combinations of a set with n elements when repetition is allowed.

There are $n!/(n_1! n_2! \cdots n_k!)$ permutations of n objects where there are n_i indistinguishable objects of type i for $i = 1, 2, 3, \ldots, k$.

The algorithm for generating the permutations of the set $\{1, 2, \ldots, n\}$.

Review Questions

1. Explain how the sum and product rules can be used to find the number of bit strings with a length not exceeding 10.

2. Explain how to find the number of bit strings of length not exceeding 10 that have at least one 0 bit.

3. a) How can the product rule be used to find the number of functions from a set with m elements to a set with n elements?

b) How many functions are there from a set with five elements to a set with ten elements?

c) How can the product rule be used to find the number of one-to-one functions from a set with m elements to a set with n elements?

d) How many one-to-one functions are there from a set with five elements to a set with ten elements?

e) How many onto functions are there from a set with five elements to a set with ten elements?

4. How can you find the number of possible outcomes of a playoff between two teams where the first team that wins four games wins the playoff?

5. How can you find the number of bit strings of length ten that either begin with 101 or end with 010?

6. a) State the pigeonhole principle.

b) Explain how the pigeonhole principle can be used to show that among any 11 integers, at least two must have the same last digit.

7. a) State the generalized pigeonhole principle.

b) Explain how the generalized pigeonhole principle can be used to show that among any 91 integers, there are at least ten that end with the same digit.

8. a) What is the difference between an r-combination and an r-permutation of a set with n elements?

b) Derive an equation that relates the number of r-combinations and the number of r-permutations of a set with n elements.

c) How many ways are there to select six students from a class of 25 to serve on a committee?

d) How many ways are there to select six students from a class of 25 to hold six different executive positions on a committee?

9. a) What is Pascal's triangle?

b) How can a row of Pascal's triangle be produced from the one above it?

10. What is meant by a combinatorial proof of an identity? How is such a proof different from an algebraic one?

11. Explain how to prove Pascal's Identity using a combinatorial argument.

12. a) State the Binomial Theorem.

b) Explain how to prove the Binomial Theorem using a combinatorial argument.

c) Find the coefficient of $x^{100}y^{101}$ in the expansion of $(2x + 5y)^{201}$.

13. a) Explain how to find a formula for the number of ways to select r objects from n objects when repetition is allowed and order does not matter.

b) How many ways are there to select a dozen objects from among objects of five different types if objects of the same type are indistinguishable?

c) How many ways are there to select a dozen objects from these five different types if there must be at least three objects of the first type?

d) How many ways are there to select a dozen objects from these five different types if there cannot be more than four objects of the first type?

e) How many ways are there to select a dozen objects from these five different types if there must be at least two objects of the first type but no more than three objects of the second type?

14. a) Let n and r be positive integers. Explain why the number of solutions of the equation $x_1 + x_2 + \cdots + x_n = r$, where x_i is a nonnegative integer for $i = 1, 2, 3, \ldots, n$, equals the number of r-combinations of a set with n elements.

b) How many solutions in nonnegative integers are there to the equation $x_1 + x_2 + x_3 + x_4 = 17$?

c) How many solutions in positive integers are there to the equation in part (b)?

15. a) Derive a formula for the number of permutations of n objects of k different types where there are n_1 indistinguishable objects of type one, n_2 indistinguishable objects of type two, $\ldots$, and n_k indistinguishable objects of type k.

b) How many ways are there to order the letters of the word *INDISCREETNESS*?

16. Describe an algorithm for generating all the permutations of the set of the n smallest positive integers.

17. a) How many ways are there to deal hands of five cards to six players from a standard 52-card deck?

b) How many ways are there to distribute n distinguishable objects into k distinguishable boxes so that n_i objects are placed in box i?

18. Describe an algorithm for generating all the combinations of the set of the n smallest positive integers.

Supplementary Exercises

1. How many ways are there to choose 6 items from 10 distinct items when

a) the items in the choices are ordered and repetition is not allowed?

b) the items in the choices are ordered and repetition is allowed?

c) the items in the choices are unordered and repetition is not allowed?

d) the items in the choices are unordered and repetition is allowed?

2. How many ways are there to choose 10 items from 6 distinct items when

   a) the items in the choices are ordered and repetition is not allowed?

   b) the items in the choices are ordered and repetition is allowed?

   c) the items in the choices are unordered and repetition is not allowed?

   d) the items in the choices are unordered and repetition is allowed?

3. A test contains 100 true/false questions. How many different ways can a student answer the questions on the test, if answers may be left blank?

4. How many bit strings of length 10 either start with 000 or end with 1111?

5. How many bit strings of length 10 over the alphabet $\{a, b, c\}$ have either exactly three as or exactly four bs?

6. The internal telephone numbers in the phone system on a campus consist of five digits, with the first digit not equal to zero. How many different numbers can be assigned in this system?

7. An ice cream parlor has 28 different flavors, eight different kinds of sauce, and 12 toppings.

   a) In how many different ways can a dish of three scoops of ice cream be made where each flavor can be used more than once and the order of the scoops does not matter?

   b) How many different kinds of small sundaes are there if a small sundae contains one scoop of ice cream, a sauce, and a topping?

   c) How many different kinds of large sundaes are there if a large sundae contains three scoops of ice cream, where each flavor can be used more than once and the order of the scoops does not matter; two kinds of sauce, where each sauce can be used only once and the order of the sauces does not matter; and three toppings, where each topping can be used only once and the order of the toppings does not matter?

8. How many positive integers less than 1000

   a) have exactly three decimal digits?

   b) have an odd number of decimal digits?

   c) have at least one decimal digit equal to 9?

   d) have no odd decimal digits?

   e) have two consecutive decimal digits equal to 5?

   f) are palindromes (that is, read the same forward and backward)?

9. When the numbers from 1 to 1000 are written out in decimal notation, how many of each of these digits are used?

   a) 0   **b)** 1   **c)** 2   **d)** 9

10. There are 12 signs of the zodiac. How many people are needed to guarantee that at least six of these people have the same sign?

11. A fortune cookie company makes 213 different fortunes. A student eats at a restaurant that uses fortunes from this company. What is the largest possible number of times that the student can eat at the restaurant without getting the same fortune four times?

12. How many people are needed to guarantee that at least two were born on the same day of the week and in the same month (perhaps in different years)?

13. Show that there are at least two different five-element subsets of a set of 10 positive integers not exceeding 50 that have the same sum.

14. A package of baseball cards contains 20 cards. How many packages must be purchased to ensure that two cards in these packages are identical if there are a total of 550 different cards?

15. **a)** How many cards must be chosen from a deck to guarantee that at least two aces are chosen?

    b) How many cards must be chosen from a deck to guarantee that at least two aces and two kinds are chosen?

    c) How many cards must be chosen from a deck to guarantee that there are at least two cards of the same kind?

    d) How many cards must be chosen from a deck to guarantee that there are at least two cards of two different kinds?

*16. Show that in any set of $n + 1$ positive integers not exceeding $2n$ there must be two that are relatively prime.

*17. Show that in a sequence of m integers there exists one or more consecutive terms with a sum divisible by m.

18. Show that if five points are picked in the interior of a square with a side length of 2, then at least two of these points are no farther than $\sqrt{2}$ apart.

19. Show that the decimal expansion of a rational number must repeat itself from some point onward.

20. How many diagonals does a regular polygon with n sides have, where n is a positive integer with $n \geq 3$?

21. How many ways are there to choose a dozen donuts from 20 varieties

    a) if there are no two donuts of the same variety?

    b) if all donuts are of the same variety?

    c) if there are no restrictions?

    d) if there are at least two varieties?

    e) if there must be at least six blueberry-filled donuts?

    f) if there can be no more than six blueberry-filled donuts?

22. Find n if

    a) $P(n, 2) = 110$.   **b)** $P(n, n) = 5040$.

    c) $P(n, 4) = 12P(n, 2)$.

23. Find n if

  a) $C(n, 2) = 45$.   **b)** $C(n, 3) = P(n, 2)$.
  c) $C(n, 5) = C(n, 2)$.

24. Show that if n and r are nonnegative integers and $n \geq r$, then

$$P(n + 1, r) = P(n, r)(n + 1)/(n + 1 - r).$$

*25. Suppose that S is a set with n elements. How many ordered pairs (A, B) are there such that A and B are subsets of S with $A \subseteq B$? (*Hint:* Show that each element of S belongs to A, $B - A$, or $S - B$.)

26. Give a combinatorial proof of Corollary 2 of Section 4.4 by setting up a correspondence between the subsets of a set with an even number of elements and the subsets of this set with an odd number of elements. (*Hint:* Take an element a in the set. Set up the correspondence by putting a in the subset if it is not already in it and taking it out if it is in the subset.)

27. Let n and r be nonnegative integers with $r < n$. Show that

$$C(n, r - 1) = C(n + 2, r + 1)$$
$$- 2C(n + 1, r + 1) + C(n, r + 1).$$

28. Prove using mathematical induction that $\sum_{j=2}^{n} C(j, 2) = C(n+1, 3)$ whenever n is an integer greater than 1.

29. Show that if n is an integer then

$$\sum_{k=0}^{n} 3^k \binom{n}{k} = 4^n.$$

30. In this exercise we will derive a formula for the sum of the squares of the n smallest positive integers. We will count the number of triples (i, j, k) such that $i, j,$ and k are integers such that $0 \leq i < k, 0 \leq j < k,$ and $1 \leq k \leq n$ in two ways.

  a) Show that there are k^2 such triples with a fixed k. Conclude that there are $\sum_{k=1}^{n} k^2$ such triples.
  b) Show that the number of such triples with $0 \leq i < j < k$ and the number of such triples with $0 \leq j < i < k$ both equal $C(n + 1, 3)$.
  c) Show that the number of such triples with $0 \leq i = j < k$ equals $C(n + 1, 2)$.
  d) Combining part (a) with parts (b) and (c), conclude that

$$\sum_{k=1}^{n} k^2 = 2C(n + 1, 3) + C(n + 1, 2)$$

$$= n(n + 1)(2n + 1)/6.$$

*31. How many bit strings of length n, where $n \geq 4$, contain exactly two occurrences of 01?

32. Let S be a set. We say that a collection of subsets $A_1, A_2, \ldots, A_n$ each containing d elements, where $d \geq 2$, is *2-colorable* if it is possible to assign to each

element of S one of two different colors such that in every subset A_i there are elements that have been assigned each color. Let $m(d)$ be the largest integer such that every collection of fewer than $m(d)$ sets each containing d elements is 2-colorable.

  a) Show that the collection of all subsets with d elements of a set S with $2d - 1$ elements is not 2-colorable.
  b) Show that $m(2) = 3$.
  ** c) Show that $m(3) = 7$. (*Hint:* Show that the collection $\{1, 3, 5\}, \{1, 2, 6\}, \{1, 4, 7\}, \{2, 3, 4\}, \{2, 5, 7\},$ $\{3, 6, 7\}, \{4, 5, 6\}$ is not 2-colorable. Then show that all collections of six sets with three elements each are 2-colorable.)

33. A professor writes 20 multiple-choice questions, each with the possible answer $a, b, c,$ or d, for a discrete mathematics test. If the number of questions with $a,$ $b, c,$ and d as their answer is 8, 3, 4, and 5, respectively, how many different answer keys are possible, if the questions can be placed in any order?

34. How many different arrangements are there of eight people seated at a round table, where two arrangements are considered the same if one can be obtained from the other by a rotation?

35. How many ways are there to assign 24 students to five faculty advisors?

36. How many ways are there to choose a dozen apples from a bushel containing 20 indistinguishable Delicious apples, 20 indistinguishable Macintosh apples, and 20 indistinguishable Granny Smith apples, if at least three of each kind must be chosen?

37. How many solutions are there to the equation $x_1 + x_2 + x_3 = 17$, where $x_1, x_2,$ and x_3 are nonnegative integers with

  a) $x_1 > 1, x_2 > 2,$ and $x_3 > 3$?
  b) $x_1 < 6$ and $x_3 > 5$?
  c) $x_1 < 4, x_2 < 3,$ and $x_3 > 5$?

38. a) How many different strings can be made from the word *PEPPERCORN* when all the letters are used?
  b) How many of these strings start and end with the letter *P*?
  c) In how many of these strings are the three letter *P*s consecutive?

39. How many subsets of a set with ten elements

  a) have fewer than five elements?
  b) have more than seven elements?
  c) have an odd number of elements?

40. A witness to a hit-and-run accident tells the police that the license plate of the car in the accident, which contains three letters followed by three digits, starts with the letters *AS* and contains both the digits 1 and 2. How many different license plates can fit this description?

41. How many ways are there to put n identical objects into m distinct containers so that no container is empty?
42. How many ways are there to seat six boys and eight girls in a row of chairs so that no two boys are seated next to each other?
43. Devise an algorithm for generating all the r-permutations of a finite set when repetition is allowed.
44. Devise an algorithm for generating all the r-combinations of a finite set when repetition is allowed.
*45. Show that if m and n are integers with $m \geq 3$ and $n \geq 3$, then $R(m, n) \leq R(m, n - 1) + R(m - 1, n)$.
*46. Show that $R(3, 4) \geq 7$ by showing that in a group of six people, where any two people are friends or enemies, there are not necessarily three mutual friends or four mutual enemies.

Computer Projects

WRITE PROGRAMS WITH THESE INPUT AND OUTPUT.

1. Given a positive integer n and a nonnegative integer not exceeding n, find the number of r-permutations and r-combinations of a set with n elements.
2. Given positive integers n and r, find the number of r-permutations when repetition is allowed and r-combinations when repetition is allowed of a set with n elements.
3. Given a sequence of positive integers, find the longest increasing and the longest decreasing subsequence of the sequence.
*4. Given an equation $x_1 + x_2 + \cdots + x_n = C$, where C is a constant, and $x_1, x_2, \ldots, x_n$ are nonnegative integers, list all the solutions.
5. Given a positive integer n, list all the permutations of the set $\{1, 2, 3, \ldots, n\}$ in lexicographic order.
6. Given a positive integer n and a nonnegative integer r not exceeding n, list all the r-combinations of the set $\{1, 2, 3, \ldots, n\}$ in lexicographic order.
7. Given a positive integer n and a nonnegative integer r not exceeding n, list all the r-permutations of the set $\{1, 2, 3, \ldots, n\}$ in lexicographic order.
8. Given a positive integer n, list all the combinations of the set $\{1, 2, 3, \ldots, n\}$.
9. Given positive integers n and r, list all the r-permutations, with repetition allowed, of the set $\{1, 2, 3, \ldots, n\}$.
10. Given positive integers n and r, list all the r-combinations, with repetition allowed, of the set $\{1, 2, 3, \ldots, n\}$.

Computations and Explorations

USE A COMPUTATIONAL PROGRAM OR PROGRAMS YOU HAVE WRITTEN TO DO THESE EXERCISES.

1. Find the number of possible outcomes in a two-team playoff when the winner is the first team to win 5 out of 9, 6 out of 11, 7 out of 13, and 8 out of 15.
2. Which binomial coefficients are odd? Can you formulate a conjecture based on numerical evidence?
3. It is not known whether the binomial coefficient $C(2n, n)$ must be divisible by the square of a prime or whether the largest exponent in the prime factorization of $C(2n, n)$ grows without bound as n grows. Explore these questions by finding the small-est and largest powers of primes in the factorization of $C(2n, n)$ for as many positive integers n as feasible.
4. Generate all the permutations of a set with eight elements.
5. Generate all the 6-permutations of a set with nine elements.
6. Generate all combinations of a set with eight elements.
7. Generate all 5-combinations with repetition allowed of a set with seven elements.

Writing Projects

RESPOND TO THESE WITH ESSAYS USING OUTSIDE SOURCES.

1. Describe some of the earliest uses of the pigeonhole principle by Dirichlet and other mathematicians.

2. Discuss ways in which the current telephone numbering plan can be extended to accommodate the rapid demand for more telephone numbers. (See if you can find some of the proposals coming from the telecommunications industry.) For each new numbering plan you discuss, show how to find the number of different telephone numbers it supports.

3. Many combinatorial identities are described in this book. Find some sources of such identities and describe important combinatorial identities besides those already introduced in this book. Give some representative proofs, including combinatorial ones, of some of these identities.

4. Describe the different models used to model the distribution of particles in statistical mechanics, including Maxwell–Boltzmann, Bose–Einstein, and Fermi–Dirac statistics. In each case, describe the counting techniques used in the model.

5. Define the Stirling numbers of the first kind and describe some of their properties and the identities they satisfy.

6. Define the Stirling numbers of the second kind and describe some of their properties and the identities they satisfy.

7. Describe the latest discoveries of values and bounds for Ramsey numbers.

8. Describe additional ways to generate all the permutations of a set with n elements besides those found in Section 4.6. Compare these algorithms and the algorithms described in the text and exercises of Section 4.6 in terms of their computational complexity.

9. Describe at least one way to generate all the partitions of a positive integer n. (See Exercise 47 in Section 3.4.)

286 Introduction to Discrete Logic & Digital System

string)   **15.** 475,255 (counting the empty string)
17. 1,321,368,961   **19. a)** 128 **b)** 450 **c)** 9 **d)** 675
e) 450 **f)** 450 **g)** 225 **h)** 75   **21.   a)** 990 **b)** 500
c) 27   **23.** 3^{50} **25.** 52,457,600   **27.** 20,077,200
29. a) 37,822,859,361 **b)** 8,204,716,800 **c)** 40,159,050,880
d) 12,113,640,000 **e)** 171,004,205,215 **f)** 72,043,541,640
g) 6,230,721,635 **h)** 223,149,655   **31. a)** 0 **b)** 120 **c)** 720
d) 2520   **33. a)** 2 if $n = 1$, 2 if $n = 2$, 0 if $n \geq 3$ **b)** 2^{n-2}
for $n > 1$; 1 if $n = 1$ **c)** $2(n-1)$ **35.** $(n+1)^m$ **37.** If n is
even $2^{n/2}$; if n is odd $2^{(n+1)/2}$ **39. a)** 240 **b)** 480   **c)** 360
41. 352   **43.** 147   **45.** 33   **47.** 7,104,000,000,000
49. 18   **51.** 17   **53.** 22   **55.** Let $P(m)$ be the sum
rule for m tasks. For the basis case take $m = 2$. This is just
the sum rule for two tasks. Now assume that $P(m)$ is true.
Consider $m + 1$ tasks, $T_1, T_2, \ldots, T_m, T_{m+1}$, which can be
done in $n_1, n_2, \ldots, n_m, n_{m+1}$ ways, respectively, such that
no two of these tasks can be done at the same time. To
do one of these tasks, we can either do one of the first m
of these, or do task T_{m+1}. By the sum rule for two tasks,
the number of ways to do this is the sum of the number
of ways to do one of the first m tasks, plus n_{m+1}. By the
inductive hypothesis this is $n_1 + n_2 + \cdots + n_m + n_{m+1}$, as
desired.   **57.** $n(n - 3)/2$

SECTION 4.2

1. Since there are six classes, but only five weekdays, the pigeonhole principle shows that at least two classes must be
held on the same day.   **3. a)** 3 **b)** 14   **5.** Since there
are four possible remainders when an integer is divided
by 4, the pigeonhole principle implies that given five integers, at least two have the same remainder.   **7.** Let
$a, a+1, \ldots, a+n-1$ be the integers in the sequence. The
integers $(a + i) \bmod n, i = 0, 1, 2, \ldots, n - 1$, are distinct,
since $0 < (a+j)-(a+k) < n$ whenever $0 \leq k < j \leq n-1$.
Since there are n possible values for $(a + i) \bmod n$, and
there are n different integers in the set, each of these values is taken on exactly once. It follows that there is exactly
one integer in the sequence that is divisible by n.   **9.** 4951
11. The midpoint of the segment joining the points (a, b, c)
and (d, e, f) is $((a+d)/2, (b+e)/2, (c+f)/2)$. It has integer coefficients if and only if a and d have the same parity,
b and e have the same parity, and c and f have the same
parity. Since there are eight possible triples of parity [such
as (*even*, *odd*, *even*)], by the pigeonhole principle at least
two of the nine points have the same triple of parities. The
midpoint of the segment joining two such points has integer coefficients.   **13. a)** Group the first eight positive
integers into four subsets of two integers each so that the
integers of each subset add up to 9: {1, 8}, {2, 7}, {3, 6}, and
{4, 5}. If five integers are selected from the first eight positive integers, by the pigeonhole principle at least two of
them come from the same subset. Two such integers have
a sum of 9, as desired.   **b)** No. Take {1, 2, 3, 4}, for example.   **15.** 4   **17.** 21,251   **19. a)** If there were fewer
than 9 freshmen, fewer than 9 sophomores, and fewer than

CHAPTER 4

SECTION 4.1

1. a) 5850 **b)** 343   **3. a)** 4^{10} **b)** 5^{10} **5.** 42   **7.** 26^3
9. 676   **11.** 2^8 **13.** $n + 1$ (counting the empty

9 juniors in the class, there would be no more than 8 of each of these three class standings, for a total of at most 24 students, contradicting the fact that there are 25 students in the class.   **b)** If there were fewer than 3 freshmen, fewer than 19 sophomores, and fewer than 5 juniors, then there would be at most 2 freshmen, at most 18 sophomores, and at most 4 juniors, for a total of at most 24 students. This contradicts the fact that there are 25 students in the class.
21. 4, 3, 2, 1, 8, 7, 6, 5, 12, 11, 10, 9, 16, 15, 14, 13
23. **procedure** *long*($a_1, \ldots, a_n$: positive integers)
{first find longest increasing subsequence}
   $max := 0; set := 00 \ldots 00$ {n bits}
   for $i := 1$ **to** 2^n
   begin
     $last := 0; count := 0, OK := $ **true**
     for $j := 1$ **to** n
     begin
       if $set(j) = 1$ **then**
       begin
         if $a_j > last$ **then** $last := a_j$
         $count := count + 1$
       end
       else $OK := false$
     end
     if $count > max$ **then**
     begin
       $max := count$
       $best := set$
     end
     $set := set + 1$ (binary addition)
   end {*max* is length and *best* indicates the sequence}
   {repeat for decreasing subsequence with only
       changes being $a_j < last$ instead of $a_j > last$
       and $last := \infty$ instead of $last := 0$}
25. By symmetry we need prove only the first statement. Let A be one of the people. Either A has at least four friends, or A has at least six enemies among the other nine people (since $3 + 5 < 9$). Suppose, in the first case, that B, C, D, and E are all A's friends. If any two of these are friends with each other, then we have found three mutual friends. Otherwise $\{B, C, D, E\}$ is a set of four mutual enemies. In the second case, let $\{B, C, D, E, F, G\}$ be a set of enemies of A. By Example 11, among B, C, D, E, F, and G there are either three mutual friends or three mutual enemies, who form, with A, a set of four mutual enemies.
27. We need to show two things: that if we have a group of n people, then among them we must find either a pair of friends or a subset of n of them all of whom are mutual enemies; and that there exists a group of $n - 1$ people for which this is not possible. For the first statement, if there is any pair of friends, then the condition is satisfied, and if not, then every pair of people are enemies, so the second condition is satisfied. For the second statement, if we have a group of $n - 1$ people all of whom are enemies of each other, then there is neither a pair of friends nor a subset of n of them all of whom are mutual enemies.

29. There are 6,432,816 possibilities for the three initials and a birthday. So, by the generalized pigeonhole principle, there are at least $\lceil 34,000,000/6,432,816 \rceil = 6$ people who share the same initials and birthday.   **31.** 18   **33.** Since there are six computers, the number of other computers a computer is connected to is an integer between 0 and 5, inclusive. However, 0 and 5 cannot both occur. To see this, note that if some computer is connected to no others, then no computer is connected to all five others, and if some computer is connected to all five others, then no computer is connected to no others. Hence, by the pigeonhole principle, since there are at most five possibilities for the number of computers a computer is connected to, there are at least two computers in the set of six connected to the same number of others.   **35.** Label the computers C_1 through C_{100}, and label the printers P_1 through P_{20}. If we connect C_k to P_k for $k = 1, 2, \ldots, 20$ and connect each of the computers C_{21} through C_{100} to *all* the printers, then we have used a total of $20 + 80 \cdot 20 = 1620$ cables. Clearly this is sufficient, because if computers C_1 through C_{20} need printers, then they can use the printers with the same subscripts, and if any computers with higher subscripts need a printer instead of one or more of these, then they can use the printers that are not being used, since they are connected to all the printers. Now we must show that 1619 cables is not enough. Since there are 1619 cables and 20 printers, the average number of computers per printer is $1619/20$, which is less than 81. Therefore some printer must be connected to fewer than 81 computers. That means it is connected to 80 or fewer computers, so there are 20 computers that are not connected to it. If those 20 computers all needed a printer simultaneously, then they would be out of luck, since they are connected to at most the 19 other printers.   **37.** Let a_i be the number of matches completed by hour i. Then $1 \le a_1 < a_2 < \cdots < a_{75} \le 125$. Also $25 \le a_1 + 24 < a_2 + 24 < \cdots < a_{75} + 24 \le 149$. There are 150 numbers $a_1, \ldots, a_{75}, a_1 + 24, \ldots, a_{75} + 24$. By the pigeonhole principle, at least two are equal. Since all the a_is are distinct and all the $(a_i + 24)$s are distinct, it follows that $a_i = a_j + 24$ for some $i > j$. Thus, in the period from the $(j + 1)$st to the ith hour, there are exactly 24 matches.   **39.** Use the generalized pigeonhole principle, placing the $|S|$ objects $f(s)$ for $s \in S$ in $|T|$ boxes, one for each element of T.   **41.** Let d_j be $jx - N(jx)$, where $N(jx)$ is the integer closest to jx for $1 \le j \le n$. Each d_j is an irrational number between $-1/2$ and $1/2$. We will assume that n is even; the case where n is odd is messier. Consider the n intervals $\{x \mid j/n < x < (j+1)/n\}$, $\{x \mid -(j+1)/n < x < -j/n\}$ for $j = 0, 1, \ldots, (n/2) - 1$. If d_j belongs to the interval $\{x \mid 0 < x < 1/n\}$ or to the interval $\{x \mid -1/n < x < 0\}$ for some j, we are done. If not, since there are $n - 2$ intervals and n numbers d_j, the pigeonhole principle tells us that there is an interval $\{x \mid (k-1)/n < x < k/n\}$ containing d_r and d_s with $r < s$. The proof can be finished by showing that $(s - r)x$ is within $1/n$ of its nearest integer.   **43. a)** Assume that $i_k \le n$

for all k. Then by the generalized pigeonhole principle, at least $\lceil (n^2+1)/n \rceil = n+1$ of the numbers $i_1, i_2, \ldots, i_{n^2+1}$ are equal. **b)** If $a_{k_j} < a_{k_{j+1}}$, then the subsequence consisting of a_{k_j}, followed by the increasing subsequence of length $i_{k_{j+1}}$ starting at $a_{k_{j+1}}$ contradicts the fact that $i_{k_j} = i_{k_{j+1}}$. Hence $a_{k_j} > a_{k_{j+1}}$. **c)** If there is no increasing subsequence of length greater than n, then parts (a) and (b) apply. Therefore we have $a_{k_{n+1}} > a_{k_n} > \cdots > a_{k_2} > a_{k_1}$, a decreasing sequence of length $n + 1$.

SECTION 4.3

1. $abc, acb, bac, bca, cab, cba$ **3.** 720 **5. a)** 120 **b)** 720 **c)** 8 **d)** 6720 **e)** 40,320 **f)** 3,628,800 **7.** 15,120 **9.** 1320 **11. a)** 210 **b)** 386 **c)** 848 **d)** 252 **13.** $2(n!)^2$ **15.** 65,780 **17.** $2^{100} - 5051$ **19. a)** 1024 **b)** 45 **c)** 176 **d)** 252 **21. a)** 120 **b)** 24 **c)** 120 **d)** 24 **e)** 6 **f)** 0 **23.** 609,638,400 **25. a)** 94,109,400 **b)** 941,094 **c)** 3,764,376 **d)** 90,345,024 **e)** 114,072 **f)** 2328 **g)** 24 **h)** 79,727,040 **i)** 3,764,376 **j)** 109,440 **27. a)** 12,650 **b)** 303,600 **29. a)** 37,927 **b)** 18,915 **31. a)** 122,523,030 **b)** 72,930,375 **c)** 223,149,655 **d)** 100,626,625 **33.** 54,600 **35.** 45 **37.** 912 **39.** 11,232,000 **41.** 13 **43.** 873

SECTION 4.4

1. $x^4 + 4x^3y + 6x^2y^2 + 4xy^3 + y^4$ **3.** $x^6 + 6x^5y + 15x^4y^2 + 20x^3y^3 + 15x^2y^4 + 6xy^5 + y^6$ **5.** 101 **7.** $-2^{10}\binom{19}{9} = -94,595,072$ **9.** $-2^{101}3^{99}\binom{200}{99}$ **11.** $(-1)^{(200-k)/3}\binom{100}{(200-k)/3}$ if $k \equiv 2 \pmod 3$ and $-100 \le k \le 200$; 0 otherwise **13.** 1 9 36 84 126 126 84 36 9 1 **15.** The sum of *all* the positive numbers $\binom{n}{k}$, as k runs from 0 to n, is 2^n, so each one of them is no bigger than this sum. **17.** $\binom{n}{k} = \frac{n(n-1)(n-2)\cdots(n-k+1)}{k(k-1)(k-2)\cdots 2} \le \frac{n \cdot n \cdots n}{2 \cdot 2 \cdots 2} = n^k/2^{k-1}$ **19.** $\binom{n}{k-1} + \binom{n}{k} = \frac{n!}{(k-1)!(n-k+1)!} + \frac{n!}{k!(n-k)!} = \frac{n!}{k!(n-k+1)!} \cdot [k + (n - k + 1)] = \frac{(n+1)!}{k!(n+1-k)!} = \binom{n+1}{k}$ **21. a)** We show that each side counts the number of ways to choose from a set with n elements a subset with k elements and a distinguished element of that set. For the left-hand side, first choose the k-set [this can be done in $\binom{n}{k}$ ways] and then choose one of the k elements in this subset to be the distinguished element (this can be done in k ways). For the right-hand side, first choose the distinguished element out of the entire n-set [this can be done in n ways], and then choose the remaining $k - 1$ elements of the subset from the remaining $n - 1$ elements of the set (this can be done in $\binom{n-1}{k-1}$ ways). **b)** $k\binom{n}{k} = k \cdot \frac{n!}{k!(n-k)!} = \frac{n \cdot (n-1)!}{(k-1)!(n-k)!} = n\binom{n-1}{k-1}$ **23.** $\binom{n+1}{k} = \frac{(n+1)!}{k!(n+1-k)!} = \frac{(n+1)}{k} \frac{n!}{(k-1)!(n-(k-1))!} = (n+1)\binom{n}{k-1}/k$. This identity together with $\binom{n}{0} = 1$ gives a recursive definition. **25.** $\binom{2n}{n+1} + \binom{2n}{n} = \binom{2n+1}{n+1} = \frac{1}{2}\left(\binom{2n+1}{n+1} + \binom{2n+1}{n+1}\right) = \frac{1}{2}\left(\binom{2n+1}{n+1} + \binom{2n+1}{n}\right) = \frac{1}{2}\left(\binom{2n+2}{n+1}\right)$ **27. a)** $\binom{n+r+1}{r}$ counts the number of ways to choose a sequence of r 0s and $n + 1$ 1s by choosing the positions of the 0s. Alternately, suppose that the $(j + 1)$st term is the last term equal to 1, so $n \le j \le n+r$. Once we have determined where the last 1 is, we decide

where the 0s are to be placed in the j spaces before the last 1. There are n 1s and $j - n$ 0s in this range. By the sum rule it follows that there are $\sum_{j=n}^{n+r} \binom{j}{j-n} = \sum_{k=0}^{r} \binom{n+k}{k}$ ways to do this. **b)** Let $P(r)$ be the statement to be proved. The basis step is the equation $\binom{n}{0} = \binom{n+1}{0}$, which is just $1 = 1$. Assume that $P(r)$ is true. Then $\sum_{k=0}^{r+1} \binom{n+k}{k} = \sum_{k=0}^{r} \binom{n+k}{k} + \binom{n+r+1}{r+1} = \binom{n+r+1}{r} + \binom{n+r+1}{r+1} = \binom{n+r+2}{r+1}$, using the inductive hypothesis and Pascal's identity. **29.** We can choose the leader first in n different ways. We can then choose the rest of the committee in 2^{n-1} ways. Hence there are $n2^{n-1}$ ways to choose the committee and its leader. Meanwhile, the number of ways to select a committee with k people is $\binom{n}{k}$. Once we have chosen a committee with k people, there are k ways to choose its leader. Hence there are $\sum_{k=1}^{n} k\binom{n}{k}$ ways to choose the committee and its leader. Hence $\sum_{k=1}^{n} k\binom{n}{k} = n2^{n-1}$. **31.** Let the set have n elements. From Corollary 2 we have $\binom{n}{0} - \binom{n}{1} + \binom{n}{2} - \cdots + (-1)^n\binom{n}{n} = 0$. It follows that $\binom{n}{0} + \binom{n}{2} + \binom{n}{4} + \cdots = \binom{n}{1} + \binom{n}{3} + \binom{n}{5} + \cdots$. The left-hand side gives the number of subsets with an even number of elements, and the right-hand side gives the number of subsets with an odd number of elements. **33. a)** A path of the desired type consists of m moves to the right and n moves up. Each such path can be represented by a bit string of length $m + n$ with m 0s and n 1s, where a 0 represents a move to the right and a 1 a move up. **b)** The number of bit strings of length $m + n$ containing exactly n 1s equals $\binom{m+n}{n} = \binom{m+n}{m}$ since such a string is determined by specifying the positions of the n 1s or by specifying the positions of the m 0s. **35.** By Exercise 33 the number of paths of length n of the type described in that exercise equals 2^n, the number of bit strings of length n. On the other hand, a path of length n of the type described in Exercise 33 must end at a point that has n as the sum of its coordinates, say $(n - k, k)$ for some k between 0 and n, inclusive. By Exercise 33, the number of such paths ending at $(n - k, k)$ equals $\binom{n-k+k}{k} = \binom{n}{k}$. Hence $\sum_{k=0}^{n}\binom{n}{k} = 2^n$. **37.** By Exercise 33 the number of paths from $(0, 0)$ to $(n + 1, r)$ of the type described in that exercise equals $\binom{n+r+1}{r}$. But such a path starts by going j steps vertically for some j with $0 \le j \le r$. The number of these paths beginning with j vertical steps equals the number of paths of the type described in Exercise 33 that go from $(1, j)$ to $(n+1, r)$. This is the same as the number of such paths that go from $(0, 0)$ to $(n, r - j)$, which by Exercise 33 equals $\binom{n+r-j}{r-j}$. Since $\sum_{j=0}^{r}\binom{n+r-j}{r-j} = \sum_{k=0}^{r}\binom{n+k}{k}$, it follows that $\sum_{k=1}^{r}\binom{n+k}{k} = \binom{n+r+1}{r} - 1$. **39. a)** $\binom{n+1}{2}$ **b)** $\binom{n+2}{3}$ **c)** $\binom{2n-2}{n-1}$ **d)** $\binom{n-1}{\lfloor (n-1)/2 \rfloor}$ **e)** Largest odd entry in nth row of Pascal's triangle **f)** $\binom{3n-3}{n-1}$

SECTION 4.5

1. 243 **3.** 26^6 **5.** 125 **7.** 35 **9. a)** 1716 **b)** 50,388 **c)** 2,629,575 **d)** 330 **e)** 9,724 **11.** 9 **13.** 4,504,501 **15. a)** 10,626 **b)** 1,365 **c)** 11,649 **d)** 106 **17.** 2,520

19. 302,702,400 **21.** 3003 **23.** 7,484,400 **25.** 30,492
27. $C(59, 50)$ **29.** 35 **31.** 83,160 **33.** 63
35. 19,635 **37.** 210 **39.** 27,720 **41.** $52!/(7!^5 17!)$
43. $24 \cdot 13^4/(52 \cdot 51 \cdot 50 \cdot 49)$ **45. a)** $C(k + n - 1, n)$
b) $(k + n - 1)!/(k - 1)!$ **47.** There are $C(n, n_1)$ ways
to choose n_1 objects for the first box. Once these objects
are chosen, there are $C(n - n_1, n_2)$ ways to choose objects
for the second box. Similarly, there are $C(n - n_1 - n_2, n_3)$
ways to choose objects for the third box. Continue in
this way until there is $C(n - n_1 - n_2 - \cdots - n_{k-1}, n_k) =$
$C(n_k, \ln_k) = 1$ way to choose the objects for the last box
(since $n_1 + n_2 + \cdots + n_k = n$). By the product rule, the number of ways to make the entire assignment is $C(n, n_1)C(n -$
$n_1, n_2)C(n - n_1 - n_2, n_3) \cdots C(n - n_1 - n_2 - \cdots - n_{k-1}, n_k)$,
which equals $n!/(n_1!n_2! \cdots n_k!)$, as straightforward simplification shows. **49. a)** Since $x_1 \le x_2 \le \cdots \le x_r$, it follows
that $x_1 + 0 < x_2 + 1 < \cdots < x_r + r - 1$. The inequalities are
strict since $x_j + j - 1 < x_{j+1} + j$ as long as $x_j \le x_{j+1}$. Since
$1 \le x_j \le n + r - 1$, this sequence is made up of r distinct
elements from T. **b)** Suppose that $1 \le x_1 < x_2 < \cdots <$
$x_r \le n + r - 1$. Let $y_k = x_k - (k - 1)$. Then it is not hard to see
that $y_k \le y_{k+1}$ for $k = 1, 2, \ldots, r - 1$ and that $1 \le y_k \le n$
for $k = 1, 2, \ldots r$. It follows that $\{y_1, y_2, \ldots, y_r\}$ is an r-
combination with repetition allowed of S. **c)** From (a)
and (b) it follows that there is a one-to-one correspondence of r-combinations with repetition allowed of S and
r-combinations of T, a set with $n + r - 1$ elements. We
conclude that there are $C(n + r - 1, r)$ r-combinations
with repetitions allowed of S. **51.** 5 **53.** The terms
in the expansion are of the form $x_1^{n_1} x_2^{n_2} \cdots x_m^{n_m}$, where
$n_1 + n_2 + \cdots + n_m = n$. Such a term arises from choosing
the x_1 in n_1 factors, the x_2 in n_2 factors,..., and the x_m in
n_m factors. This can be done in $C(n; n_1, n_2, \ldots, n_m)$ ways,
since a choice is a permutation of n_1 labels "1," n_2 labels
"2," ...and n_m labels "m." **55.** 2520

SECTION 4.6

1. a) 2134 **b)** 54132 **c)** 12534 **d)** 45312 **e)** 6714253
f) 31542678 **3.** 14532, 15432, 21345, 23451, 23514, 31452,
31542, 43521, 45213, 45321 **5.** 1234, 1243, 1324, 1342,
1423, 1432, 2134, 2143, 2314, 2341, 2413, 2431, 3124, 3142,
3214, 3241, 3412, 3421, 4123, 4132, 4213, 4231, 4312, 4321
7. $\{1, 2, 3\}, \{1, 2, 4\}, \{1, 2, 5\}, \{1, 3, 4\}, \{1, 3, 5\}, \{1, 4, 5\}$,
$\{2, 3, 4\}, \{2, 3, 5\}, \{2, 4, 5\}, \{3, 4, 5\}$ **9.** The bit string representing the next largest r-combination must differ from
the bit string representing the original one in position i
since positions $i + 1, \ldots, r$ are occupied by the largest possible numbers. Also $a_i + 1$ is the smallest possible number
we can put in position i if we want a combination greater
than the original one. Then $a_i + 2, \ldots, a_i + r - i + 1$ are the
smallest allowable numbers for positions $i + 1$ to r. Thus
we have produced the next r-combination. **11.** 123, 132,
213, 231, 312, 321, 124, 142, 214, 241, 412, 421, 125, 152, 215,
251, 512, 521, 134, 143, 314, 341, 413, 431, 135, 153, 315,
351, 513, 531, 145, 154, 415, 451, 514, 541, 234, 243, 324, 342,

423, 432, 235, 253, 325, 352, 523, 532, 245, 254, 425, 452, 524,
542, 345, 354, 435, 453, 534, 543 **13.** We will show it is
a bijection by showing it has an inverse. Given a positive
integer less than $n!$, let $a_1, a_2, \ldots, a_{n-1}$ be its Cantor digits.
Put n in position $n - a_{n-1}$, so clearly a_{n-1} is the number of
integers less than n that follow n in the permutation. Then
put $n - 1$ in free position $(n - 1) - a_{n-2}$, where we have
numbered the free positions $1, 2, \ldots, n - 1$ (excluding the
position that n is already in). Continue until 1 is placed in
the only free position left. Since we have constructed an
inverse, the correspondence is a bijection.
15. procedure *Cantor permutation*(n, i: integers with
   $n \ge 1$ and $0 \le i < n!$)
   $x := n$
   for $j := 1$ **to** n
     $p_j := 0$
   for $k := 1$ **to** $n - 1$
   begin
     $c := \lfloor x/(n - k)! \rfloor; x := x - c(n - k)!; h := n$
     while $p_h \ne 0$
       $h := h - 1$
     for $j := 1$ **to** c
     begin
       $h := h - 1$
       while $p_h \ne 0$
         $h := h - 1$
     end
     $p_h := n - k + 1$
   end
   $h := 1$
   while $p_h \ne 0$
     $h := h + 1$
   $p_h := 1$
   $\{p_1 p_2 \cdots p_n$ is the permutation corresponding to $i\}$

SUPPLEMENTARY EXERCISES

1. a) 151,200 **b)** 1,000,000 **c)** 210 **d)** 5005 **3.** 3^{100}
5. 24,600 **7. a)** 4,060 **b)** 2688 **c)** 25,009,600 **9. a)** 192
b) 301 **c)** 300 **d)** 300 **11.** 639 **13.** The maximum possible sum is 240, and the minimum possible
sum is 15. So the number of possible sums is 226. Since
there are 252 subsets with five elements of a set with
10 elements, by the pigeonhole principle it follows that
at least two have the same sum. **15. a)** 50 **b)** 50
c) 14 **d)** 5 **17.** Let $a_1, a_2, \ldots, a_m$ be the integers, and
let $d_i = \sum_{j=1}^{i} a_j$. If $d_i \equiv 0 \pmod{m}$ for some i, we are
done. Otherwise $d_1 \bmod m, d_2 \bmod m, \ldots, d_m \bmod m$ are
m integers with values in $\{1, 2, \ldots, m - 1\}$. By the pigeonhole principle $d_k = d_l$ for some $1 \le k < l \le m$. Then
$\sum_{j=k+1}^{l} a_j = d_l - d_k \equiv 0 \pmod{m}$. **19.** The decimal expansion of the rational number a/b can be obtained by
division of b into a, where a is written with a decimal point
and an arbitrarily long string of 0s following it. The basic
step is finding the next digit of the quotient, namely, $\lfloor r/b \rfloor$,
where r is the remainder with the next digit of the div-

idend brought down. The current remainder is obtained from the previous remainder by subtracting b times the previous digit of the quotient. Eventually the dividend has nothing but 0s to bring down. Furthermore, there are only b possible remainders. Thus, at some point, by the pigeonhole principle, we will have the same situation as had previously arisen. From that point onward, the calculation must follow the same pattern. In particular, the quotient will repeat. **21. a)** 125,970 **b)** 20 **c)** 141,120,525 **d)** 141,120,505 **e)** 177,100 **f)** 141,078,021 **23. a)** 10 **b)** 8 **c)** 7 **25.** 3^n **27.** $C(n+2, r+1) = C(n+1, r+1) + C(n+1, r) = 2C(n+1, r+1) - C(n+1, r+1) + C(n+1, r) = 2C(n+1, r+1) - (C(n, r+1) + C(n, r)) + (C(n, r) + C(n, r-1)) = 2C(n+1, r+1) - C(n, r+1) + C(n, r-1)$ **29.** Substitute $x = 1$ and $y = 3$ into the binomial theorem. **31.** $C(n+1, 5)$ **33.** 3,491,888,400 **35.** 5^{24} **37. a)** 45 **b)** 57 **c)** 12 **39. a)** 386 **b)** 56 **c)** 512 **41.** 0 if $n < m$; $C(n-1, n-m)$ if $n \geq m$

43. procedure *next permutation* (n: positive integer,
$\quad a_1, a_2, \ldots, a_r$: positive integers not exceeding
$\quad n$ with $a_1 a_2 \cdots a_r \neq nn \cdots n$)
$i := r$
while $a_i = n$
begin
$\quad a_i := 1$
$\quad i := i - 1$
end
$a_i := a_i + 1$
$\{a_1 a_2 \cdots a_r$ is the next permutation in lexicographic
$\quad$ order$\}$

45. We must show that if there are $R(m, n-1) + R(m-1, n)$ people at a party, then there must be at least m mutual friends or n mutual enemies. Consider one person; let's call him Jerry. Then there are $R(m-1, n) + R(m, n-1) - 1$ other people at the party, and by the pigeonhole principle there must be at least $R(m-1, n)$ friends of Jerry or $R(m, n-1)$ enemies of Jerry among these people. First let's suppose there are $R(m-1, n)$ friends of Jerry. By the definition of R, among these people we are guaranteed to find either $m-1$ mutual friends or n mutual enemies. In the former case these $m-1$ mutual friends together with Jerry are a set of m mutual friends; and in the latter case we have the desired set of n mutual enemies. The other situation is similar: Suppose there are $R(m, n-1)$ enemies of Jerry; we are guaranteed to find among them either m mutual friends or $n-1$ mutual enemies. In the former case we have the desired set of m mutual friends, and in the latter case these $n-1$ mutual enemies together with Jerry are a set of n mutual enemies.

C h a p t e r 1

Introduction

This book concerns the design of digital systems, a process often referred to as logic design. A digital system is one in which all of the signals are represented by discrete values. Computers and calculators are obvious examples, but most electronic systems contain a large amount of digital logic. Internally, digital systems usually operate with two-valued signals, which we will label 0 and 1. Although multi-valued systems have been built, two-valued systems are more reliable, and thus almost all digital systems use two-valued signals. Such a system, as shown in Figure 1.1, may have an arbitrary number of inputs $(A, B, \ldots)$ and an arbitrary number of outputs $(W, X, \ldots)$.

In addition to the data inputs shown, some circuits require a timing signal, called a clock (which is just another input signal that alternates between 0 and 1 at a regular rate). We will discuss the details of clock signals in Chapter 6.

A simple example of digital systems is shown in Example 1.1.

Figure 1.1 A digital system.

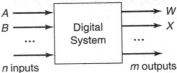

A system with three inputs, A, B, and C, and one output, Z, such that $Z = 1$ if and only if[1] two of the inputs are 1.

EXAMPLE 1.1

The inputs and outputs of a digital system represent real quantities. Sometimes, as in Example 1.1, these are naturally binary, that is, they take on one of two values. Other times, they may be multivalued. For example, an input may be a decimal digit or the output might be the letter grade for this course. Each must be represented by a set of binary digits (often called bits). This process is referred to as coding the inputs and outputs into binary. (We will discuss the details of this later.)

---

[1]The term *if and only if* is often abbreviated iff. It means that the output is 1 if the condition is met and is not 1 (which means it must be 0) if the condition is not met.

2

Chapter 1 Introduction

The physical manifestation of these binary quantities may be one of two voltages, for example, 0 volts or ground for logic 0 and 5 volts for logic 1, as in the laboratory implementations we will be discussing in Appendix A.1. It may also be a magnetic field in one direction or another (as on diskettes), a switch in the up or down position (for an input), or a light on or off (as an output). Except in the discussion of specific laboratory experiments and in the translation of verbal descriptions into more formal ones, the physical representation will be irrelevant in this text; we will be concerned with 0's and 1's.

Table 1.1 A truth table for Example 1.1.

A	B	C	Z
0	0	0	0
0	0	1	0
0	1	0	0
0	1	1	1
1	0	0	0
1	0	1	1
1	1	0	1
1	1	1	1

We can describe the behavior of a digital system, such as that of Example 1.1, in tabular form. Since there are only eight possible input combinations, we can list all of them and what the output is for each. Such a table (referred to as a truth table) is shown in Table 1.1. We will leave the development of truth tables (including one similar to this) to later in the chapter.

Three other examples are given in Examples 1.2, 1.3, and 1.4.

EXAMPLE 1.2	A system with eight inputs, representing two 4-bit binary numbers, and one 5-bit output, representing the sum. (Each input number can range from 0 to 15; the output can range from 0 to 30.)
EXAMPLE 1.3	A system with one input, A, plus a clock, and one output, Z, which is 1 iff the input was one at the last three consecutive clock times.
EXAMPLE 1.4	A more complex example is a traffic controller. In the simplest case, there are just two streets, and the light is green on each street for a fixed period of time. It then goes to yellow for another fixed period and finally to red. There are no inputs to this system other than the clock. There are six outputs, one for each color in each direction. (Each output may control multiple bulbs.) Traffic controllers may have many more outputs, if, for example, there are left-turn signals. Also, there may be several inputs to indicate when there are vehicles waiting at a red signal or passing a green one.

The first two examples are *combinational*, that is, the output depends only on the present value of the input. In Example 1.1, if we know the value of A, B, and C right now, we can determine what Z is now.[2] Examples 1.3 and 1.4 are *sequential*, that is, they require *memory*, since we need to know something about inputs at an earlier time (previous clock times).

We will concentrate on combinational systems in the first half of the book and leave the discussion about sequential systems until later. As we

---

[2]In a real system, there is a small amount of delay between the input and output, that is, if the input changes at some point in time, the output changes a little after that. The time frame is typically in the nanosecond (10^{-9} sec) range. We will ignore those delays almost all of the time, but we will return to that issue in Chapter 5.

will see, sequential systems are composed of two parts, memory and combinational logic. Thus, we need to be able to design combinational systems before we can begin designing sequential ones.

A word of caution about natural language in general, and English in particular, is in order. English is not a very precise language. The examples given above leave some room for interpretation. In Example 1.1, is the output to be 1 if all three of the inputs are 1, or only if exactly two inputs are 1? One could interpret the statement either way. When we wrote the truth table, we had to decide; we interpreted "two" as "two or more" and thus made the output 1 when all three inputs were 1. (In problems in this text, we will try to be as precise as possible, but even then, different people may read the problem statement in different ways.)

The bottom line is that we need a more precise description of logic systems. We will develop that for combinational systems in the first two chapters and for sequential systems in Chapter 6.

1.1 A BRIEF REVIEW OF NUMBER SYSTEMS

This section gives an introduction to some topics in number systems, primarily those needed to understand the material in the remainder of the book. We will only deal with integers. If this is familiar material from another course, skip to Section 1.2 (page 19).

Integers are normally written using a positional number system, where each digit represents the coefficient in a power series

$$N = a_{n-1}r^{n-1} + a_{n-2}r^{n-2} + \cdots + a_2r^2 + a_1r + a_0$$

where n is the number of digits, r is the radix or base, and the a_i are the coefficients, where each is an integer in the range

$$0 \leq a_i < r$$

For decimal, $r = 10$, and the a's are in the range 0 to 9. For binary, $r = 2$, and the a's are all either 0 or 1. Other commonly used notations in computer documentation are octal, $r = 8$, and hexadecimal, $r = 16$. In binary, the digits are usually referred to as *bits*, a contraction for *b*inary dig*its*.

The decimal number 7642 (sometimes written 7642_{10} to emphasize that it is radix 10, that is, decimal) thus stands for

$$7642_{10} = 7 \times 10^3 + 6 \times 10^2 + 4 \times 10 + 2$$

and the binary number

$$101111_2 = 1 \times 2^5 + 0 \times 2^4 + 1 \times 2^3 + 1 \times 2^2 + 1 \times 2 + 1$$
$$= 32 + 8 + 4 + 2 + 1 = 47_{10}$$

From this last example,[3] it is clear how to convert from binary to decimal; just evaluate the power series. To do that easily, it is useful to know the powers of 2, rather than compute them each time they are needed. (It would save a great deal of time and effort if at least the first ten powers of 2 were memorized; the first 20 are shown in the Table 1.2.)

Table 1.2 Powers of 2.

n	2^n	n	2^n
1	2	11	2,048
2	4	12	4,096
3	8	13	8,192
4	16	14	16,384
5	32	15	32,768
6	64	16	65,536
7	128	17	131,072
8	256	18	262,144
9	512	19	524,288
10	1,024	20	1,048,576

We will often be using the first 16 positive binary integers, and sometimes the first 32, as shown in the Table 1.3. (As in decimal, leading 0's are often left out, but we have shown the 4-bit number including leading 0's for the first 16.) When the size of the storage place for a positive binary number is specified, then leading 0's are added so as to obtain the correct number of bits.

Table 1.3 First 32 binary integers.

Decimal	Binary	4-bit	Decimal	Binary
0	0	0000	16	10000
1	1	0001	17	10001
2	10	0010	18	10010
3	11	0011	19	10011
4	100	0100	20	10100
5	101	0101	21	10101
6	110	0110	22	10110
7	111	0111	23	10111
8	1000	1000	24	11000
9	1001	1001	25	11001
10	1010	1010	26	11010
11	1011	1011	27	11011
12	1100	1100	28	11100
13	1101	1101	29	11101
14	1110	1110	30	11110
15	1111	1111	31	11111

Note that the number one less than 2^n consists of n 1's (for example, $2^4 - 1 = 1111 = 15$ and $2^5 - 1 = 11111 = 31$).

---

[3]Section 1.6, Solved Problems, contains additional examples of each of the types of problems discussed in this chapter. There is a section of Solved Problems in each of the chapters.

An *n*-bit number can represent the positive integers from 0 to $2^n - 1$. Thus, for example, 4-bit numbers have the range of 0 to 15, 8-bit numbers 0 to 255 and 16-bit numbers 0 to 65,535.

To convert from decimal to binary, we could evaluate the power series of the decimal number, by converting each digit to binary, that is

$$746 = 111 \times (1010)^{10} + 0100 \times 1010 + 0110$$

but that requires binary multiplication, which is rather time-consuming.

There are two straightforward algorithms using decimal arithmetic. First, we can subtract from the number the largest power of 2 less than that number and put a 1 in the corresponding position of the binary equivalent. We then repeat that with the remainder. A 0 is put in the position for those powers of 2 that are larger than the remainder.

EXAMPLE 1.5

For 746, $2^9 = 512$ is the largest power of 2 less than or equal to 746, and thus there is a 1 in the 2^9 (512) position. We then compute $746 - 512 = 234$. The next smaller power of 2 is $2^8 = 256$, but that is larger than 234 and thus, there is a 0 in the 2^8 position. Next, we compute $234 - 128 = 106$, putting a 1 in the 2^7 position. (Now, the binary number begins 101.) Continuing, we subtract 64 from 106, resulting in 42 and a 1 in the 2^6 position (and now the number begins with 1011). Since 42 is larger than 32, we have a 1 in the 2^5 position, and compute $42 - 32 = 10$. Since $2^4 = 16$ is greater than 10, there is a 0 in the 2^4 position. At this point, we can continue subtracting (8 next) or recognize that the binary equivalent of the remainder, 10, is 1010, giving

$$746_{10} = 1 \times 2^9 + 0 \times 2^8 + 1 \times 2^7 + 1 \times 2^6 + 1 \times 2^5 + 0 \times 2^4$$
$$+ 1 \times 2^3 + 0 \times 2^2 + 1 \times 2 + 0$$

$$= 1011101010_2$$

The other approach is to divide the decimal number by 2 repeatedly. The remainder each time gives a digit of the binary answer, starting at the least significant bit (a_0). The remainder is then discarded and the process is repeated.

EXAMPLE 1.6

Converting 746 from decimal to binary, we compute

746/2 = 373 with a remainder of 0	0
373/2 = 186 with a remainder of 1	10
186/2 = 93 with a remainder of 0	010
93/2 = 46 with a remainder of 1	1010
46/2 = 23 with a remainder of 0	01010
23/2 = 11 with a remainder of 1	101010
11/2 = 5 with a remainder of 1	1101010
5/2 = 2 with a remainder of 1	11101010
2/2 = 1 with a remainder of 0	011101010
1/2 = 0 with a remainder of 1	1011101010

We could continue dividing by 2 and get additional leading 0's. Thus, the answer is 101101010 as before. In this method, we could also stop when we recognize the number that is left and convert it to binary. Thus, when we had 23, we could recognize that as 10111 (from Table 1.3) and place that in front of the bits we had produced, giving 10111 01010.

EXAMPLE 1.7

Convert 105 to binary

105/2 = 52, rem 1	produces	1
52/2 = 26, rem 0		01
26/2 = 13, rem 0		001
but 13 = 1101		1101 001

The method works because all of the terms in the power series except the last divide evenly by 2. Thus, since

$$746 = 1 \times 2^9 + 0 \times 2^8 + 1 \times 2^7 + 1 \times 2^6 + 1 \times 2^5 + 0 \times 2^4$$
$$+ 1 \times 2^3 + 0 \times 2^2 + 1 \times 2 + 0$$

$$746/2 = 373 \text{ and remainder of } 0$$
$$= 1 \times 2^8 + 0 \times 2^7 + 1 \times 2^6 + 1 \times 2^5 + 1 \times 2^4 + 0 \times 2^3$$
$$+ 1 \times 2^2 + 0 \times 2 + 1 + \text{rem } 0$$

The last bit became the remainder. If we repeat the process, we get

$$373/2 = 186 \text{ and remainder of } 1$$
$$= 1 \times 2^7 + 0 \times 2^6 + 1 \times 2^5 + 1 \times 2^4 + 1 \times 2^3$$
$$+ 0 \times 2^2 + 1 \times 2 + 0 + \text{rem } 1$$

That remainder is the second digit from the right. On the next division, the remainder will be 0, the third digit. This process continues until the most significant bit is found.

[SP 1, 2; EX 1, 2][4]

1.1.1 Octal and Hexadecimal

Octal ($r = 8$) and *hexadecimal,* often referred to as *hex* ($r = 16$) are two other bases that are commonly used in computer documentation. Each is just a shorthand notation for binary. In octal, binary digits are grouped in threes (starting at the least significant). For example, a 9-bit number,

$$N = (b_8 2^8 + b_7 2^7 + b_6 2^6) + (b_5 2^5 + b_4 2^4 + b_3 2^3)$$
$$+ (b_2 2^2 + b_1 2^1 + b_0)$$
$$= 2^6(b_8 2^2 + b_7 2^1 + b_6) + 2^3(b_5 2^2 + b_4 2^1 + b_3)$$
$$+ (b_2 2^2 + b_1 2^1 + b_0)$$
$$= 8^2 o_2 + 8 o_1 + o_0$$

---

[4]At the end of most sections, a list of solved problems and exercises that are appropriate to that section is given.

where the o_i represent the octal digits and must fall in the range 0 to 7. Each term in parentheses is just interpreted in decimal. If the binary number does not have a multiple of 3 bits, leading 0's are added.

	EXAMPLE 1.8
(from Examples 1.5 and 1.6)	

$$1011101010_2 = 001\ 011\ 101\ 010_2$$
$$= 1\ 3\ 5\ 2_8$$

To convert from octal to binary, we just replace each octal digit by its 3-bit binary equivalent, the inverse of the last step in Example 1.8.

To convert from octal to decimal, we can evaluate the power series (where the powers of 8 can be obtained from Table 1.2 since $8^i = 2^{3i}$).

	EXAMPLE 1.9

$$1352_8 = 1 \times 8^3 + 3 \times 8^2 + 5 \times 8 + 2$$
$$= 512 + 3 \times 64 + 40 + 2$$
$$= 746_{10}$$

To convert from decimal to octal, we can first convert to binary, or we can (more easily) adapt the second algorithm used to convert from decimal to binary, replacing divide by 2 by divide by 8.

	EXAMPLE 1.10

$746/8 = 93$	rem 2	produces	2
$93/8 = 11$	rem 5		52
$11/8 = 1$	rem 3		352
$1/8 = 0$	rem 1		1352_8

Since it involves less work to convert decimal to octal than to binary, we often first convert to octal and then go to binary. Thus,

$$746_{10} = 1352_8 = 001\ 011\ 101\ 110_2$$

Hexadecimal ($r = 16$) groups bits by 4's. This is now the most common representation, since most computer word sizes are multiples of 4 bits (for example, 16, 32, 64). Each digit can then be in the range 0 to 15, where the digits above 9 are represented by the first six letters of the alphabet (upper case):

10 A
11 B
12 C
13 D
14 E
15 F

EXAMPLE 1.11

$1011101010_2 = 0010\ 1110\ 1010_2$

$= 2\,E\,A_{16}$

To convert from hex to decimal, we evaluate the power series.

EXAMPLE 1.12

$2\,E\,A_{16} = 2 \times 16^2 + 14 \times 16 + 10$

$= 512 + 224 + 10 = 746_{10}$

Finally, to convert from decimal to hex, repeatedly divide by 16, producing the hex digits as the remainder.

EXAMPLE 1.13

$746/16 = 46$	rem 10	produces	A
$46/16 = 2$	rem 14		E A
$2/16 = 0$	rem 2		$2\,E\,A_{16}$

[SP 3, 4; EX 3, 4]

1.1.2 Binary Addition

A common operation required in computers and other digital systems is the addition of two numbers. In this section, we will describe the process for adding binary numbers.

To compute the sum of two binary numbers, say

```
0 1 1 0    6
0 1 1 1   +7
```

Table 1.4 Binary addition.

$0 + 0 = 0$
$0 + 1 = 1$
$1 + 0 = 1$
$1 + 1 = 10$ (2, or a sum of 0 and a carry of 1 to the next bit)

we add one digit at a time (as we do in decimal), producing a sum and a carry to the next bit. Just as we have an addition table for decimal, we need one for binary (but it is of course much shorter). (See Table 1.4.) A step-by-step addition is shown in Example 1.14.

EXAMPLE 1.14

First, the least significant bits (the rightmost bits) are added, producing a sum of 1 and a carry of 0, as shown in green.

```
      0
  0 1 1 0
  0 1 1 1
        1
```

Next, we must add the second digit from the right,

$0 + 1 + 1 = 0 + (1 + 1) = 0 + 10 = 10$

(a sum of 0 and a carry of 1)

or $(0 + 1) + 1 = 1 + 1 = 10$

(the order of addition does not matter).

That addition is highlighted below.

```
  1 0
0 1 1 0
0 1 1 1
    0 1
```

The final two additions then become

```
  1 1            0 1
0 1 1 0        0 1 1 0
0 1 1 1        0 1 1 1
  1 0 1        1 1 0 1
```

Notice that in the third bit of addition, we had three 1's (the carry in plus the two digits). That produced a sum of 3 (11 in binary), that is, a sum bit of 1 and a carry of 1. The sum, of course, comes to 13 (in decimal). In this case, the last addition produced a carry out of 0, and thus the answer was 4-bits long. If the operands were larger (say, 13 + 5), the answer would require 5 bits as shown below, where the last carry is written as part of the sum. (This is, of course, no different from decimal addition, where the sum of two 4-digit numbers might produce a 4- or 5-digit result.)

```
  1 0 1
  1 1 0 1          1 3
  0 1 0 1             5
1 0 0 1 0          1 8
```

In a computer with n-bit words, when an arithmetic operation produces a result that is out of range [for example, addition of n-bit positive integers produces an $(n + 1)$-bit result], it is called *overflow*. With the addition of 4-bit positive integers, overflow occurs when the sum is greater than or equal to 16 (that is, 2^4). In the last example, there was overflow since the answer, 18, is greater than 15, the largest 4-bit positive integer.

After the addition of the least significant bits (which only has two operands), each remaining addition is a three-operand problem. We will denote the carry that is added in as c_{in} and the resulting carry from the addition c_{out}. The addition problem then becomes

$$
\begin{array}{r}
c_{in} \\
a \\
b \\
\hline
c_{out} \; s
\end{array}
$$

A complete table defining the addition process is shown in Table 1.5.

Table 1.5 One-bit adder.

a	b	c_{in}	c_{out}	s
0	0	0	0	0
0	0	1	0	1
0	1	0	0	1
0	1	1	1	0
1	0	0	0	1
1	0	1	1	0
1	1	0	1	0
1	1	1	1	1

A device that does this 1-bit computation is referred to as a *full adder*. To add 4-bit numbers, we might build four of these and connect them as shown in Figure 1.2. Notice that the carry input of the bit 1 adder has a 0 on it, since there is no carry into that bit. Sometimes a simpler circuit (called a *half adder*) is built for that bit. We will return to this problem in Chapter 2, when we are prepared to design the full adder.

Figure 1.2 A 4-bit adder.

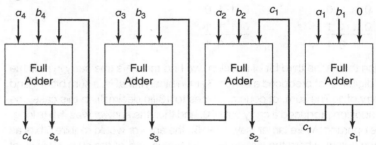

[SP 5; EX 5]

1.1.3 Signed Numbers

Up to this point, we have only considered positive integers, sometimes referred to as *unsigned numbers*. Computers must deal with *signed numbers*, that is, both positive and negative numbers. The human friendly notation is referred to as *signed-magnitude* (+5 or −3 as decimal examples). This could be incorporated into a computer, using the first bit of a number as a sign indicator (normally 0 for positive and 1 for negative) and the remaining bits for the magnitude. Thus, in a 4-bit system, we would represent

$$+5 \rightarrow 0101 \quad -5 \rightarrow 1101 \quad -3 \rightarrow 1011$$

With 3 bits for magnitude, the range of numbers available would be from −7 to +7. (Of course, most computers use a larger number of bits to store numbers and thus have a much larger range.) Note that such a representation has both a positive (0000) and negative (1000) zero. Although that might cause confusion (or at least complicate the internal logic of the computer), the major problem with signed-magnitude is the complexity of arithmetic. Consider the following addition problems:

+5	−5	+5	−5	−3	+3
+3	−3	−3	+3	+5	−5
+8	−8	+2	−2	+2	−2

In the first two, where the signs of the two operands are the same, we just add the magnitudes and retain the sign. For these two, the computation is 5 + 3. In each of the other examples, we must determine which is the larger magnitude. (It could be the first operand or the second.) Then, we must subtract the smaller from the larger, and finally, attach the sign of the larger magnitude. For these four, the computation is 5 − 3. Although this could all be done, the complexity of the hardware involved (an adder, a subtractor, and a comparator) has led to another solution.

Signed binary numbers are nearly always stored in *two's complement* format. The leading bit is still the sign bit (0 for positive). Positive numbers (and zero) are just stored in normal binary. The largest number that can be stored is $2^{n-1} - 1$ (7 for $n = 4$). Thus, in a 4-bit system, +5 would be stored as 0101.

The negative number, $-a$, is stored as the binary equivalent of $2^n - a$ in an n-bit system. Thus, for example, −3 is stored as the binary for 16 − 3 = 13, that is, 1101.

The most negative number that can be stored is -2^{n-1} (−8 in a 4-bit system). The largest number available in two's complement is about half that of unsigned numbers with the same number of bits, since half of the 2^n representations are used for negative numbers. This method extends to other bases than binary. It is referred to as *radix complement*. Negative numbers, $-a$, in n digits are stored as $r^n - a$. In decimal for example, this is called ten's complement. In a 2-digit system, −16 would be stored as 100 − 16 = 84. (Numbers from 0 to 49 would be considered positive and those between 50 and 99 would be representations of negative numbers.)

An easier way to find the storage format for negative numbers in two's complement is the following three-step approach:

1. Find the binary equivalent of the magnitude.
2. Complement each bit (that is, change 0's to 1's and 1's to 0's)
3. Add 1.

EXAMPLE 1.15

	−5	−1	−0
1.	5: 0 1 0 1	1: 0 0 0 1	0: 0 0 0 0
2.	1 0 1 0	1 1 1 0	1 1 1 1
3.	1	1	1
	−5: 1 0 1 1	−1: 1 1 1 1	0 0 0 0
	(a)	(b)	(c)

Note that there is no negative zero; the process of complementing +0 produces an answer of 0000. In two's complement addition, the carry out of the most significant bit is ignored.

Table 1.6 lists the meaning of all 4-bit numbers both as positive (unsigned) numbers and as two's complement signed numbers.

Table 1.6 Signed and unsigned 4-bit numbers.

Binary	Positive	Signed (two's complement)
0000	0	0
0001	1	+1
0010	2	+2
0011	3	+3
0100	4	+4
0101	5	+5
0110	6	+6
0111	7	+7
1000	8	−8
1001	9	−7
1010	10	−6
1011	11	−5
1100	12	−4
1101	13	−3
1110	14	−2
1111	15	−1

To find the magnitude of a negative number stored in two's complement format (that is, one that begins with a 1), the second and third steps of the negation process are followed.

EXAMPLE 1.16

		−5:	1 0 1 1	−1:	1 1 1 1
2.	Bit by bit complement		0 1 0 0		0 0 0 0
3.	Add 1		1		1
		5:	0 1 0 1	1:	0 0 0 1

(One could subtract 1 and then complement, instead; that will give the same answer.)

The reason that two's complement is so popular is the simplicity of addition. To add any two numbers, no matter what the sign of each is, we just do binary addition on their representations. Three sample computations are shown in Example 1.17. In each case, the carry out of the most significant bit is ignored.

EXAMPLE 1.17

−5	1 0 1 1	−5	1 0 1 1	−5	1 0 1 1
+7	0 1 1 1	+5	0 1 0 1	+3	0 0 1 1
+2	(1) 0 0 1 0	0	(1) 0 0 0 0	−2	(0) 1 1 1 0

In the first, the sum is 2. In the second, the sum is zero. In the third, the sum is −2, and, indeed, the representation of −2 is produced.

Overflow occurs when the sum is out of range. For 4-bit numbers, that range is $-8 \leq \text{sum} \leq +7$.

+5	0 1 0 1	
+4	0 1 0 0	
	(0) 1 0 0 1	(looks like −7)

EXAMPLE 1.18

The answer produced is clearly wrong, since the correct answer (+9) is out of range.

Indeed, whenever we add two positive numbers (each beginning with a 0) and get a result that looks negative (begins with a 1), there is overflow. Similarly, adding two negative numbers and obtaining a sum more negative than −8 also produces overflow.

−5	1 0 1 1	
−4	1 1 0 0	
	(1) 0 1 1 1	(looks like +7)

EXAMPLE 1.19

This time, two negative numbers produced a sum that looks positive.

The addition of two numbers of the opposite sign never produces overflow, since the magnitude of the sum is somewhere between the magnitudes of the two operands. (Although overflow seems rather common when dealing with 4-bit examples, it is an unusual occurrence in most computer applications, where numbers are 16 or 32 bits or longer.)   *[SP 6, 7, 8; EX 6, 7, 8, 9]*

1.1.4 Binary Subtraction

Subtraction (whether dealing with signed or unsigned numbers) is generally accomplished by first taking the two's complement of the second operand, and then adding. Thus, $a - b$ is computed as $a + (-b)$.

Consider the computation of $7 - 5$.

5:	0 1 0 1	7:		0 1 1 1
	1 0 1 0	−5:		+ 1 0 1 1
	+ 1	2	(1)	0 0 1 0
−5:	1 0 1 1			

EXAMPLE 1.20

The 5 is first complemented. This same process is followed whether the computation involves signed or unsigned numbers. Then, the representation of −5 is added to 7, producing an answer of 2.

For signed numbers, the carry out of the high-order bit is ignored and overflow occurs if the addition process operates on two numbers of the same sign and produces a result of the opposite sign. For unsigned numbers, the carry out of the high-order bit is the indicator of overflow, as in addition. However, in subtraction, a 0 indicates overflow. In Example 1.20, there was no overflow for either signed or unsigned numbers, since the answer, 2, is within range. The carry out of 1 indicates no overflow, for unsigned numbers. For signed numbers, the addition of a positive number to a negative one never produces overflow.

In most computer applications, the two additions (of the 1 in the complement computation and of the two operands) are done in one step. The least significant bit of the adder (bit 0) has no carry input for addition. The 1 that was added in the process of complementing can be input to that carry input for subtraction. Thus, to compute $7 - 5$, we take the bit by bit complement of 5 (0101 becomes 1010) and add.

EXAMPLE 1.21

$$7 - 5$$

$$
\begin{array}{r}
1 \\
0\,1\,1\,1 \\
1\,0\,1\,0 \\
\hline
(1)\ 0\,0\,1\,0
\end{array}
$$

Of course, we could design a subtractor (in addition to the adder), but that is unnecessary additional hardware for most computers.

Note that this process works for unsigned numbers even if the operands are larger than could be represented in a two's complement system, as shown in Example 1.22, where the difference $14 - 10$ is computed.

EXAMPLE 1.22

$$
\begin{array}{r}
1 \\
1\,1\,1\,0 \\
+0\,1\,0\,1 \\
\hline
(1)\ 0\,1\,0\,0 = 4
\end{array}
$$

We see overflow for unsigned numbers in Example 1.23a and for signed numbers in Example 1.23b.

EXAMPLE 1.23

$$
\begin{array}{cc}
5 - 7 & 7 - (-5) \\
1 & 1 \\
0\,1\,0\,1 & 0\,1\,1\,1 \\
1\,0\,0\,0 & 0\,1\,0\,0 \\
\hline
(0)\ 1\,1\,1\,0 & 1\,1\,0\,0 \\
(a) & (b)
\end{array}
$$

For unsigned numbers, overflow is indicated by the carry of 0. The result of (a) should be negative (-2), which cannot be represented in an unsigned system. For signed numbers, the result is correct. For signed numbers, overflow may occur if we subtract a negative number from a positive one or a positive number from a negative one, as shown in Example 1.23b. That is overflow since the addition process involved two positive numbers and the result looked negative. (Indeed, the answer should be 12, but that is greater than the largest 4-bit signed number, 7.)

[SP 9, 10; EX 10]

1.1.5   Binary Coded Decimal (BCD)

Internally, most computers operate on binary numbers. However, when they interface with humans, the mode of communication is generally decimal. Thus, it is necessary to convert from decimal to binary on input and from binary to decimal on output. (It is straightforward to write software to do this conversion.) However, even this decimal input and output must be coded into binary, digit by digit. If we use the first 10 binary numbers to represent the 10 decimal digits (as in the first binary column in Table 1.7), then the number 739, for example, would be stored as

0111   0011   1001

Table 1.7   Binary coded decimal codes.

Decimal digit	8421 code	5421 code	2421 code	Excess 3 code	2 of 5 code
0	0000	0000	0000	0011	11000
1	0001	0001	0001	0100	10100
2	0010	0010	0010	0101	10010
3	0011	0011	0011	0110	10001
4	0100	0100	0100	0111	01100
5	0101	1000	1011	1000	01010
6	0110	1001	1100	1001	01001
7	0111	1010	1101	1010	00110
8	1000	1011	1110	1011	00101
9	1001	1100	1111	1100	00011
unused	1010	0101	0101	0000	any of
	1011	0110	0110	0001	the 22
	1100	0111	0111	0010	patterns
	1101	1101	1000	1101	with 0, 1,
	1110	1110	1001	1110	3, 4, or 5
	1111	1111	1010	1111	1's

Each decimal digit is represented by 4 bits, and thus a 3-digit decimal number requires 12 bits (whereas, if it were converted to binary, it would require only 10 bits, since numbers up to 1023 can be represented with 10 bits). In addition to the inefficiency of storage, arithmetic on binary coded decimal (BCD) numbers is much more complex than that on binary, and thus BCD is only used internally in small systems requiring limited computation.

We have already discussed the simplest code, using the first 10 binary numbers to represent the 10 digits. The remaining 4-bit binary numbers (1010, 1011, 1100, 1101, 1110, 1111) are unused. This code, and those in the next two columns of Table 1.7 are referred to as *weighted codes,* since the value represented is computed by taking the sum of each digit times its weight. This first code is referred to as the 8421 code, since those are the weights of the bits. Each decimal digit is represented by

$$8 \times a_3 + 4 \times a_2 + 2 \times a_1 + 1 \times a_0$$

It is also referred to as straight binary. Two other weighted codes (5421 and 2421) that are occasionally used are shown next.

Two other codes that are not weighted are shown in the Table 1.7. The first is *excess 3* (XS3) where the decimal digit is represented by the binary equivalent of 3 more than the digit. For example, 0 is stored as the binary 3 (0011) and 6 as the binary of $6 + 3 = 9$ (1001). The final column shows a 2 of 5 code, where each digit is represented by a 5-bit number, 2 of which are 1 (and the remaining 3 bits are 0). This provides some error detection capabilities, since if an error is made in just one of the bits (during storage or transmission), the result will contain either one or three 1's and can be detected as an error.

Note that in both the 5421 and 2421 codes, other combinations can be used to represent some of the digits (such as 0101 for 5). However, those shown in the table are the standard representations; the others are included in the unused category.

Each of the representations has advantages in various applications. For example, if signed (10's complement) numbers were stored, the first digit of that number would be in the range 5 to 9 for negative numbers. In the 5421, 2421, and excess 3 codes, that would correspond to the first bit of the number being 1. (We would only need to check 1 bit to determine if a number is negative.) In the 8421 code, however, more complex logic is required, since the first bit might be either 0 or 1 for negative numbers. In both 5421 and excess 3 codes, the 10's complement is computed by complementing each bit and adding 1 (as in two's complement). The process is more complex using the other codes. We will make use of some of these codes in later examples.

[SP 11, 12; EX 11, 12]

1.1.6 Other Codes

There are other codes that appear in the digital world. Alphanumeric information is transmitted using the American Standard Code for Information Interchange (ASCII). Seven digits are used to represent the various characters on the standard keyboard as well as a number of control signals (such as carriage return). Table 1.8 lists the printable codes. (Codes beginning with 00 are for control signals.)

Table 1.8 ASCII code.

$a_3a_2a_1a_0$	$a_6a_5a_4$					
	010	**011**	**100**	**101**	**110**	**111**
0000	space	0	@	P	`	p
0001	!	1	A	Q	a	q
0010	"	2	B	R	b	r
0011	#	3	C	S	c	s
0100	$	4	D	T	d	t
0101	%	5	E	U	e	u
0110	&	6	F	V	f	v
0111	'	7	G	W	g	w
1000	(	8	H	X	h	x
1001	)	9	I	Y	i	y
1010	*	:	J	Z	j	z
1011	+	;	K	[	k	{
1100	,	<	L	\	l		
1101	-	=	M	]	m	}
1110	.	>	N	^	n	~
1111	/	?	O	_	o	delete

This allows one to code anything that can be printed from the standard keyboard. For example, *Logic* would be coded

1001100	1101111	1100111	1101001	1100011
L	o	g	i	c

In a *Gray code*, consecutive numbers differ in only one bit. Table 1.9 shows a 4-bit Gray code sequence.

Table 1.9 Gray code.

Number	Gray code	Number	Gray code
0	0000	8	1100
1	0001	9	1101
2	0011	10	1111
3	0010	11	1110
4	0110	12	1010
5	0111	13	1011
6	0101	14	1001
7	0100	15	1000

A Gray code is particularly useful in coding the position of a continuous device. As the device moves from one section to the next, only 1 bit of the code changes. If there is some uncertainty as to the exact position, only 1 bit is in doubt. If a normal binary code were used, all 4 bits would change as it moved from 7 to 8.

The *Hamming code* (proposed by Richard Hamming in 1950) is a single error-correcting code. Check bits are added to the information bits so that if at most 1 bit is changed in transmission or storage, the original value can be restored. The simplest organization is to number the bits starting at 1; those bits that are a power of 2 (1, 2, 4, 8) are check bits. The pattern of checking is shown below for 4 information bits and 3 check bits:

	a_1	a_2	a_3	a_4	a_5	a_6	a_7
Bit 1	X		X		X		X
Bit 2		X	X			X	X
Bit 4				X	X	X	X

The check bit is chosen so that the total number of 1's in the bits selected is even. (This is referred to as a *parity* check.) Thus,

$$a_1 = a_3 \oplus a_5 \oplus a_7$$
$$a_2 = a_3 \oplus a_6 \oplus a_7$$
$$a_4 = a_5 \oplus a_6 \oplus a_7$$

Table 1.10 shows the 16 coded words.

Table 1.10 Hamming Code.

Data\Bit	a_1	a_2	a_3	a_4	a_5	a_6	a_7
0000	0	0	0	0	0	0	0
0001	1	1	0	1	0	0	1
0010	0	1	0	1	0	1	0
0011	1	0	0	0	0	1	1
0100	1	0	0	1	1	0	0
0101	0	1	0	0	1	0	1
0110	1	1	0	0	1	1	0
0111	0	0	0	1	1	1	1
1000	1	1	1	0	0	0	0
1001	0	0	1	1	0	0	1
1010	1	0	1	1	0	1	0
1011	0	1	1	0	0	1	1
1100	0	1	1	1	1	0	0
1101	1	0	1	0	1	0	1
1110	0	0	1	0	1	1	0
1111	1	1	1	1	1	1	1

When a word is received, the same bits are checked:

$$e_1 = a_1 \oplus a_3 \oplus a_5 \oplus a_7$$
$$e_2 = a_2 \oplus a_3 \oplus a_6 \oplus a_7$$
$$e_4 = a_4 \oplus a_5 \oplus a_6 \oplus a_7$$

If no errors were made, all three computations would produce 0. If one error was made, the checks produce the number of the bit in error,

$$4\,e_4 + 2\,e_2 + e_1.$$

(Multiple errors will be misinterpreted.)

EXAMPLE 1.24

Received: 0010011

$$e_1 = 0 \qquad e_2 = 1 \qquad e_4 = 0$$

Bit 2 (a check bit) is in error. The correct word is 0110011, the data is 1011.
Received: 1101101

$$e_1 = 1 \qquad e_2 = 0 \qquad e_4 = 1$$

Bit 5 is in error. The correct word is 1101001, the data is 0001.

With n check bits (where $n \geq 2$), there can be $2^n - n - 1$ information bits.

Check bits	Data bits
2	1
3	4
4	11
5	26

[SP 13, 14; EX 13, 14]

1.2 THE DESIGN PROCESS FOR COMBINATIONAL SYSTEMS

We are now ready to develop the tools needed to design combinational systems. We will concentrate first on rather small systems, which will enable us to better understand the process. We will look at somewhat larger problems in Chapter 5.

In this section, we will outline the process to be used to design combinational systems. (A similar process will be developed in Chapter 7 for sequential systems.) The design process typically starts with a problem statement, a verbal description of the intended system. The goal is to develop a block diagram of that system, utilizing available components and meeting the design objectives and constraints.

We will use the following five examples to illustrate the steps in the design process and, indeed, continue to follow some of them in subsequent chapters, as we develop the tools necessary to do that design.

Continuing Examples (CE)

CE1. A system with four inputs, A, B, C, and D, and one output, Z, such that Z = 1 iff three of the inputs are 1.

CE2. A single light (that can be on or off) that can be controlled by any one of three switches. One switch is the master on/off switch. If it is down, the lights are off. When the master switch is up, a change in the position of one of the other switches (from up to down or from down to up) will cause the light to change state.

CE3. A system to do 1 bit of binary addition. It has three inputs (the 2 bits to be added plus the carry from the next lower order bit) and produces two outputs, a sum bit and a carry to the next higher order position.

CE4. A display driver; a system that has as its input the code for a decimal digit, and produces as its output the signals to drive a seven-segment display, such as those on most digital watches and numeric displays (more later).

CE5. A system with nine inputs, representing two 4-bit binary numbers and a carry input, and one 5-bit output, representing the sum. (Each input number can range from 0 to 15; the output can range from 0 to 31.)

Step 1: Represent each of the inputs and outputs in binary.

Sometimes, as in CE1, 3, and 5, the problem statement is already given in terms of binary inputs and outputs. Other times, it is up to the designer. In CE2, we need to create a numeric equivalence for each of the inputs and outputs. We might code the light on as a 1 output and off as 0. (We could just as well have used the opposite definition, as long as we are coordinated with the light designer.) Similarly, we will define a switch in the up position as a 1 input and down as 0. For CE4, the input is a decimal digit. We must determine what BCD code is to be used. That might be provided for us by whoever is providing the input, or we may have the ability to specify it in such a way as to make our system simplest. We must also code the output; we need to know the details of the display and whether a 1 or a 0 lights each segment. (We will discuss those details in Section 1.4.) In general, the different input and output representations may result in a significant difference in the amount of logic required.

Step 2: Formalize the design specification either in the form of a *truth table* or of an *algebraic expression*.

We will concentrate on the idea of a truth table here and leave the development of algebraic expressions for Chapter 2. The truth table format is the most common result of Step 2 of the design process. A *truth table* is a listing of all the possible input combinations and the value of each of the outputs for each of these input combinations. We can do this in a digital system because each of the inputs only takes on one of two values (0 or 1). Thus, if we have n inputs, there are 2^n input combinations and thus the truth table has 2^n rows. These rows are normally written in binary order (if, for no other reason, than to make sure that we do not leave any out). The truth table has two sets of columns—n input columns, one for each input variable, and m output columns, one for each of the m outputs.

An example of a truth table with two inputs, A and B, and one output, Y, is shown as Table 1.11, where there are two input columns, one output column, and $2^2 = 4$ rows (not including the title row). We will look at truth tables for some of the continuing examples shortly, after presenting the other steps of the design process.

Table 1.11 A two-input truth table.

A	B	Y
0	0	0
0	1	1
1	0	1
1	1	1

> **Step 1.5:** If necessary, break the problem into smaller subproblems.

This step is listed here because sometimes it is possible to do this after having developed the truth table and sometimes, we must really break up the problem before we can even begin to do such a table.

It is not possible to apply most of the design techniques that we will develop to very large problems. Even CE5, the 4-bit adder, has nine inputs and would thus require a truth table of $2^9 = 512$ rows with nine input columns and five output columns. Although we can easily produce the entries for any line of that table, the table would spread over several pages and be very cumbersome. Furthermore, the minimization techniques of Chapters 2 through 4 would be strained. The problem becomes completely unmanageable if we go to a realistic adder for a computer—say one that adds 32-bit numbers. There the table would be 2^{64} lines long, even without a carry input (approximately 1.84×10^{19}). (That means that if we were to write one million lines on each page and put one million pages in a book, we would still need over 18 million volumes to list the entire truth table. Or, if we had a computer that could process one billion lines of the truth table per second (somewhat faster than today's technology), it would still take over 584 years to process the whole table.)

Obviously, we have been able to solve such problems. In the case of the adder, we can imitate how we do it by hand, namely, add 1 bit at a time producing 1 bit of the sum and the carry to the next bit. That is the problem proposed in CE3; it only requires an eight line truth table. We can build 32 such systems and connect them together.

Also, it is often most economical to take advantage of subsystems that already have been implemented. For example, we can buy the 4-bit adder described in CE5 (on a single integrated circuit chip). We might want to use that as a component in our design. We will examine this part of the design process further in Chapter 5.

> **Step 3:** Simplify the description.

The truth table will lead directly to an implementation in some technologies (see, for example, the ROM in Chapter 5). More often, we must convert that to an algebraic form in order to implement it. But the algebraic form we get from the truth table tends to lead to rather complex systems. Thus, we will develop techniques for reducing the complexity of algebraic expressions in Chapters 2 through 4.

> **Step 4:** Implement the system with the available components, subject to the design objectives and constraints.

A *gate* is a network with one output. Most of the implementations of Chapters 2 and 3 use gates as the components. The truth table used to illustrate Step 2 describes the behavior of one type of gate, a two-input OR gate. The final form of the solution may be a block diagram of the gate implementation, where the OR gate is usually depicted by the symbol of Figure 1.3. We may build it in the laboratory using integrated circuit packages that contain a few such gates or we may simulate it on a computer. We will discuss each of these in more detail later.

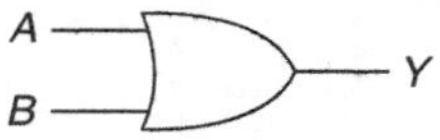

As mentioned earlier, more complex components, such as adders and decoders, may be available as building blocks, in addition to (or in place of) gates. (Of course, when we get to sequential systems, we will introduce storage devices and other larger building blocks.)

The design objective is often to build the least expensive circuit. That usually corresponds to the simplest algebraic expression, although not always. Since gates are usually obtained in packages (say 4 two-input OR gates in a package), the cost may be measured in terms of the number of packages. Thus, whether we need one of the four gates in a package, or all four, the cost would be the same. Sometimes, one of the objectives is speed, that is, to build as fast a circuit as possible. As we will see later, each time a signal passes through a gate, there is a small delay, slowing down the system. Thus, if speed is a factor, we may have a limit on the number of gates any one signal must pass through.

Figure 1.3 OR gate symbol.

Table 1.12 A truth table with a don't care.

a	b	f
0	0	0
0	1	1
1	0	1
1	1	X

Table 1.13 Acceptable truth tables.

a	b	f_1	f_2
0	0	0	0
0	1	1	1
1	0	1	1
1	1	0	1

1.3   DON'T CARE CONDITIONS

Before we can develop the truth table for the BCD example (CE4), we must understand the concept of the *don't care*. In some systems, the value of the output is specified for only some of the input conditions. (Such functions are sometimes referred to as *incompletely specified functions*.) For the remaining input combinations, it does not matter what the output is, that is, we don't care. In a truth table, don't cares are indicated by an X. (Some of the literature uses d, ϕ, or φ.) Table 1.12 is such a truth table.

This table states that the f must be 0 when a and b are 0, that it must be 1 when $a = 0$ and $b = 1$ or when $a = 1$ and $b = 0$, and that it does not matter what f is when a and b are both 1. In other words, either f_1 or f_2 of Table 1.13 are acceptable.

When we design a system with don't cares, we may make the output either 0 or 1 for each don't care input combination. In the example of Table 1.13, that means that we can implement either f_1 or f_2. One of these might be much less costly to implement. If there are several don't cares, the number of acceptable solutions greatly increases, since each can be either 0 or 1, independently. The techniques we develop in Chapters 3 and 4 handle don't cares very easily; they do not require solving separate problems.

In real systems, don't cares occur in several ways. First, there may be some input combinations that never occur. That is the case in CE4, where the input is the code for a decimal digit; there are only 10 possible input combinations. If a 4-bit code is used, then six of the input combinations never occur. When we build a system, we can design it such that the output would be either 0 or 1 for each of these don't care combinations, since that input never happens.

A second place where don't cares occur is in the design of one system to drive a second system. Consider the block diagram of Figure 1.4. We are designing System One to make System Two behave in a certain way. There will be occasions when, for certain values of A, B, and C, System Two will behave the same way whether J is 0 or 1. In that case, the output J of System One is a don't care for that input combination. We will see this behavior arise in Chapter 6, where System Two is a flip flop (a binary storage device).

Figure 1.4   Design example with don't cares.

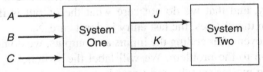

We will see a third kind of don't care in CE4; we may really not care what one of the outputs is.

1.4 THE DEVELOPMENT OF TRUTH TABLES

Given a word problem, the first step is to decide how to code the inputs. Then, the development of a truth table is usually rather straightforward. The number of inputs determines the number of rows and the major problem generally revolves about the ambiguity of English (or any natural language).

For CE1, a 16 row truth table is required. There are four input columns and one output column. (In Table 1.14, there are actually three output columns shown, Z_1, Z_2, and Z_3 to account for the three interpretations of the problem statement.) There is little room for controversy on the behavior of the system for the first 15 rows of the table. If there are

Table 1.14 Truth table for CE1.

A	B	C	D	Z_1	Z_2	Z_3
0	0	0	0	0	0	0
0	0	0	1	0	0	0
0	0	1	0	0	0	0
0	0	1	1	0	0	0
0	1	0	0	0	0	0
0	1	0	1	0	0	0
0	1	1	0	0	0	0
0	1	1	1	1	1	1
1	0	0	0	0	0	0
1	0	0	1	0	0	0
1	0	1	0	0	0	0
1	0	1	1	1	1	1
1	1	0	0	0	0	0
1	1	0	1	1	1	1
1	1	1	0	1	1	1
1	1	1	1	0	1	X

less than three 1's on the input lines, the output is 0. If three of the inputs are 1 and the other is 0, then the output is 1. The only question in completing the table is in relation to the last row. Does "three of the inputs are 1" mean *exactly* three or does it mean at *least* three? If the former is true, then the last line of the truth table is 0, as shown for Z_1. If the latter is true, then the last line of the table is 1, as shown in Z_2. Two other options, both shown as Z_3, are that we know that all four inputs will not be 1 simultaneously, and that we do not care what the output is if all four inputs are 1. In those cases, the last entry is don't care, X.

For CE2, even after coding the inputs and outputs, we do not have a unique solution to the problem. We will label the switches a, b, and c (where a is the master switch) and use a 1 to represent up (and a 0 for down). The light output is labeled f (where a 1 on f means that the light is on). When $a = 0$, the light is off (0), no matter what the value of b and c. The problem statement does not specify the output when $a = 1$; it only specifies what effect a change in the other inputs will have. We still have two possible solutions to this problem. If we assume that switches b and c in the down position cause the light to be off, then the fifth row of the table (100) will have an output of 0, as shown in Table 1.15a. When one of these switches is up (101, 110), then the light must be on. From either of these states, changing b or c will either return the system to the 100 input state or move it to state 111; for this, the output is 0.

We could have started with some other fixed value, such as switches b and c up means that the light is on or that switches b and c down means that the light is on. Either of these would produce the truth table of Table 1.15b, which is equally acceptable.

We have already developed the truth table for CE3, the 1-bit binary full adder, in Section 1.1.2, Table 1.5 (although we did not refer to it as a truth table at that time).

Table 1.15 Truth tables for CE2.

a	b	c	f		a	b	c	f
0	0	0	0		0	0	0	0
0	0	1	0		0	0	1	0
0	1	0	0		0	1	0	0
0	1	1	0		0	1	1	0
1	0	0	0		1	0	0	1
1	0	1	1		1	0	1	0
1	1	0	1		1	1	0	0
1	1	1	0		1	1	1	1

(a)		(b)

Although we could easily construct a truth table for CE5, the 4-bit adder, we would need 512 rows. Furthermore, once we had done this, we would still find it nearly impossible to simplify the function by hand (that is, without the aid of a computer). We will defer further discussion of this problem to Chapter 5.

We will now examine the display driver of CE 4. The first thing we must do is to choose a code for the decimal digit. That will (obviously) affect the table and, indeed, make a significant difference in the cost of the implementation. We will call the binary inputs W, X, Y, and Z and the outputs a, b, c, d, e, f, and g. For the sake of this example, we will assume that decimal digits are stored in the 8421 code. (We will look at variations on this in Chapter 5.)

The next thing we need to know is whether the display requires a 0 or 1 on each segment input to light that segment. Both types of displays exist. In the solution presented in Table 1.16, we assume that a 1 is needed to light a segment.

The display has seven inputs, labeled a, b, c, d, e, f, g, one for each of the segments. A block diagram of the system is shown in Figure 1.5, along with the layout of the display and how each digit is displayed. The solid lines represent segments to be lit and the dashed ones segments that are not lit for that digit. Note that there are alternate displays for the

Figure 1.5 A seven-segment display.

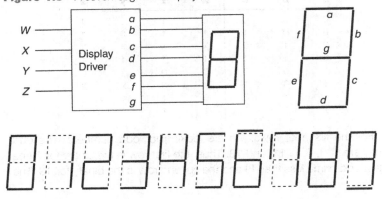

digits 6, 7, and 9. For 6, sometimes segment a is lit, and sometimes it is not. The design specification might state that it must be lit or that it must not be lit or that it doesn't matter; choose whatever is easier. The latter is the choice shown in Table 1.16. We will return to this problem in Chapter 5.

Table 1.16   A truth table for the seven-segment display driver.

Digit	W	X	Y	Z	a	b	c	d	e	f	g
0	0	0	0	0	1	1	1	1	1	1	0
1	0	0	0	1	0	1	1	0	0	0	0
2	0	0	1	0	1	1	0	1	1	0	1
3	0	0	1	1	1	1	1	1	0	0	1
4	0	1	0	0	0	1	1	0	0	1	1
5	0	1	0	1	1	0	1	1	0	1	1
6	0	1	1	0	X	0	1	1	1	1	1
7	0	1	1	1	1	1	1	0	0	X	0
8	1	0	0	0	1	1	1	1	1	1	1
9	1	0	0	1	1	1	1	X	0	1	1
—	1	0	1	0	X	X	X	X	X	X	X
—	1	0	1	1	X	X	X	X	X	X	X
—	1	1	0	0	X	X	X	X	X	X	X
—	1	1	0	1	X	X	X	X	X	X	X
—	1	1	1	0	X	X	X	X	X	X	X
—	1	1	1	1	X	X	X	X	X	X	X

EXAMPLE 1.25

As a final example, we want to develop a truth table for a system with three inputs, a, b, and c, and four outputs, w, x, y, z. The output is a binary number equal to the largest integer that meets the input conditions:

$a = 0$: odd	$a = 1$: even
$b = 0$: prime	$b = 1$: not prime
$c = 0$: less than 8	$c = 1$: greater than or equal to 8

Some inputs may never occur; the output is never all 0's.
(A prime is a number that is only evenly divisible by itself and 1.) A truth table for this is shown next.

a	b	c	w	x	y	z
0	0	0	0	1	1	1
0	0	1	1	1	0	1
0	1	0	X	X	X	X
0	1	1	1	1	1	1
1	0	0	0	0	1	0
1	0	1	X	X	X	X
1	1	0	0	1	1	0
1	1	1	1	1	1	0

For the first four rows, we are looking for odd numbers. The odd primes are 1, 3, 5, 7, 11, and 13. Thus, the first row is the binary for 7 (the largest odd prime less than 8) and the second row is the binary for 13. The next two rows contain nonprimes. All odd numbers less than 8 are prime; therefore, the input is never 010 and the outputs are don't cares. Finally, 9 and 15 are odd nonprimes; 15 is larger. For the second half of the table, the only even prime is 2; thus, 101 never occurs. The larger even nonprimes are 6 and 14.

[SP 15, 16; EX 15, 16]

1.5 THE LABORATORY

Although the material in this text can be studied without any practical examples, implementing some systems in the laboratory greatly aids the learning process. We include, in Appendix A, the description of four platforms and a set of laboratory exercises that can be performed on each.

The traditional laboratory involves wiring logic blocks and probing them with meters or displaying the signals with lights. In Appendix A.1, we will introduce the features of the IDL-800 Digital Lab[5]. It provides switches, pulsers, and clock signals for inputs, and a set of lights and two seven-segment displays for outputs. There is a place to put a breadboard and to plug in a number of integrated circuit packages (such as those described throughout the text). Also, power supplies and meters are built in. It is not necessary to have access to this system to execute the experiments; but it does have everything needed in one place (except the integrated circuit packages and the wires for connectors). Students should build some of the circuits that they have designed and test them, by applying various inputs and checking that the correct output is produced. For small numbers of inputs, try all input combinations (the complete truth table). For larger numbers of inputs, the 4-bit adder, for example, a sample of the inputs is adequate as long as the sample is chosen in such a way as to exercise all of the circuit. (For example, adding many pairs of small numbers is not adequate, since it does not test the high-order part of the adder.)

We will also introduce, in Appendix A.2, a breadboard simulator (MacBreadboard and WinBreadboard[6,7]). It contains switches, pulsers, a clock signal, and lights, very much like the hardware laboratory. Integrated circuits can be placed on the breadboard and wires "connected."

The computer-aided laboratory allows one to build a simulation of the circuit on a computer and test it. We will introduce the basics of LogicWorks 4[8] in Appendix A.3, enough to allow us to "build" and test the various circuits discussed in the text. The system has available individual gates, as well as all of the standard integrated circuit packages that are discussed in the text (and many others). A complete description of

---

[5]Manufactured by K & H Mfg. Co., Ltd.

[6]A trademark of Yoeric Software.

[7]Copies of WinBreadboard and Altera tools are included on the CD accompanying this text.

[8]A trademark of Capilano Computing Systems, Ltd.

LogicWorks, including a CD-ROM for either Windows or Macintosh is available through Prentice Hall.

In Appendix A.4, we will introduce the Altera[9] schematic capture tool, MAX+plusII. Like LogicWorks 4, it allows us to draw circuits and test them. It has an excellent tool for creating test waveforms.

Appendix A.5 contains a set of 25 experiments (keyed to the appropriate chapter) that can be performed on each of the platforms.

Finally, Appendix A.6 contains the pinouts for all of the integrated circuits discussed in the text and the experiments.

1.6 SOLVED PROBLEMS

1. Convert the following positive binary numbers to decimal.
   a. 110100101
   b. 00010111

   a. $110100101 = 1 + 4 + 32 + 128 + 256 = 421$
   Starting the evaluation from right (1's position) to left (2^8 position). (There are 0's in the 2, 8, 16, and 64 bits.)
   b. $00010111 = 1 + 2 + 4 + 16 = 23$
   Leading 0's do not change the result.

2. Convert the following decimal numbers to binary. Assume all numbers are unsigned (positive) and represented by 12 bits.
   a. 47
   b. 98
   c. 5000
   d. 3163

   a. 47

$47 < 64$	**Thus** no 2^6 bit or greater	
$47 - 32 = 15$	gives a 2^5 bit	
$15 < 16$	no 2^4 bit	
$15 - 8 = 7$	2^3 bit	
$7 = 111$	thus last 3 bits are 111	

   $47 = 000000101111$

   b. 98

$98/2 = 49$	remainder $= 0$		0
$49/2 = 24$	remainder $= 1$		10
$24/2 = 12$	remainder $= 0$		010
$12/2 = 6$	**remainder $= 0$**		0010
$6/2 = 3$	remainder $= 0$		00010
$3/2 = 1$	remainder $= 1$		100010
$1/2 = 0$	remainder $= 1$		1100010

---

[9]Altera Corporation. For a more complete description of the Altera Tool Set, see Brown & Vranesic, "Fundamentals of Digital Logic with VHDL Design," McGraw Hill, 2000.

We could keep dividing 0 by 2 and getting remainders of 0 until we had 12 bits or recognize that the leading bits must be 0.

$98 = 000001100010$

As in part a, we could have stopped dividing when we recognized the number, say that $12 = 1100$. We would take what we had already found, the three least significant bits of 010 and put the binary for 12 ahead of that, getting the same answer, of course, 1100010 (with enough leading 0's to make up the appropriate number of bits).

c. 5000: cannot represent in 12 bits, since $5000 > 2^{12}$.

d. We can first convert to octal

$3163/8 = 395$	remainder $= 3$	3
$395/8 = 49$	remainder $= 3$	33
$49/8 = 6$	remainder $= 1$	133
$6/8 = 0$	remainder $= 6$	6133

That becomes

110001011011

---

3. Convert the following to

    i. octal

    ii. hexadecimal

a. 11010110111_2

b. 611_{10}

a. Leading 0's are added when necessary to make the number of bits a multiple of 3 for octal and 4 for hexadecimal.

    i. 011   010   110   111 $= 3267_8$

    ii. 0110   1011   0111 $= 6B7_{16}$

b.
  i.

$611/8 = 76$	rem 3	3
$76/8 = 9$	rem 4	43
$9/8 = 1$	rem 1	143
$1/8 = 0$	rem 1	1143

  ii.

$611/16 = 38$	rem 3	3
$38/16 = 2$	rem 6	63
$2/16 = 0$	rem 2	263

---

4. Convert the following to decimal

a. 2170_8

b. $1C3_{16}$

a. $0 + 7 \times 8 + 8^2 + 2 \times 8^3 = 56 + 64 + 1024 = 1144$

b. $3 + 12 \times 16 + 16^2 = 3 + 192 + 256 = 451$

5. Compute the sum of the following pairs of 6-bit unsigned numbers. If the answer is to be stored in a 6-bit location, indicate which of the sums produces overflow. Also, show the decimal equivalent of the problem.

a. $001011 + 011010$

b. $101111 + 000001$

c. $101010 + 010101$

d. $101010 + 100011$

a.

		0		1 0		0 1
11		0 0 1 0 1 1		0 0 1 0 1 1		0 0 1 0 1 1
26		0 1 1 0 1 0		0 1 1 0 1 0		0 1 1 0 1 0
37		1		0 1		1 0 1

	1 0		1 1		1
	0 0 1 0 1 1		0 0 1 0 1 1		0 0 1 0 1 1
	0 1 1 0 1 0		0 1 1 0 1 0		0 1 1 0 1 0
	0 1 0 1		0 0 1 0 1		0 1 0 0 1 0 1 = 37

Note that in this case the last carry result is 0 (it is shown as part of the sum) and thus the answer does fit in 6 bits (there is no overflow).

b.

	0 1 1 1 1	(carries)
	1 0 1 1 1 1	47
	0 0 0 0 0 1	1
	0 1 1 0 0 0 0	48

c.

	0 0 0 0 0	
	1 0 1 0 1 0	42
	0 1 0 1 0 1	21
	0 1 1 1 1 1 1	63

d.

	0 0 0 1 0		
	1 0 1 0 1 0	42	
	1 0 0 0 1 1	35	
	1 0 0 1 1 0 1	77	overflow (looks like 13)

Note that the answer is larger than 63, which is the largest 6-bit number.

6. The following decimal numbers are to be stored in a 6-bit two's complement format. Show how they are stored.

a. $+14$

b. -20

c. 37

a. $+14 = 001110$ Positive numbers are just converted to binary.

b. -20: $+20 = 010100$

Complement every bit 101011

Add 1 $\underline{1}$

$-20 \Rightarrow 101100$

c. 37: Cannot be stored, the range of 6-bit numbers is $-32 \leq n \leq 31$. Converting 37 to binary would give 100101, but that represents a negative number.

7. The following 6-bit two's complement numbers were found in a computer. What decimal number do they represent?

a. 001011

b. 111010

a. 001011: Since it begins with 0, it is positive $= 1 + 2 + 8 = 11$

b. 111010: Since it begins with a 1, it is negative; take two's complement: 000101

$\underline{1}$

$000110 = 6$

Thus $111010 \Rightarrow -6$

8. Each of the following pairs of signed (two's complement) numbers are stored in computer words (6 bits). Compute the sum as it is stored in a 6-bit computer word. Show the decimal equivalents of each operand and the sum. Indicate if there is overflow.

a. $111111 + 001011$

b. $001001 + 100100$

c. $001001 + 010011$

d. $001010 + 011000$

e. $111010 + 110001$

f. $101001 + 110001$

g. $110101 + 001011$

a. 111111 -1

$\underline{001011}$ $+11$ The carry out is ignored and will not

(1) 001010 $+10$ be shown in the remaining examples.

b. 001001 $+9$

$\underline{100100}$ -28

101101 -19

c. 001001 $+9$

$\underline{010011}$ $+19$

011100 $+28$

d.   0 0 1 0 1 0   +10
         0 1 1 0 0 0   +24
         1 0 0 0 1 0   looks like −30; should be +34; overflow
                       sum of two positive numbers looks
                       negative

e.   1 1 1 0 1 0   −6
         1 1 0 0 0 1   −15
         1 0 1 0 1 1   −21

f.   1 0 1 0 0 1   −23
         1 1 0 0 0 1   −15
         0 1 1 0 1 0   looks like +26; should be −38; overflow
                       sum of two negative numbers looks
                       positive

g.   1 1 0 1 0 1   −11
         0 0 1 0 1 1   +11
         0 0 0 0 0 0   0

9. Subtract each of the following pairs of unsigned numbers.
   a. 0 0 1 1 0 1 − 0 0 0 1 1 0
   b. 1 1 0 1 0 1 − 0 0 0 0 1 1
   c. 0 0 0 1 1 1 − 0 1 0 0 1 1

   a. (This example is the same for either signed or unsigned
   numbers.)

	1	
0 0 1 1 0 1	0 0 1 1 0 1	13
− 0 0 0 1 1 0	1 1 1 0 0 1	−6
	(1) 0 0 0 1 1 1	7

   b.

	1	
1 1 0 1 0 1	1 1 0 1 0 1	53
− 0 0 0 0 1 1	1 1 1 1 0 0	−3
	(1) 1 1 0 0 1 0	50

   c.

	1	
0 0 0 1 1 1	0 0 0 1 1 1	7
− 0 1 0 0 1 1	1 0 1 1 0 0	−19
	(0) 1 1 0 1 0 0	overflow, answer negative

10. Subtract each of the following pairs of signed numbers.
    a. 1 1 0 1 0 1 − 0 0 0 0 1 1
    b. 1 1 0 1 0 1 − 0 1 1 0 0 0
    c. 0 1 0 0 0 0 − 1 0 0 1 0 0

a.
$$
\begin{array}{r}
1 \\
1\,1\,0\,1\,0\,1 \\
-0\,0\,0\,0\,1\,1 \\
\end{array}
\qquad
\begin{array}{r}
1\,1\,0\,1\,0\,1 \\
1\,1\,1\,1\,0\,0 \\
\hline
(1)\ 1\,1\,0\,0\,1\,0
\end{array}
\qquad
\begin{array}{r}
-11 \\
-(+3) \\
\hline
-14
\end{array}
$$

Note that this is the same binary number as in Solved Problem 9b.

b.
$$
\begin{array}{r}
1 \\
1\,1\,0\,1\,0\,1 \\
-0\,1\,1\,0\,0\,0 \\
\end{array}
\qquad
\begin{array}{r}
1\,1\,0\,1\,0\,1 \\
1\,0\,0\,1\,1\,1 \\
\hline
(1)\ 0\,1\,1\,1\,0\,1
\end{array}
\qquad
\begin{array}{l}
-11 \\
-(+24) \\
\hline
\text{overflow, answer looks} \\
\text{positive}
\end{array}
$$

c.
$$
\begin{array}{r}
1 \\
0\,1\,0\,0\,0\,0 \\
-1\,0\,0\,1\,0\,0 \\
\end{array}
\qquad
\begin{array}{r}
0\,1\,0\,0\,0\,0 \\
0\,1\,1\,0\,1\,1 \\
\hline
(0)\ 1\,0\,1\,1\,0\,0
\end{array}
\qquad
\begin{array}{l}
16 \\
-(-28) \\
\hline
\text{overflow, answer looks} \\
\text{negative}
\end{array}
$$

11. We have a computer that can store 3 decimal digits. How are the following two numbers stored in each of the five codes?

   a. 491

   b. 27

   a. 8421   0100 1001 0001

       5421   0100 1100 0001

       2421   0100 1111 0001

       XS3   0111 1100 0100

       2 of 5   01100 00011 10100

   Note that the first four codes require 12-bit words; the 2 of 5 code requires 15-bit words.

   b. 8421   0000 0010 0111

       5421   0000 0010 1010

       2421   0000 0010 1101

       XS3   0011 0101 1010

       2 of 5   11000 10010 00110

12. We have the following numbers stored in a computer. What is the decimal value represented if the number is stored as

   i. BCD 8421   iv. BCD excess 3

   ii. BCD 5421   v. Binary unsigned

   iii. BCD 2421   vi. Binary signed

   a. 1000 0111

   b. 0011 0100

   c. 1100 1001

a. 1000 0111

i. BCD 8421	87	
ii. BCD 5421	−	0111 not used
iii. BCD 2421	−	1000, 0111 not used
iv. BCD excess 3	54	
v. Binary unsigned	135	
vi. Binary signed	−121	

b. 0011 0100

i. BCD 8421	34
ii. BCD 5421	34
iii. BCD 2421	34
iv. BCD excess 3	01
v. Binary unsigned	52
vi. Binary signed	+52

c. 1100 1001

i. BCD 8421	−	1100 not used
ii. BCD 5421	96	
iii. BCD 2421	−	1001 not used
iv. BCD excess 3	96	
v. Binary unsigned	201	
vi. Binary signed	−55	

13. a. Code the following into ASCII.

    i. HELLO

    ii. hello

b. Translate the following into English.

    i. 1011001 1100101 1110011 0100001

    ii. 0110010 0101011 0110001 0111101 0110011

a.   i. 1001000 1000101 1001100 1001100 1001111

    ii. 1101000 1100101 1101100 1101100 1101111

b.   i. Yes!

    ii. 2+1=3

14. Using the version of the Hamming Code shown

a. Code the following data

    i. 1000

    ii. 0011

b. If the following word was received, what word was sent (assuming no more than a single error)?

    i. 1111011

    ii. 1111010

a.   i. **1110000**

     ii. **1000011**

b.   i. $e_1 = 1 \oplus 1 \oplus 0 \oplus 1 = 1$

        $e_2 = 1 \oplus 1 \oplus 1 \oplus 1 = 0$

        $e_4 = 1 \oplus 0 \oplus 1 \oplus 1 = 1$

   bit 5 error, word sent 1111111, data sent 1111

     ii. $e_1 = 1 \oplus 1 \oplus 0 \oplus 0 = 0$

        $e_2 = 1 \oplus 1 \oplus 1 \oplus 0 = 1$

        $e_4 = 1 \oplus 0 \oplus 1 \oplus 0 = 0$

   bit 2 error, word sent 1011010, data sent 1010

15. For each of the following problems, there are four inputs, A, B, C, and D. Show a truth table for the functions specified. (One truth table with four outputs is shown for the four examples.)

a. The inputs represent a 4-bit unsigned binary number. The output, W, is 1 if and only if the number is a multiple of 2 or of 3 but not both.

b. The inputs represent a 4-bit positive binary number. The output, X, is 0 if and only if the input is a prime (where 0 never occurs).

c. The first two inputs (A, B) represent a 2-bit unsigned binary number (in the range 0 to 3). The last two (C, D) represent a second unsigned binary number (in the same range). The output, Y, is 1 if and only if the two numbers differ by two or more.

d. The inputs represent a BCD number in excess 3 code. Those combinations that do not represent one of the digits never occur. The output, Z, is 1 if and only if that number is a perfect square.

The truth table contains the answer to all four parts.

A	B	C	D	W	X	Y	Z
0	0	0	0	0	X	0	X
0	0	0	1	0	0	0	X
0	0	1	0	1	0	1	X
0	0	1	1	1	0	1	1
0	1	0	0	1	1	0	1
0	1	0	1	0	0	0	0
0	1	1	0	0	1	0	0
0	1	1	1	0	0	1	1
1	0	0	0	1	1	1	0
1	0	0	1	1	1	0	0
1	0	1	0	1	1	0	0
1	0	1	1	0	0	0	0
1	1	0	0	0	1	1	1
1	1	0	1	0	0	1	X
1	1	1	0	1	1	0	X
1	1	1	1	1	1	0	X

a. We don't care whether one considers 0 a multiple of 2 or 3, since it is either a multiple of neither or of both. In both cases, $W = 0$. For the next row, 1 is not a multiple of either 2 or 3; thus, $W = 0$. For the next three rows $W = 1$, since 2 and 4 are multiples of 2, but not 3, and 3 is a multiple of 3, but not 2. Both 5 and 7 are multiples of neither and 6 is a multiple of both; thus, for the next three rows, $W = 0$.

b. A prime number is one that is evenly divisible only by 1 or itself. Note that the problem specifies that the output is 0 for primes and is thus 1 for numbers that are not prime. The first nonprime is $4(2 \times 2)$. Indeed, all of the even numbers (other than 2) are nonprimes. Since 0 never occurs, the output is a don't care.

c. For the first four rows, the first number is 0. It is compared on successive rows with 0, 1, 2, and 3. Only 2 and 3 differ from 0 by 2 or more. In the next group of four rows, the first number is 1; it only differs from 3 by 2 or more. In the next four rows, 2 differs only from 0 by 2 or more. Finally, in the last 4 rows, 3 differs from 0 and 1 by 2 or more.

d. A perfect square is an integer obtained by multiplying some integer by itself. Thus, 0, 1, 4, and 9 are perfect squares. Note that the first three rows and the last three rows are all don't cares, since those input combinations never occur.

16. The system is a speed warning device. It receives, on two lines, an indication of the speed limit on the highway. There are three possible values—45, 55, or 65 MPH. It receives from the automobile, on two other lines, an indication of the speed of the vehicle. There are four possible values—under 45, between 46 and 55, between 56 and 65, and over 65 MPH. It produces two outputs. The first, f, indicates whether the car is going above the speed limit. The second, g, indicates that the car is driving at a "dangerous speed"—defined as either over 65 MPH or more than 10 MPH above the speed limit. Show how each of the inputs and outputs are coded (in terms of binary values) and complete the truth table for this system.

The first step is to code the inputs, as shown in the tables below.

Speed limit	a	b	Speed	c	d
45	0	0	<45	0	0
55	0	1	46–55	0	1
65	1	0	56–65	1	0
unused	1	1	>65	1	1

The outputs will be 1 if the car is speeding or driving dangerously.

	a	b	c	d	f	g
	0	0	0	0	0	0
45	0	0	0	1	1	0
	0	0	1	0	1	1
	0	0	1	1	1	1
	0	1	0	0	0	0
55	0	1	0	1	0	0
	0	1	1	0	1	0
	0	1	1	1	1	1
	1	0	0	0	0	0
65	1	0	0	1	0	0
	1	0	1	0	0	0
	1	0	1	1	1	1
	1	1	0	0	X	X
	1	1	0	1	X	X
	1	1	1	0	X	X
	1	1	1	1	X	X

1.7 EXERCISES[10]

1. Convert the following unsigned binary numbers to decimal.

  *a. 11111   e. 10101010

   b. 1000000   f. 000011110000

   c. 1001101101   g. 110011001100

  *d. 101111   *h. 000000000000

2. Convert the following decimal numbers to binary. Assume all numbers are unsigned (positive) and represented by 12 bits.

  *a. 73   c. 402   *e. 1000   *g. 4200

   b. 127   d. 512   f. 17   h. 1365

3. Convert the following to

   i. octal

   ii. hexadecimal

  *a. 100101101011_2 *c. 791_{10}

   b. 10110100000101_2 d. 1600_{10}

4. Convert the following to decimal.

   a. 777_8 *b. 1040_8 c. $ABCD_{16}$ *d. $3FF_{16}$

5. Compute the sum of the following pairs of 6-bit unsigned numbers. If the answer is to be stored in a 6-bit location, indicate which of the sums produce overflow. Also, show the decimal equivalent of both operands and the result.

  *a. 000011 + 001100   c. 011100 + 011010

   b. 010100 + 101101   *d. 110011 + 001110

---

[10]Answers to Exercises marked with an asterisk (∗) are given in Appendix B.

Chapter 1 Introduction

    *e.   001011 + 100111   g.   101100 + 100100

    f.   000101 + 000111

6. The following decimal numbers are to be stored in a 6-bit two's complement format. Show how they are stored.

    *a.   +25   *c.   +32   *e.   −15   g. −1

    b.   0   d.   +15   f.   −45   h. −16

7. The following 6-bit two's complement numbers were found in a computer. What decimal number do they represent?

    a.   000101   *c.   010101   e.   011111   g.   101010

    b.   111111   *d.   100100   f.   111001   *h.   100000

8. We have a computer which stores binary signed numbers in two's complement form. All numbers are 8 bits long.

    a.   What decimal number is represented by 01101011?

    b.   What decimal number is represented by 10101110?

   *c.   How is the number −113 stored?

   *d.   How is the number +143 stored?

    e.   How is the number +43 stored?

    f.   How is the number −43 stored?

9. Each of the following pairs of signed (two's complement) numbers are stored in computer words (6 bits). Compute the sum as it is stored in a 6-bit computer word. Show the decimal equivalents of each operand and the sum. Indicate if there is overflow.

    *a.   110101   c.   001100   e.   011010

          001111   110100   001100

    b.   111010   *d.   101010   *f.   111101

          000111   100110   110000

10. For each of the following pairs of numbers, subtract the second from the first. Show the operands and the answers in decimal, assuming

   i.   the numbers are unsigned

   ii.   the numbers are signed (two's complement).

   Indicate overflow where appropriate.

    a.   010101   *c.   111010   e.   110010

          001100   000111   110111

   *b.   010001   *d.   100100   f.   111010

          011000   011000   101101

11. We have a computer that can store 3 decimal digits. How are each of the following numbers stored in each of the five codes?

   i.   8421   iv.   excess 3

   ii.   5421   v.   2 of 5

   iii.   2421

   *a.   103   b.   999   c.   1   d.   0

12. We have the following numbers stored in a computer. What is the decimal value represented if the number is stored as

    i.   BCD 8421   iv. BCD excess 3
    ii. BCD 5421   v.   binary unsigned
    iii. BCD 2421   vi. binary signed

    a. 1111 1010   *d. 1001 0101
   *b. 0001 1011   e. 1110 1101
    c. 1000 0011   f. 0100 1000

13. a. Code the following into ASCII

    i.   Problem 5   iii. $2 + 1 = 3$
   *ii. "OK"   iv.   ABM

   b. Translate the following into English

    i.   1000001 1101100 1100001 1101110
    ii. 0100100 0110111 0101110 0111001 0110101
   *iii. 0111001 0101111 0110011 0111101 0110011
    iv. 1010100 1101000 1100101 0100000 1100101
            1101110 1100100

14. Using the version of the Hamming code shown

   a. Code the following data

    i.   0000   iii. 0101
   *ii. 1011   iv. 1111

   b. If the following word was received, what word was sent (assuming no more than a single error)?

   *i. 1011010   *iii. 0000110
    ii. 0011010   iv.   1100110

15. Show a truth table for a 1-bit full subtractor that has a borrow input b_{in} and inputs x and y, and produces a difference, d, and a borrow output, b_{out}.

$$b_{in}$$
$$x$$
$$\frac{-y}{b_{out}\ d}$$

16. Show truth tables for each of the following.

   *a. There are four inputs and three outputs. The inputs, w, x, y, z, are codes for the grade that may be received:

0000 A	0100 B−	1000 D+	1100 Incomplete
0001 A−	0101 C+	1001 D	1101 Satisfactory
0010 B+	0110 C	1010 D−	1110 Unsatisfactory
0011 B	0111 C−	1011 F	1111 Pass

The outputs are

    1:   a 1 if and only if the grade is C or better (only letter grades; C− is not C or better)

    2:   a 1 if and only if the university will count it toward the 120 credits required for a degree (passing grade only)

    3:   a 1 if and only if it will be counted in computing a grade point average (letter grades only).

b.   This system has four inputs and three outputs. The first two inputs, a and b, represent a 2-bit binary number (range of 0 to 3). A second binary number (same range) is represented by the other two inputs, c and d. The output f is to be 1 if and only if the two numbers differ by exactly 2. Output g is to be 1 if and only if the numbers are equal. Output h is to be 1 if and only if the second number is larger than the first.

c.   The system has four inputs. The first two, a and b, represent a number in the range 1 to 3 (0 is not used). The other two, c and d, represent a second number in the same range. The output, y, is to be 1 if and only if the first number is greater than the second or the second is 2 greater than the first.

*d.   A system has one output, F, and four inputs, where the first two inputs (A, B) represent one 2-bit binary number (in the range 0 to 3) and the second two inputs (C, D) represent another binary number (same range). F is to be 1 if and only if the two numbers are equal or if they differ by exactly 1.

e.   A system has one output, F, and four inputs, where the first two inputs (A, B) represent one 2-bit binary number (in the range 0 to 3) and the second two inputs (C, D) represent another binary number (same range). F is to be 1 if and only if the sum of the two numbers is odd.

f.   The system has four inputs. The first two, a and b, represent a number in the range 0 to 2 (3 is not used). The other two, c and d, represent a second number in the same range. The output, y, is to be 1 if and only if the two numbers do not differ by more than 1.

g.   The problem is to design a ball and strike counter for baseball. The inputs are how many balls (0, 1, 2, or 3) before this pitch, how many strikes (0, 1, 2) before this pitch, and what happens on this pitch. The outputs are how many balls after this pitch (0, 1, 2, 3, 4) or how many strikes after this pitch (0, 1, 2, 3).

In baseball, there are four outcomes of any pitch (from the point of view of this problem). It can be a strike, a foul ball, a ball, or anything else that will end this batter's turn (such as a hit or a fly out).

A foul ball is considered a strike, except when there are already two strikes, in which case the number of strikes remain 2. The output is to indicate the number of balls and strikes after this pitch (even if the pitch is the fourth ball or the third strike, in which case the batter's turn is over). If the batter's turn is over for any other reason, the output should indicate 0 balls and 0 strikes.

Show the code for the inputs (there are six inputs, two for what happened on that pitch, two for the number of balls, and two for the number of strikes) and for the outputs (there should be 5, 3 for balls and 2 for strikes). Then show the 64 line truth table.

*h. The months of the year are coded in four variables, *abcd*, such that January is 0000, February is 0001, . . . , and December is 1011. The remaining 4 combinations are never used. (Remember: 30 days has September, April, June, and November. All the rest have 31, except February. . . .) Show a truth table for a function, *g*, that is 1 if the month has 31 days and 0 if it does not.

i. The months of the year are coded as in 10h, except that February of a leap year is coded as 1100. Show a truth table with five outputs, v, w, x, y, z that indicates the number of days in the selected month.

j. Repeat 10i, except that the outputs are to be in BCD (8421 code). There are now six outputs, u, v, w, x, y, z (where the first decimal digit is coded 0, 0, u, v and the second digit is coded w, x, y, z).

k. The system has four inputs, $a, b, c,$ and d and one output, f. The last three inputs (b, c, d) represent a binary number, n, in the range 0 to 7; however, the input 0 never occurs. The first input (a) specifies which of two computations is made.

$a = 0$: f is 1 iff n is a multiple of 2

$a = 1$: f is 1 iff n is a multiple of 3

l. The system has four inputs, $a, b, c,$ and d and one output, f. The first two inputs (a, b) represent one binary number (in the range 0 to 3) and the last two (c, d) represent another number in the range 1 to 3 (0 never occurs). The output, f, is to be 1 iff the second number is at least two larger than the first.

1.8   CHAPTER 1 TEST (50 MINUTES)[11]

1. Convert the decimal number 347 to
   a.   binary.
   b.   hexadecimal.
   c.   octal.

   Show your work.

2. Add the two unsigned binary numbers; show both operands and the result in decimal as well as binary. (Be sure to show the carry as you add.) Indicate if there is overflow.

   $$0\ 1\ 0\ 1\ 1 \qquad\qquad 1\ 0\ 1\ 0\ 1\ 1$$
   $$\underline{0\ 1\ 1\ 1\ 0} \qquad\qquad \underline{0\ 1\ 1\ 0\ 0\ 1}$$

3. Show the decimal equivalent of each of the numbers if they are interpeted as (six answers).

   $$1\ 0\ 0\ 1\ 0\ 1\ 0\ 1 \qquad\qquad 0\ 1\ 1\ 1\ 0\ 0\ 1\ 1$$

   a.   Unsigned binary
   b.   Signed binary
   c.   BCD (8421 code)

4. Add the three pairs of signed (two's complement) numbers. Be sure to show the carry as you add. Show both operands and the result of each addition in decimal as well as binary. Indicate if there is overflow.

   $$1\ 1\ 0\ 0 \qquad\qquad 1\ 0\ 1\ 0 \qquad\qquad 0\ 1\ 0\ 1$$
   $$\underline{1\ 1\ 0\ 1} \qquad\qquad \underline{0\ 1\ 1\ 1} \qquad\qquad \underline{0\ 0\ 1\ 1}$$

5. Subtract the two pairs of numbers. Show the operands and the results in decimal and binary
   a.   assuming they are unsigned.
   b.   assuming they are signed.

   $$1\ 1\ 0\ 1\ -\ 1\ 1\ 0\ 0 \qquad\qquad 1\ 0\ 1\ 0\ -\ 0\ 1\ 1\ 0$$

   Indicate if there is overflow.

6. The inputs of this system A and B represent one binary number in the range 0:3. The inputs C and D represent a second binary number (also in the range 0:3). There are three outputs, X, Y, and Z.

---

[11]Tests assume students are allowed one sheet of $8\frac{1}{2} \times 11$ paper with any notes they wish on both sides. Solutions to Chapter Tests are given in Appendix C.

Chapter 2 Switching Algebra and Logic Circuits

The most basic circuit element is the *gate*. A gate is a circuit with one output that implements one of the basic functions, such as the OR and AND. (We will define additional gate types later.) Gates are available with two inputs, as well as three, four, and eight inputs. (They could be built with other numbers of inputs, but these are the standard sizes that are commercially available.) The symbols most commonly used (and which we will use throughout this text) are shown in Figure 2.1. (Note in Figure 2.1 the rounded input for the OR and the flat for the AND; and the pointed output on the OR and the rounded output on the AND.)

Figure 2.1 Symbols for OR and AND gates.

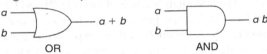

Property 2b is stating that the three circuits of Figure 2.2 all produce the same output.

Figure 2.2 AND gate implementation of Property 2b.

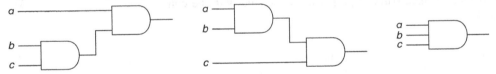

Figure 2.3 A NOT gate.

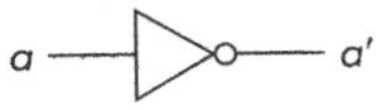

The third gate that we will include for now is the NOT, which has the symbol shown in Figure 2.3. The triangle is just the symbol for an amplifier (from electronics). The circle (sometimes referred to as a bubble) on the output is the symbol for inversion (NOT) and, as we will see later, is often shown attached to other gate inputs and outputs to indicate the NOT function.

Parentheses are used as in other mathematics; expressions inside the parentheses are evaluated first. When evaluating expressions without parentheses, the order of precedence is

NOT

AND

OR

Thus, for example,

$$ab' + c'd = (a(b')) + ((c')d)$$

Even without parentheses, the input b is complemented first and then ANDed with a. Input c is complemented and ANDed with d and then the two product terms are ORed. If the intent is to AND a and b and then complement them, it must be written $(ab)'$ rather than ab' and if the intent is to do the OR before the ANDs, it must be written $a(b' + c')d$.

In each of the properties, we use a single letter, such as $a, b, c, \ldots$ to represent any expression, not just a single variable. Thus, for example, Property 1a also states that

$$xy'z + w' = w' + xy'z$$

One other thing to note is that properties always appear in *dual* pairs. To obtain the dual of a property, interchange OR and AND, and the constants 0 and 1. The first interchange is obvious in P1 and P2; the other will be used in the next three properties. It can be shown that whenever two expressions are equal, the duals of those expressions are also equal. That could save some work later on, since we do not have to prove both halves of a pair of properties.

[SP 1; EX 1]

2.2 BASIC PROPERTIES OF SWITCHING ALGEBRA

We will next look at three pairs of properties associated with the constants 0 and 1.

P3a. $a + 0 = a$	**P3b.** $a \cdot 1 = a$	identity
P4a. $a + 1 = 1$	**P4b.** $a \cdot 0 = 0$	null
P5a. $a + a' = 1$	**P5b.** $a \cdot a' = 0$	complement

Properties 3a and 4b follow directly from the first and third lines of the truth tables; Properties 3b and 4a follow from the second and fourth lines. Property 5 follows from the definition of the NOT, namely, that either a or a' is always 1 and the other is always 0. Thus, P5a must be either $0 + 1$ or $1 + 0$, both of which are 1, and P5b must be either $0 \cdot 1$ or $1 \cdot 0$, both of which are 0. Once again, each of the properties comes in dual pairs.

Note that by combining the commutative property (P1a) with 3, 4, and 5, we also have

P3aa. $0 + a = a$	**P3bb.** $1 \cdot a = a$	
P4aa. $1 + a = 1$	**P4bb.** $0 \cdot a = 0$	
P5aa. $a' + a = 1$	**P5bb.** $a' \cdot a = 0$	

Often, as we manipulate expressions, we will use one of these versions, rather than first interchanging the terms using the commutative law (P1).

Another property that follows directly from the first and last lines of the truth table is

P6a. $a + a = a$	**P6b.** $a \cdot a = a$	idempotency

Chapter 2 Switching Algebra and Logic Circuits

By repeated application of Property 6a, we can see that

$$a + a + a + a = a$$

In the process of manipulating logic functions, it should be understood that each of these equalities is bidirectional. For example, $xyz + xyz$ can be replaced in an expression by xyz; but, also, it is sometimes useful to replace xyz by $xyz + xyz$.

The final property that we will obtain directly from the truth tables of the operators is the only one we will include on our list that is a self-dual.

involution   **P7.** $(a')' = a$

If $a = 0$, then $a' = 1$. However, when that is complemented again, that is, $(a')' = 1' = 0 = a$. Similarly, if $a = 1$, $a' = 0$ and $(a')' = 1$. Since there are no ANDs, ORs, 0's, or 1's, the dual is the same property.

The next pair of properties, referred to as the *distributive* law, are most useful in algebraic manipulation.

distributive   **P8a.** $a(b + c) = ab + ac$ **P8b.** $a + bc = (a + b)(a + c)$

P8a looks very familiar; we use it commonly with addition and multiplication. In right to left order, it is referred to as *factoring*. On the other hand, P8b is not a property of regular algebra. (Substitute 1, 2, 3 for a, b, c and the computation is $1 + 6 = 7$ on the left and $4 \times 3 = 12$ on the right.) The simplest way to prove these properties of switching algebra is to produce a truth table for both sides of the equality and show that they are equal. That is shown for Property 8b in Table 2.2. The left three columns are the input columns. The left hand side (LHS) of the equality is constructed by first forming a column for bc. That column has a 1 in each of the rows where both b and c are 1 and 0 elsewhere. Then LHS = $a + bc$ is computed using the column for a and that for bc. LHS is 1 wherever either of those columns contains a 1 or both are 1 and is 0 where they are both 0. Similarly, the right hand side (RHS) is computed by first constructing a column for $a + b$, which contains a 1 wherever $a = 1$ or $b = 1$. The column for $a + c$ is constructed in a similar fashion and finally RHS = $(a + b)(a + c)$ is 1 wherever both of the previous columns are 1.

Table 2.2 Truth table to prove Property 8b.

a	b	c	bc	**LHS**	$a + b$	$a + c$	**RHS**
0	0	0	0	0	0	0	0
0	0	1	0	0	0	1	0
0	1	0	0	0	1	0	0
0	1	1	1	1	1	1	1
1	0	0	0	1	1	1	1
1	0	1	0	1	1	1	1
1	1	0	0	1	1	1	1
1	1	1	1	1	1	1	1

The table could have been constructed by evaluating each of the expression for each row (input combination). For the first row,

$$a + bc = 0 + (0 \cdot 0) = 0 + 0 = 0$$
$$(a + b)(a + c) = (0 + 0)(0 + 0) = 0 + 0 = 0$$

and for the sixth row (101)

$$a + bc = 1 + (0 \cdot 1) = 1 + 0 = 1$$
$$(a + b)(a + c) = (1 + 0)(1 + 1) = 1 \cdot 1 = 1$$

We would need to do this for all eight rows. If we need the whole table, the first method usually requires less work.

This method can also be used to determine whether or not functions are equal. To be equal, the functions must have the same value for all input combinations. If they differ in any row of the truth table, they are not equal.

Construct a truth table and show which of the three functions are equal. (Be sure to state whether or not they are equal.)

EXAMPLE 2.1

$$f = y'z' + x'y + x'yz'$$

$$g = xy' + x'z' + x'y$$

$$h = (x' + y')(x + y + z')$$

x y z	y'z'	x'y	x'yz'	f	xy'	x'z'	x'y	g	x' + y'	x + y + z'	h
0 0 0	1	0	0	1	0	1	0	1	1	1	1
0 0 1	0	0	0	0	0	0	0	0	1	0	0
0 1 0	0	1	1	1	0	1	1	1	1	1	1
0 1 1	0	1	0	1	0	0	1	1	1	1	1
1 0 0	1	0	0	1	1	0	0	1	1	1	1
1 0 1	0	0	0	0	1	0	0	1	1	1	1
1 1 0	0	0	0	0	0	0	0	0	0	1	0
1 1 1	0	0	0	0	0	0	0	0	0	1	0

The truth table was constructed for each of the three functions (using the same technique as we did in developing Table 2.2). For input combination 1 0 1, $f = 0$, but $g = h = 1$. Thus, f is not equal to either of the other functions. The columns for g and h are identical; thus, $g = h$.

[SP 2, 3; EX 2, 3]

2.3 MANIPULATION OF ALGEBRAIC FUNCTIONS

Before adding some properties that are useful in simplifying algebraic expressions, it is helpful to introduce some terminology that will make the discussion simpler.

Chapter 2 Switching Algebra and Logic Circuits

A *literal* is the appearance of a variable or its complement. Examples are a and b'. In determining the complexity of an expression, one of the measures is the number of literals. Each appearance of a variable is counted. Thus, for example, the expression

$$ab' + bc'd + a'd + e'$$

contains eight literals.

A *product term* is one or more literals connected by AND operators. In the above example, there are four product terms, ab', $bc'd$, $a'd$, and e'. Notice that a single literal is a product term.

A *standard product term,* also called a *minterm,* is a product term that includes each variable of the problem, either uncomplemented or complemented. Thus, for a function of four variables, w, x, y, and z, the terms $w'xyz'$ and $wxyz$ are standard product terms, but $wy'z$ is not.

A *sum of products* expression (often abbreviated SOP) is one or more product terms connected by OR operators. The expression above meets this definition as do each of the following:

$w'xyz' + wx'y'z' + wx'yz + wxyz$	(4 product terms)
$x + w'y + wxy'z$	(3 product terms)
$x' + y + z$	(3 product terms)
wy'	(1 product term)
z	(1 product term)

It is usually possible to write several different sum of product expressions for the same function.

A *canonical sum* or *sum of standard product terms* is just a sum of products expression where all of the terms are standard product terms. The first example above is the only canonical sum (if there are four variables in all of the problems). Often, the starting point for algebraic manipulations is with canonical sums.

A *minimum sum of products* expression is one of those SOP expressions for a function that has the fewest number of product terms. If there is more than one expression with the fewest number of terms, then minimum is defined as one or more of those expressions with the fewest number of literals. As implied by the wording above, there may be more than one minimum solution to a given problem. Each of the expressions below are equal (meaning that whatever values are chosen for x, y, and z, each expression produces the same value). Note that the first is a sum of standard product terms.

(1) $x'yz' + x'yz + xy'z' + xy'z + xyz$	5 terms, 15 literals
(2) $x'y + xy' + xyz$	3 terms, 7 literals
(3) $x'y + xy' + xz$	3 terms, 6 literals
(4) $x'y + xy' + yz$	3 terms, 6 literals

Expressions (3) and (4) are the minima. (It should be clear that those are minimum among the expressions shown; it is not so obvious that there is not yet another expression with fewer terms or literals.) (A word of caution: When looking for all of the minimum solutions, do NOT include any solution with more terms or more literals than the best already found.)

Actually, we have enough algebra at this point to be able to go from the first expression to the last two. First, we will reduce the first expression to the second:

$$
\begin{aligned}
x'yz' + x'yz &+ xy'z' + xy'z + xyz \\
&= (x'yz' + x'yz) + (xy'z' + xy'z) + xyz && \text{associative} \\
&= x'y(z' + z) + xy'(z' + z) + xyz && \text{distributive} \\
&= x'y \cdot 1 + xy' \cdot 1 + xyz && \text{complement} \\
&= x'y + xy' + xyz && \text{identity}
\end{aligned}
$$

The first step takes advantage of P2a, which allows us to group terms in any way that we wish. We then utilized P8a to factor $x'y$ out of the first two terms and xy' out of the third and fourth terms. Next we used P5aa to replace $z' + z$ by 1. In the final step, we used P3b to reduce the expression.

The last three steps can be combined into a single step. We can add a property

P9a. $ab + ab' = a$ **P9b.** $(a + b)(a + b') = a$ **adjacency**

where, in the first case, $a = x'y$ and $b = z'$. Thus, if there are two product terms in a sum that are identical, except that one of the variables is uncomplemented in one and complemented in the other, they can be combined, using P9a. (The proof of this property follows the same three steps we used above—P8a to factor out the a, P5a to replace $b + b'$ by 1, and finally P3b to produce the result.) The dual can be proved using the dual steps, P8b, P5b, and P3a.

The easiest way to get to expression (3), that is, to go to six literals, is to use P6a, and make two copies of $xy'z$, that is,

$$xy'z = xy'z + xy'z$$

The expression becomes

$$
\begin{aligned}
x'yz' + x'yz &+ xy'z' + xy'z + xyz + xy'z \\
&= (x'yz' + x'yz) + (xy'z' + xy'z) + (xyz + xy'z) \\
&= x'y(z' + z) + xy'(z' + z) + xz(y + y') \\
&= x'y \cdot 1 + xy' \cdot 1 + xz \cdot 1 \\
&= x'y + xy' + xz
\end{aligned}
$$

We added the second copy of $xy'z$ at the end and combined it with the last term (xyz). The manipulation then proceeded in the same way as before. The other expression can be obtained in a similar manner by using P6a on $x'yz$ and combining the second copy with xyz. Notice that we freely

Chapter 2 Switching Algebra and Logic Circuits

reordered the terms in the first sum of products expression when we utilized P6a to insert a second copy of one of the terms.

In general, we may be able to combine a term on the list with more than one other term. If that is the case, we can replicate a term as many times as are needed.

Another property that will allow us to reduce the system to six literals without the need to make extra copies of a term is

simplification   **P10a.** $a + a'b = a + b$ **P10b.** $a(a' + b) = ab$

We can demonstrate the validity of P10a by using P8b, P5a, and P3bb as follows:

$$
\begin{aligned}
a + a'b &= (a + a')(a + b) & \text{distributive} \\
&= 1 \cdot (a + b) & \text{complement} \\
&= a + b & \text{identity}
\end{aligned}
$$

P10b can be demonstrated as follows:

$$a(a' + b) = aa' + ab = 0 + ab = ab$$

We can apply this property to the example by factoring x out of the last two terms:

$$
\begin{aligned}
x'y + xy' &+ xyz \\
&= x'y + x(y' + yz) & \text{distributive} \\
&= x'y + x(y' + z) & \text{simplification} \\
&= x'y + xy' + xz & \text{distributive}
\end{aligned}
$$

We used P10a where $a = y'$ and $b = z$ in going from line 2 to 3. Instead, we could have factored y out of the first and last terms, producing

$$
\begin{aligned}
y(x' + xz) &+ xy' \\
&= y(x' + z) + xy' \\
&= x'y + yz + xy'
\end{aligned}
$$

which is the other six literal equivalent.

Consider the following example, an expression in canonical form.

EXAMPLE 2.2

$a'b'c' + a'bc' + a'bc + ab'c'$

The first two terms can be combined using P9a, producing

$a'c' + a'bc + ab'c'$

Now, we can factor a' from the first two terms and use P10a to reduce this to

$a'c' + a'b + ab'c'$

and repeat the process with c' and the first and last terms, resulting in an expression

$a'c' + a'b + b'c'$

Although this expression is simpler than any of the previous ones, it is not minimum. With the properties we have developed so far, we have reached a dead end, and we have no way of knowing that this is not the minimum. Returning to the original expression, we can group the first term with the last and the middle two terms. Then, when we apply P9a, we get an expression with only two terms and four literals:

$$a'b'c' + a'bc' + a'bc + ab'c'$$
$$= b'c' + a'b$$

Later, we will see a property that allows us to go from the three-term expression to the one with only two terms.

Each terminology defined earlier has a dual that will also prove useful.

A *sum term* is one or more literals connected by OR operators. Examples are $a + b' + c$ and b' (just one literal).

A *standard sum term,* also called a *maxterm,* is a sum term that includes each variable of the problem, either uncomplemented or complemented. Thus, for a function of four variables, w, x, y, and z, the terms $w' + x + y + z'$ and $w + x + y + z$ are standard sum terms, but $w + y' + z$ is not.

A *product of sums* expression (POS) is one or more sum terms connected by AND operators. Examples of product of sums expressions:

$(w + x)(w + y)$	2 terms
$w(x + y)$	2 terms
w	1 term
$w + x$	1 term
$(w + x' + y' + z')(w' + x + y + z')$	2 terms

A *canonical product* or *product of standard sum terms* is just a product of sums expression where all of the terms are standard sum terms. The last example above is the only canonical sum (if there are four variables in all of the problems). Often, the starting point for algebraic manipulations is with canonical sums.

Minimum is defined the same way for both POS and SOP, namely, the expressions with the fewest number of terms, and, among those with the same number of terms, those with the fewest number of literals. A given function (or expression) can be reduced to minimum sum of products form and to minimum product of sums form. They may both have the same number of terms and literals or either may have fewer than the other. (We will see examples later, when we have further developed our minimization techniques.)

Chapter 2 Switching Algebra and Logic Circuits

An expression may be in sum of products form, product of sums form, both, or neither. Examples are

SOP: $x'y + xy' + xyz$

POS: $(x + y')(x' + y)(x' + z')$

both: $x' + y + z$ or xyz'

neither: $x(w' + yz)$ or $z' + wx'y + v(xz + w')$

We will now look at an example of the simplification of functions in product of sums form. (Later, we will look at methods of going from sum of products to product of sums and from product of sums to sum of products forms.)

$$g = (w' + x' + y + z')(w' + x' + y + z)(w + x' + y + z')$$

The first two terms can be combined, using P9b, where

$$a = w' + x' + y \quad \text{and} \quad b = z'$$

producing

$$g = (w' + x' + y)(w + x' + y + z')$$

That can most easily be reduced further by using P6b, to create a second copy of the first term, which can be combined with the last term, where

$$a = x' + y + z' \quad \text{and} \quad b = w$$

producing the final answer

$$g = (w' + x' + y)(x' + y + z')$$

We could also do the following manipulation (parallel to what we did with the sum of product expression)

$$g = (w' + x' + y)(w + x' + y + z')$$
$$= x' + y + w'(w + z') \qquad \text{[P8b]}$$
$$= x' + y + w'z' \qquad \text{[P10b]}$$
$$= (x' + y + w')(x' + y + z') \qquad \text{[P8b]}$$

[SP 4, 5, 6; EX 4, 5, 6]   which, after reordering the literals in the first set of parentheses, is the same expression as before.

2.4 IMPLEMENTATION OF FUNCTIONS WITH AND, OR, AND NOT GATES

We will first look at the implementation of switching functions using networks of AND, OR, and NOT gates. (After all, the goal of our design is to produce the block diagram of a circuit to implement the given switching function.) When we defined minimum sum of products expressions, we introduced, as an example, the function

$$f = x'yz' + x'yz + xy'z' + xy'z + xyz$$

A block diagram of a circuit to implement this is shown in Figure 2.4. Each of the product terms is formed by an AND gate. In this example, all of the AND gates have three inputs. The outputs of the AND gates are used as inputs to an OR (in this case a five-input OR). This implementation assumes that all of the inputs are available both uncomplemented and complemented (that is, for example, both x and x' are available as inputs). This is usually the case if the input to the combinational logic circuit comes from a flip flop, a storage device in sequential systems. It is not usually true, however, if the input is a system input.

Figure 2.4   Block diagram of f in sum of standard products form.

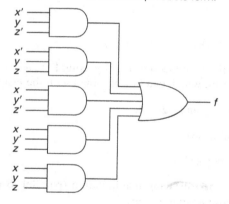

This is an example of a *two-level* circuit. The number of levels is the maximum number of gates through which a signal must pass from the input to the output. In this example, all signals go first through an AND gate and then through an OR. When inputs are available both uncomplemented and complemented, implementations of both sum of product and product of sum expressions result in two-level circuits.

We saw that this same function can be manipulated to a minimum sum of products expression, one version of which is

$$f = x'y + xy' + xz$$

This, of course, leads to a less complex circuit, namely, the one shown in Figure 2.5.

We have reduced the complexity of the circuit from six gates with 20 gate inputs (three to each of the five ANDs and five to the OR) to one with four gates and 9 gate inputs. The simplest definition of minimum for a gate network is minimum number of gates and, among those with the

Figure 2.5   Minimum sum of product implementation of f.

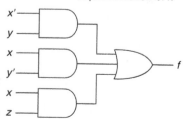

58   **Chapter 2** Switching Algebra and Logic Circuits

same number of gates, minimum number of gate inputs. For two-level circuits, this always corresponds to minimum sum of products or minimum product of sums functions.

If complemented inputs are not available, then an inverter (a NOT gate) is needed for each input that is required to be complemented (x and y in this example). The circuit of Figure 2.6 shows the NOT gates that must be added to the circuit of Figure 2.5 to implement f. Note that in this version we showed each input once, with that input line connected to whatever gates required it. That is surely what happens when we actually construct the circuit. However, for clarity, we will draw circuits more like the previous one (except, of course, we will only have one NOT gate for each input, with the output of that gate going to those gates that require it). (This is a three-level circuit, since some of the paths pass through three gates, a NOT, an AND, and then an OR.)

Figure 2.6   Circuit with only uncomplemented inputs.

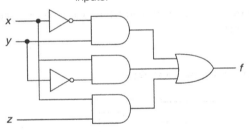

Figure 2.7   A product of sums implementation.

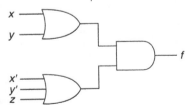

A product of sums expression (assuming all inputs are available both uncomplemented and complemented) corresponds to a two-level OR-AND network. For this same example, the minimum product of sums (although that is not obvious based on the algebra we have developed to this point)

$$f = (x + y)(x' + y' + z)$$

is implemented with the circuit of Figure 2.7.

When we implement functions that are in neither SOP nor POS form, the resulting circuits are more than two levels. As an example, consider the following function:

$$h = z' + wx'y + v(xz + w')$$

We begin inside the parentheses and build an AND gate with inputs x and z. The output of that goes to an OR gate, the other input of which is w'. That is ANDed with v, which is ORed with the input z' and the output of the AND gate producing $wx'y$, resulting in the circuit of Figure 2.8.

Figure 2.8 A multilevel circuit.

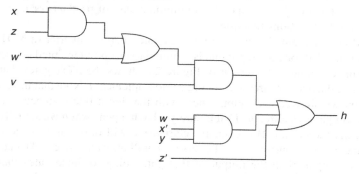

This is a four-level circuit, since the signals x and z pass first through an AND gate, then an OR, then an AND and finally through an OR, a total of four gates.

EXAMPLE 2.3

If we took the version of f used for Figure 2.5, and factored x from the last two terms, we obtain

$$f = x'y + x(y' + z)$$

That would result in the three-level circuit

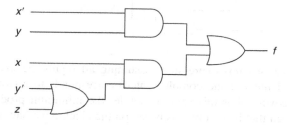

This (three-level) solution uses 4 two-input gates.

Gates are typically available in dual in-line pin packages (DIPs) of 14 connector pins. These packages are often referred to as *chips*. (Larger packages of 16, 18, 22, and more pins are used for more complex logic.) These packages contain *integrated circuits* (ICs). Integrated circuits are categorized as *small-scale integration* (SSI) when they contain just a few gates. Those are the ones that we will refer to in this chapter. Medium-scale (MSI) circuits contain as many as 100 gates; we will see examples of these later. The terminology *large-scale integration* (LSI) and *very large-scale integration* (VLSI) is used for even more complex packages, including complete computers.

Two of the connector pins are used to provide power to the chip. That leaves 12 pins for logic connections (on a 14-pin chip). Thus, we can fit 4 two-input gates on a chip. (Each gate has two input connections and one output connection. There are enough pins for four such gates.) Similarly, there are enough pins for 6 one-input gates (NOTs), 3 three-input gates, and 2 four-input gates (with two pins unused). In examples that refer to specific integrated circuits, we will discuss *transistor-transistor logic* (TTL) and, in particular, the 7400 series of chips.[3] For these chips, the power connections are 5 V and ground (0 V).

A list of the common AND, OR, and NOT integrated circuits that might be encountered in the laboratory is

7404	6 (hex) NOT gates
7408	4 (quadruple) two-input AND gates
7411	3 (triple) three-input AND gates
7421	2 four-input (dual) AND gates
7432	4 (quadruple) two-input OR gates

Details of the pin connections are shown in Appendix A.6.

At this point in the text, we have provided enough background to begin the laboratory exercises in the Appendices. In the laboratory, if a three-input OR (or AND) is needed, and only two-input ones are available, it can be constructed

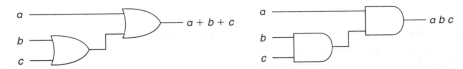

This idea can be extended to gates with larger numbers of inputs.[4]

Also, if we need a two-input gate and there is a left over three-input one (since they come three to a package), we can either connect the same signal to two of the inputs (since $aa = a$, and $a + a = a$)

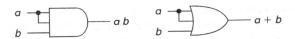

Also, we could connect a logic 1 (+5 V) to one of the inputs of an AND or a logic 0 (ground) to one of the inputs of an OR:

$$1 \cdot ab = ab \qquad 0 + a + b = a + b$$

---

[3]Even within the 7400 series, there are a number of variations, indicated by a letter or letters after the 74 (such as 74H10). We will not be concerned with that detail; it is left for a course on digital electronics.

[4]Caution: This approach does not work for NAND and NOR gates (which we will introduce in Section 2.8).

In the laboratory, logic 0 and logic 1 are represented by two voltages, often 0 and 5 V. Most commonly, the higher voltage is used to represent 1 and the lower voltage to represent 0. This is referred to as *positive logic*. The opposite choice is also possible, that is, use the higher voltage to represent 0. That is referred to as *negative logic*. When dealing with 1's and 0's, the concept does not really come up. However, the same electronic circuit has different logic meanings depending upon which choice we make.

Consider the truth table of Table 2.3a, where the behavior of the gate is described just in terms of high (H) and low (L). The positive logic interpretation of Table 2.3b produces the truth table for an OR gate. The negative logic interpretation of Table 2.3c is that of an AND gate.

Table 2.3

a. High/Low			b. Positive logic			c. Negative logic		
a	b	f	a	b	f	a	b	f
L	L	L	0	0	0	1	1	1
L	H	H	0	1	1	1	0	0
H	L	H	1	0	1	0	1	0
H	H	H	1	1	1	0	0	0

Most implementations use positive logic; we will do that consistently throughout this book. Occasionally, negative logic, or even a mixture of the two, is used.

[SP 7, 8; EX 7, 8; LAB[5]]

2.5   FROM THE TRUTH TABLE TO ALGEBRAIC EXPRESSIONS

Often, a design problem is stated in terms of the truth table that describes the output in terms of the inputs. Other times, verbal descriptions of systems can most easily be translated into the truth table. Thus, we need the ability to go from the truth table to an algebraic expression. To understand the process, consider the two-variable truth table of Table 2.4.

Since this is a two-variable problem, the truth table has $4(= 2^2)$ rows, that is, there are 4 possible combinations of inputs. (This is the truth table for the OR as we defined it at the beginning of this chapter, but that is irrelevant to this discussion.) What the table says is that

Table 2.4   A two-variable truth table.

a	b	f
0	0	0
0	1	1
1	0	1
1	1	1

f is 1   if $a = 0$ AND $b = 1$ OR
          if $a = 1$ AND $b = 0$ OR
          if $a = 1$ AND $b = 1$

---

[5]LAB refers to experiments in Appendix A.

Chapter 2 Switching Algebra and Logic Circuits

However, this is the same as saying

f is 1   if $a' = 1$ AND $b = 1$ OR
             if $a = 1$ AND $b' = 1$ OR
             if $a = 1$ AND $b = 1$

But $a' = 1$ AND $b = 1$ is the same as saying $a'b = 1$ and thus

f is 1   if $a'b = 1$ OR if $ab' = 1$ OR if $ab = 1$

That finally produces the expression

$$f = a'b + ab' + ab$$

Each row of the truth table corresponds to a product term. A sum of products expression is formed by ORing those product terms corresponding to rows of the truth table for which the function is 1. Each product term has each variable included, with that variable complemented when the entry in the input column for that variable contains a 0 and uncomplemented when it contains a 1. Thus, for example, row 10 produces the term ab'. These product terms include all of the variables; they are minterms. Minterms are often referred to by number, by just converting the binary number in the input row of the truth table to decimal. Both of the following notations are common:

$$f(a, b) = m_1 + m_2 + m_3$$

$$f(a, b) = \Sigma m(1, 2, 3)$$

For a three-variable function, we show, in Table 2.5, the minterms and minterm numbers that are used for all functions of three variables.

For a specific function, those terms for which the function is 1 are used. This is illustrated in Example 2.4.

Table 2.5 Minterms.

ABC	Minterm	Number
0 0 0	$A'B'C'$	0
0 0 1	$A'B'C$	1
0 1 0	$A'BC'$	2
0 1 1	$A'BC$	3
1 0 0	$AB'C'$	4
1 0 1	$AB'C$	5
1 1 0	ABC'	6
1 1 1	ABC	7

EXAMPLE 2.4

ABC	f	f'
0 0 0	0	1
0 0 1	1	0
0 1 0	1	0
0 1 1	1	0
1 0 0	1	0
1 0 1	1	0
1 1 0	0	1
1 1 1	0	1

where the truth table shows both the function, f, and its complement, f'. We can write

$$f(A, B, C) = \Sigma m(1, 2, 3, 4, 5)$$
$$= A'B'C + A'BC' + A'BC + AB'C' + AB'C$$

Either from the truth table, or by recognizing that every minterm is included in either f or f', we can then write

$$f'(A, B, C) = \Sigma m(0, 6, 7)$$
$$= A'B'C' + ABC' + ABC$$

The two sum of minterm forms are sum of product expressions. In most cases, including this one, the sum of minterms expression is not a minimum sum of products expression. We could reduce f from 5 terms with 15 literals to either of two functions with 3 terms and 6 literals as follows:

$$f = A'B'C + A'BC' + A'BC + AB'C' + AB'C$$
$$= A'B'C + A'B + AB' \qquad \textbf{[P9a, P9a]}$$
$$= A'C + A'B + AB'$$
$$= B'C + A'B + AB'$$

where the final expressions are obtained using P8a and P10a on the first term and either the second or the third. Similarly, we can reduce f' from 3 terms with 9 literals to 2 terms with 5 literals, using P9a:

$$f' = A'B'C' + AB$$

In much of the material of Chapters 3 and 4, we will specify functions by just listing their minterms (by number). We must, of course, list the variables of the problem as part of that statement. Thus,

$$f(w, x, y, z) = \Sigma m(0, 1, 5, 9, 11, 15)$$

is the simplest way to specify the function

$$f = w'x'y'z' + w'x'y'z + w'xy'z + wx'y'z + wx'yz + wxyz$$

If the function includes don't cares, then those terms are included in a separate sum (Σ).

$$f(a, b, c) = \Sigma m(1, 2, 5) + \Sigma d(0, 3)$$

EXAMPLE 2.5

implies that minterms 1, 2, and 5 are included in the function and that 0 and 3 are don't cares, that is the truth table is as follows:

abc	f
0 0 0	X
0 0 1	1
0 1 0	1
0 1 1	X
1 0 0	0
1 0 1	1
1 1 0	0
1 1 1	0

Let us now return to the first three of our continuing examples and develop algebraic expressions for them.

EXAMPLE 2.6	Using Z_2 for CE1, we get

$$Z_2 = A'BCD + AB'CD + ABC'D + ABCD' + ABCD$$

directly from the truth table. The last term ($ABCD$) can be combined with each of the others (using P10a). Thus, if we make four copies of it (using P6a repeatedly) and then utilize P10a four times, we obtain

$$Z_2 = BCD + ACD + ABD + ABC$$

No further simplification is possible; this is the minimum sum of products expression. Notice that if we used Z_1, we would have

$$Z_1 = A'BCD + AB'CD + ABC'D + ABCD'$$

No simplification is possible. This expression also has four terms, but it has 16 literals, whereas the expression for Z_2 only has 12.

EXAMPLE 2.7	For CE2, we have either

$$f = ab'c + abc' \quad \text{or} \quad f = ab'c' + abc$$

depending upon which truth table we choose. Again, no simplification is possible.

EXAMPLE 2.8	For the full adder, CE3, (using c for the carry in, c_{in}, to simplify the algebraic expressions, we get from the truth table

$$c_{out} = a'bc + ab'c + abc' + abc$$
$$s = a'b'c + a'bc' + ab'c' + abc$$

The simplification of carry out is very much like that of Z_2 in Example 2.6, resulting in

$$c_{out} = bc + ac + ab$$

but s is already in minimum sum of product form. We will return to the implementation of the full adder in Section 2.10.

We will next take a brief look at a more general approach to switching functions. How many different functions of n variables are there?

For two variables, there are 16 possible truth tables, resulting in 16 different functions. The truth table of Table 2.6 shows all of these functions. (Each output column of the table corresponds to one of the 16 possible 4-bit binary numbers.)

Table 2.6 All two-variable functions.

a	b	f_0	f_1	f_2	f_3	f_4	f_5	f_6	f_7	f_8	f_9	f_{10}	f_{11}	f_{12}	f_{13}	f_{14}	f_{15}
0	0	0	0	0	0	0	0	0	0	1	1	1	1	1	1	1	1
0	1	0	0	0	0	1	1	1	1	0	0	0	0	1	1	1	1
1	0	0	0	1	1	0	0	1	1	0	0	1	1	0	0	1	1
1	1	0	1	0	1	0	1	0	1	0	1	0	1	0	1	0	1

Some of the functions are trivial, such as f_0 and f_{15}, and some are really just functions of one of the variables, such as f_3. The set of functions, reduced to minimum sum of product form, are

$$f_0 = 0$$
$$f_1 = ab$$
$$f_2 = ab'$$
$$f_3 = a$$
$$f_4 = a'b$$
$$f_5 = b$$

$$f_6 = a'b + ab'$$
$$f_7 = a + b$$
$$f_8 = a'b'$$
$$f_9 = a'b' + ab$$
$$f_{10} = b'$$
$$f_{11} = a + b'$$

$$f_{12} = a'$$
$$f_{13} = a' + b$$
$$f_{14} = a' + b'$$
$$f_{15} = 1$$

Table 2.7 Number of functions of n variables.

Variables	Terms
1	4
2	16
3	256
4	65,536
5	4,294,967,296

[SP 9, 10; EX 9, 10, 11, 12]

For n variables, the truth table has 2^n rows and thus, we can choose any 2^n bit number for a column. Thus, there are 2^{2^n} different functions of n variables. That number grows very quickly, as can be seen from Table 2.7.

(Thus, we can find a nearly unlimited variety of problems of four or more variables for exercises or tests.)

2.6 INTRODUCTION TO THE KARNAUGH MAP

Although our main discussion of the Karnaugh map[6] (often called the K-map) is reserved for Chapter 3, it is useful to see how it relates to the algebraic manipulation that we have been doing (and will continue to do). In this section, we will look at the layout of two-, three-, and four-variable maps.

The Karnaugh map consists of one square for each possible minterm in a function. Thus, a two-variable map has 4 squares, a three-variable map has 8 squares, and a four-variable map has 16 squares.

Three views of the two-variable map are shown in Map 2.1. In each, the upper right square, for example, corresponds to $A = 1$ and $B = 0$, minterm 2.

Map 2.1 Two-variable Karnaugh maps.

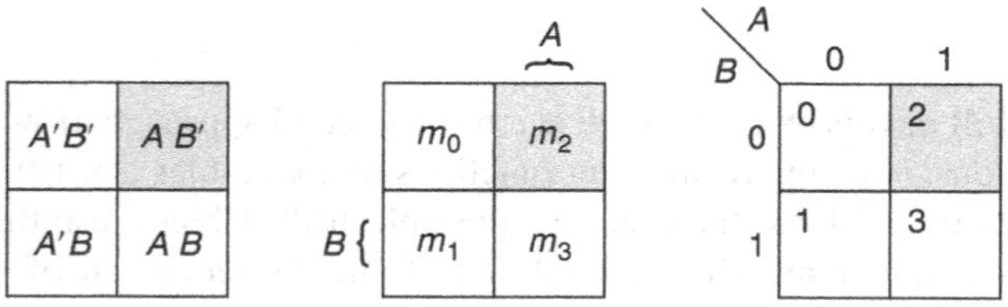

---

[6]This tool was introduced in 1953 by Maurice Karnaugh.

Chapter 2 Switching Algebra and Logic Circuits

When we plot a function, we put a 1 in each square corresponding to a minterm that is included in the function, and put a 0 in or leave blank those squares not included in the function. For functions with don't cares, an X goes in the square for which the minterm is a don't care. Map 2.2 shows examples of these.

Map 2.2   Plotting functions.

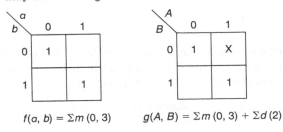

$$f(a, b) = \Sigma m\,(0, 3) \qquad g(A, B) = \Sigma m\,(0, 3) + \Sigma d\,(2)$$

Three-variable maps have eight squares, arranged in a rectangle as shown in Map 2.3.[7]

Map 2.3   Three-variable maps.

C \ AB	A' B' 00	A' B 01	A B 11	A B' 10
C' 0	A' B' C'	A' B C'	A B C'	A B' C'
C 1	A' B' C	A' B C	A B C	A B' C

C \ AB	00	01	11	10
0	0	2	6	4
1	1	3	7	5

Notice that the last two columns are not in numeric order. That is the key idea that makes the map work. By organizing the map that way, the minterms in adjacent squares can always be combined using

P9a. $ab + ab' = a$

---

[7]Some people label the row(s) of the map with the first variable(s) and the columns with the others. The three-variable map then looks like

A \ BC	00	01	11	10
0	0	1	3	2
1	4	5	7	6

This version of the map produces the same results as the other.

EXAMPLE 2.9

$m_0 + m_1$: $A'B'C' + A'B'C = A'B'$

$m_4 + m_6$: $AB'C' + ABC' = AC'$

$m_7 + m_5$: $ABC + AB'C = AC$

Also, the outside columns (and the outside rows when there are four rows) are adjacent. Thus,

$m_0 + m_4$: $A'B'C' + AB'C' = B'C'$

$m_1 + m_5$: $A'B'C + AB'C = B'C$

If we had ordered the columns in numeric order, as shown in Map 2.4 (where the algebraic version of the minterms is shown only for m_2 and m_4), we would not be able to combine adjacent squares:

Map 2.4 **Incorrect** arrangement of the map.

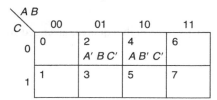

$$m_2 + m_4 = A'BC' + AB'C' = C'(A'B + AB')$$

However, we cannot manipulate that into a single term.

Product terms that correspond to the sum of two minterms appear as two adjacent 1's on the map. The terms of Example 2.9 are shown in Map 2.5.

Map 2.5 Product terms corresponding to groups of two.

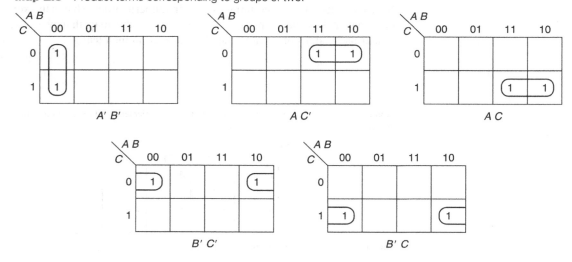

It is sometimes more convenient to draw the map in a vertical orientation (that is, two columns and four rows) as shown in Map 2.6. Both versions of the map produce the same results.

Map 2.6   Vertical orientation of three-variable map.

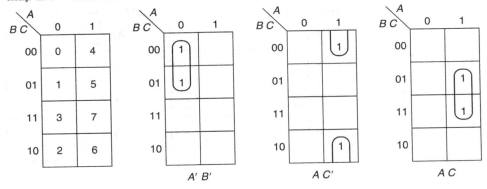

Map 2.7   Map with columns labeled.

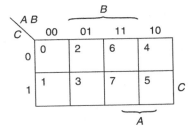

In reading the map, it is useful to label the pairs of columns (in those arrangements where there are four columns) as shown in Map 2.7. Thus, 1's in squares 4 and 6 are in the A columns and the C' row (that is, not in the C row), producing the AC' term as above.

The four-variable map consists of 16 squares in the 4 by 4 arrangement shown in Map 2.8.

As with the three-variable map, 1's in two adjacent squares (where the top and bottom rows as well as the left and right columns are considered to be adjacent) correspond to a single product term (combined using P9a). Example 2.10 shows three such terms.

Map 2.8   The four-variable map.

CD \ AB	00	01	11	10
00	0	4	12	8
01	1	5	13	9
11	3	7	15	11
10	2	6	14	10

CD \ AB	00	01	11	10
00	$A'B'C'D'$	$A'BC'D'$	$ABC'D'$	$AB'C'D'$
01	$A'B'C'D$	$A'BC'D$	$ABC'D$	$AB'C'D$
11	$A'B'CD$	$A'BCD$	$ABCD$	$AB'CD$
10	$A'B'CD'$	$A'BCD'$	$ABCD'$	$AB'CD'$

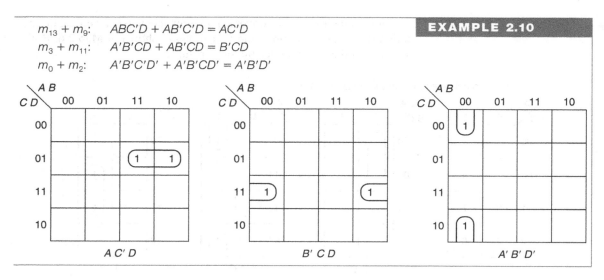

$m_{13} + m_9$: $ABC'D + AB'C'D = AC'D$

$m_3 + m_{11}$: $A'B'CD + AB'CD = B'CD$

$m_0 + m_2$: $A'B'C'D' + A'B'CD' = A'B'D'$

EXAMPLE 2.10

$A C'D$ $B'CD$ $A'B'D'$

Up to this point, all of the product terms that we have shown correspond to two minterms combined using P9a. These correspond to a product term with one literal missing, that is, with only two literals in a three-variable function and three literals in a four-variable function. Let us next look at the maps of Map 2.9 with a group of four 1's.

On the map to the left, we have circled two groups of two, one forming the term $A'C$ and the other forming the term AC. Obviously, P9a can be applied again to these two terms, producing

$$A'C + AC = C$$

Map 2.9   A group of four 1's.

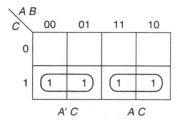

$A'C$ AC

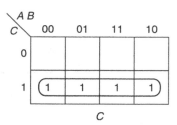

C

That is shown on the map to the right as a rectangle of four 1's. In general, rectangles of four 1's will correspond to a product term with two of the variables missing (that is, a single literal for three-variable problems and a two-literal term for four-variable problems).

We could have factored C from all of the terms producing

$$A'B'C + A'BC + ABC + AB'C = C(A'B' + A'B + AB + AB')$$

However, the sum inside the parentheses is just a sum of all of the minterms of A and B; that must be 1. Thus, we can get the result in just

Chapter 2 Switching Algebra and Logic Circuits

that one step. Indeed, we could have added a secondary property to P9, namely,

P9aa. $a'b' + a'b + ab + ab' = 1$

P9bb. $(a' + b')(a' + b)(a + b)(a + b') = 0$

These can be proved by repeated application of P9, first to the first two terms, then to the last two terms, and finally to the resulting terms as shown below

$$(a'b' + a'b) + (ab + a'b) = (a') + (a) = 1$$

$$[(a' + b')(a' + b)][(a + b)(a + b')] = [a'][a] = 0$$

Some examples of such groups for four-variable problems are shown in Map 2.10.

Map 2.10 Examples of groups of four.

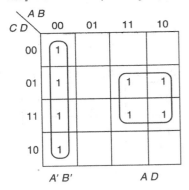

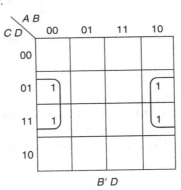

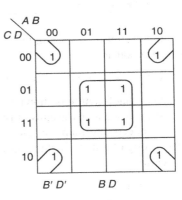

The easiest way to identify the term from the map is by determining in which row(s) and column(s) all of the 1's are located. Thus, on the first map, the 1's in the group on the left are all in the 0 0 ($A'B'$) column and thus the term is $A'B'$. The other group has its 1's in the 11 and 10 columns; the common feature is the 1 in the A position (which corresponds to A). Furthermore, the 1's are in the 01 and 11 rows; there is a common 1 in the D position. Thus, the term is AD. In the middle map, the 1's are in the 00 and 10 columns, producing B' and the 01 and 11 rows, resulting in D; the term is thus $B'D$. (Notice, by the way, that that term also appears on the first map, even though it was not circled.) On the last map, the four corners produce the term $B'D'$ (since all the 1's are in the 00 or 10 columns and the 00 or 10 rows). The middle group is BD. Any of these terms could also be obtained algebraically by first writing the minterms, then applying P10a to pairs of terms, and then applying it again to the two terms that resulted (as we did for the three-variable example). However, the whole idea of the map is to eliminate the need to do algebra.

Introduction to Discrete Logic & Digital System

Two adjacent groups of four can be combined in a similar way to form a group of eight squares (with three of the literals missing). Two such groups are shown in Map 2.11. The terms are A' for the map on the left and D' for the map on the right.

Map 2.11 Groups of eight.

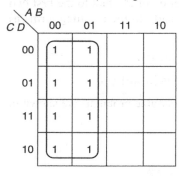
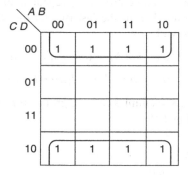

Let us now look back at the expressions used to illustrate minimum sum of products:

$$x'yz' + x'yz + xy'z' + xy'z + xyz$$

A map of that function is shown in Map 2.12.

We can see many groups of two adjacent 1's that will form product terms. Indeed, the map can guide us into which terms to choose. We need enough terms to include all of the 1's. The second version of the expression,

$$x'y + xy' + xyz$$

is illustrated on the Map 2.13, where each of the terms used has been circled. Note that minterm 7 (xyz) has been circled; but a larger group, including that minterm, could have been circled. Indeed, the remaining two solutions are indicated on Map 2.14.

Map 2.12 $x'yz' + x'yz + xy'z'$ $+ xy'z + xyz.$

Map 2.13 A better solution.

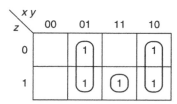

Map 2.14 The minimum solutions.

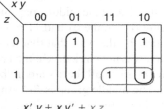
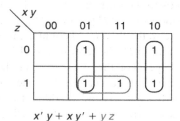

$$x'y + xy' + xz \qquad\qquad x'y + xy' + yz$$

Each of these solutions required us to make a second copy of one of the terms in order to use P9a. That is seen in the maps by the fact that the term duplicated is circled twice. (That just means that, in the first case, both xy' and xz are 1 when the inputs are $x = 1$, $y = 0$, and $z = 1$. That is surely not a problem, however, since $1 + 1 = 1$.)

P10a groups a smaller group with part of a larger one. On the left part of Map 2.15, the terms xy' and xyz are circled. P10a produces the terms circled on the map to the right.

Map 2.15   Illustration of P10a.

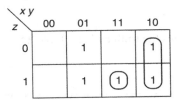 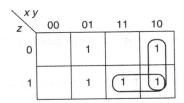

The map helps us to choose minterms to group, as illustrated in the function of Example 2.2 (from Section 2.3).

EXAMPLE 2.11

$f = a'b'c' + a'bc' + a'bc + ab'c'$

The map is shown below, with all three groups of two circled.

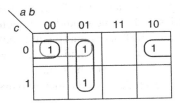

In the first attempt at algebraic manipulation, we grouped the first two minterms. But, as can be seen on the left map below, the two 1's that are left could not be combined, and resulted in a three-term solution. If, on the other hand, we used the map, we could see that choosing the two groups on the right map includes all of the minterms and produces the solution

$f = a'b + b'c'$

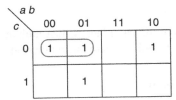 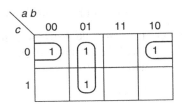

We will leave until Chapter 3 techniques for finding minimum sum of product (and product of sums) solutions for more complex functions.

2.7 THE COMPLEMENT AND PRODUCT OF SUMS

Before we discuss the most common types of gates, NANDs and NORs, and go further with algebraic simplification, we need to develop one more property. This property is the only one for which a person's name is commonly attached—*DeMorgan's* theorem.

P11a. $(a + b)' = a'b'$ **P11b.** $(ab)' = a' + b'$ DeMorgan

The simplest proof of this property utilizes the truth table of Table 2.8.

Table 2.8 Proof of DeMorgan's theorem.

a	b	$a + b$	$(a + b)'$	a'	b'	$a'b'$	ab	$(ab)'$	$a' + b'$
0	0	0	1	1	1	1	0	1	1
0	1	1	0	1	0	0	0	1	1
1	0	1	0	0	1	0	0	1	1
1	1	1	0	0	0	0	1	0	0
			11a			11a		11b	11b

In Table 2.8, we have produced a column for each of the expressions in the property. (The entries in the table should be obvious, since they just involve the AND, OR, and NOT operations on other columns.) Note that the columns (labeled 11a) for $(a + b)'$ and $a'b'$ are the same and those (labeled 11b) for $(ab)'$ and $a' + b'$ are the same.

The property can be extended to more than two operands easily.

P11aa. $(a + b + c...)' = a'b'c'...$

         P11bb. $(abc...)' = a' + b' + c'...$

For P11aa, with three variables, the proof goes

$$(a + b + c)' = ((a + b) + c)' = (a + b)'c' = a'b'c'$$

CAUTION: The most common mistakes in algebraic manipulation involve the misuse of DeMorgan's theorem:

$$(ab)' \neq a'b' \quad \text{rather} \quad (ab)' = a' + b'$$

The NOT (') cannot be distributed through the parentheses. Just look at the $(ab)'$ and $a'b'$ columns of the truth table and compare the expressions for $a = 0$ and $b = 1$ (or for $a = 1$ and $b = 0$):

$$(0 \cdot 1)' = 0' = 1 \quad\quad 0' \cdot 1' = 1 \cdot 0 = 0$$

The dual of this is also false, that is,

$$(a + b)' \neq a' + b'$$

Once again, the two sides differ when a and b differ.

There will be times when we are given a function and need to find its complement, that is, given $f(w, x, y, z)$, we need $f'(w, x, y, z)$. The straightforward approach is to use DeMorgan's theorem repeatedly.

EXAMPLE 2.12

$$f = wx'y + xy' + wxz$$

then

$$\begin{aligned} f' &= (wx'y + xy' + wxz)' \\ &= (wx'y)'(xy')'(wxz)' \qquad \text{[P11a]} \\ &= (w' + x + y')(x' + y)(w' + x' + z') \qquad \text{[P11b]} \end{aligned}$$

Note that if the function is in sum of products form, the complement is in product of sums form (and the complement of a product of sums expression is a sum of products one).

To find the complement of more general expressions, we can repeatedly apply DeMorgan's theorem or we can follow this set of rules:

1. Complement each variable (that is, a to a' or a' to a).
2. Replace 0 by 1 and 1 by 0.
3. Replace AND by OR and OR by AND, being sure to preserve the order of operations. That sometimes requires additional parentheses.

EXAMPLE 2.13

$$f = ab'(c + d'e) + a'bc'$$
$$f' = (a' + b + c'(d + e'))(a + b' + c)$$

Note that in f, the last operation to be performed is an OR of the complex first term with the product term. To preserve the order, parentheses were needed in f'; making the AND the last operation. We could have used square brackets, [ ], in order to make the expression more readable, making it

$$f' = [a' + b + c'(d + e')][a + b' + c]$$

We would produce the same result, with much more work, by using P11a and P11b over and over again:

$$\begin{aligned} f' &= [ab'(c + d'e) + a'bc']' \\ &= [ab'(c + d'e)]'[a'bc']' \\ &= [a' + b + (c + d'e)'][a + b' + c] \\ &= [a' + b + c'(d'e)'][a + b' + c] \\ &= [a' + b + c'(d + e')][a + b' + c] \end{aligned}$$

With DeMorgan's theorem, we can now obtain product of sum expressions from the truth table. Returning to Example 2.4 of Section 2.5,

EXAMPLE 2.14

ABC	f	f'
0 0 0	0	1
0 0 1	1	0
0 1 0	1	0
0 1 1	1	0
1 0 0	1	0
1 0 1	1	0
1 1 0	0	1
1 1 1	0	1

we found that

$$f' = A'B'C' + ABC' + ABC$$

Using P11, we can then obtain the product of sums expression[8] for f,

$$f = (f')' = (A + B + C)(A' + B' + C)(A' + B' + C').$$

To find a minimum product of sums expression, we can either manipulate the product of sums expression above (using P9b on the last two terms) to obtain

$$f = (A + B + C)(A' + B')$$

or we could simplify the sum of products expression for f' and then use DeMorgan to convert it to a product of sums expression. Both approaches produce the same result.

[SP 13, 14; EX 14, 15, 16]

2.8 NAND, NOR, AND EXCLUSIVE-OR GATES

In this section we will introduce three other commonly used types of gates, the NAND, the NOR, and the Exclusive-OR, and see how to implement circuits using them.

The NAND has the symbol shown in Figure 2.9. Like the AND and the OR, the NAND is commercially available in several sizes, typically two-, three-, four-, and eight-input varieties. When first introduced, it was

Figure 2.9 NAND gates.

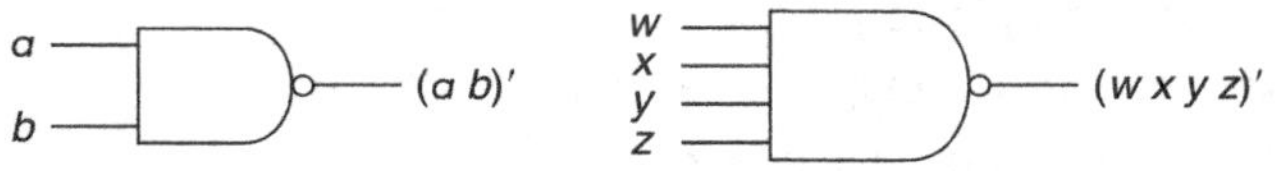

[8]It is possible to obtain product of sums expressions directly from the truth table without first finding the sum of product expression. Each 0 of f produces a maxterm in the product of sums expression. We have omitted that approach here, because it tends to lead to confusion.

referred to as an AND-NOT, which perfectly describes its function, but the shorter name, NAND, has become widely accepted. Note that DeMorgan's theorem states that

$$(ab)' = a' + b'$$

and thus an alternate symbol for the two-input NAND is shown in Figure 2.10. The symbols may be used interchangeably; they refer to the same component.

The NOR gate (OR-NOT) uses the symbols shown in Figure 2.11. Of course, $(a + b)' = a'b'$. NOR gates, too, are available with more inputs.

Figure 2.10 Alternate symbol for NAND.

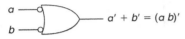

Figure 2.11 Symbols for NOR gate.

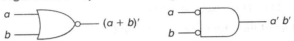

Why use NAND and NOR gates, rather than AND, OR, and NOT gates? After all, the logic expressions are in terms of AND, OR, and NOT operators and thus the implementation with those gates is straightforward. Many electronic implementations naturally invert (complement) signals; thus, the NAND is more convenient to implement than the AND. The most important reason is that with either NAND or NOR, only one type of gate is required. On the other hand, both AND and OR gates are required; and, often, NOT gates are needed, as well. As can be seen from the circuits of Figure 2.12, NOT gates and two-input AND and OR gates can be replaced by just two-input NANDs. Thus, these operators are said to be *functionally complete*. (We could implement gates with more than two inputs using NANDs with more inputs. We could also implement AND, OR, and NOT gates using only NORs; that is left as an exercise.)

Figure 2.12 Functional completeness of NAND.

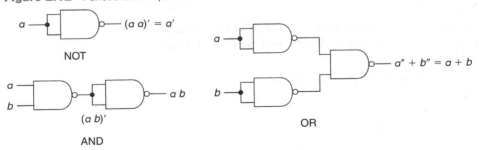

Using these gate equivalences, the function $f(= x'y + xy' + xz)$ that we first implemented with AND and OR gates in Figure 2.5 (Section 2.4) can now be implemented with NAND gates, as shown in Figure 2.13. But note that we have two NOT gates in a row in each of the green paths. They serve no purpose logically (P7 states $(a')' = a$), and thus they can be removed from the circuit, yielding that of Figure 2.14. That is, all of

Figure 2.13 NAND gate implementation.

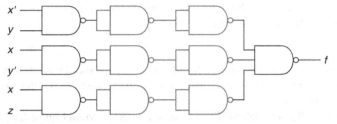

Figure 2.14 Better NAND gate implementation.

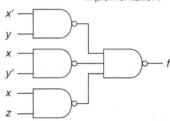

the AND and OR gates of the original circuit became NANDs. Nothing else was changed.

This process can be greatly simplified when we have a circuit consisting of AND and OR gates such that

1. the output of the circuit comes from an OR,
2. the inputs to all OR gates come either from a system input or from the output of an AND, and
3. the inputs to all AND gates come either from a system input or from the output of an OR.

All gates are replaced by NAND gates, and any input coming directly into an OR is complemented.

We can obtain the same result by starting at the output gate and putting a bubble (a NOT) at both ends of each input line to that OR gate. If the circuit is not two-level, we repeat this process at the input of each of the OR gates. Thus, the AND/OR implementation of f becomes that of Figure 2.15, where all of the gates have become NAND gates (in one of the two notations we introduced earlier).

This approach works with any circuit that meets the conditions above, with only one additional step. If an input comes directly into an OR gate, there is no place for the second NOT; thus, that input must be complemented. For example, the circuit for h

$$h = z' + wx'y + v(xz + w')$$

is shown in Figure 2.16. Again, all of the AND and OR gates become NANDs, but the two inputs that came directly into the OR gates were complemented.

Figure 2.15 Double NOT gate approach.

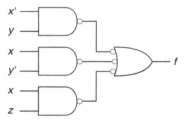

Figure 2.16 A multilevel NAND implementation.

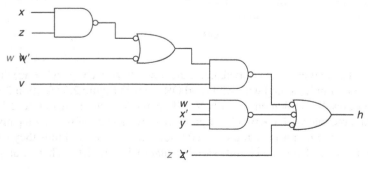

| **EXAMPLE 2.15** | $f = wx(y + z) + x'y$ |

This would be implemented with AND and OR gates in either of two ways.

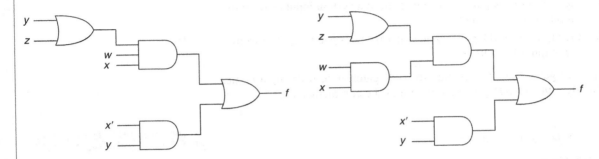

The first version can be directly converted to NAND gates, as shown below.

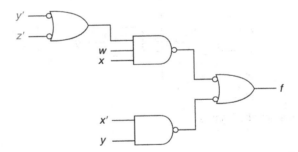

The second version cannot be converted to NAND gates without adding an extra NOT gate, since it violates the third rule—an AND gets an input from another AND. Thus, this circuit would become

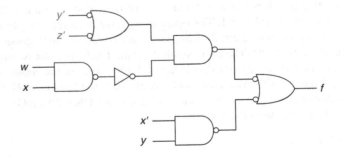

where the NOT is required to implement the AND that forms wx. Expressions such as this one are often obtained starting from sum of product solutions. We will see some examples of this in Section 2.10.

The dual approach works for implementing circuits with NOR gates. When we have a circuit consisting of AND and OR gates such that

1. the output of the circuit comes from an AND,
2. the inputs to OR gates come either from a system input or from the output of an AND, and
3. the inputs to AND gates come either from a system input or from the output of an OR.

Then all gates can be converted to NOR gates, and, if an input comes directly into an AND gate, that input must be complemented.

EXAMPLE 2.16

$$g = (x + y')(x' + y)(x' + z')$$

is implemented

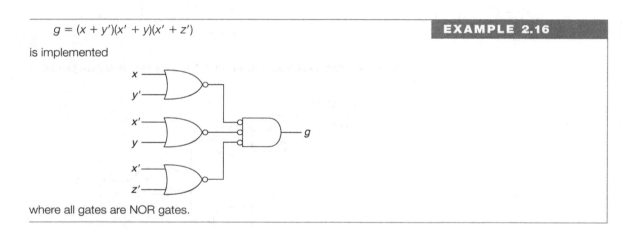

where all gates are NOR gates.

The Exclusive-OR gate implements the expression

$$a'b + ab'$$

which is sometimes written $a \oplus b$. The terminology comes from the definition that $a \oplus b$ is 1 if $a = 1$ (and $b = 0$) **or** if $b = 1$ (and $a = 0$), but not both $a = 1$ and $b = 1$. The operand we have been referring to as OR $(+)$ is sometimes referred to as the Inclusive-OR to distinguish it from the Exclusive-OR. The logic symbol for the Exclusive-OR is similar to that for the OR except that it has a double line on the input, as shown in Figure 2.17a. Also commonly available is the Exclusive-NOR gate, as shown in Figure 2.17b. It is just an Exclusive-OR with a NOT on the output and produces the function

$$(a \oplus b)' = a' b' + a b$$

This sometimes is referred to as a comparator, since the Exclusive-NOR is 1 if $a = b$, and is 0 if $a \neq b$.

A NAND gate implementation of the Exclusive-OR is shown in Figure 2.18a, where only uncomplemented inputs are assumed.

Figure 2.17 (a) An Exclusive-OR gate. (b) An Exclusive-NOR gate.

$a \oplus b$

(a)

$(a \oplus b)'$

(b)

The two NOT gates (implemented as two-input NANDs) can be replaced by a single gate, as shown in Figure 2.18b, since

$$a(a' + b') + b(a' + b') = aa' + ab' + ba' + bb' = ab' + a'b$$

Figure 2.18 Exclusive-OR gates.

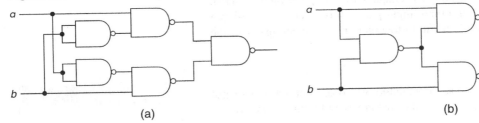

(a)   (b)

Some useful properties of the Exclusive-OR are

$$(a \oplus b)' = (a'b + ab')' = (a + b')\,(a' + b) = a'b' + ab$$
$$a' \oplus b = (a')'b + (a')b' = ab + a'b' = (a \oplus b)'$$
$$(a \oplus b') = (a \oplus b)'$$
$$a \oplus 0 = a = (a' \cdot 0 + a \cdot 1)$$
$$a \oplus 1 = a' = (a' \cdot 1 + a \cdot 0)$$

The Exclusive-OR has both the commutative and associative properties, that is,

$$a \oplus b = b \oplus a$$
$$(a \oplus b) \oplus c = a \oplus (b \oplus c)$$

The first of these is obvious from the definition; the second can be shown algebraically:

$$(a \oplus b) \oplus c = (a'b + ab')c' + (a'b' + ab)c$$
$$= a'bc' + ab'c' + a'b'c + abc$$
$$a \oplus (b \oplus c) = a'(b'c + bc') + a(b'c' + bc)$$
$$= a'b'c + a'bc' + ab'c' + abc$$

These two expressions have the same terms.

A list of some of the more common NAND, NOR, and Exclusive-OR integrated circuit packages that we may encounter in the laboratory is as follows:

7400   4 (quadruple) two-input NAND gates
7410   3 (triple) three-input NAND gates
7420   2 (dual) four-input NAND gates

7430   1 eight-input NAND gate

7402   4 (quadruple) two-input NOR gates

7427   3 (triple) three-input NOR gates

7486   4 (quadruple) two-input Exclusive-OR gates

To build a circuit, we utilize packages. Even if we only need 1 three-input NAND gate, we must buy a package with three gates on it (a 7410). Recognize, however, that a three-input gate can be used as a two-input gate by connecting two of the inputs together or by connecting one of the inputs to a logic 1.

Consider the following circuit, constructed with ANDs and ORs; the input variables have been omitted since they are irrelevant to the discussion.

EXAMPLE 2.17

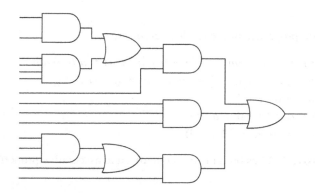

The number of gates and packages are shown in the left part of the table below

| | **Gates** | | **Packs** | | | | |
Inputs	AND	OR	AND	OR	NAND	Packs
2	3	2	1		5	1
3	2	1	1	1	3	1
4	1		1		1	1
Total	6	3	3	1	9	3

With AND and OR gates, four packages are needed—three ANDs and one OR package (since the 2 two-input OR gates can be constructed with the leftover three-input gates.

If all of the gates are converted to NANDs (and some of the inputs are complemented) the gate and package count is shown in the right part of the table. Only three packages are needed. The second four-input gate on the 7420 would be used as the fifth two-input gate (by tying three of the inputs together).

[SP 15, 16, 17; EX 17, 18; LAB]

2.9 SIMPLIFICATION OF ALGEBRAIC EXPRESSIONS

We have already looked at the process of simplifying algebraic expressions, starting with a sum of minterms or a product of maxterms. The primary tools were

P9a. $ab + ab' = a$ **P9b.** $(a + b)(a + b') = a$

P10a. $a + a'b = a + b$ **P10b.** $a(a' + b) = ab$

although many of the other properties were used, particularly,

P6a. $a + a = a$ **P6b.** $a \cdot a = a$

P8a. $a(b + c) = ab + ac$ **P8b.** $a + bc = (a + b)(a + c)$

If the function is stated in other than one of the standard forms, two other properties are useful. First,

absorption   **P12a.** $a + ab = a$ **P12b.** $a(a + b) = a$

The proof of P12a uses P3b, P8a, P4aa, and P3b (again).

$$a + ab = a \cdot 1 + ab = a(1 + b) = a \cdot 1 = a$$

Remember that we only need to prove one half of the property, since the dual of a property is always true. However, we could have proven P12b using the duals of each of the theorems we used to prove P12a. Instead, we could distribute the a from the left side of P12b, producing

$$a \cdot a + ab = a + ab$$

However, that is just the left side of P12a, which we have already proved is equal to a.

EXAMPLE 2.18

P12a states that

$$w'xy + w'y = w'y$$

From the map below,

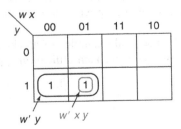

$$w'\ y \qquad w'\ x\ y$$

we can see that the term $w'y$ circles the 1 of $w'xy$, and thus the latter term is unnecessary.

P10a and P12a look very similar; yet we used two very different approaches to demonstrate their validity. In P10a, we did

$$a + a'b = (a + a')(a + b) = 1 \cdot (a + b) = a + b$$

[P8b, P5a, P3bb]

whereas for P12a, we used P3b, P8a, P4aa, and P3b. How did we know not to start the proof of P11a by using P8b to obtain

$$a + ab = (a + a)(a + b) = a(a + b)?$$

Those steps are all valid, but they do not get us anywhere toward showing that these expressions equal a. Similarly, if we started the proof of P10a by using P3b, that is,

$$a + a'b = a \cdot 1 + a'b$$

we also do not get anywhere toward a solution. How does the novice know where to begin? Unfortunately, the answer to that is either trial and error or experience. After solving a number of problems, we can often make the correct guess as to where to start on a new one. If that approach does not work, then we must try another one. This is not much of a problem in trying to demonstrate that two expressions are equal. We know that we can quit when we have worked one side to be the same as the other.

Before proceeding with a number of examples, some comments on the process are in order. There is no algorithm for algebraic simplification, that is, there is no ordered list of properties to apply. On the other hand, of the properties we have up to this point, 12, 9, and 10 are the ones most likely to reduce the number of terms or literals. Another difficulty is that we often do not know when we are finished, that is, what is the minimum. In most of the examples we have worked so far, the final expressions that we obtained appear to be as simple as we can go. However, we will see a number of examples where it is not obvious that there is not a more minimum expression. We will not be able to get around this until Chapter 3 when we develop other simplification methods. (Note that in the Solved Problems and the Exercises, the number of terms and literals in the minimum solution is given. Once that is reached, we know we are done; if we end up with more, we need to try another approach.)

We will now look at several examples of algebraic simplification, and show, for the first two, how each simplification appears on the map.

EXAMPLE 2.19

$$xyz + x'y + x'y'$$
$$= xyz + x' \qquad \text{[P9a]}$$
$$= x' + yz \qquad \text{[P10a]}$$

where $a = x'$, $a' = x$, and $b = yz$

84   **Chapter 2**   Switching Algebra and Logic Circuits

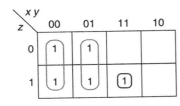

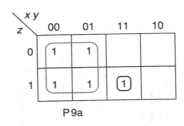

P 9a

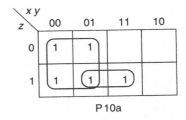

P 10a

The first map shows the terms of the original function circled. We next combined the last two terms, using P9a, to get a group of four, as shown in the middle. Finally, P10a produced the group of two.

EXAMPLE 2.20	$wx + wxy + w'yz + w'y'z + w'xyz'$

$$= (wx + wxy) + (w'yz + w'y'z) + w'xyz'$$

$$= wx + w'z + w'xyz' \qquad\qquad \textbf{[P12a, P9a]}$$

$$= wx + w'(z + xyz')$$

$$= wx + w'(z + xy) \qquad\qquad\qquad \textbf{[P10a]}$$

$$= wx + w'z + w'xy$$

$$= w'z + x(w + w'y)$$

$$= w'z + x(w + y) \qquad\qquad\qquad \textbf{[P10a]}$$

$$= w'z + wx + xy$$

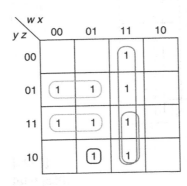

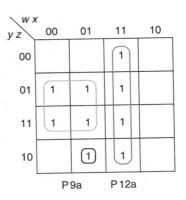

P 9a   P 12a

P9a allowed us to combine the two groups of two into a group of four; P12a was used to remove the term wxy, which was included in wx. Next, P10a is used twice on the minterm $w'xyz'$, once with each of the other terms, first forming a group of two, and then a group of four.

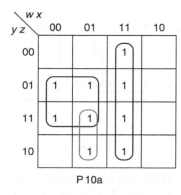 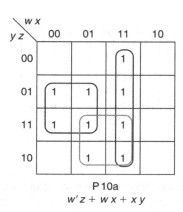

P 10a

P 10a

$w'z + wx + xy$

That property could have been used first with wx (resulting in xyz'). That term is shown circled on the map below. That approach, however, would leave us with an expression

$w'z + wx + xyz'$

for which there are no algebraic clues as to how to proceed (as shown on the map below). The only way we can now reduce it is to add terms to the expression. Shortly, we will introduce another property that will enable us to go from this expression to the minimum one.

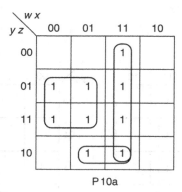

P 10a

$(x + y)(x + y + z') + y' = (x + y) + y'$	**[P12b]**	**EXAMPLE 2.21**
$= x + (y + y') = x + 1 = 1$	**[P5a, P4a]**	

$(a + b' + c)(a + c')(a' + b' + c)(a + c + d)$		**EXAMPLE 2.22**
$= (b' + c)(a + c')(a + d)$	**[P9b, P10b]**	

where the second simplification really took several steps

$(a + c')(a + c + d) = a + c'(c + d) = a + c'd = (a + c')(a + d)$

One more tool is useful in the algebraic simplification of switching functions. The operator *consensus* (indicated by the symbol ¢) is defined as follows:

For any two product terms where exactly one variable appears uncomplemented in one and complemented in the other, the consensus is defined as the product of the remaining literals. If no such variable exists or if more than one such variable exists, then the consensus is undefined. If we write one term as at_1 and the second as $a't_2$ (where t_1 and t_2 represent product terms), then, if the consensus is defined,

$$at_1 \text{ ¢ } a't_2 = t_1t_2$$

EXAMPLE 2.23

$ab'c$ ¢ $a'd = b'cd$

$ab'c$ ¢ $a'cd = b'cd$

abc' ¢ $bcd' = abd'$

$b'c'd'$ ¢ $b'cd' = b'd'$

abc' ¢ $bc'd$ = undefined—no such variable

$a'bd$ ¢ $ab'cd$ = undefined—two variables, a and b

We then have the following property that is useful in reducing functions.

consensus
    P13a. $at_1 + a't_2 + t_1t_2 = at_1 + a't_2$
            P13b. $(a + t_1)(a' + t_2)(t_1 + t_2) = (a + t_1)(a' + t_2)$

P13a states that the consensus term is redundant and can be removed from a sum of product expression. (Of course, this property, like all of the others, can be used in the other direction to add a term. We will see an example of that shortly.)

CAUTION: It is the consensus term that can be removed (t_1t_2), NOT the other two terms (NOT $at_1 + a't_2$). A similar kind of simplification can be obtained in product of sum expressions using the dual (P13b). We will not pursue that further.

First, we will derive this property from the others. Using P12a twice, the right hand side becomes

$$at_1 + a't_2 = (at_1 + at_1t_2) + (a't_2 + a't_1t_2) \qquad \textbf{[P12a]}$$
$$= at_1 + a't_2 + (at_1t_2 + a't_1t_2)$$
$$= at_1 + a't_2 + t_1t_2 \qquad \textbf{[P9a]}$$

It is also useful to look at both the map and the truth table for this theorem. A map (in the vertical orientation) is shown in Map 2.16, first with the two terms from both sides of P13a on the left, and then with the consensus term, as well, on the right. It is clear that the consensus term is redundant.

Map 2.16 Consensus.

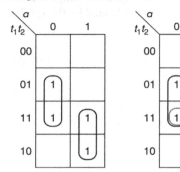

Similarly, from Table 2.9, we see that the consensus term, t_1t_2, is 1 only where one of the other terms is already 1. Thus, if we OR that term with RHS, it does not change anything, that is, LHS is the same as RHS.

Table 2.9 Consensus.

a	t_1	t_2	at_1	$a't_2$	**RHS**	t_1t_2	**LHS**
0	0	0	0	0	0	0	0
0	0	1	0	1	1	0	1
0	1	0	0	0	0	0	0
0	1	1	0	1	1	1	1
1	0	0	0	0	0	0	0
1	0	1	0	0	0	0	0
1	1	0	1	0	1	0	1
1	1	1	1	0	1	1	1

EXAMPLE 2.24

In Example 2.2 (Section 2.3), we reduced the function as

$$f = a'b'c' + a'bc' + a'bc + ab'c'$$

to

$$f_1 = a'c' + a'b + b'c'$$

by combining the first two terms using P9a, and then applying P10a twice. At that point, we were at a dead end. However, we found by starting over with a different grouping that we could reduce this to

$$f_2 = b'c' + a'b$$

Indeed, the term eliminated, $a'c'$, is the consensus of the other terms; we could use P13a to go from f_1 to f_2.

EXAMPLE 2.25	

$g = bc' + abd + acd$

Since Properties 1 through 12 produce no simplification, we now try consensus. The only consensus term defined is

$bc' \ ¢ \ acd = abd$

Property 13 now allows us to remove the consensus term. Thus,

$g = bc' + acd$

With the following function, there is no way to apply Properties 12, 9 and 10:

$f = w'y' + w'xz + wxy + wyz'$

Next, we try consensus. An approach that assures that we try to find the consensus of all pairs of terms is to start with consensus of the second term with the first; then try the third with the second and the first; and so forth. Following this approach (or any other) for this example, the only consensus that exists is

$w'xz \ ¢ \ wxy = xyz$

When a consensus term was part of the sum of product expression, P13a allowed us to remove that term and thus simplify the expression. If the consensus term is not one of the terms in the SOP expression, the same property allows us to add it to the expression. Of course, we don't add another term automatically, since that makes the expression less minimum. However, we should keep track of such a term, and, as a last resort, consider adding it to the function. Then, see if that term can be used to form other consensus terms and thus reduce the function. In this example, by adding xyz, f becomes

$f = w'y' + w'xz + wxy + wyz' + xyz$

Now, however,

$xyz \ ¢ \ wyz' = wxy$ and $xyz \ ¢ \ w'y' = w'xz$

Thus, we can remove both wxy and $w'xz$, leaving

$f = w'y' + wyz' + xyz$ (3 terms, 8 literals)

The original function is shown on the left of Map 2.17. On the right, the new term that was formed, xyz, is shown in green. The two terms that can then be eliminated are shown in gray.

We will now consider two examples making use of consensus, as well as all of the other properties. The usual approach is to try to utilize properties 12, 9, and then 10. When we get as far as we can with these, we then turn to consensus.

Map 2.17 Adding the consensus term.

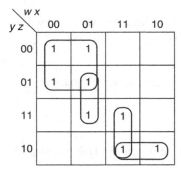
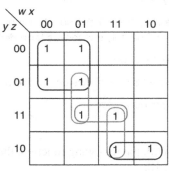

EXAMPLE 2.26

$A'BCD + A'BC'D + B'EF + CDE'G + A'DEF + A'B'EF$

$= A'BD + B'EF + CDE'G + A'DEF$ [P12a, P9a]

But $A'BD \not\subset B'EF = A'DEF$ and this reduces to

$A'BD + B'EF + CDE'G$

EXAMPLE 2.27

$w'xy + wz + xz + w'y'z + w'xy' + wx'z$

$= wz + w'x + xz + w'y'z$ [P12a, P9a]

$= wz + w'x + w'y'z$ since $wz \not\subset w'x = xz$ [P13a]

But,

$wz + w'y'z = z(w + w'y') = z(w + y')$ [P10a]

$= wz + w'x + y'z$

The maps shown below illustrate the algebraic steps.

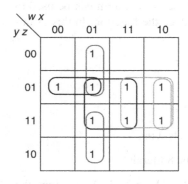
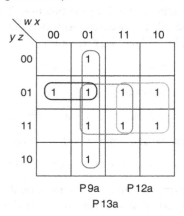
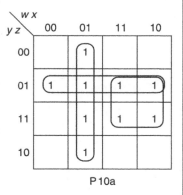

P 9a   P 12a

P 13a

P 10a

The green terms on the first map are eliminated using P9a and P12a. On the middle map, the gray term is the consensus of the two groups of four. Finally, P10a creates the row of four 1's.

[SP 18; EX 19, 20, 21]

2.10 MANIPULATION OF ALGEBRAIC FUNCTIONS AND NAND GATE IMPLEMENTATIONS

In addition to the need to minimize algebraic expressions, there is sometimes the requirement to put an expression in a certain format, such as sum of products, sum of minterms, product of sums, or product of maxterms. Secondly, to meet design constraints, we sometimes must manipulate the algebra. In this section we will look at some examples and introduce one more property.

If we have a sum of product expression and need to expand it to sum of minterms, there are three options. First, we can create a truth table, and, from that, follow the approach of Section 2.5 to produce a sum of minterms. Indeed, this approach will work for an expression in any format. Second, we could map the function and obtain the minterms from the map. The other approach is to use P9a to add variables to a term.

EXAMPLE 2.28	

$$f = bc + ac + ab$$
$$= bca + bca' + ac + ab$$

We can repeat the process on the other two terms, producing

$$f = bca + bca' + acb + acb' + abc + abc'$$
$$= abc + a'bc + abc + ab'c + abc + abc'$$
$$= a'bc + ab'c + abc' + abc$$

where P6a was used to remove the duplicate terms.

If two literals were missing from a term, that term would produce four minterms, using P9a repeatedly.

EXAMPLE 2.29	

$$g = x' + xyz = x'y + x'y' + xyz$$
$$= x'yz + x'yz' + x'y'z + x'y'z' + xyz$$
$$g(x, y, z) = \Sigma m(3, 2, 1, 0, 7) = \Sigma m(0, 1, 2, 3, 7)$$

since minterm numbers are usually written in numeric order.

To convert to product of maxterms, P9b can be used. For example,

EXAMPLE 2.30	

$$f = (A + B + C)(A' + B')$$
$$= (A + B + C)(A' + B' + C)(A' + B' + C')$$

One other property is useful in manipulating functions from one form to another.

P14a. $\quad ab + a'c = (a + c)(a' + b)$

(The dual of this is also true; but it is the same property with the variables b and c interchanged.) This property can be demonstrated by first applying P8a to the right side three times:

$$(a + c)(a' + b) = (a + c)a' + (a + c)\, b = aa' + a'c + ab + bc$$

However, $aa' = 0$ and $bc = a'c \not\subset ab$ and thus, using P3aa and P13a, we get

$$aa' + a'c + ab + bc = a'c + ab$$

which is the left side of the property.

This property is particularly useful in converting product of sums expressions to sum of products and vice versa. In Example 2.4, we found a sum of products expression. Then, in Example 2.14, we found the product of sums expression and minimized it. In Example 2.30, we converted that function to product of maxterms. Now, we will utilize P14a to go back to sum of products form.

$$f = (A + B + C)(A' + B') = AB' + A'(B + C) = AB' + A'B + A'C$$

EXAMPLE 2.31

where the a of P14a is A, the b is $B + C$, and the c is B'. This, indeed, is one of the sum of product solutions we found in Example 2.4 for this problem. Although the utilization of this property does not always produce a minimum sum of product expression (as it does in this case), it does produce a simpler expression than we would get just using P8a.

To go from a product of sum expression (or a more general expression that is neither sum of product nor product of sum) to a sum of products expression, we use primarily the following three properties:

P8b. $\quad a + bc = (a + b)(a + c)$

P14a. $\quad ab + a'c = (a + c)(a' + b)$

P8a. $\quad a(b + c) = ab + ac$

We try to apply them in that order, using the first two from right to left.

$$A(B + C')(B + D) + BC(A + D')(A' + D)$$
$$= A(B + C'D) + BC(AD + A'D') \qquad \textbf{[P8b, P14a]}$$
$$= AB + AC'D + ABCD + A'BCD' \qquad \textbf{[P8a]}$$

EXAMPLE 2.32

(This expression is not minimum; we have no reason to believe that it would be. It can be reduced to $AB + AC'D + BCD'$ using P12a on the first and third terms and P10a on the first and fourth.)

92   **Chapter 2** Switching Algebra and Logic Circuits

EXAMPLE 2.33	$(A + B' + C)(A + B + D)(A' + C' + D')$	
	$= (A + (B' + C)(B + D))(A' + C' + D')$	**[P8b]**
	$= (A + B'D + BC)(A' + C' + D')$	**[P14a]**
	$= A(C' + D') + A'(B'D + BC)$	**[P14a]**
	$= AC' + AD' + A'B'D + A'BC$	**[P8a]**

The dual of these properties can be used to convert to product of sums as can be seen in Example 2.34.

EXAMPLE 2.34	$wxy' + xyz + w'x'z'$	
	$= x(wy' + yz) + w'x'z'$	**[P8a]**
	$= x(y' + z)(y + w) + w'x'z'$	**[P14a]**
	$= (x + w'z')(x' + (y' + z)(y + w))$	**[P14a]**
	$= (x + w')(x + z')(x' + y' + z)(x' + y + w)$	**[P8b]**

Another application of P14a and this type of algebraic manipulation comes when we wish to implement functions using only two-input NAND or NOR gates (or two- and three-input gates). (We will only consider examples of NAND gate implementations.) Consider the following problem.

The expression below is the only minimum sum of products expression for the function f. Assume all inputs are available both uncomplemented and complemented. Find a NAND gate circuit that uses only two-input gates. No gate may be used as a NOT gate.[9]

$$f = ab'c' + a'c'd' + bd$$

(A two-level solution would require four gates, three of which would be three-input gates, and 11 gate inputs.)

---

[9]We could always produce a circuit using two-input gates by replacing a three-input gate by 2 twos and a NOT. For example, a three-input NAND could be implemented as follows:

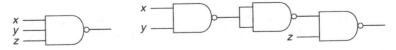

Larger gates could be replaced in a similar fashion. But this approach almost always leads to circuits with more gates than is necessary.

To solve this problem, we must eliminate three-input gates. Thus, the starting point is to attempt to factor something from the three literal terms. In this example, there is a common c' in the first two terms and we can thus obtain

$$f = c'(ab' + a'd') + bd$$

This, indeed, solves the whole problem in one step since not only did we reduce the 2 three-input product terms to two inputs each, but we also got the final OR to a two-input one. Thus, the resulting circuit is shown in Figure 2.19, where we first implemented it with AND and OR gates and then, starting at the output, added double inverters in each path from the input of an OR back to the output of an AND. (In this example, no inputs came directly into an OR.) This solution requires 6 gates and 12 inputs. It should be noted that either solution, this one or the two-level one mentioned earlier requires two integrated circuit packages. This requires two 7400s (4 two-input NANDs each) and would leave two of the gates unused. The two-level solution would require a 7410 (3 three-input gates) and a 7400 for the remaining two-input gate and would leave three of those gates unused. (If we had replaced each three-input gate by 2 two-input ones plus a NOT, the implementation would require 7 two-input gates plus three NOT gates.)

Figure 2.19 A two-input NAND gate circuit.

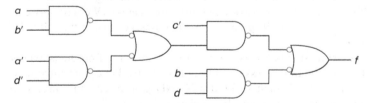

More complex examples of finding a two-input gate implementation often require the use of P14a as well as P8a. Consider the function in Example 2.35 (already in minimum sum of products form).

$$G = DE' + A'B'C' + CD'E + ABC'E$$ **EXAMPLE 2.35**

The four-literal product term is the first place we must attack. We could factor E from the last two terms. That would produce

$$G = DE' + A'B'C' + E(CD' + ABC')$$

But now, there is no way of eliminating the three-input gate corresponding to $A'B'C'$. Instead, we can factor C' from the second and the fourth terms, producing

$$G = C'(A'B' + ABE) + DE' + CD'E$$

Chapter 2   Switching Algebra and Logic Circuits

We can apply P14a to the expression within the parentheses to get

$$G = C'(A' + BE)(A + B') + DE' + CD'E$$

or, using B instead of A,

$$G = C'(B' + AE)(B + A') + DE' + CD'E$$

In either case, we still have 2 three-input AND terms, that first product and the last one. (We cannot take the output of the OR gate that forms $B' + AE$ and the output of the OR gate that forms $B + A'$ and connect them to a two-input AND gate. We would then need to connect the output of that AND gate to the input of another AND gate with C' as its other input. This would violate the third rule for conversion to NAND gates—the inputs to AND gates may not come from the output of another AND gate.) We can reduce it to all two-input gates by applying P14a again, using the C' from the first complex term and the C from the last product term, producing (from the second version) the following expression:

$$G = (C' + D'E)[C + (B' + AE)(B + A')] + DE'$$

This requires 10 gates, as shown in the NAND gate circuit shown below.

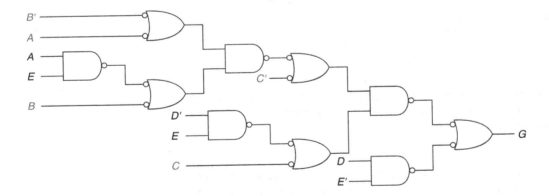

Again, we began by implementing the circuit with ANDs and ORs, starting at the inner most parentheses. Five of the inputs went directly to OR gates and were thus complemented (as shown in green in the circuit).

There is still another approach to manipulating this algebra.

$$\begin{aligned} G &= C'(A' + BE)(A + B') + DE' + CD'E \\ &= C'(A' + BE)(A + B') + (D + CE)(D' + E') \\ &= (A' + BE)(AC' + B'C') + (D + CE)(D' + E') \end{aligned}$$

In this case, we eliminated the three-input AND by distributing the C' (P8a) and used P14a on the last two product terms. We will leave the implementation of this as an exercise, but we can count 11 gates (one more than before) from the algebraic expression, as seen from the count below.

$$G = (A' + BE)(AC' + B'C') + (D + CE)(D' + E')$$
$$\quad\;\; 1\;\; 2\; 3\; 4\;\;\;\; 5\;\; 6\;\;\;\; 7\;\;\;\;\; 8\;\; 9\; 10\;\; 11$$

where each gate is numbered below the operator corresponding to that gate.

As an example of sharing a gate, consider the implementation of the following function with two-input NAND gates:

EXAMPLE 2.36

$$G = C'D' + ABC' + A'C + B'C$$
$$\;\;\; = C'(D' + AB) + C(A' + B')$$

The circuit for that is shown below.

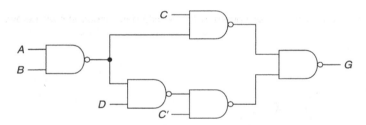

Note that only one NAND gate is needed for the product term AB and for the sum term $A' + B'$ (since inputs coming directly to an OR are complemented).

As a final example, we will return to the implementation of the full adder (CE3). The sum of product expressions developed in Example 2.8 are repeated below (where the carry input, c_{in}, is represented by just c).

EXAMPLE 2.37

$$s = a'b'c + a'bc' + ab'c' + abc$$
$$c_{out} = bc + ac + ab$$

A two-level implementation of these would require 1 four-input NAND gate (for s), 5 three-input NAND gates (four for s and one for c_{out}), and 3 two-input NANDs (for c_{out}), assuming all inputs are available both uncomplemented and complemented. But this assumption is surely not valid for c, since that is just the output of combinational logic just like this (from the next less significant bit of the sum). Thus, we need at least one NOT gate (for c') and possibly three. The implementation of this adder would thus require four integrated circuit packages (one 7420, two 7410s, and one 7400). (There would be one gate left over of each size which could be used to create whatever NOTs are needed.)

Although s and c_{out} are in minimum sum of product form, we can manipulate the algebra to reduce the gate requirements by first factoring c from two terms of s and from two terms of c_{out}, and factoring c' from the other two terms of s, yielding

$$s = c(a'b' + ab) + c'(ab' + a'b)$$
$$c_{out} = c(a + b) + ab$$

This requires 11 two-input NAND gates, not including the three NOTs (since ab need only be implemented once for the two terms and $a + b$ is implemented using the same gate as $a'b'$).

Returning to the expression for sum, note that

$$s = c(a \oplus b)' + c'(a \oplus b) = c \oplus (a \oplus b)$$

Furthermore, we could write

$$c_{out} = c(a \oplus b) + ab$$

(That is a little algebraic trick that is not obvious from any of the properties. However, the difference between $a + b$ and $a \oplus b$ is that the former is 1 when both a and b are 1, but the latter is not. But the expression for c_{out} is 1 for $a = b = 1$ because of the ab term.)

Using these last two expressions, we could implement both the sum and carry using three Exclusive-ORs and 3 two-input NANDs as follows:

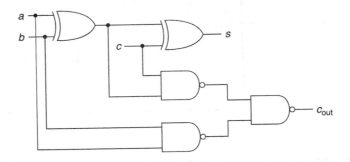

Packages with four Exclusive-OR gates are available (7486) and thus this circuit could be implemented with one of those packages and one 7400. Note that complemented inputs are not necessary for this implementation.

2.10 Manipulation of Algebraic Functions

Finally, since we can implement each Exclusive-OR with 4 two-input NAND gates, without requiring complemented inputs, we obtain

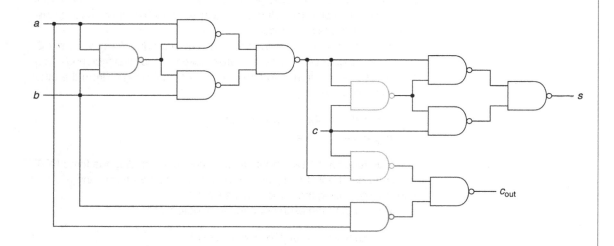

Note that the two green NAND gates have the same inputs and the two light green ones also have the same inputs. Only one copy of each is necessary, yielding the final circuit with only nine NAND gates.

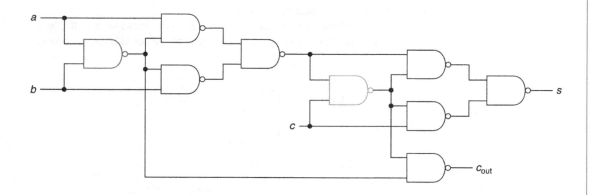

This implementation would require three 7400s if we were only building one bit of an adder. However, a 4-bit adder could be built with nine packages.

[SP 19, 20, 21, 22, 23;
EX 22, 23, 24, 25, 26; LAB]

2.11 A MORE GENERAL BOOLEAN ALGEBRA

The basis for switching algebra is *Boolean algebra*, first published by George Boole in 1849. It allows more than two elements. It is defined in terms of a set of postulates and then the remaining properties are developed from them as theorems. The postulates have been stated in a variety of ways, but the following development seems most straightforward. Indeed, several of these postulates are identical in form to the properties of switching algebra listed in Sections 2.1 and 2.2. But there, we began with the definition of the operators (limited to a two-valued algebra) and proved the properties either directly from the definition or by way of a truth table. Here, the operators are not defined, but can be derived from the postulates.

1. A Boolean algebra consists of a set of $k \geq 2$ elements. (For the switching algebra developed in Section 2.1, $k = 2$.)

2. There are two binary operators, $+$ and $\cdot$, and one unary operator, $'$.

3. The algebra is closed, that is, if a and b are members of the set, then

    $$a + b, a \cdot b, a'$$

    are also members of the set. (This property is not true of all operators and all sets in normal algebra. For example, if the set is the set of positive integers, subtraction is not closed since it may result in a negative integer, and division is not closed since the quotient may be a non integer.)

4. Commutative law (same as P1):
    i. $a + b = b + a$
    ii. $a \cdot b = b \cdot a$

5. Associative law (same as P2):
    i. $a + (b + c) = (a + b) + c$
    ii. $a \cdot (b \cdot c) = (a \cdot b) \cdot c$

6. Distributive law (same as P8):
    i. $a + b \cdot c = (a + b) \cdot (a + c)$
    ii. $a \cdot (b + c) = a \cdot b + a \cdot c$

7. Identity (similar to P3):
    i.   There exists a unique element in the set, 0, such that
         $a + 0 = a$
    ii. There exists a unique element in the set, 1, such that
         $a \cdot 1 = a$

8. Complement (same as P5): For each element a, there exists a unique element a' such that

   i. $a + a' = 1$

   ii. $a \cdot a' = 0$

We have now defined Boolean algebra. It works for a two-valued system (the switching algebra we have been discussing throughout this chapter) as well as a more general one.

For switching algebra, we can use these postulates to define the operators. First, we can recognize that there are the two elements, 0 and 1, postulated in number 7. Using that postulate and the commutative law, we can complete the first three lines of Table 2.10a for the OR ($+$) operator and the last three for the AND($\cdot$). For the OR, the postulate

$$a + 0 = a$$

implies that $0 + 0 = 0$ (first line) and $1 + 0 = 1$ (third line). In addition, using the commutative law, we get

$$0 + a = a$$

and thus the second line is completed ($0 + 1 = 1$).

Using the other part of postulate 7, we get $0 \cdot 1 = 0$, $1 \cdot 1 = 1$, and with the commutative property, $1 \cdot 0 = 0$. For the remaining lines, we need to prove the idempotency property (P6 from before). We can do that in the following steps

$$
\begin{aligned}
a + a &= (a + a) \cdot 1 && \text{[7ii]}\\
&= (a + a) \cdot (a + a') && \text{[8i]}\\
&= a + a \cdot a' && \text{[6i]}\\
&= a + 0 && \text{[8ii]}\\
&= a && \text{[7i]}
\end{aligned}
$$

Using this theorem, we can complete the first row of the OR truth table ($0 + 0 = 0$). We can prove the dual of this theorem,

$$a \cdot a = a$$

using the other half of each of the postulates and thus complete the last line of the AND Table 2.10b ($1 \cdot 1 = 1$).

Finally, we can define the NOT ($'$) operator from postulate 8. Part i says that either a or a' (or both) is 1; part ii says that either a or a' (or both) is 0. Thus, one of them must be 1 and the other 0, that is, if $a = 0$, then a' must be 1, and if $a = 1$, then a' must be 0.

From here, we can prove all of the properties of switching algebra as before. Most of them are also properties of a general Boolean algebra, but that is beyond the scope of this book.

Table 2.10a Defining OR and AND.

a	b	$a + b$	$a \cdot b$
0	0	0	
0	1	1	0
1	0	1	0
1	1		1

Table 2.10b Completed definition of OR and AND.

a	b	$a + b$	$a \cdot b$
0	0	0	0
0	1	1	0
1	0	1	0
1	1	1	1

2.12 SOLVED PROBLEMS

1. Show a block diagram of a circuit using AND and OR gates for each side of P8b: $a + bc = (a + b)(a + c)$

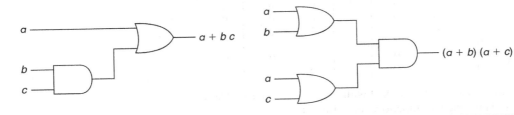

2. Show a truth table for the following functions:
   a. $F = XY' + YZ + X'Y'Z'$
   b. $G = X'Y + (X + Z')(Y + Z)$

(a)

XYZ	XY'	YZ	X'Y'Z'	F
000	0	0	1	1
001	0	0	0	0
010	0	0	0	0
011	0	1	0	1
100	1	0	0	1
101	1	0	0	1
110	0	0	0	0
111	0	1	0	1

(b)

XYZ	X'Y	X + Z'	Y + Z	( )( )	G
000	0	1	0	0	0
001	0	0	1	0	0
010	1	1	1	1	1
011	1	0	1	0	1
100	0	1	0	0	0
101	0	1	1	1	1
110	0	1	1	1	1
111	0	1	1	1	1

3. Determine, using truth tables, whether or not each of the groups of expressions are equal:
   a. $f = a'c' + a'b + ac$
      $g = bc + ac + a'c'$
   b. $f = P'Q' + PR + Q'R$
      $g = Q' + PQR$

(a)

abc	a'c'	a'b	ac	f	bc	ac	a'c'	g
000	1	0	0	1	0	0	1	1
001	0	0	0	0	0	0	0	0
010	1	1	0	1	0	0	1	1
011	0	1	0	1	1	0	0	1
100	0	0	0	0	0	0	0	0
101	0	0	1	1	0	1	0	1
110	0	0	0	0	0	0	0	0
111	0	0	1	1	1	1	0	1

The two functions are equal.

(b)

PQR	P'Q'	PR	Q'R	f	Q'	PQR	g
000	1	0	0	1	1	0	1
001	1	0	1	1	1	0	1
010	0	0	0	0	0	0	0
011	0	0	0	0	0	0	0
100	0	0	0	0	1	0	1 ←
101	0	1	1	1	1	0	1
110	0	0	0	0	0	0	0
111	0	1	0	1	0	1	1

Note that for row 100 (marked with a green arrow), $f = 0$ and $g = 1$. Thus, the two functions are different.

4. For each of the following expressions, indicate which (if any) of the following apply (more than one may apply):

   i.   Product term
   ii. Sum of products expression
   iii. Sum term
   iv. Product of sums expression

   a. ab'
   b. $a'b + ad$
   c. $(a + b)(c + a'd)$
   d. $a' + b'$
   e. $(a + b')(b + c)(a' + c + d)$

   a. i.   product of two literals
        ii. sum of one product term
        iv. product of two sum terms
   b. ii. sum of two product terms
   c. none; second term is not a sum term
   d. ii. sum of two product terms
        iii. sum of two literals
        iv. product of one sum term
   e. iv. product of three sum terms

5. In the expressions of problem 4, how many literals are in each?

   a. 2   **b.** 4   **c.** 5   **d.** 2   **e.** 7

6. Using Properties 1 to 10, reduce the following expressions to a minimum sum of products form. Show each step (number of terms and number of literals in minimum shown in parentheses).

   a. $xyz' + xyz$ (1 term, 2 literals)
   b. $x(y + w'z) + wxz$ (2 terms, 4 literals)
   c. $x'y'z' + x'y'z + x'yz + xy'z + xyz$ (2 terms, 3 literals)
   d. $f = abc' + ab'c + a'bc + abc$ (3 terms, 6 literals)

a. $xyz' + xyz = xy(z' + z) = xy \cdot 1 = xy$ **[P8a, P5aa, P3b]**

or, in one step, using P9a, where $a = xy$ and $b = z'$

b. $x(y + w'z) + wxz = xy + w'xz + wxz$ **[P8a]**

$\qquad = xy + (w' + w)xz$ **[P8a]**

$\qquad = xy + 1 \cdot xz$ **[P5aa]**

$\qquad = xy + xz$ **[P3bb]**

Note that throughout, we freely apply P1 and P2 (without noting them) to regroup and reorder literals and terms.

c. $x'y'z' + x'y'z + x'yz + xy'z + xyz$

Make two copies of $x'y'z$

$\qquad = (x'y'z' + x'y'z) + (x'y'z + x'yz) + (xy'z + xyz)$ **[P6a]**

$\qquad = x'y'(z' + z) + x'z(y' + y) + xz(y' + y)$ **[P8a]**

$\qquad = x'y' \cdot 1 + x'z \cdot 1 + xz \cdot 1$ **[P5aa]**

$\qquad = x'y' + x'z + xz$ **[P3b]**

$\qquad = x'y' + (x' + x)z = x'y' + 1 \cdot z$ **[P8a, P5aa]**

$\qquad = x'y' + z$ **[P3bb]**

or, without using P6a,

$\qquad = (x'y'z' + x'y'z) + x'yz + (xy'z + xyz)$

$\qquad = x'y' + x'yz + xz$ **[P9a]**

$\qquad = x'(y' + yz) + xz$

$\qquad = x'(y' + z) + xz$ **[P10a]**

$\qquad = x'y' + x'z + xz$ **[P8a]**

$\qquad = x'y' + z$ **[P9a]**

Note that we could follow a path that does not lead us to the correct answer, by combining the last two terms in the second line of this second sequence, yielding

$\qquad = x'y' + z(x'y + x)$

$\qquad = x'y' + z(y + x)$ **[P10a]**

$\qquad = x'y' + yz + xz$ **[P8a]**

This is a dead end. It has more terms than the minimum (which was given) and we do not have the tools (in Properties 1 to 10) to reduce this further without backing up to the original expression (or, at least, the first reduction). We should then go back and start again.

d. There are two approaches to this problem. In the first, we note that abc can be combined with each of the other terms. Thus, we make three copies of it, using

$abc = abc + abc + abc$ **[P6a]**

$\qquad f = (abc' + abc) + (ab'c + abc) + (a'bc + abc)$

$\qquad = ab + ac + bc$ **[P9a]**

In the second approach, we just use abc to combine with the term next to it, producing

$$f = abc' + ab'c + a'bc + abc = abc' + ab'c + bc \qquad \text{[P9a]}$$
$$= abc' + c(b + b'a) = abc' + c(b + a)$$
$$= abc' + bc + ac \qquad \text{[P10a]}$$
$$= a(c + c'b) + bc = a(c + b) + bc$$
$$= ac + ab + bc \qquad \text{[P10a]}$$

or, in place of the last two lines,

$$= b(c + c'a) + ac = b(c + a) + ac$$
$$= bc + ab + ac \qquad \text{[P10a]}$$

In this approach, we used P10a twice to eliminate a literal from the second term and then the first. We could have done it in any order. Indeed, there were two ways to do the last step (as shown on the last two lines).

7. Show a block diagram of a system using AND, OR, and NOT gates to implement the following function. Assume that variables are available only uncomplemented. Do not manipulate the algebra.

$$F = (A (B + C)' + BDE)(A' + CE)$$

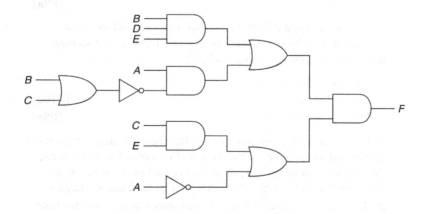

8. For each of the following circuits,
   i. find an algebraic expression
   ii. put it in sum of product form.

104   **Chapter 2**   Switching Algebra and Logic Circuits

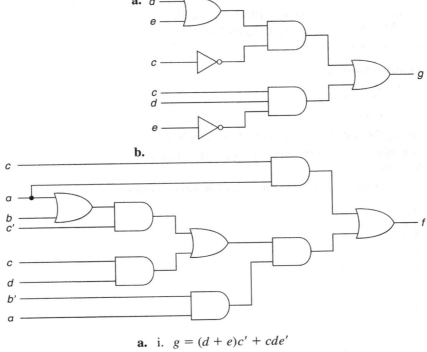

a. i. $g = (d + e)c' + cde'$

    ii. $g = c'd + c'e + cde'$

b. i. $f = ac + ab'(cd + c'(a + b))$

    ii. $f = ac + ab'cd + ab'c' + ab'c'b$

       $= ac + ab'cd + ab'c'$

9. For the following truth table,

a b c	f
0 0 0	0
0 0 1	1
0 1 0	0
0 1 1	1
1 0 0	1
1 0 1	0
1 1 0	1
1 1 1	1

a. Show the minterms in numerical form.

b. Show an algebraic expression in sum of minterm form.

c. Show a minimum sum of product expression (two solutions, three terms, six literals each).

d. Show the minterms of f' (complement of f) in numeric form.

a. $f(a, b, c) + \Sigma m(1, 3, 4, 6, 7)$

b. $f = a'b'c + a'bc + ab'c' + abc' + abc$

c. $f = a'c + ac' + abc$
   $\quad = a'c + ac' + ab$ (using P10a on last two terms)
   $\quad = a'c + ac' + bc$ (using P10a on first and last term)

d. $f'(a, b, c) = \Sigma m(0, 2, 5)$

10. For the following function,

$\quad f(x, y, z) = \Sigma m(2, 3, 5, 6, 7)$

a. Show the truth table.

b. Show an algebraic expression in sum of minterm form.

c. Show a minimum sum of product expression (two terms, three literals).

d. Show the minterms of f' (complement of f) in numeric form.

a.

$x\,y\,z$	f
0 0 0	0
0 0 1	0
0 1 0	1
0 1 1	1
1 0 0	0
1 0 1	1
1 1 0	1
1 1 1	1

b. $f = x'y\,z' + x'y\,z + x\,y'z + xyz' + xyz$

c. $f = x'y + xy'z + xy$
   $\quad = y + xy'z$
   $\quad = y + xz$

d. $f'(x, y, z) = \Sigma m(0, 1, 4)$

11. Plot the following functions on a Karnaugh map:

a. $f(a, b, c) = \Sigma m(0, 1, 3, 6)$

b. $g(w, x, y, z) = \Sigma m(3, 4, 7, 10, 11, 14) + \Sigma d(2, 13, 15)$

c. $F = BD' + ABC + AD + A'B'C$

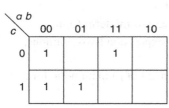

a.

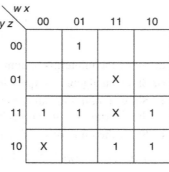

b.

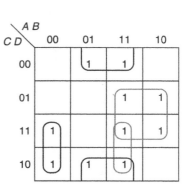

c.

In c, we have two choices. We could expand F, using P10a to

$$F = (A'BC'D' + ABC'D' + A'BCD' + ABCD')$$
$$+ (ABCD' + ABCD) + (AB'C'D + ABC'D + AB'CD$$
$$+ ABCD) + (A'B'CD' + A'B'CD)$$
$$= \Sigma m(4, 12, 6, 14, 14, 15, 9, 13, 11, 15, 2, 3)$$

which, when reordered and duplicates are removed, gives

$$F(A, B, C, D) = \Sigma m(2, 3, 4, 6, 9, 11, 12, 13, 14, 15)$$

Alternately, BD' produces 1's in the B columns (where $B = 1$), that is the middle two columns, and the D' rows (where $D = 0$), that is the first and last rows. ABC corresponds to two 1's, in the AB (11) column and the C (last two) rows. The term AD produces 1's in the last two columns and the middle two rows, and the term $A'B'C$ gives 1's in the first (00) column and the last two rows.

12. Reduce the following expressions to a minimum sum of products form, using P1 through P10. Show each step (number of terms and number of literals in minimum shown in parentheses). Also, show how the steps appear on Karnaugh maps.

    a. $p'q'r + p'qr' + p'qr + pqr' + pq'r'$ (3 terms, 6 literals)

    b. $x'y'z' + x'y'z + x'yz + xy'z + xyz + xyz'$ (3 terms, 5 literals)

    a. $p'q'r + p'qr' + p'qr + pqr' + pq'r'$

    $\quad = p'q'r + (p'qr' + p'qr) + (pqr' + pq'r')$

    $\quad = p'q'r + p'q + pr'$ **[P9a, P9a]**

    $\quad = p'(q'r + q) + pr'$

    $\quad = p'r + p'q + pr'$ **[P10a]**

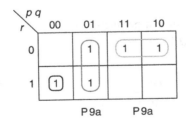

P 9a   P 9a

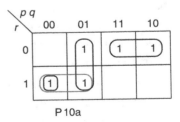

P 10a

    b. $(x'y'z' + x'y'z) + x'yz + (xy'z + xyz) + xyz'$

    $\quad = x'y' + x'yz + xz + xyz'$ **[P9a, P9a]**

    $\quad = x'(y' + yz) + x(z + yz')$

    $\quad = x'y' + (x'z + xz) + xy$ **[P10a, P10a]**

    $\quad = z + x'y' + xy$ **[P9a]**

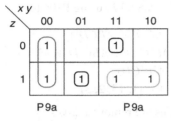 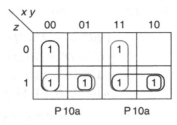 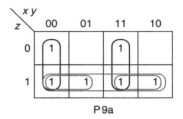

Better, if we look at the map, we note a group of four and can first do

$$z(x'y' + x'y + xy' + xy) + x'y'z' + xyz'$$

$$= z \cdot 1 + x'y'z' + xyz' \qquad \text{[P9aa]}$$

$$= z + z'(x'y' + xy)$$

$$= z + x'y' + xy \qquad \text{[P10a]}$$

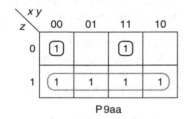 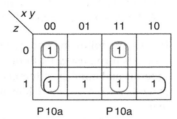

13. Find the complement of the following expressions. Only single variables may be complemented in the answer.

  a. $f = x'yz' + xy'z' + xyz$

  b. $g = (w + x' + y)(w' + x + z)(w + x + y + z)$

  c. $h = (a + b'c)d' + (a' + c')(c + d)$

  a. $f' = (x + y' + z)(x' + y + z)(x' + y' + z')$

    Sum of products becomes product of sums.

  b. $g' = w'xy' + wx'z' + w'x'y'z'$

    Product of sums becomes sum of products.

  c. $h' = [a'(b + c') + d][ac + c'd']$

  or, step by step

$$h' = [(a + b'c)d']'[(a' + c')(c + d)]'$$

$$= [(a + b'c)' + d][(a' + c')' + (c + d)']$$

$$= [a'(b'c)' + d][ac + c'd']$$

$$= [a'(b + c') + d][ac + c'd']$$

14. For the functions of Problem 9 and 10,

  a. Show an algebraic expression in product of maxterm form.

  b. Show a minimum product of sums expression (two terms, five literals).

i. From Problem 9

a. $f'(a, b, c) = \Sigma m(0, 2, 5)$
$$= a'b'c' + a'bc' + ab'c$$
$$f = (a + b + c)(a + b' + c)(a' + b + c')$$

b. Reordering the first two terms of f, we see that adjacency (P9b) is useful
$$f = (a + c + b)(a + c + b')(a' + b + c')$$
$$= (a + c)(a' + b + c')$$

Or, we can minimize f' and then use DeMorgan:
$$f' = a'c' + ab'c$$
$$f = (a + c)(a' + b + c')$$

Note that if we convert the answer of part b to an SOP expression, using P14a, we get
$$f = a(b + c') + a'c = ab + ac' + a'c$$

which is the same as the first answer to Problem 9c.

ii. From Problem 10

a. $f'(x, y, z) = \Sigma m(0, 1, 4)$
$$= x'y'z' + x'y'z + xy'z'$$
$$f = (x + y + z)(x + y + z')(x' + y + z)$$

b. $f' = x'y'z' + x'y'z + xy'z' + x'y'z'$
$$= x'y' + y'z'$$
$$f = (x + y)(y + z)$$

15. Show a block diagram corresponding to each of the expressions below using only NAND gates. Assume all inputs are available both uncomplemented and complemented. There is no need to manipulate the functions to simplify the algebra.

a. $f = ab'd' + bde' + bc'd + a'ce$

b. $g = b(c'd + c'e') + (a + ce)(a' + b'd')$

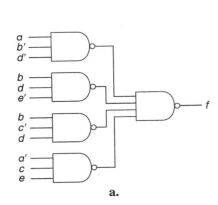

a.

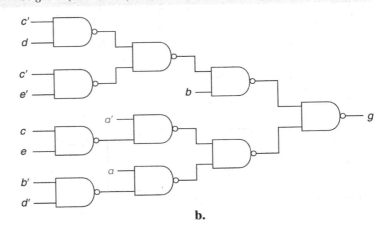

b.

Note that in part a, this is a two-level circuit. In part b, the only inputs that go directly into an OR are a and a'; they are complemented.

16. Show a block diagram corresponding to each of the expressions below using only NOR gates. Assume all inputs are available both uncomplemented and complemented. There is no need to manipulate the functions to simplify the algebra.

    a. $f = (a + b')(a' + c + d)(b + d')$

    b. $g = [a'b' + a(c + d)](b + d')$

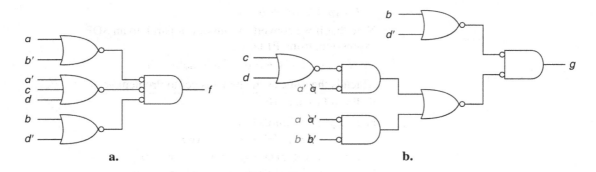

                   a.   **b.**

17. For each of the following circuits,
    i. Find an algebraic expression.
    ii. Put it in sum of product form.

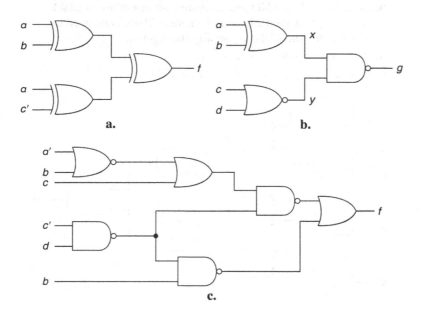

a. i. $f = (a \oplus b) \oplus (a \oplus c')$

    ii. $f = (a'b + ab') \oplus (a'c' + ac)$

$$= (a'b + ab')' \, (a'c' + ac)$$
$$\quad + (a'b + ab') \, (a'c' + ac)'$$
$$= (a'b' + ab) \, (a'c' + ac)$$
$$\quad + (a'b + ab')(a'c + ac')$$
$$= a'b'c' + abc + a'bc + ab'c'$$
$$= b'c' + bc$$

b. i. $g = x' + y' = (a'b + ab')' + c + d$

$$= ab + a'b' + c + d$$

c. i. $f = \{[(a' + b)' + c](c'd)'\}' + [(b(c'd)']'$

    ii. $f = \{[(a' + b)' + c]' + (c'd)\} + [b' + c'd]$

$$= (a' + b)c' + c'd + b' + c'd$$
$$= a'c' + bc' + c'd + b' = a'c' + c' + c'd + b'$$
$$= c' + a'c' + c'd' + b' = c' + b'$$

18. Reduce the following expressions to a minimum sum of products form. Show each step (number of terms and number of literals in minimum shown in parentheses).

  a. $F = A + B + A'B'C'D$ (3 terms, 4 literals)

  b. $f = x'y'z + w'xz + wxyz' + wxz + w'xyz$

                                      (3 terms, 7 literals)

  c. $g = wxy' + xyz + wx'yz + xyz' + wy'$

                                        (3 terms, 6 literals)

  d. $H = AB + B'C + ACD + ABD' + ACD'$

                                        (2 terms, 4 literals)

  e. $G = ABC' + A'C'D + AB'C' + BC'D + A'D$

                                        (2 terms, 4 literals)

  f. $f = abc + b'cd + acd + abd'$ (3 terms, 9 literals)

a. $F = A + B + A'B'C'D$

$$= (A + A'B'C'D) + B$$
$$= (A + B'C'D) + B \qquad\qquad \textbf{[P10a]}$$
$$= A + (B + B'C'D)$$
$$= A + B + C'D \qquad\qquad\qquad \textbf{[P10a]}$$

We can also achieve the same result using a different approach.

$$A + B + A'B'C'D = (A + B) + (A + B)'C'D \qquad \textbf{[P11a]}$$
$$= (A + B) + C'D \qquad\qquad\qquad\qquad \textbf{[P10a]}$$

b. $f = x'y'z + w'xz + wxyz' + wxz + w'xyz$

$$= x'y'z + w'xz + wxyz' + wxz \qquad \textbf{[P12a]}$$

$$= x'y'z + xz + wxyz' \qquad \textbf{[P9a]}$$
$$= x'y'z + x(z + wyz')$$
$$= x'y'z + x(z + wy) \qquad \textbf{[P10a]}$$
$$= x'y'z + xz + wxy$$
$$= z(x'y' + x) + wxy$$
$$= z(y' + x) + wxy \qquad \textbf{[P10a]}$$
$$= y'z + xz + wxy$$

c. $g = wxy' + xyz + wx'yz + xyz' + wy'$

$\qquad = wy' + xy + wx'yz \qquad$ **[P10a, P11a]**

They produce the map on the right.

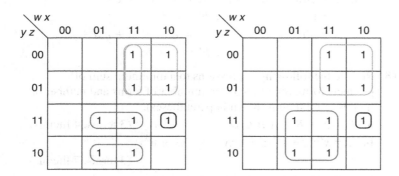

There are two ways to apply P11a next. If we use it with the first and third terms, we get

$$g = w(y' + yx'z) + xy$$
$$\; = w(y' + x'z) + xy$$
$$\; = wy' + wx'z + xy$$

But now, there is nothing further we can do (without a great deal of backtracking or P13a). This is shown on the left map below.

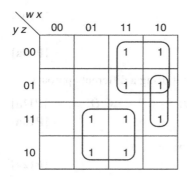
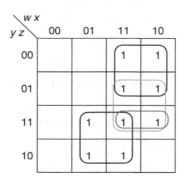

However, if we first used P11a with the second and third terms,

$$g = wy' + y(x + x'wz)$$
$$= wy' + y(x + wz)$$
$$= wy' + xy + wyz$$

That produces the green term on the map to the right. Now, we can apply P11a again to the first and third terms to produce the solution with six literals (including the solid terms on the right map).

$$g = w(y' + yz) + xy = w(y' + z) + xy = wy' + wz + xy$$

d. $H = AB + B'C + ACD + ABD' + ACD'$

$\qquad = AB + B'C + AC$ **[P12a, P9a]**

$\qquad = AB + B'C$ **[P13a]**

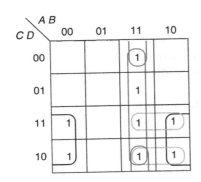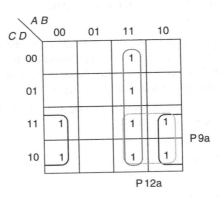

P 9a

P 12a

Note that the consensus term covers only 1's that are part of the other terms.

e. $G = ABC' + A'C'D + AB'C' + BC'D + A'D$

$\qquad = ABC' + AB'C' + A'D + BC'D$ **[P12a]**

$\qquad = AC' + A'D + BC'D$ **[P9a]**

But,

$$AC' \notin A'D = C'D$$
$$G = AC' + A'D + BC'D + C'D \qquad \textbf{[P13a]}$$
$$= AC' + A'D + C'D \qquad \textbf{[P12a]}$$
$$= AC' + A'D \qquad \textbf{[P13a]}$$

Note that we used consensus to first add a term and then to remove that same term. That term is showed in gray on the third map.

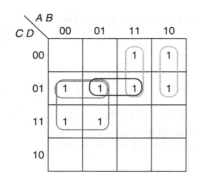

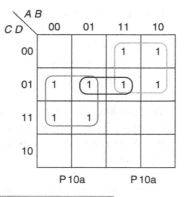

P 10a P 10a

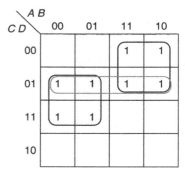

f. $f = abc + b'cd + acd + abd'$

Since

$abc \not\!\!c\ b'cd = acd$

the consensus term can be removed and thus

$f = abc + b'cd + abd'$

No further reduction is possible; the only consensus that exists among the terms in this reduced expression produces the term *acd*, the one that we just removed. None of the other properties can be used to reduce this function further.

However, if we go back to the original function, we note that another consensus does exist:

$acd \not\!\!c\ abd' = abc$

and thus the term *abc* can be removed, producing

$f = b'cd + acd + abd'$

That is another equally good minimum solution (since no further minimization is possible). Even though we found two applications of consensus in this function, we cannot take advantage of both of them since, no matter which one we use first, the term needed to form the second consensus has been removed.

The map below shows the four terms of the original expression circled.

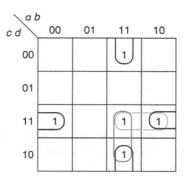

The two terms in black are the ones that are used in both solutions. Once they are chosen, only minterm 15 is left to be covered; we can use either of the other terms, eliminating the fourth.

19. Expand the following function to sum of minterms form

$$F(A, B, C) = A + B'C$$

We have a choice of two approaches. We could use P3b, P5aa (both from right to left) and P8a repeatedly to produce

$$A + B'C = A(B' + B) + (A' + A)B'C$$
$$= AB' + AB + A'B'C + AB'C$$
$$= AB'(C' + C) + AB(C' + C) + A'B'C + AB'C$$
$$= AB'C' + AB'C + ABC' + ABC + A'B'C + AB'C$$
$$= AB'C' + AB'C + ABC' + ABC + A'B'C$$

having removed the duplicated term $(AB'C)$. Or we could use a truth table, such as

A B C	B'C	F
0 0 0	0	0
0 0 1	1	1
0 1 0	0	0
0 1 1	0	0
1 0 0	0	1
1 0 1	1	1
1 1 0	0	1
1 1 1	0	1

and thus,

$$F = A'B'C + AB'C' + AB'C + ABC' + ABC$$

which is the same expression as above reordered, or

$$F(A, B, C) = \Sigma m(1, 4, 5, 6, 7)$$

20. Convert each of the following expressions to sum of products form:
a. $(w + x' + z)(w' + y + z')(x + y + z)$
b. $(a + b + c + d')(b + c + d)(b' + c')$

a. $(w + x' + z)(w' + y + z')(x + y + z)$
$$= [z + (w + x')(x + y)](w' + y + z') \qquad \text{[P8b]}$$
$$= (z + wx + x'y)(w' + y + z') \qquad \text{[P14a]}$$
$$= z(w' + y) + z'(wx + x'y) \qquad \text{[P14a]}$$
$$= w'z + yz + wxz' + x'yz' \qquad \text{[P8a]}$$

Note that this is not a minimum sum of products expression, even though the original was a minimum product of sums expression. Using P10a, we could reduce this to

$$w'z + yz + wxz' + x'y$$

b. $(a + b + c + d')(b + c + d)(b' + c')$

$= [b + c + (a + d')\, d](b' + c')$	**[P8b]**
$= (b + c + ad)(b' + c')$	**[P8b, P5b, P3a]**
$= bc' + b'(c + ad)$	**[P14a]**
$= bc' + b'c + ab'd$	**[P8a]**

or using c instead of b for P14a

$= (b + c + ad)(b' + c')$

$= b'c + c'(b + ad)$

$= b'c + bc' + ac'd$

These are two equally good solutions.

21. Convert each of the following expressions to product of sums form:

a. $a'c'd + a'cd' + bc$

b. $wxy' + xy'z + wx'z'$

a. $a'c'd + a'cd' + bc$

$= c(b + a'd') + c'a'd$	**[P8a]**
$= (c + a'd)(c' + b + a'd')$	**[P14a]**
$= (c + a')(c + d)\,(c' + b + a')(c' + b + d')$	**[P8b]**

Two comments are in order. This is not in minimum product of sums form. P12b allows us to manipulate the first and third terms so as to replace the third term by $(a' + b)$. We could have started the process by factoring a' from the first two terms, but that would require more work.

b. $wxy' + xy'z + wx'z'$

$= xy'(w + z) + x'wz'$	**[P8a]**
$= (x + wz')(x' + y'(w + z))$	**[P14a]**
$= (x + w)(x + z')(x' + y')(x' + w + z)$	**[P8b]**

22. Implement each of the following expressions (which are already in minimum sum of product form) using only two-input NAND gates. No gate may be used as a NOT. All inputs are available both uncomplemented and complemented. (The number of gates required is shown in parentheses.)

a. $f = w'y' + xyz + wyz' + x'y'z$ (8 gates)

b. $F = B'C'D' + BD + ACD + ABC$ (7 gates)

c. $g = a'b'c'd' + abcd' + a'ce + ab'd + be$ (12 gates)

116   **Chapter 2** Switching Algebra and Logic Circuits

a. $f = y'(w' + x'z) + y(xz + wz')$

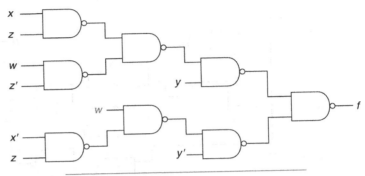

b. $F = AC(B + D) + B'C'D' + BD$

$\quad = (C + B'D')(C' + A(B + D)) + BD$

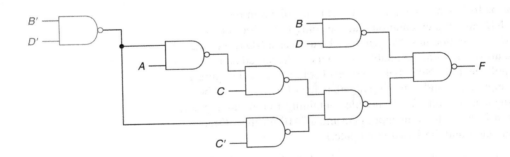

Note that the gate on the left is used to implement both the $B'D'$ term and the $(B + D)$ term.

c. $g = a'b'c'd' + abcd' + a'ce + ab'd + be$

The first attempt at a solution yields one with 13 gates.

$$g = d'(a'b'c' + abc) + e(b + a'c) + ab'd$$
$$= (d' + ab')(d + a'b'c' + abc) + e(b + a'c)$$
$$= (d' + ab')(d + (a + b'c')(a' + bc)) + e(b + a'c)$$
$$\quad\;\, 1\; 2\; 3\quad 4\qquad 5\quad 6\; 7\quad 8\; 9\quad 10\,11\; 12\; 13$$

Another approach is

$$g = a'(b'c'd' + ce) + a(bcd' + b'd) + be$$
$$= [a + b'c'd' + ce][a' + bcd' + b'd] + be$$
$$= [a + (c + b'd')(c' + e)][a' + (b + d)(b' + cd')] + be$$
$$\quad\; 1\quad\; 2\quad 3\; 4\quad 5\quad 6\quad\; 7\quad\; 3\quad 8\quad\; 9\; 10\quad 11\; 12$$

where gate three is used twice, as shown below.

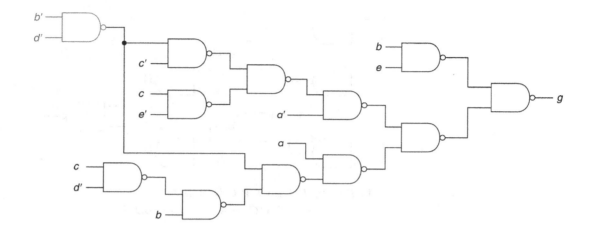

23. For the following function, show the block diagram for a NAND gate implementation that uses only four 7400 series NAND gate modules. No gate may be used as a NOT. Assume that all variables are available both uncomplemented and complemented. (Note that a two-level solution would require 2 six-input gates and a five-input gate (each of which would be implemented with a 7430 module containing 1 eight-input gate), plus a 7420 for the four-input gate and a 7410 for the 2 three-input gates and the 1 two-input gate.)

$$g = abcdef + d'e'f + a'b' + c'd'e' + a'def' + abcd'f'$$

$$g = abc(def + d'f') + d'e'(c' + f) + a'(b' + def')$$

This requires 1 four-input gate (for the first term), 4 three-input gates, and 5 two-input gates (one 7420, with the second gate used as a three-input one, one 7410, and two 7400s with three gates unused). If we required that no four-input gates be used, we could further manipulate the algebra as follows:

$$g = [a' + bc(def + d'f')][a + b' + def'] + d'e'(c' + f)$$

using P14a on the first and last terms, which would require 5 three-input gates and 6 two-input gates (still four modules).

We could also do a completely different factoring, yielding

$$g = de(abcf + a'f') + d'(abcf' + e'f + c'e') + a'b'$$
$$= [d' + e(abcf + a'f')][d + abcf' + e'f + c'e'] + a'b'$$
$$= [d' + e(a' + f)(f' + abc)][d + c'e'$$
$$+ (f + abc)(f' + e')] + a'b'$$

This requires 3 three-input gates and 10 two-input gates (also four modules), as shown below.

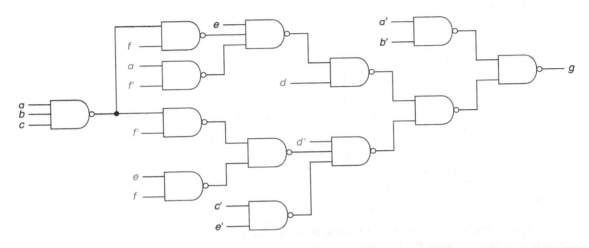

24. The following is already in minimum sum of products form.

$$F = B'DE' + A'B'D + A'BC'D' + ABD'E' + ABDE + ACDE$$

All variables are available both uncomplemented and complemented. Find two solutions, each of which uses no more than three integrated circuit packages of NAND gates (4 two-input or 3 three-input or 2 four-input gates per package). One solution must use only two- and three-input gates; the other must use at least 1 four-input gate package.

The easiest starting point is to factor pairs of terms as follows:

$$F = B'D(A' + E') + BD'(A'C' + AE') + ADE(B + C)$$

This indeed corresponds to a solution that satisfies the problem requirements. There are 3 three-input gates (corresponding to the first AND of $B'D$ ( ), the second AND of BD' ( ), and the output OR). There is 1 four-input gate, corresponding to the last AND, and 5 two-input gates. We thus need one 7420 for the four-input gate; the second gate on that package can be used as the fifth two-input gate. The 3 three-input gates require one 7410, and the remaining 4 two-input gates require one 7400.

By utilizing P14a, we obtain

$$F = B'D(A' + E') + BD'(A' + E')(A + C') + ADE(B + C)$$

Note that the term $A' + E'$ appears twice in the expression, and we can thus share the output of the NAND gate that creates it. This requires 2 four-input gates, 2 three-input gates, and 3 two-input gates, leaving an extra two- and three-input gate unused.

(This might be useful if we were building other circuits at the same time and physically close to this one.) A block diagram of this circuit follows.

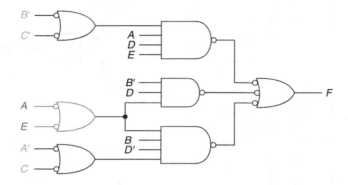

If we wish to find a solution that does not use four-input gates, then we can factor D from the four terms containing it, as follows:

$$F = D[B'(A' + E') + AE(B + C)] + BD'(A'C' + AE')$$
$$\quad\;\; 2\;\; 2 \quad\;\; 2 \quad\;\; 2\;\; 3 \quad 2 \quad\;\; 2\;\; 3 \quad 2\;\; 2\;\; 2$$

As can be seen from the listing under the expression, this implementation requires 9 two-input gates and 2 three-input ones, a total of three chips. There are several other solutions which we will not enumerate here (but none of them use only two-input gates).

2.13   EXERCISES

1. Show a block diagram of a circuit using AND and OR gates for each side of each of the following equalities:
   a.   P2a: $a + (b + c) = (a + b) + c$
   b.   P8a: $a(b + c) = ab + ac$
2. Show a truth table for the following functions:
   a. $F = X'Y + Y'Z' + XYZ$
   b. $G = XY + (X' + Z)(Y + Z')$
   c. $H = WX + XY' + WX'Z + XYZ' + W'XY'$
3. Determine, using truth tables, which expressions in each of the groups are equal:
   a. $f = ac' + a'c + bc$
   $\quad\;\; g = (a + c)(a' + b + c')$

Chapter 2 Switching Algebra and Logic Circuits

*b. $f = a'c' + bc + ab'$
    $g = b'c' + a'c' + ac$
    $h = b'c' + ac + a'b$

c. $f = ab + ac + a'bd$
    $g = bd + ab'c + abd'$

4. For each of the following expressions, indicate which (if any) of the following apply (more than one may apply):

    i. Product term

    ii. Sum of products expression

    iii. Sum term

    iv. Product of sums expression

    a. $abc'd + b'cd + ad'$
  *b. $a' + b + cd$
    c. $b'c'd'$
  *d. $(a + b)c'$
    e. $a' + b$
  *f. a'
  *g. $a(b + c) + a'(b' + d)$
    h. $(a + b' + d)(a' + b + c)$

5. For the expressions of problem 2, how many literals are in each?

6. Using properties 1 to 10, reduce the following expressions to a minimum sum of products form. Show each step (number of terms and number of literals in minimum shown in parentheses).

    *a. $x'z + xy'z + xyz$ (1 term, 1 literal)
    b. $x'y'z' + x'yz + xyz$ (2 terms, 5 literals)
    c. $x'y'z' + x'y'z + xy'z + xyz'$ (3 terms, 7 literals)
    *d. $a'b'c' + a'b'c + abc + ab'c$ (2 terms, 4 literals)
    e. $x'y'z' + x'yz' + x'yz + xyz$ (2 terms, 4 literals)
    *f. $x'y'z' + x'y'z + x'yz + xyz + xyz'$

    (2 solutions, each with 3 terms, 6 literals)

    g. $x'y'z' + x'y'z + x'yz + xy'z + xyz + xyz'$

    (3 terms, 5 literals)

    h. $a'b'c' + a'bc' + a'bc + ab'c + abc' + abc$

    (3 terms, 5 literals)

7. Show a block diagram of a system using AND, OR, and NOT gates to implement the following functions. Assume that variables are available only uncomplemented. Do not manipulate the algebra.

    a. $P'Q' + PR + Q'R$
    b. $ab + c(a + b)$
    *c. $wx'(v + y'z) + (w'y + v')(x + yz)'$

8. For each of the following circuits,

    i. find an algebraic expression

    ii. put it in sum of product form.

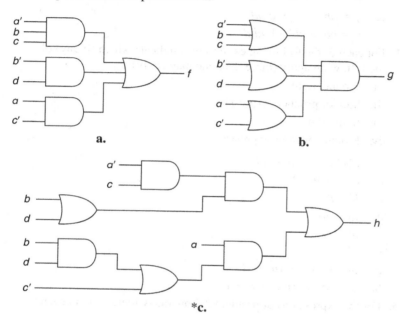

        a.   **b.**

                                  *c.

9. For each of the following functions:

    $*f(x, y, z) = \Sigma m(1, 3, 6)$

    $g(x, y, z) = \Sigma m(0, 2, 4, 6)$

  a.   Show the truth table.

  b.   Show an algebraic expression in sum of minterms form.

  c.   Show a minimum sum of products expression (*a*: 2 terms, 5 literals; *b*: 1 term, 1 literal).

  d.   Show the minterms of f' (complement of f) in numeric form.

*10. For each of the following functions,

a b c	f	g
0 0 0	0	1
0 0 1	1	1
0 1 0	0	0
0 1 1	0	0
1 0 0	0	1
1 0 1	1	1
1 1 0	1	1
1 1 1	1	0

  a.   Show the minterms in numerical form.

  b.   Show an algebraic expression in sum of minterms form.

Chapter 2 Switching Algebra and Logic Circuits

   c.   Show a minimum sum of products expression (f: 2 terms, 4 literals; g: 2 terms, 3 literals).

   d.   Show the minterms of f' (complement of f) in numeric form.

11. For each of the following functions:

$$F = AB' + BC + AC$$
$$G = (A + B)(A + C') + AB'$$

   a.   Show the truth table.

   b.   Show an algebraic expression in sum of minterms form.

   c.   Show a minimum sum of products expression (F: 2 terms, 4 literals; G: 2 terms, 3 literals).

   d.   Show the minterms of the complement of each term in numeric form.

* **12.** Consider the following function with don't cares:

$$G(X, Y, Z) = \Sigma m(5, 6) + \Sigma d(1, 2, 4)$$

For each of the following expressions, indicate whether it could be used as a solution for G. (Note: it may not be a minimum solution.)

   a. $XYZ' + XY'Z$ d. $Y'Z + XZ' + X'Z$

   b. $Z' + XY'Z$ e. $XZ' + X'Z$

   c. $X(Y' + Z')$ f. $YZ' + Y'Z$

13. Plot the following functions on the Karnaugh map:

   a. $f(a, b, c) = \Sigma m(1, 2, 3, 4, 6)$

*   b. $g(w, x, y, z) = \Sigma m(1, 3, 5, 6, 7, 13, 14) + \Sigma d(8, 10, 12)$

   c. $F = WX'Y'Z + W'XYZ + W'X'Y'Z' + W'XY'Z + WXYZ$

*   d. $g = a'c + a'bd' + bc'd + ab'd + ab'cd'$

   e. $h = x + yz' + x'z$

14. Find the complement of the following expressions. Only single variables may be complemented in the answer.

*   a. $f = abd' + b'c' + a'cd + a'bc'd$

   b. $g = (a + b' + c)(a' + b + c)(a + b' + c')$

   c. $h = (a + b)(b' + c) + d'(a'b + c)$

15. For the functions of Problems 9, 10, and 11:

   a.   Show an algebraic expression in product of maxterms form.

   b.   Show a minimum product of sums expression (3 terms, 6 literals; 1, 1; 2, 4; 2, 4; 2, 4; 2, 4, respectively).

16. Show that the NOR is functionally complete by implementing a NOT, a two-input AND, and a two-input OR using only two-input NORs.

17. For each of the following circuits,

   i.   find an algebraic expression

   ii.   put it in sum of products form.

2.13 Exercises

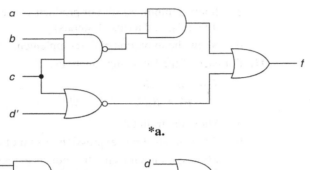

*a.

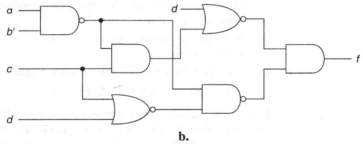

b.

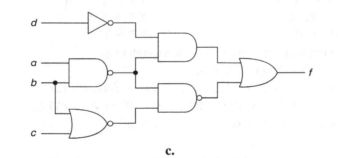

c.

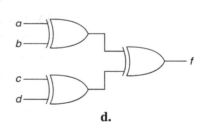

d.

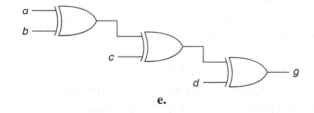

e.

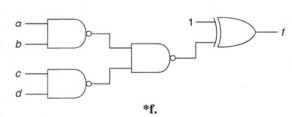

*f.

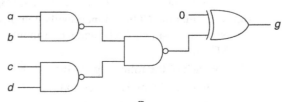

g.

18. Show a block diagram corresponding to each of the expressions below using only NAND gates. Assume all inputs are available both uncomplemented and complemented. Do not manipulate the functions to simplify the algebra.

a. $f = wy' + wxz' + xy'z + w'x'z$

b. $g = wx + (w' + y)(x + y')$

c. $h = z(x'y + w'x') + w(y' + xz')$

*d. $F = D[B'(A' + E') + AE(B + C)] + BD'(A'C' + AE')$

19. Reduce the following expressions to a minimum sum of products form, using P1 through P12. Show each step (number of terms and number of literals in minimum shown in parentheses).

a. $h = ab'c + bd + bcd' + ab'c' + abc'd$ (3 terms, 6 literals)

b. $h = ab' + bc'd' + abc'd + bc$ (3 terms, 5 literals)

*c. $f = ab + a'bd + bcd + abc' + a'bd' + a'c$
    (2 terms, 3 literals)

d. $g = abc + abd + bc'd'$ (2 terms, 5 literals)

e. $f = xy + w'y'z + w'xy' + wxyz' + w'yz + wz$
    (3 terms, 5 literals)

20. Reduce the following expressions to a minimum sum of products form. Show each step and the property used (number of terms and number of literals in minimum shown in parentheses). Also, show how the steps appear on Karnaugh maps.

a. $f = x'yz + w'x'z + x'y + wxy + w'y'z$ (3 terms, 7 literals)

b. $G = A'B'C' + AB'D + BCD' + A'BD + CD + A'D$
    (4 terms, 9 literals)

*c. $F = W'YZ' + Y'Z + WXZ + WXYZ' + XY'Z + W'Y'Z'$
    (3 terms, 7 literals)

d. $g = wxz + xy'z + wz' + xyz + wxy'z + w'y'z'$
    (3 terms, 6 literals)

e. $F = ABD' + B'CE + AB'D' + B'D'E + ABCD'E + B'C'D'$
    (3 terms, 8 literals)

f. $f = b'c + abc + b'cd + a'b'd + a'c'd$ (3 terms, 7 literals)

*g. $G = B'C'D + BC + A'BD + ACD + A'D$
    (3 terms, 6 literals)

h. $f = ab + bcd + ab'c' + abd + bc + abc'$
    (2 terms, 4 literals)

i. $h = abc' + ab'd + bcd + a'bc$ (3 terms, 8 literals)

*j. $g = a'bc' + bc'd + abd + abc + bcd' + a'bd'$
    (2 solutions, 3 terms, 9 literals)

21. i. For the following functions, use consensus to add as many new terms to the sum of product expression given.

   ii. Then reduce each to a minimum sum of products, showing each step and the property used.

    *a. $f = a'b'c' + a'bd + a'cd' + abc$ (3 terms, 8 literals)

    b. $g = wxy + w'y'z + xyz + w'yz'$ (3 terms, 8 literals)

22. Expand the following functions to sum of minterms form:

    *a. $f(a, b, c) = ab' + b'c'$

    b. $g(x, y, z) = x' + yz + y'z'$

    c. $h(a, b, c, d) = ab'c + bd + a'd'$

23. Convert each of the following expressions to sum of products form:

    a. $(a + b + c + d')(b + c' + d)(a + c)$

    b. $(a' + b + c')(b + c' + d)(b' + d')$

    *c. $(w' + x)(y + z)(w' + y)(x + y' + z)$

    d. $(A + B + C)(B' + C + D)(A + B' + D)(B + C' + D')$

24. Convert each of the following expressions to product of sums form:

    a. $AC + A'D'$

    b. $w'xy' + wxy + xz$

    *c. $bc'd + a'b'd + b'cd'$

25. Implement each of the following expressions (which are already in minimum sum of products form) using only two-input NAND gates. No gate may be used as a NOT. All inputs are available both uncomplemented and complemented. (The number of gates required is shown in parentheses.)

    *a. $f = wy' + wxz' + y'z + w'x'z$ (7 gates)

    b. $ab'd' + bde' + bc'd + a'ce$ (10 gates)

    c. $H = A'B'E' + A'B'CD' + B'D'E' + BDE' + BC'E + ACE'$
                                                  (14 gates)

    *d. $F = A'B'D' + ABC' + B'CD'E + A'B'C + BC'D$ (11 gates)

    e. $G = B'D'E' + A'BC'D + ACE + AC'E' + B'CE$
                               (12 gates, one of which is shared)

    f. $h = b'd'e' + ace + c'e' + bcde$ (9 gates)

26. Each of the following is already in minimum sum of products form. All variables are available both uncomplemented and complemented. Find two solutions each of which uses no more than the number of integrated circuit packages of NAND gates (4 two-input or 3 three-input or 2 four-input gates per package) listed. One solution must use only two and three input gates; the other must use at least 1 four-input gate package.

    *a. $F = ABCDE + B'E' + CD'E' + BC'D'E + A'B'C$
        $+ A'BC'E$ (3 packages)

    b. $G = ABCDEF + A'B'D' + C'D'E + AB'CE' + A'BC'DF$
        $+ ABE'F'$ (4 packages)

Chapter 2 Switching Algebra and Logic Circuits

2.14 CHAPTER 2 TEST (100 MINUTES, OR TWO 50-MINUTE TESTS)

1. Use a truth table to demonstrate whether or not the following functions are equal:

$$f = a'b' + a'c' + ab$$
$$g = (b' + c')(a' + b)$$

a b c	f	g
0 0 0		
0 0 1		
0 1 0		
0 1 1		
1 0 0		
1 0 1		
1 1 0		
1 1 1		

2. Reduce the expression below to a sum of products expression with two terms and four literals. Show each step.

$$a'b'c + a'bc + ab'c + ab'c'$$

3. Reduce the expression below to a sum of products expression with two terms and three literals. Show each step.

$$x'y'z' + x'y'z + x'yz' + x'yz + xyz$$

4. For each part, assume all variables are available both uncomplemented and complemented.

$$f = ab'c + ad + bd$$

   a. Show a block diagram for a two-level implementation of f using AND and OR gates.

   b. Show a block diagram for an implementation of f using only two-input AND and OR gates.

5. For the following truth table

x	y	z	f
0	0	0	1
0	0	1	0
0	1	0	1
0	1	1	1
1	0	0	0
1	0	1	1
1	1	0	0
1	1	1	1

   a. Write a sum of minterms function in numeric form, for example,

   $$\Sigma m(0, \ldots)$$

b. Write a sum of minterms function in algebraic form, for example,

$$x'y\,z + \ldots$$

c. Find one minimum sum of products expression (3 terms, 6 literals).

d. Find a product of sums expression in product of maxterms form.

e. Find a minimum product of sums form (2 terms, 5 literals).

6. Map each of the following functions (be sure to label the maps):

a. $f(x, y, z) = \Sigma m(1, 2, 7) + \Sigma d(4, 5)$

	00	01	11	10
0				
1				

b. $g = a'c + ab'c'd + a'bd + abc'$

Circle each of the terms.

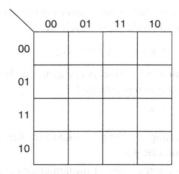

	00	01	11	10
00				
01				
11				
10				

7. Assume all inputs are available both uncomplemented and complemented. Show a two-level implementation of

$$g = w\,x + w\,z + w'\,x' + w'\,y'\,z'$$
$$= (w' + x + z)\,(w + x' + y')\,(w + x' + z')$$

a. using NAND gates of any size

b. using NOR gates of any size

c. using two-input NAND gates (none of which may be used as a NOT)

8. For the each of the following functions find a minimum sum of products expression (3 terms, 6 literals). Show each algebraic step and show maps corresponding to those steps.

a. $f = b'd' + bc'd + b'cd' + bcd + ab'd$

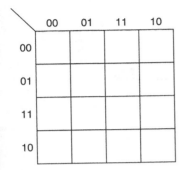

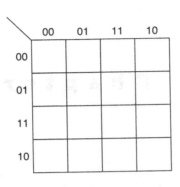

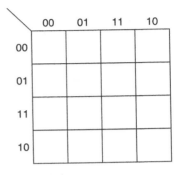

5-POINT BONUS: Find a second minimum sum of products (no maps needed).

b. $g = xy'z' + yz + xy'z + wxy + xz$

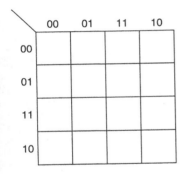

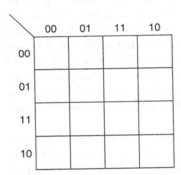

9. a.   Expand the following to sum of minterms (sum of standard product terms). Eliminate any duplicates.

$$g = a' + ac + b'c$$

b.   Manipulate the following to a sum of products expression.

$$f = (x' + y)(w' + y + z')(y' + z)(w + y' + z')$$

10. Implement each of the following functions using only two-input NAND gates. NO GATE MAY BE USED AS A NOT GATE. The functions are in minimum sum of product form. Assume all inputs are available both uncomplemented and complemented.

a. $f = ac + bcd + a'b'd'$ (7 gates)

b. $g = abc + ac'd'e' + a'd'e + ce + cd$

Full credit for 11 gates, 5 point bonus for 10

Chapter 3

The Karnaugh Map

The algebraic methods developed in Chapter 2 allow us, in theory, to simplify any function. However, there are a number of problems with that approach. There is no formal method, such as first apply Property 10, then P14, etc. The approach is totally heuristic, depending heavily on experience. After manipulating a function, we often cannot be sure whether or not it is a minimum. We may not always find the minimum, even though it appears that there is nothing else to do. Furthermore, it gets rather difficult to do algebraic simplification with more than four or five variables. Finally, it is easy to make copying mistakes as we rewrite the equations.

In this chapter we will examine an approach that is easier to implement, the *Karnaugh map* (sometimes referred to as a K-map). This is a graphical approach to finding suitable product terms for use in sum of product expressions. (The product terms that are "suitable" for use in minimum sum of products expressions are referred to as *prime implicants*. We will define that term shortly.) The map is useful for problems of up to six variables and is particularly straightforward for most problems of three or four variables. Although there is no guarantee of finding a minimum solution, the methods we will develop nearly always produce a minimum. We will adapt the approach (with no difficulty) to finding minimum product of sums expressions, to problems with don't cares, and to multiple output problems.

We introduced the Karnaugh map in Section 2.6. In this chapter, we will develop techniques to find minimum sum of product expressions using the map. We will start with three- and four-variable maps and will include five- and six-variable maps later.

We can plot any function on the map. Either, we know the minterms, and use that form of the map (as we did earlier), or we put the function in sum of products form and plot each of the product terms.

EXAMPLE 3.1

Map

$$F = AB' + AC + A'BC'$$

The map for F is shown below, with each of the product terms circled. Each of the two-literal terms corresponds to two squares on the map (since one of the variables is missing). The AB' term is in the 10 column. The AC term is in the $C = 1$ row and in the 11 and 10 columns (with a common 1 in the A position). Finally, the minterm $A'BC'$ corresponds to one square, in the 01 ($A'B$) column and in the $C = 0$ row.

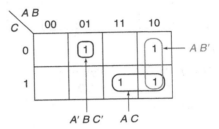

We could have obtained the same map by first expanding F to minterm form algebraically, that is,

$$F = AB'(C' + C) + AC(B' + B) + A'BC'$$
$$= AB'C' + AB'C + AB'C + ABC + A'BC'$$
$$= m_4 + m_5 + m_5 + m_7 + m_2$$
$$= m_2 + m_4 + m_5 + m_7$$

(removing duplicates and reordering)

We can then use the numeric map and produce the same result.

	00	01	11	10
0	0	2 — 1	6	4 — 1
1	1	3	7 — 1	5 — 1

We are now ready to define some terminology related to the Karnaugh map. An *implicant* of a function is a product term that can be used in a sum of products expression for that function, that is, the function is 1 whenever the implicant is 1 (and maybe other times, as well). From the point of view of the map, an implicant is a rectangle of 1, 2, 4, 8, ... (any power of 2) 1's. That rectangle may not include any 0's. All minterms are implicants.

Consider the function, F, of Map 3.1. The second map shows the first four groups of 2; the third map shows the other groups of 2 and the group of 4.

Map 3.1 A function to illustrate definitions.

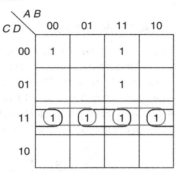

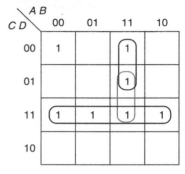

The implicants of *F* are

Minterms	Groups of 2	Groups of 4
A'B'C'D'	A'CD	CD
A'B'CD	BCD	
A'BCD	ACD	
ABC'D'	B'CD	
ABC'D	ABC'	
ABCD	ABD	
AB'CD		

Any sum of products of expression for *F* must be a sum of implicants. Indeed, we must choose enough implicants such that each of the 1's of *F* are included in at least one of these implicants. Such a sum of products expression is sometimes referred to as a *cover* of *F* and we sometimes say that an implicant *covers* certain minterms (for example, *ACD* covers m_{11} and m_{15}).

Implicants must be rectangular in shape and the number of 1's in the rectangle must be a power of 2. Thus, neither of the functions whose maps are shown in Example 3.2 are covered by a single implicant, but rather by the sum of two implicants each (in their simplest form).

EXAMPLE 3.2

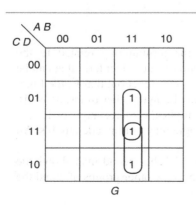

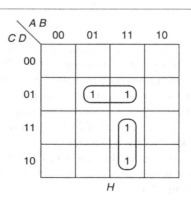

Chapter 3 The Karnaugh Map

G consists of three minterms, $ABC'D$, $ABCD$, and $ABCD'$, in the shape of a rectangle. It can be reduced no further than is shown on the map, namely, to $ABC + ABD$, since it is a group of three 1's, not two or four. Similarly, H has the same three minterms plus $A'BC'D$; it is a group of four, but not in the shape of a rectangle. The minimum expression is, as shown on the map, $BC'D + ABC$. (Note that ABD is also an implicant of G, but it includes 1's that are already included in the other terms.)

Map 3.2 Prime implicants.

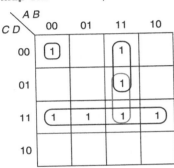

A *prime implicant* is an implicant that (from the point of view of the map) is not fully contained in any one other implicant. For example, it is a rectangle of two 1's that is not part of a single rectangle of four 1's. On Map 3.2, all of the prime implicants of F are circled. They are $A'B'C'D'$, ABC', ABD, and CD. Note that the only minterm that is not part of a larger group is m_0 and that the other four implicants that are groups of two 1's are all part of the group of four.

From an algebraic point of view, a prime implicant is an implicant such that if any literal is removed from that term, it is no longer an implicant. From that viewpoint, $A'B'C'D'$ is a prime implicant because $B'C'D'$, $A'C'D'$, $A'B'D'$, and $A'B'C'$ are not implicants (that is, if we remove any literal from that term, we get a term that is 1 for some input combinations for which the function is to be 0). However, ACD is not a prime implicant since when we remove A, leaving CD, we still have an implicant. (Surely, the graphical approach of determining which implicants are prime implicants is easier than the algebraic method of attempting to delete literals.)

The purpose of the map is to help us find minimum sum of products expressions (where we defined minimum as being minimum number of product terms (implicants) and among those with the same number of implicants, the ones with the fewest number of literals. However, the only product terms that we need consider are prime implicants. Why? Say we found an implicant that was not a prime implicant. Then, it must be contained in some larger implicant, a prime implicant, one that covers more 1's. But that larger implicant (say four 1's rather than two) has fewer literals. That alone makes a solution using the term that is not a prime implicant not a minimum. (For example, CD has two literals, whereas, ACD has three.) Furthermore, that larger implicant covers more 1's, which often will mean that we need fewer terms.

An *essential prime implicant* is a prime implicant that includes at least one 1 that is not included in any other prime implicant. (If we were to circle all of the prime implicants of a function, the essential prime implicants are those that circle at least one 1 that no other prime implicant circles.) In the example of Map 3.2, $A'B'C'D'$, ABC', and CD are essential prime implicants; ABD is not. The term *essential* is derived from the idea that we must use that prime implicant in any minimum sum of products expression. A word of caution is in order. There will often be a prime implicant that is used in a minimum solution (even in all minimum solutions when more than one equally good solution exists) that is not "essential." That happens when each of the 1's covered by this prime implicant could be covered in other ways. We will see examples of that in Section 3.1.

3.1 MINIMUM SUM OF PRODUCT EXPRESSIONS USING THE KARNAUGH MAP

In this section, we will describe two methods for finding minimum sum of products expressions using the Karnaugh map. Although these methods involve some heuristics, we can all but guarantee that they will lead to a minimum sum of products expression (or more than one when multiple solutions exist) for three- and four-variable problems. (They also work for five- and six-variable maps, but our visualization in three dimensions is more limited. We will discuss this in detail in Section 3.5.)

In the process of finding prime implicants, we will be considering each of the 1's on the map starting with the most *isolated* 1's. By isolated, we mean that there are few (or no) adjacent squares with a 1 in it. In an **n**-variable map, each square has **n** adjacent squares. Examples for three- and four-variable maps are shown in Map 3.3.

Map 3.3   Adjacencies on three- and four-variable maps.

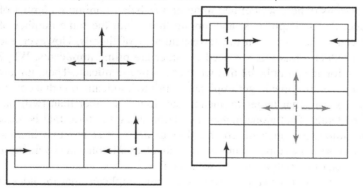

Map Method 1

1.   Find all essential prime implicants. Circle them on the map and mark the minterm(s) that make them essential with an asterisk (*). Do this by examining each 1 on the map that has not already been circled. It is usually quickest to start with the most isolated

   Chapter 3   The Karnaugh Map

1's, that is, those that have the fewest adjacent squares with 1's in them.

2. Find *enough* other prime implicants to cover the function. Do this using two criteria:
   a. Choose a prime implicant that covers as many new 1's (that is, those not already covered by a chosen prime implicant).
   b. Avoid leaving isolated uncovered 1's.

It is often obvious what "enough" is. For example, if there are five uncovered 1's and no prime implicants cover more than two of them, then we need at least three more terms. Sometimes, three may not be sufficient, but it usually is.

We will now look at a number of examples to demonstrate this method. First, we will look at the example used to illustrate the definitions.

EXAMPLE 3.3

As noted, m_0 has no adjacent 1's; therefore, it ($A'B'C'D'$) is a prime implicant. Indeed, it is an essential prime implicant, since no other prime implicant covers this 1. (That is always the case when minterms are prime implicants.) The next place that we look is m_{12}, since it has only one adjacent 1. Those 1's are covered by prime implicant ABC'. Indeed, no other prime implicant covers m_{12}, and thus ABC' is essential. (Whenever we have a 1 with only one adjacent 1, that group of two is an essential prime implicant.) At this point, the map has become

CD \ AB	00	01	11	10
00	1*		1*	
01			1	
11	1	1	1	1
10				

and

$$F = A'B'C'D' + ABC' + \cdots$$

Each of the 1's that have not yet been covered are part of the group of four, CD. Each has two adjacent squares with 1's that are part of that group. That will always be the case for a group of four. (Some squares, such as m_{15} may have more than two adjacent 1's.) CD is essential because no other prime implicant covers m_3, m_7, or m_{11}. However, once that group is circled, as shown below, we have covered the function:

resulting in

$$F = A'B'C'D + ABC' + CD$$

In this example, once we have found the essential prime implicants, we are done; all of the 1's have been covered by one (or more) of the essential prime implicants. We do not need step 2. There may be other prime implicants that were not used (such as ABD in this example).

Another function that is covered using only essential prime implicants is shown in Example 3.4.

We start looking at the most isolated 1, m_{11}. It is covered only by the group of two shown, wyz. The other essential prime implicant is $y'z'$, because of m_0, m_8, or m_{12}. None of these are covered by any other prime implicant; each makes that prime implicant essential. The second map shows these two terms circled.

EXAMPLE 3.4

That leaves two 1's uncovered. Each of these can be covered by two different prime implicants; but the only way to cover them both with one term is shown on the first map below.

Thus, the minimum sum of product solution is

$$f = y'z' + wyz + w'xz$$

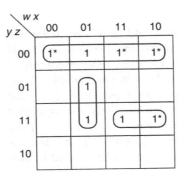 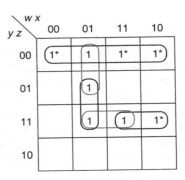

The other two prime implicants are $w'xy'$ and xyz, circled in green on the second map. They are redundant, however, since they cover no new 1's. Even though $w'xz$ must be used in a minimum solution, it does not meet the definition of an essential prime implicant; each of the 1's covered by it can be covered by other prime implicants.

Sometimes, after selecting all of the essential prime implicants, there are two choices for covering the remaining 1's, but only one of these produces a minimum solution, as in Example 3.5.

EXAMPLE 3.5 $f(a, b, c, d) = \Sigma m(0, 2, 4, 6, 7, 8, 9, 11, 12, 14)$

The first map shows the function and the second shows all essential prime implicants circled. In each case, one of the 1's (as indicated with an asterisk, *) can be covered by only that prime implicant. (That is obvious from the last map, where the remaining two prime implicants are circled.)

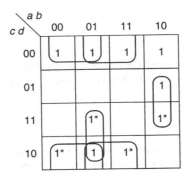 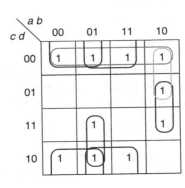

3.1   Minimum Sum of Product Expressions Using the Karnaugh Map   **137**

Only one 1 (m_8) is not covered by an essential prime implicant. It can be covered in two ways, by a group of four (in green) and a group of two (light green). Clearly, the group of four provides a solution with one less literal, namely,

$$f = a'd' + bd' + a'bc + ab'd + c'd'$$

When asking whether a 1 makes a group of four an essential prime implicant on a four-variable map, we need find only two adjacent 0's. If there are fewer than two adjacent 0's, this 1 must be either in a group of eight or part of two or more smaller groups. Note that in Example 3.5, m_2 and m_{14} have two adjacent 0's, and thus each makes a prime implicant essential. In contrast, m_0, m_4, m_8, and m_{12} each have only one adjacent 0 and are each covered by two or three prime implicants. For a 1 to make a group of two essential, it must have three adjacent 0's. That is true for m_7 and m_{11}, but not for m_8 or m_9, each of which can be covered by two prime implicants.

We will now consider some examples with multiple minimum solutions, starting with a three-variable function.

There are two essential prime implicants, as shown on the following maps: **EXAMPLE 3.6**

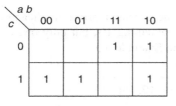 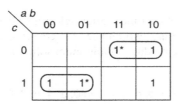 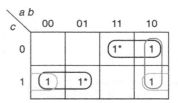

After finding the two essential prime implicants, ac' and $a'c$, as shown on the center map, m_5 is still uncovered. As can be seen from the map on the right, there are two ways to cover that term, yielding two, equally good, minimum solutions:

$$f = ac' + a'c + ab'$$
$$= ac' + a'c + b'c$$

As an aside, we can show that these two solutions are mathematically equal. We can take the first expression and add to it the consensus of the last two terms, $a'c \, ¢ \, ab' = b'c$, leaving

$$f = ac' + a'c + ab' + b'c$$

Notice that the consensus term is the third term of the second expression. We could do the same thing with the first and third terms of the second expression, $ac' \notin b'c = ab'$ and add that to the second expression, obtaining

$$f = ac' + a'c + b'c + ab'$$

These two expressions are indeed the same set of terms in a different order.

EXAMPLE 3.7 $g(w, x, y, z) = \Sigma m(2, 5, 6, 7, 9, 10, 11, 13, 15)$

The function is mapped first, and the two essential prime implicants are shown on the second map, giving

$$g = xz + wz + \cdots$$

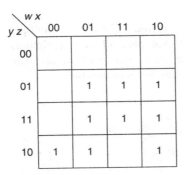
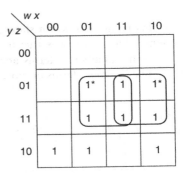

Although m_2 looks rather isolated, it can indeed be covered by $w'yz'$ (with m_6) or by $x'yz'$ (with m_{10}). After choosing the essential prime implicants, the remaining three 1's can each be covered by two different prime implicants. Since there are three 1's left to be covered (after choosing the essential prime implicants), and since all the remaining prime implicants are groups of two and thus have three literals, we need at least two more of these prime implicants. Indeed, there are three ways to cover the remaining 1's with two more prime implicants. Using the first criteria, we choose one of the prime implicants that covers two new 1's, $w'yz'$, as shown on the left map below.

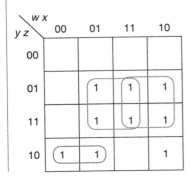
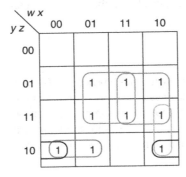
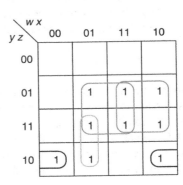

Then, only m_{10} remains and it can be covered either by $wx'y$ or by $x'yz'$, as shown on the center map. Similarly, we could have started with $x'yz'$, in which case we could use $w'xy$ to complete the cover, as on the third map. (We could also have chosen $w'yz'$, but that repeats one of the answers from before.) Thus, the three solutions are

$$g = xz + wz + w'yz' + wx'y$$

$$g = xz + wz + w'yz' + x'yz'$$

$$g = xz + wz + x'yz' + w'xy$$

All three minimum solutions require four terms and 10 literals.

At this point, it is worth stating the obvious. If there are multiple minimum solutions (as was true in this example), all such minimums have the same number of terms and the same number of literals. Any solution that has more terms or more literals is not minimum!

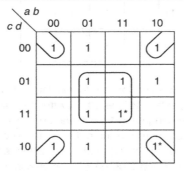

EXAMPLE 3.8

Once again there are two essential prime implicants, as shown on the right map. The most isolated 1's are m_{10} and m_{15}. Each has only two adjacent 1's. But all of the 1's in groups of four have at least two adjacent 1's; if there are only two, then that minterm will make the prime implicant essential. (Each of the other 1's in those groups of four has at least three adjacent 1's.) The essential prime implicants give us

$$f = b'd' + bd + \cdots$$

There are three 1's not covered by the essential prime implicants. There is no single term that will cover all of them. However, the two in the 01 column can be covered by either of two groups of four, as shown on the map on the left (one circled in green, the other in light green). And, there are two groups of two that cover m_9 (also one circled in green, the other in light green), shown on the map to the right.

Chapter 3   The Karnaugh Map

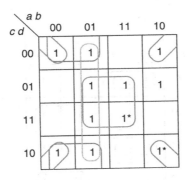
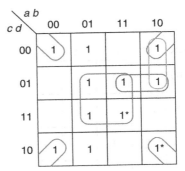

We can choose one term from the first pair and (independently) one from the second pair. Thus, there are four solutions. We can write the solution as shown, where we take one term from within each bracket

$$f = b'd' + bd + \begin{Bmatrix} a'd' \\ a'b \end{Bmatrix} + \begin{Bmatrix} ac'd \\ ab'c' \end{Bmatrix}$$

or we can write out all four expressions

$$f = b'd' + bd + a'd' + ac'd$$
$$= b'd' + bd + a'd' + ab'c'$$
$$= b'd' + bd + a'b + ac'd$$
$$= b'd' + bd + a'b + ab'c'$$

EXAMPLE 3.9

This example is one we call "don't be greedy."

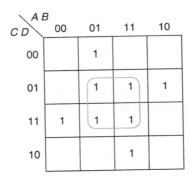
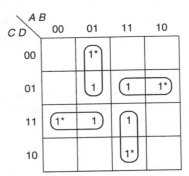

At first glance, one might want to take the only group of four (circled in light green). However, that term is not an essential prime implicant, as is obvious once we circle all of the essential prime implicants and find that the four 1's in the center are covered. Thus, the minimum solution is

$$G = A'BC' + A'CD + ABC + AC'D$$

EXAMPLE 3.10

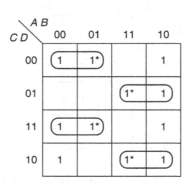
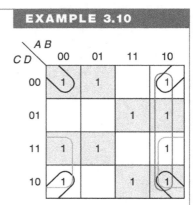

The four essential prime implicants are shown on the second map, leaving three 1's to be covered:

$$F = A'C'D' + AC'D + A'CD + ACD' + \cdots$$

These squares are shaded on the third map. The three other prime implicants, all groups of four, are also shown on the third map. Each of these covers two of the remaining three 1's (no two the same). Thus any two of $B'D'$, AB', and $B'C$ can be used to complete the minimum sum of products expression. The resulting three equally good answers are

$$F = A'C'D' + AC'D + A'CD + ACD' + B'D' + AB'$$
$$F = A'C'D' + AC'D + A'CD + ACD' + B'D' + B'C$$
$$F = A'C'D' + AC'D + A'CD + ACD' + AB' + B'C$$

Before doing additional (more complex) examples, we will introduce a somewhat different method for finding minimum sum of products expressions.

Map Method 2

1.   Circle all of the prime implicants.
2.   Select all essential prime implicants; they are easily identified by finding 1's that have only been circled once.
3.   Then choose enough of the other prime implicants (as in Method 1). Of course, these prime implicants have already been identified in step 1.

142   **Chapter 3** The Karnaugh Map

EXAMPLE 3.11

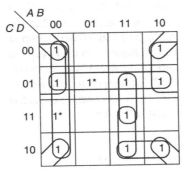

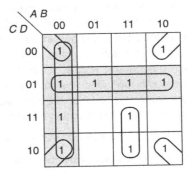

All of the prime implicants have been circled on the center map. Note that m_0 has been circled three times and that several minterms have been circled twice. However, m_3 and m_5 have only been circled once. Thus, the prime implicants that cover them, $A'B'$ and $C'D$ are essential. On the third map, we have shaded the part of the map covered by essential prime implicants to highlight what remains to be covered. There are four 1's, each of which can be covered in two different ways, and five prime implicants not used yet. No prime implicant covers more than two new 1's; thus, we need at least two more terms. Of the groups of four, only $B'D'$ covers two new 1's; $B'C'$ covers only one. Having chosen the first group, we must use ABC to cover the rest of the function, producing

$$F = A'B' + C'D + B'D' + ABC$$

Notice that this is the only set of four prime implicants (regardless of size) that covers the function.

EXAMPLE 3.12 $G(A, B, C, D) = \Sigma m(0, 1, 3, 7, 8, 11, 12, 13, 15)$

This is a case with more 1's left uncovered after finding the essential prime implicant. The first map shows all the prime implicants circled. The only essential prime implicant is YZ; there are five 1's remaining to be covered. Since all of the other prime implicants are groups of two, we need three more prime implicants. These 1's are organized in a chain, with each prime implicant linked to one on either side. If we are looking for just one solution, we should follow the guidelines from Method 1, choosing two terms that

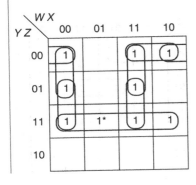

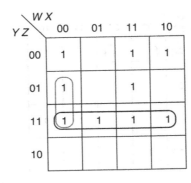

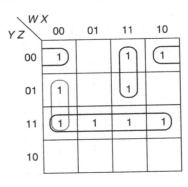

3.1 Minimum Sum of Product Expressions Using the Karnaugh Map

each cover new 1's and then select a term to cover the remaining 1. One such example is shown on the third map, starting with WXY' and $X'Y'Z'$. If we wish to find all of the minimum solutions, one approach is to start at one end of the chain (as shown in the second map). (We could have started at the other end, with m_{13}, and achieved the same results.) To cover m_1, we must either use $W'X'Z$, as shown in green above, or $W'X'Y'$ (as shown on the maps below). Once we have chosen $W'X'Z$, we have no more freedom, since the terms shown on the third map above are the only way to cover the remaining 1's in two additional terms. Thus, one solution is

$$F = YZ + W'X'Z + X'Y'Z' + WXY'$$

The next three maps show the solutions using $W'X'Y'$ to cover m_0.

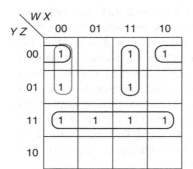 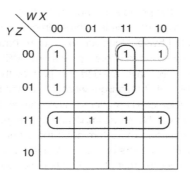 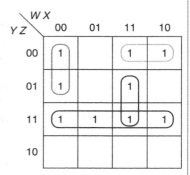

After choosing $W'X'Y'$, there are now three 1's to be covered. We can use the same last two terms as before (left) or use $WY'Z'$ to cover m_8 (right two maps). The other three solutions are thus

$$F = YZ + W'X'Y' + X'Y'Z' + WXY'$$
$$F = YZ + W'X'Y' + WY'Z' + WXY'$$
$$F = YZ + W'X'Y' + WY'Z' + WXZ$$

We will now look at some examples with no essential prime implicants. A classic example of such a function is shown in Example 3.13.

EXAMPLE 3.13

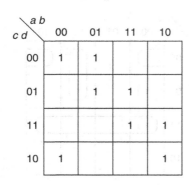 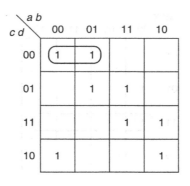 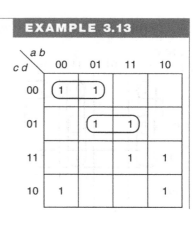

There are eight 1's; all prime implicants are groups of two. Thus, we need at least four terms in a minimum solution. There is no obvious place to start; thus, in the second map, we arbitrarily chose one of the terms, $a'c'd'$. Following the guidelines of step 2, we should then choose a second term that covers two new 1's, in such a way as not to leave an isolated uncovered 1. One such term is $bc'd$, as shown on the third map. Another possibility would be $b'cd'$ (the group in the last row). As we will see, that group will also be used. Repeating that procedure, we get the cover on the left map below,

$$f = a'c'd' + bc'd + acd + b'cd'$$

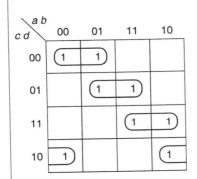

Notice, that if, after starting with $a'c'd'$, we chose one of the prime implicants not included in this solution above, such as abd, shown on the middle map, we leave an isolated uncovered 1 (which would require a third term) plus three more 1's (which would require two more terms). A solution using those two terms would require five terms (obviously not minimum since we found one with four). Another choice would be a term such as $a'b'd'$, which covers only one new 1, leaving five 1's uncovered. That, too, would require at least five terms.

The other solution to this problem starts with $a'b'd'$, the only other prime implicant to cover m_0. Using the same process, we obtain the map on the right and the expression

$$f = a'b'd' + a'bc' + abd + ab'c$$

EXAMPLE 3.14

$$G(A, B, C, D) = \Sigma m(0, 1, 3, 4, 6, 7, 8, 9, 11, 12, 13, 14, 15)$$

All of the prime implicants are groups of four. Since there are 13 1's, we need at least four terms. The first map shows all of the prime implicants circled; there are nine. There are no 1's circled only once, and thus, there are no essential prime implicants.

As a starting point, we choose one of the minterms covered by only two prime implicants, say m_0. On the second map, we used $C'D'$ to cover it. Next, we found two additional prime implicants that cover four new 1's each, as shown on the third map. That leaves just m_{13} to be covered. As can be seen on the fourth map (shown below), there are three different prime implicants that can be used. Now, we have three of the minimum solutions.

$$F = C'D' + B'D + BC + \{AB \quad \text{or} \quad AC' \quad \text{or} \quad AD\}$$

If, instead of using $C'D'$ to cover m_0, we use $B'C'$ (the only other prime implicant that covers m_0), as shown on the next map, we can find two other groups of four that each cover four new 1's and leave just m_{13} to be covered. Once again, we have three different ways to complete the cover (the same three terms as before).

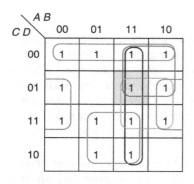
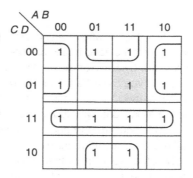
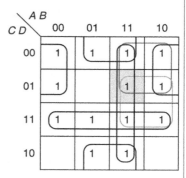

Thus, there are six equally good solutions

$$F = \begin{Bmatrix} C'D' + B'D + BC \\ B'C' + BD' + CD \end{Bmatrix} + \begin{Bmatrix} AB \\ AC' \\ AD \end{Bmatrix}$$

where one group of terms is chosen from the first bracket and an additional term from the second. We are sure that there are no better solutions, since each uses the minimum number of prime implicants, four. Although it may not be obvious without trying other combinations, there are no additional minimum solutions.

A number of other examples are included in Solved Problems 1 and 2. Example 3.15 is one of the most complex four-variable problems, requiring more terms than we might estimate at first.

EXAMPLE 3.15

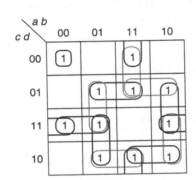

This function has one essential prime implicant (a minterm) and ten other 1's. All of the other prime implicants are groups of two. The second map shows all 13 prime implicants. Note that every 1 (other than m_0) can be covered by two or three different terms.

Since there are ten 1's to be covered by groups of two, we know that we need at least five terms, in addition to $a'b'c'd'$. The third map shows the beginnings of an attempt to cover the function. Each term covers two new 1's without leaving any isolated uncovered 1. (The 1 at the top could be combined with m_{14}.) The four 1's that are left require three additional terms. After trying several other groupings, we can see that it is not possible to cover this function with less than seven terms. There are 32 different minimum solutions to this problem. A few of the solutions are listed below. The remainder are left as an exercise (Ex 1p).

$$f = a'b'c'd' + a'cd + bc'd + ab'd + abc' + a'bc + acd'$$
$$= a'b'c'd' + a'cd + bc'd + ab'd + abd' + bcd' + ab'c$$
$$= a'b'c'd' + b'cd + a'bd + ac'd + abd' + acd' + bcd'$$
$$= a'b'c'd' + b'cd + abc' + bcd' + a'bd + ab'c + ab'd$$

[SP 1, 2; EX 1, 2, 3]

3.2 DON'T CARES

Finding minimum solutions for functions with don't cares does not significantly change the methods we developed in the last section. We need to modify slightly the definitions of a prime implicant and clarify the definition of an essential prime implicant.

A *prime implicant* is a rectangle of 1, 2, 4, 8, . . . 1's or X's not included in any one larger rectangle. Thus, from the point of view of finding prime implicants, X's (don't cares) are treated as 1's.

An *essential prime implicant* is a prime implicant that covers at least one 1 not covered by any other prime implicant (as always). Don't cares (X's) do not make a prime implicant essential.

Now, we just apply either of the methods of the last section. When we are done, some of the X's may be included and some may not. But we *don't care* whether or not they are included in the function.

$$F(A, B, C, D) = \Sigma m(1, 7, 10, 11, 13) + \Sigma d(5, 8, 15)$$

EXAMPLE 3.16

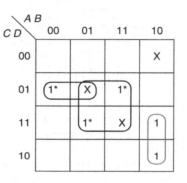

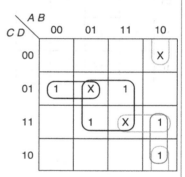

We first mapped the function, entering a 1 for those minterms included in the function and an X for the don't cares. We found two essential prime implicants, as shown on the center map. In each case, the 1's with an asterisk cannot be covered by any other prime implicant. That left the two 1's circled in green to cover the rest of the function. That is not an essential prime implicant, since each of the 1's could be covered by another prime implicant (as shown in light green on the third map). However, if we did not use $AB'C$, we would need two additional terms, instead of one. Thus, the only minimum solution is

$$F = BD + A'C'D + AB'C$$

and terms $AB'D'$ and ACD are prime implicants not used in the minimum solution. Note that if all of the don't cares were made 1's, we would need a fourth term to cover m_8, making

$$F = BD + A'C'D + AB'C + AB'D' \quad \text{or}$$
$$F = BD + A'C'D + ACD + AB'D'$$

and that if all of the don't cares were 0's, the function would become

$$F = A'B'C'D + A'BCD + ABC'D + AB'C$$

In either case, the solution is much more complex then when we treated those terms as don't cares (and made two of them 1's and the other a 0).

148   **Chapter 3**   The Karnaugh Map

EXAMPLE 3.17

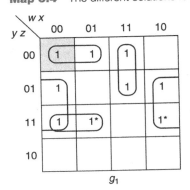

There are two essential prime implicants, as shown on the center map, $x'z$ and $w'yz$. The group of four don't cares, $w'x'$, is a prime implicant (since it is a rectangle of four 1's or X's) but it is not essential (since it does not cover any 1's not covered by some other prime implicant). Surely, a prime implicant made up of all don't cares would never be used, since that would add a term to the sum without covering any additional 1's. The three remaining 1's require two groups of two and thus there are three equally good solutions, each using four terms and 11 literals:

$$g_1 = x'z + w'yz + w'y'z' + wxy'$$
$$g_2 = x'z + w'yz + xy'z' + wxy'$$
$$g_3 = x'z + w'yz + xy'z' + wy'z$$

An important thing to note about Example 3.17 is that the three algebraic expressions are not all equal. The first treats the don't care for m_0 as a 1, whereas the other two (which are equal to each other) treat it as a 0. This will often happen with don't cares. They must treat the specified part of the function (the 1's and the 0's) the same, but the don't cares may take on different values in the various solutions. The maps of Map 3.4 show the three functions.

Map 3.4   The different solutions for Example 3.17.

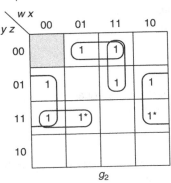
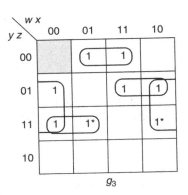

3.2   Don't Cares   149

EXAMPLE 3.18

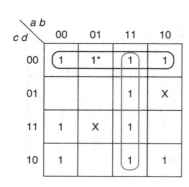
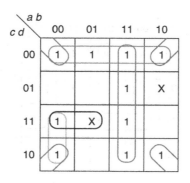

On the first map, we have shown the only essential prime implicant, $c'd'$, and the other group of four that is used in all three solutions, ab. (This must be used since the only other prime implicant that would cover m_{15} is bcd, which requires one more literal and does not cover any 1's that are not covered by ab.) The three remaining 1's require two terms, one of which must be a group of two (to cover m_3) and the other must be one of the groups of four that cover m_{10}. On the second map, we have shown two of the solutions, those that utilize $b'd'$ as the group of four. On the third map, we have shown the third solution, utilizing ad'. Thus, we have

$$g_1 = c'd' + ab + b'd' + a'cd$$
$$g_2 = c'd' + ab + b'd' + a'b'c$$
$$g_3 = c'd' + ab + ad' + a'b'c$$

We can now ask if these solutions are equal to each other. We can either map all three solutions as we did for Example 3.17 or we can make a table of the behavior of the don't cares—one column for each don't care and one row for each solution.

	m_7	m_9
g_1	1	0
g_2	0	0
g_3	0	0

From the table, it is clear that $g_2 = g_3$, but neither is equal to g_1. A more complex example is found in the solved problems.

Don't cares provide us with another approach to solving map problems for functions with or without don't cares.

Map Method 3

1. Find all essential prime implicants using either Map Method 1 or 2.

2. Replace all 1's covered by the essential prime implicants with X's. This highlights the 1's that remain to be covered.

3. Then choose enough of the other prime implicants (as in Methods 1 and 2).

Step 2 works because the 1's covered by essential prime implicants may be used again (as part of a term covering some new 1's), but need not be. Thus, once we have chosen the essential prime implicants, these minterms are, indeed, don't cares.

EXAMPLE 3.19 $F(A, B, C, D) = \Sigma m(0, 3, 4, 5, 6, 7, 8, 10, 11, 14, 15)$

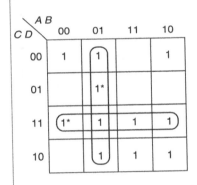 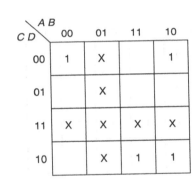

We first found the two essential prime implicants, $A'B$ and CD. On the second map, we converted all of the 1's covered to don't cares. Finally, we can cover the remaining 1's with AC and $B'C'D'$, producing

$$F = A'B + CD + AC + B'C'D'$$

Replacing covered minterms by don't cares accomplishes the same thing as the shading that we did in Examples 3.10 and 3.11; it highlights the 1's that remain to be covered.

[SP 3, 4; EX 4, 5]

3.3   PRODUCT OF SUMS

Finding a minimum product of sums expression requires no new theory. The following approach is the simplest:

1. Map the complement of the function. (If there is already a map for the function, replace all 0's by 1's, all 1's by 0's and leave X's unchanged.)

2. Find the minimum sum of products expression for the complement of the function (using the techniques of the last two sections).

3. Use DeMorgan's theorem (P11) to complement that expression, producing a product of sums expression.

Another approach, which we will not pursue here, is to define the dual of prime implicants (referred to as prime implicates) and develop a new method.

EXAMPLE 3.20

$$f(a, b, c, d) = \Sigma m(0, 1, 4, 5, 10, 11, 14)$$

Since all minterms must be either minterms of f or of f', then, f' must be the sum of all of the other minterms, that is

$$f'(a, b, c, d) = \Sigma m(2, 3, 6, 7, 8, 9, 12, 13, 15)$$

Maps of both f and f' are shown below

$c\,d$ \\ $a\,b$	00	01	11	10
00	1	1		
01	1	1		
11				1
10			1	1

f

$c\,d$ \\ $a\,b$	00	01	11	10
00			1	1
01			1	1
11	1	1	1	
10	1	1		

f'

We did not need to map f, unless we wanted both the sum of products expression and the product of sums expression. Once we mapped f, we did not need to write out all the minterms of f'; we could have just replaced the 1's by 0's and 0's by 1's. Also, instead of mapping f', we could look for rectangles of 0's on the map of f. This function is rather straightforward. The maps for the minimum sum of product expressions for both f and f' are shown below:

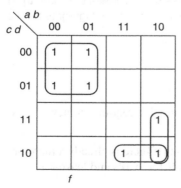

f

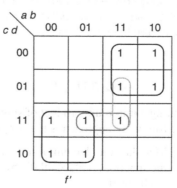

f'

Chapter 3 The Karnaugh Map

There is one minimum solution for f and there are two equally good solutions for the sum of products for f':

$$f = a'c' + ab'c + acd' \qquad f' = ac' + a'c + abd$$
$$f' = ac' + a'c + bcd$$

We can then complement the solutions for f' to get the two minimum product of sums solutions for f:

$$f = (a' + c)(a + c')(a' + b' + d')$$
$$f = (a' + c)(a + c')(b' + c' + d')$$

The minimum sum of products solution has three terms and eight literals; the minimum product of sums solutions have three terms and seven literals. (There is no set pattern; sometimes the sum of products solution has fewer terms or literals, sometimes the product of sums does, and sometimes they have the same number of terms and literals.)

EXAMPLE 3.21

Find all of the minimum sum of products and all minimum product of sums solutions for

$$g(w, x, y, z) = \Sigma m(1, 3, 4, 6, 11) + \Sigma d(0, 8, 10, 12, 13)$$

We first find the minimum sum of products expression by mapping g. However, before complicating the map by circling prime implicants, we also map g' (below g). Note that the X's are the same on both maps.

For g, the only essential prime implicant, $w'xz'$ is shown on the center map. The 1's covered by it are made don't cares on the right map and the remaining useful prime implicants are circled. We have seen similar examples before, where we have three 1's to be covered in groups of two. There are three equally good solutions:

$$g = w'xz' + \begin{cases} w'x'y' + x'yz \\ w'x'z + x'yz \\ w'x'z + wx'y \end{cases}$$

For g', there are three essential prime implicants, as shown on the center map. Once all of the 1's covered by them have been made don't cares, there is only one 1 left; it can be covered in two ways as shown on the right map:

$$g' = x'z' + xz + wy' + \begin{cases} wx \\ wz' \end{cases}$$

$$g = (x + z)(x' + z')(w' + y)\begin{cases} (w' + x') \\ (w' + z) \end{cases}$$

Note that in this example, the sum of product solutions each require only three terms (with nine literals), whereas the product of sums solutions each require four terms (with eight literals).

Finally, we want to determine which, if any, of the five solutions are equal. The complication (compared to this same question in the last section) is that when we treat a don't care as a 1 for g', that means that we are treating it as a 0 of g. Labeling the three sum of product solutions as g_1, g_2, and g_3, and the two product of sums solutions as g_4 and g_5, we produce the following table

	0	8	10	12	13
g_1	1	0	0	0	0
g_2	0	0	0	0	0
g_3	0	0	1	0	0
g_4'	1	1	1	1	1
g_4	0	0	0	0	0
g_5'	1	1	1	1	1
g_5	0	0	0	0	0

The product of sum solutions treat all of the don't cares as 1's of g' since each is circled by the essential prime implicants of g'. (Thus, they are 0's of g.) We then note that the three solutions that are equal are

$$g_2 = w'xz' + w'x'z + x'yz$$

$$g_4 = (x + z)(x' + z')(w' + y)(w' + x')$$

$$g_5 = (x + z)(x' + z')(w' + y)(w' + z)$$

[SP 5, 6; EX 6, 7]

3.4 MINIMUM COST GATE IMPLEMENTATIONS

We are now ready to take another look at implementing functions with various types of gates. In this section, we will limit our discussion to two-level solutions for systems where all inputs are available both un-complemented and complemented. (In Section 2.10, we examined multi-level circuits.) The minimization criteria is minimum number of gates, and among those with the same number of gates, minimum number of gate inputs. (Other criteria, such as minimum number of integrated circuit packages, were also discussed in Section 2.10 and will be examined further in Chapter 5.) The starting point is almost always to find the minimum sum of products solutions and/or the minimum product of sums solutions. That is because each term (other than single literal ones) corresponds to a gate. Then, unless the function has only one term, there is one output gate. Minimizing the number of literals minimizes the number of inputs to these gates.

First, we will look for solutions using AND and OR gates. We must look at both the minimum sum of products and minimum product of sums solutions. In Examples 3.20 and 3.21 from the last section, the product of sums solutions for f had one less gate input than the sum of products solution and the sum of products solutions for g had one less gate than the product of sums solutions. One of the minimum cost solutions for each is shown in Figure 3.1. (There are three equally good ones for f and two equally good ones for g.)

Figure 3.1   Minimum cost AND/OR implementations.

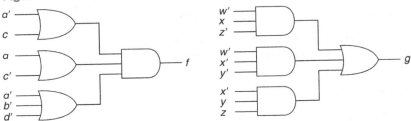

For a two-level solution using NAND gates, we need to start with a minimum sum of products solution. Thus, for g we can use the solution we obtained for AND and OR, but for f, we must use the sum of products solution, the one with one more gate input, as shown in Figure 3.2.

Similarly, for a two-level solution with NOR gates, we use a minimum product of sums solution, resulting in the circuits of Figure 3.3. Note that the NOR gate solution for g uses one more gate than the NAND gate solution.

If we are not limited to two levels, we have one additional option for implementing NAND gate solutions (or NOR gate solutions) beyond the algebraic manipulation of Section 2.8. We could find a minimum sum of

Figure 3.2   NAND gate implementations.

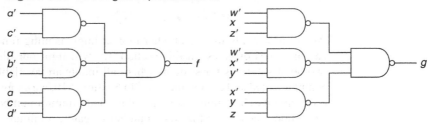

Figure 3.3   NOR gate implementations.

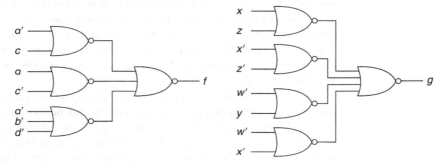

products expression for f' and implement that with NAND gates. We would then place a NOT gate at the output to produce f.

$$G(A, B, C, D) = \Sigma m(0, 1, 3, 4, 6, 7, 8, 9, 11, 12, 13, 14, 15)$$

EXAMPLE 3.22

In Example 3.14, we found six equally good minimum sum of products solutions, each of which has four terms and eight literals. These solutions would require five gates. One of them is

$$G = C'D' + B'D + BC + AB$$

The map for G' is shown below

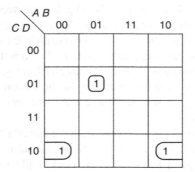

and thus

$$G' = A'BC'D + B'CD'$$

We could implement G' with three NAND gates and then use a NOT gate (or a two-input NAND with the inputs tied together) on the output as shown below:

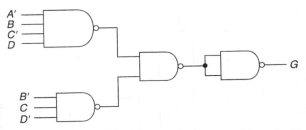

This requires only four gates compared to the sum of products solution which required five gates. (Either would require two 7400 series packages.)

[SP 7; EX 8]

3.5 FIVE- AND SIX-VARIABLE MAPS

A five-variable map consists of $2^5 = 32$ squares. Although there are several arrangements that have been used, we prefer to look at it as two layers of 16 squares each. The top layer (on the left below) contains the squares for the first 16 minterms (for which the first variable, A, is 0) and the bottom layer contains the remaining 16 squares, as pictured in Map 3.5:

Map 3.5 A five-variable map.

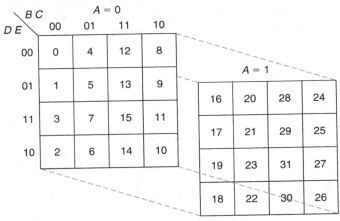

Each square in the bottom layer corresponds to the minterm numbered 16 more than the square above it. Product terms appear as rectangular solids of 1, 2, 4, 8, 16, . . . 1's or X's. Squares directly above and below each other are adjacent.

EXAMPLE 3.23

$$m_2 + m_5 = A'B'C'DE' + AB'C'DE' = B'C'DE'$$
$$m_{11} + m_{27} = A'BC'DE + ABC'DE = BC'DE$$
$$m_5 + m_7 + m_{21} + m_{23} = B'CE$$

These terms are circled on the map below.

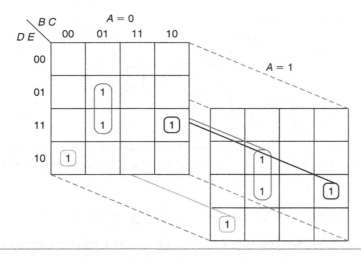

In a similar manner, six-variable maps are drawn as four layers of 16-square maps, where the first two variables determine the layer and the other variables specify the square within the layer. The layout, with minterm numbers shown, is given in Map 3.6. Note that the layers are ordered in the same way as the rows and the columns, that is 00, 01, 11, 10.

In this section, we will concentrate on five-variable maps, although we will also do an example of six-variable maps at the end. The

Map 3.6 A six-variable map.

	A B = 00			
C D E F	00	01	11	10
00	0	4	12	8
01	1	5	13	9
11	3	7	15	11
10	2	6	14	10

A B = 01

16	20	28	24
17	21	29	25
19	23	31	27
18	22	30	26

A B = 11

48	52	60	56
49	53	61	57
51	55	63	59
50	54	62	58

A B = 10

32	36	44	40
33	37	45	41
35	39	47	43
34	38	46	42

techniques are the same as for four-variable maps; the only thing new is the need to visualize the rectangular solids. Rather than drawing the maps to look like three dimensions, we will draw them side by side. The function, F, is mapped in Map 3.7.

$$F(A, B, C, D, E) = \Sigma m(4, 5, 6, 7, 9, 11, 13, 15, 16, 18, 27, 28, 31)$$

Map 3.7 A five-variable problem.

A

0

DE \ BC	00	01	11	10
00		1		
01		1	1	1
11		1	1	1
10		1		

1

DE \ BC	00	01	11	10
00	1		1	
01				
11			1	1
10	1			

As always, we first look for the essential prime implicants. A good starting point is to find 1's on one layer for which there is a 0 in the corresponding square on an adjoining layer. Prime implicants that cover that 1 are contained completely on that layer (and thus, we really only have a four-variable map problem). In this example, m_4 meets this criteria (since there is a 0 in square 20 below it). Thus, the only prime implicants covering m_4 must be on the first layer. Indeed, $A'B'C$ is an essential prime implicant. (Note that the A' comes from the fact that this group is contained completely on the $A = 0$ layer of the map and the $B'C$ from the fact that this group is in the second column.) Actually, all four 1's in this term have no counterpart on the other layer and m_6 would also make this prime implicant essential. (The other two 1's in that term are part of another prime implicant, as well.) We also note that m_9, m_{16}, m_{18}, and m_{28} have 0's in the corresponding square on the other layer and make a prime implicant essential. Although m_{14} has a 0 beneath it (m_{30}), it does not make a prime implicant on the A' layer essential. Thus Map 3.8 shows each of these circled, highlighting the essential prime implicants that are contained on one layer.

So far, we have

$$F = A'B'C + A'BE + AB'C'E' + ABCD'E' + \cdots$$

The two 1's remaining uncovered do have counterparts on the other layer. However, the only prime implicant that covers them is BDE, as shown on Map 3.9 in green. It, too, is an essential prime implicant. (Note that prime implicants that include 1's from both layers do not have the variable A in

Map 3.8   Essential prime implicants on one layer.

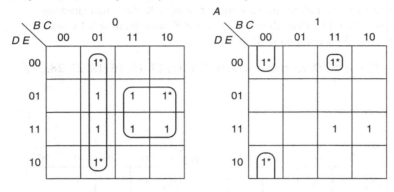

them. Such prime implicants must, of course, have the same number of 1's on each layer; otherwise, they would not be rectangular.)

Map 3.9   A prime implicant covering 1's on both layers.

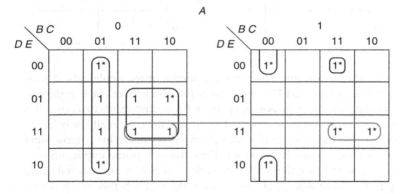

The complete solution is thus

$$F = A'B'C + A'BE + AB'C'E' + ABCD'E' + BDE$$

Groups of eight 1's are not uncommon in five-variable problems, as illustrated in Example 3.24.

$G(A, B, C, D, E) = \Sigma m(1, 3, 8, 9, 11, 12, 14, 17, 19, 20, 22, 24, 25, 27)$

The first map shows a plot of that function. On the second map, to the right, we have circled the two essential prime implicants that we found by considering 1's on one layer with 0's in the corresponding square on the other layer. The group of eight 1's, $C'E$ (also an essential prime implicant), is shown in green on the third map (where the essential prime implicants found on the second map are shown as don't cares). Groups of eight have three literals missing (leaving only two). At this point, only two 1's are left uncovered; that requires the essential prime implicant, $BC'D'$, shown on the fourth map in light green.

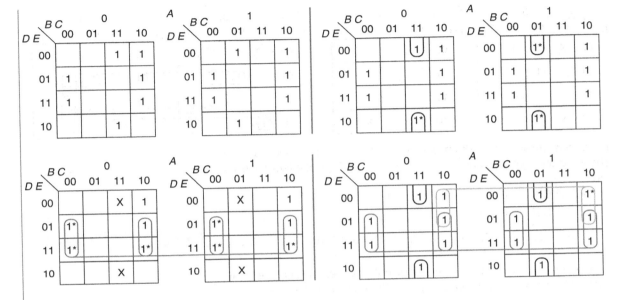

The solution is thus

$$G = A'BCE' + AB'CE' + C'E + BC'D'$$

Note that there is only one other prime implicant in this function, $A'BD'E'$; it covers no 1's not already covered.

EXAMPLE 3.25

The next problem is shown on the maps below. Once again, we start by looking for 1's that are on one layer, with a corresponding 0 on the other layer. Although there are several such 1's on the $A = 0$ layer, only m_{10} makes a prime implicant essential. Similarly, on the $A = 1$ layer, m_{30} is covered by an essential prime implicant. These terms, $A'C'E'$ and $ABCD$, are shown on the second map. The 1's covered are shown as don't cares on the next map.

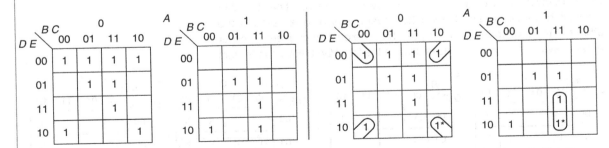

Three other essential prime implicants include 1's from both layers of the map; they are $CD'E$, BCE and $B'C'DE'$, as shown on the left map below. These were found by looking for isolated 1's, such as m_{21}, m_{15}, and m_{18}.

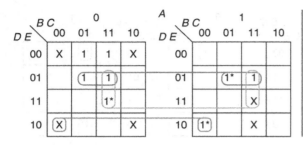

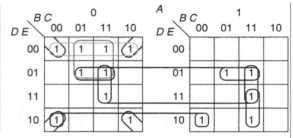

Finally, the remaining two 1's (m_4 and m_{12}) can be covered in two ways, as shown on the right map above, $A'CD'$ and $A'D'E'$. Thus, the two solutions are

$$F = A'C'E' + ABCD + CD'E + BCE + B'C'DE' + A'CD'$$

$$F = A'C'E' + ABCD + CD'E + BCE + B'C'DE' + A'D'E'$$

$$H(A, B, C, D, E) = \Sigma m(1, 8, 9, 12, 13, 14, 16, 18, 19, 22, 23, 24, 30)$$
$$+ \Sigma d(2, 3, 5, 6, 7, 17, 25, 26)$$

EXAMPLE 3.26

A map of H is shown below on the left with the only essential prime implicant, $B'D$, (a group of eight, including four 1's and four don't cares) circled.

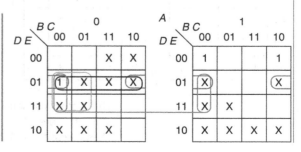

Next, we choose CDE', since otherwise separate terms would be needed to cover m_{14} and m_{30}. We also chose $A'BD'$ since it covers four new 1's. Furthermore, if that were not used, a group of two ($A'BCE'$) would be needed to cover m_{12}. That leaves us with three 1's (m_1, m_{16}, and m_{24}) to be covered. On the maps below, we have replaced all covered 1's by don't cares (X's) to highlight the remaining 1's. No term that covers m_1 also covers either of the other terms. However, m_{16} and m_{24} can be covered with one term in either of two ways ($AC'E'$ or $AC'D'$) as shown on the first map below, and m_1 can

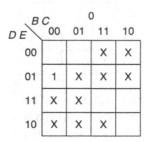

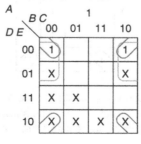

162   **Chapter 3**   The Karnaugh Map

be covered by four different groups of four, as shown on the second map ($A'D'E$, $A'B'E$, $B'C'E$, or $C'D'E$), yielding the eight solutions shown.

$$H = B'D + CDE' + A'BD' + \begin{Bmatrix} AC'E' \\ AC'D' \end{Bmatrix} + \begin{Bmatrix} A'D'E \\ A'B'E \\ B'C'E \\ C'D'E \end{Bmatrix}$$

Finally, we will look at one example of a six-variable function.

EXAMPLE 3.27 $G(A, B, C, D, E, F) = \Sigma m(1, 3, 6, 8, 9, 13, 14, 17, 19, 24, 25, 29, 32,$
$33, 34, 35, 38, 40, 46, 49, 51, 53, 55, 56, 61, 63)$

The map is drawn horizontally, with the first two variables determining the 16-square layer (numbered, of course 00, 01, 11, 10).

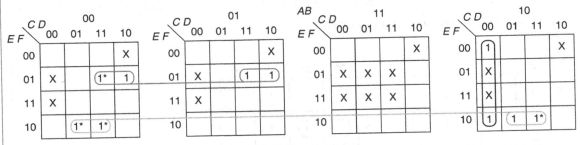

The first map shows three of the essential prime implicants. The only one that is confined to one layer is on the third layer, $ABDF$. The 1's in the upper right corner of each layer form another group of four (without the first two variables), $CD'E'F'$. The green squares form a group of eight, $C'D'F$. The next map shows 1's covered by the first three prime implicants as don't cares.

The other two essential prime implicants are $A'CE'F$ and $B'DEF'$. (Remember that the top and bottom layers are adjacent.) Finally, m_{32} and m_{34} (on the fourth layer) remain uncovered; they are covered by the term, $AB'C'D'$. (Each of them could have been covered by a group of two; but that would take two terms.) Thus, the minimum expression is

$$G = ABDF + CD'E'F' + C'D'F + A'CE'F + B'DEF' + AB'C'D'$$

[SP 8, 9; EX 9, 10]

3.6 MULTIPLE OUTPUT PROBLEMS

Many real problems involve designing a system with more than one output. If, for example, we had a problem with three inputs, A, B, and C and two outputs, F and G, we could treat this as two separate problems (as shown on the left in Figure 3.4). We would then map each of the functions, and find minimum solutions. However, if we treated this as a single system with three inputs and two outputs (as shown on the right), we may be able to economize by sharing gates.

Figure 3.4 Implementation of two functions.

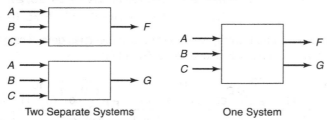

Two Separate Systems   One System

In this section, we will illustrate the process of obtaining two-level solutions using AND and OR gates (sum of products solutions), assuming all variables are available both uncomplemented and complemented. We could convert each of these solutions into NAND gate circuits (using the same number of gates and gate inputs). We could also find product of sums solutions (by minimizing the complement of each of the functions and then using DeMorgan's theorem).

We will illustrate this by first considering three very simple examples.

$F(A, B, C) = \Sigma m(0, 2, 6, 7)$ $G(A, B, C) = \Sigma m(1, 3, 6, 7)$

EXAMPLE 3.28

If we map each of these and solve them separately,

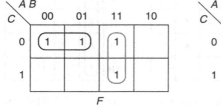

we obtain

$F = A'C' + AB$ $G = A'C + AB$

Looking at the maps, we see that the same term (AB) is circled on both. Thus, we can build the circuit on the left, rather than the two circuits on the right.

Chapter 3   The Karnaugh Map

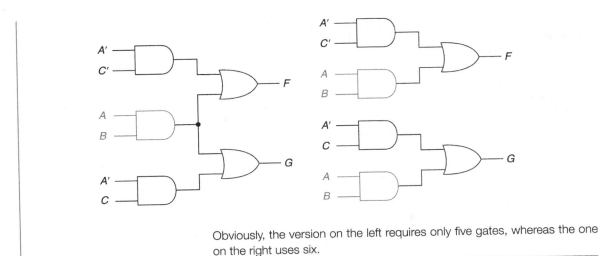

Obviously, the version on the left requires only five gates, whereas the one on the right uses six.

This example is the simplest. Each of the minimum sum of product expressions contains the same term. It would take no special techniques to recognize this and achieve the savings.

Even when the two solutions do not have a common prime implicant, we can share as illustrated in the following example:

EXAMPLE 3.29 $F(A, B, C) = \Sigma m(0, 1, 6)$ $G(A, B, C) = \Sigma m(2, 3, 6)$

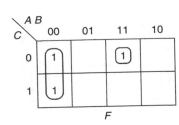

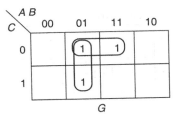

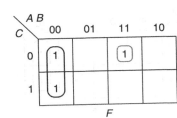

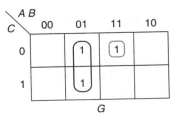

In the top maps, we considered each function separately and obtained

$$F = A'B' + ABC' \qquad G = A'B + BC'$$

This solution requires six gates (four ANDs and two ORs) with 13 inputs. However, as can be seen from the second pair of maps, we can share the term ABC' and obtain

$$F = A'B' + ABC' \qquad G = A'B + ABC'$$

(To emphasize the sharing, we have shown the shared term in green, and will do that in other examples that follow.) As can be seen from the circuit below, this only requires five gates with 11 inputs.

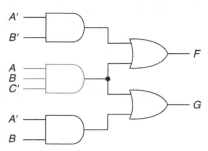

This example illustrates that a shared term in a minimum solution need not be a prime implicant. (In Example 3.29, ABC' is a prime implicant of F but not of G; in Example 3.30, we will use a term that is not a prime implicant of either function.)

$$F(A, B, C) = \Sigma m(2, 3, 7) \qquad G(A, B, C) = \Sigma m(4, 5, 7)$$

EXAMPLE 3.30

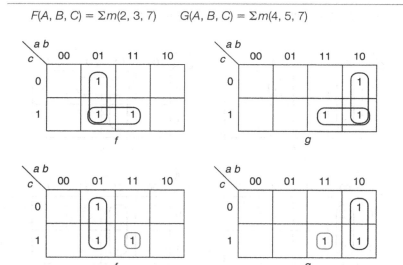

In the first pair of maps, we solved this as two problems. Using essential prime implicants of each function, we obtained

$$f = a'b + bc \qquad g = ab' + ac$$

166   **Chapter 3**   The Karnaugh Map

However, as can be seen in the second set of maps, we can share the term *abc*, even though it is not a prime implicant of either function, and once again get a solution that requires only five gates:

$$f = a'b + abc \qquad g = ab' + abc$$

The method for solving this type of problem is to begin by looking at the 1's of each function that are 0's of the other function. They must be covered by prime implicants of that function. Only the shared terms need not be prime implicants. In this last example, we chose $a'b$ for f since m_2 makes that an essential prime implicant of F and we chose ab' for g since m_4 makes that an essential prime implicant of g. That left just one 1 uncovered in each function—the same 1—which we covered with abc. We will now look at some more complex examples.

EXAMPLE 3.31

$$F(A, B, C, D) = \Sigma m(4, 5, 6, 8, 12, 13)$$
$$G(A, B, C, D) = \Sigma m(0, 2, 5, 6, 7, 13, 14, 15)$$

The maps of these functions are shown below. In them, we have shown in green the 1's that are included in one function and not the other.

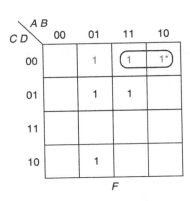

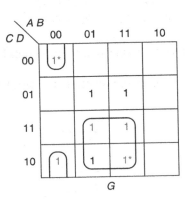

We then circled each of those prime implicants that was made essential by a green 1. The only green 1 that was not circled in F is m_4 because that can be covered by two prime implicants. Even though one of the terms would have fewer literals, we must wait. Next, we will use $A'BD'$ for F. Since m_6 was covered by an essential prime implicant of G, we are no longer looking for a term to share. Thus, m_6 will be covered in F by the prime implicant, $A'BD'$. As shown on the maps below, that leaves m_4 and m_{12} to be covered in both functions, allowing us to share the term $BC'D$, as shown on the following maps circled in green.

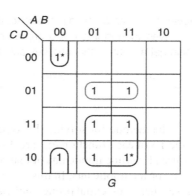

leaving

$$F = AC'D' + A'BD' + BC'D$$
$$G = A'B'D' + BC + BC'D$$

for a total of seven gates with 20 gate inputs. Notice that if we had mini-mized the functions individually, we would have used two separate terms for the third term in each expression, resulting in

$$F = AC'D' + A'BD' + BC'$$
$$G = A'B'D' + BC + BD$$

for a total of eight gates with 21 gate inputs. Clearly, the shared circuit costs less.

The shared version of the circuit is shown below.

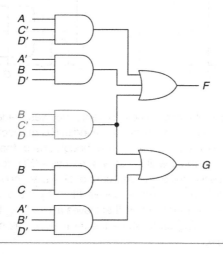

EXAMPLE 3.32

$F(A, B, C, D) = \Sigma m(0, 2, 3, 4, 6, 7, 10, 11)$

$G(A, B, C, D) = \Sigma m(0, 4, 8, 9, 10, 11, 12, 13)$

Once again the maps are shown with the unshared 1's in green and the prime implicants made essential by one of those 1's circled.

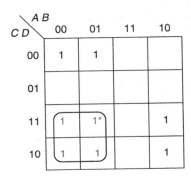   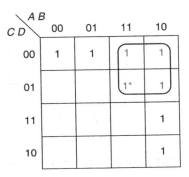

Each of the functions can be solved individually with two more groups of four, producing

$$F = A'C + A'D' + B'C \qquad G = AC' + C'D' + AB'$$

That would require eight gates with 18 gate inputs. However, sharing the groups of two as shown on the next set of maps reduces the number of gates to six and the number of gate inputs to 16. If these functions were implemented with NAND gates, the individual solutions would require a total of three packages, whereas the shared solution would require only two.

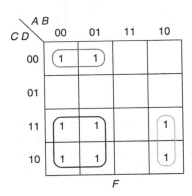   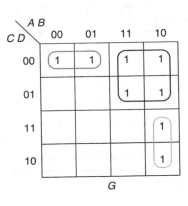

leaving the equations and the resulting AND/OR circuit.

$$F = A'C + A'C'D' + AB'C \qquad G = AC' + A'C'D' + AB'C$$

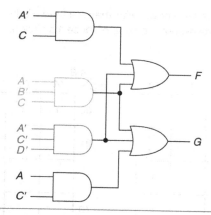

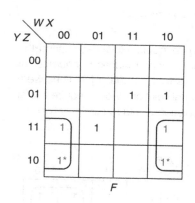

$$F(W, X, Y, Z) = \Sigma m(2, 3, 7, 9, 10, 11, 13)$$

$$G(W, X, Y, Z) = \Sigma m(1, 5, 7, 9, 13, 14, 15)$$

EXAMPLE 3.33

On the maps below, the 1's that are not shared are shown in green and the essential prime implicants that cover these 1's are circled.

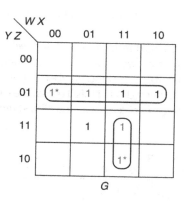

$$F = X'Y + \cdots$$

$$G = Y'Z + WXY + \cdots$$

Now, there are three 1's left in F. Since m_9 and m_{13} have been covered in G by an essential prime implicant, no sharing is possible for these terms in F. Thus, $WY'Z$, a prime implicant of F, is used in the minimum cover. Finally, there is one uncovered 1 in each function, m_7; it can be covered by a shared term, producing the solution

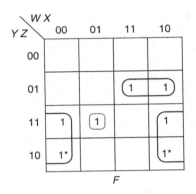

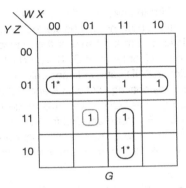

$$F = X'Y + WY'Z + W'XYZ$$
$$G = Y'Z + WXY + W'XYZ$$

This requires seven gates and 20 inputs, compared to the solution we obtain by considering these as separate problems

$$F = X'Y + WY'Z + W'YZ$$
$$G = Y'Z + WXY + XZ$$

which requires eight gates with 21 inputs.

The same techniques can be applied to problems with three or more outputs.

EXAMPLE 3.34

First, we show the solution obtained if we considered them as three separate problems.

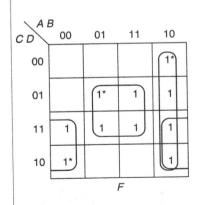

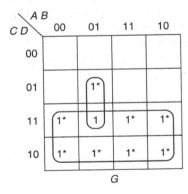

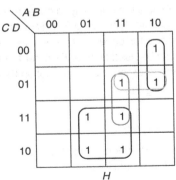

$$F = AB' + BD + B'C$$
$$G = C + A'BD$$
$$H = BC + AB'C' + (ABD \text{ or } AC'D)$$

This solution requires 10 gates and 25 gate inputs. (Note that the term C in function G does not require an AND gate.)

The technique of first finding 1's that are only minterms of one of the functions does not get us started for this example, since each of the 1's is a minterm of at least two of the functions. The starting point, instead, is to choose C for function G. The product term with only one literal does not require an AND gate and uses only one input to the OR gate. Any other solution, say sharing $B'C$ with F and BC with H, requires at least two inputs to the OR gate. Once we have made that choice, however, we must then choose $B'C$ for F and BC for H, because of the 1's shown in green on the following maps. There is no longer any sharing possible for those 1's and they make those prime implicants essential in F and H.

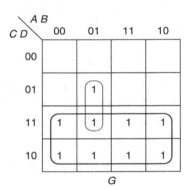
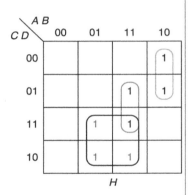

The term $AB'C'$ (circled in light green) was chosen next for H since it is an essential prime implicant of H and it can be shared (that is, all of the 1's in that term are also 1's of F, the only place where sharing is possible). $AB'C'$ is also used for F, since it covers two 1's and we would otherwise require an additional term, AB', to cover m_8. In a similar fashion, the term $A'BD$ is used for G (it is the only way to cover m_5) and can then be shared with F. Finally, we can finish covering F and H with ABD (a prime implicant of H, one of the choices for covering H when we treated that as a separate problem). It would be used also for F, rather than using another AND gate to create the prime implicant BD. The solution then becomes

$$F = B'C + AB'C' + A'BD + ABD$$
$$G = C + A'BD$$
$$H = BC + AB'C' + ABD$$

which requires only eight gates and 22 gate inputs (a savings of two gates and three-gate inputs).

$F(A, B, C, D) = \Sigma m(0, 2, 6, 10, 11, 14, 15)$

$G(A, B, C, D) = \Sigma m(0, 3, 6, 7, 8, 9, 12, 13, 14, 15)$

$H(A, B, C, D) = \Sigma m(0, 3, 4, 5, 7, 10, 11, 12, 13, 14, 15)$

EXAMPLE 3.35

The map on the next page shows these functions; the only 1 that is not shared and makes a prime implicant essential is m_9 in G. That prime implicant, AC', is shown circled.

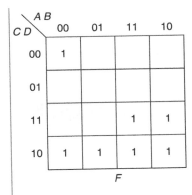

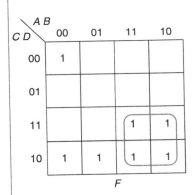

Next, we note that AC is an essential prime implicant of F (because of m_{11} and m_{15}) and of H (because of m_{10}). Furthermore, neither m_{10} nor m_{11} are 1's of G. Thus, that term is used for both F and H. Next, we chose BC' for H and BC for G; each covers four new 1's, some of which can no longer be shared (since the 1's that correspond to other functions have already been covered).

At this point, we can see that $A'B'C'D'$ can be used to cover m_0 in all three functions; otherwise, we would need three different three-literal terms. $A'CD$ can be used for G and H, and, finally, CD' is used for F, producing the following map and algebraic functions.

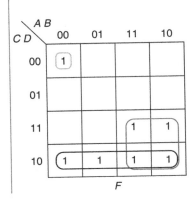

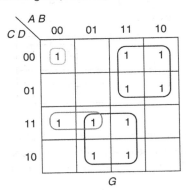

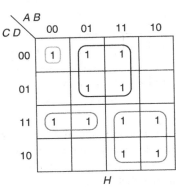

$$F = AC + A'B'C'D' + CD'$$
$$G = AC' + BC + A'B'C'D' + A'CD$$
$$H = AC + BC' + A'B'C'D' + A'CD$$

This solution requires 10 gates with 28 inputs, compared to 13 gates and 35 inputs if these were implemented separately.

Finally, we will consider an example of a system with don't cares:

EXAMPLE 3.36

$$F(A, B, C, D) = \Sigma m(2, 3, 4, 6, 9, 11, 12) + \Sigma d(0, 1, 14, 15)$$
$$G(A, B, C, D) = \Sigma m(2, 6, 10, 11, 12) + \Sigma d(0, 1, 14, 15)$$

A map of the functions, with the only prime implicant made essential by a 1 that is not shared circled, $B'D$, is shown below.

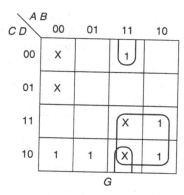

Since m_{11} has now been covered in F, we must use the essential prime implicant of G, AC, to cover m_{11} there. Also, as shown on the next maps, ABD' is used for G, since that is an essential prime implicant of G and the whole term can be shared. (We will share it in the best solution.)

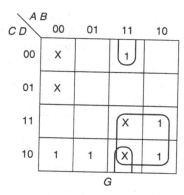

Since we need the term ABD' for G, one approach is to use it for F also. (That only costs a gate input to the OR gate.) If we do that, we could cover the rest of F with $A'D'$ and the rest of G with CD', yielding the map and equations that follow.

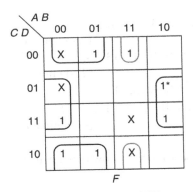
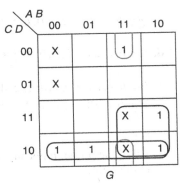

$$F = B'D + ABD' + A'D'$$
$$G = AC + ABD' + CD'$$

That solution uses seven gates and 17 inputs. Another solution using the same number of gates but one more input shares $A'CD'$. That completes G and then the cover of F is completed with BD'. The maps and equations are thus:

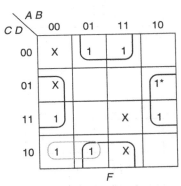
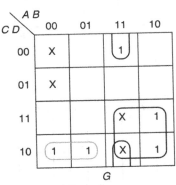

$$F = B'D + A'CD' + BD'$$
$$G = AC + ABD' + A'CD'$$

That, too, requires seven gates, but using a three-input AND gate instead of a two-input one, bringing the total number of inputs to 18.

[SP 10; EX 11, 12]

3.7 SOLVED PROBLEMS

1. For each of the following, find all minimum sum of products expressions. (If there is more than one solution, the number of solutions is given in parentheses.)

   a. $G(X, Y, Z) = \Sigma m(1, 2, 3, 4, 6, 7)$

   b. $f(w, x, y, z) = \Sigma m(2, 5, 7, 8, 10, 12, 13, 15)$

c. $g(a, b, c, d) = \Sigma m(0, 6, 8, 9, 10, 11, 13, 14, 15)$

(2 solutions)

d. $f(a, b, c, d) = \Sigma m(0, 4, 5, 6, 7, 8, 9, 10, 11, 13, 14, 15)$

(2 solutions)

e. $f(a, b, c, d) = \Sigma m(0, 1, 2, 4, 6, 7, 8, 9, 10, 11, 12, 15)$

f. $g(a, b, c, d) = \Sigma m(0, 2, 3, 5, 7, 8, 10, 11, 12, 13, 14, 15)$

(4 solutions)

a. All of the prime implicants are essential, as shown on the map to the right.

Z \ XY	00	01	11	10
0		1	1	1
1	1	1	1	

Z \ XY	00	01	11	10
0		1*	1	1*
1	1*	1	1*	

$$G = Y + XZ' + X'Z$$

b.

yz \ wx	00	01	11	10
00		1	1	
01		1	1	
11		1	1	
10	1			1

yz \ wx	00	01	11	10
00		1	1	
01		1*	1	
11		1*	1*	
10	1*			1

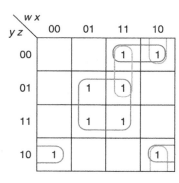

yz \ wx	00	01	11	10
00			1	1
01		1	1	
11		1	1	
10	1			1

The essential prime implicants are shown on the second map, leaving two 1's to be covered. The third map shows that each can be covered by two different prime implicants, but the green group shown is the only one that covers both with one term. We would require both light green terms. The minimum is

$$f = xz + x'yz' + wy'z'$$

c.

The three essential prime implicants are shown on the center map. The only 1 left to be covered can be covered by either of two groups of four, as shown circled in green on the third map, producing

$$g = b'c'd' + bcd' + ad + ab'$$
$$g = b'c'd' + bcd' + ad + ac$$

d.

There are no essential prime implicants. We need one group of two to cover m_0; all other 1's can be covered by groups of four. Once we have chosen $a'c'd'$ to cover m_0 (center map), we would choose ab' to cover m_8. (Otherwise, we must use $b'c'd'$, a group of two to cover that 1. Not only is that more literals, it covers nothing else new; whereas ab' covered three additional uncovered 1's.) Once that has been done, the other two prime implicants become obvious, giving

$$f = a'c'd' + ab' + bc + bd$$

In a similar fashion (on the next map), once we choose $b'c'd'$ (the other prime implicant that covers m_0), $a'b$ is the appropriate choice to cover m_4:

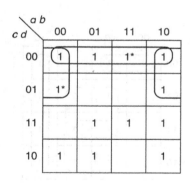

The only way to cover the remaining 1's in two terms is with ac and ad, as shown on the second map, leaving

$$f = b'c'd' + a'b + ac + ad$$

e. There are two essential prime implicants, as indicated on the first map, leaving six 1's to be covered. The essential prime implicants are shaded on the second map.

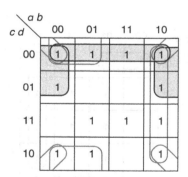

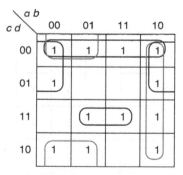

No prime implicant covers more than two of the remaining 1's; thus three more terms are needed. The three groups of four (two literal terms) are circled in green on the second map. We can cover four new 1's only using $a'd'$ and ab'. Note that m_7 and m_{15} are uncovered; they require a group of two, bcd. The only minimum solution, requiring five terms and 11 literals,

$$f = c'd' + b'c' + a'd' + ab' + bcd$$

is shown on the third map. There is another solution that uses five terms, but it requires 12 literals, namely,

$$f = c'd' + b'c' + b'd' + a'bc + acd$$

Obviously, it is not minimum (since it has an extra literal); it only used one of the groups of four instead of two.

f. On the second map, the two essential prime implicants have been highlighted ($b'd' + bd$), leaving four 1's uncovered. On the third map, we have shown the 1's covered by these prime implicants shaded.

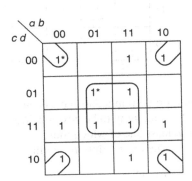
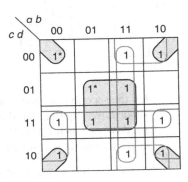

We can cover m_3 and m_{11} by either cd or $b'c$ (shown with green lines), and we can cover m_{12} and m_{14} by either ab or ad' (shown in gray lines). Thus, there are four solutions:

$$f = b'd' + bd + cd + ab$$
$$f = b'd' + bd + cd + ad'$$
$$f = b'd' + bd + b'c + ab$$
$$f = b'd' + bd + b'c + ad'$$

The term ac is also a prime implicant. However, it is not useful in a minimum solution since it leaves two isolated 1's to be covered, resulting in a five-term solution.

2. For the following functions,
   i. List all prime implicants, indicating which are essential.
   ii. Show the minimum sum of products expression(s).
   a. $G(A, B, C, D) = \Sigma m(0, 1, 4, 5, 7, 8, 10, 13, 14, 15)$
   (3 solutions)

   b. $f(w, x, y, z) = \Sigma m(2, 3, 4, 5, 6, 7, 9, 10, 11, 13)$
   c. $h(a, b, c, d) = \Sigma m(1, 2, 3, 4, 8, 9, 10, 12, 13, 14, 15)$
   (2 solutions)

a. The first map shows all of the prime implicants circled; the 1's that have been covered only once are indicated with an asterisk:

   Essential prime implicants: $A'C'$, BD
   Other prime implicants: $B'C'D'$, $AB'D'$, ACD', ABC

CD \ AB	00	01	11	10
00	1	1*		1
01	1*	1	1*	
11		1*	1	
10			1	1

CD \ AB	00	01	11	10
00	1	1		1
01	1	1	1	
11		1	1	
10			1	1

On the second map, the essential prime implicants have been shaded, highlighting the three 1's remaining to be covered. We need two terms to cover them, at least one of which must cover two of these remaining 1's. The three solutions are thus

$$F = A'C' + BD + ACD' + B'C'D'$$
$$F = A'C' + BD + AB'D' + ACD'$$
$$F = A'C' + BD + AB'D' + ABC$$

b.

yz \ wx	00	01	11	10
00		1		
01		1	1	1
11	1	1		1
10	1	1		1

yz \ wx	00	01	11	10
00		1*		
01		1	1	1
11	1	1		1
10	1	1		1*

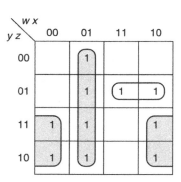

The second map shows all of the prime implicants circled and the 1's that have been covered only once are indicated with an asterisk:

Essential prime implicants: $w'x$, $x'y$

Other prime implicants: $w'y$, $xy'z$, $wy'z$, $wx'z$

With the essential prime implicants shaded on the third map, it is clear that the only minimum solution is

$$f = w'x + x'y + wy'z$$

c. All of the prime implicants are circled on the first map, with the essential prime implicants shown in green.

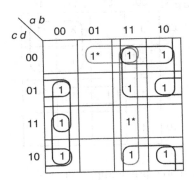

Essential prime implicants: $ab, bc'd'$

Other prime implicants: $ac', ad', b'c'd, b'cd', a'b'c, a'b'd$

Once we chose the essential prime implicants, there are six 1's left to be covered. We can only cover two at a time. There are two groups of four 1's, either of which can be used. (We cannot use both, since that would only cover three 1's.) The two solutions are shown on the maps below.

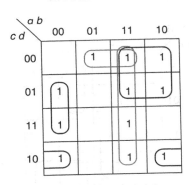

$$h = ab + bc'd' + ac' + a'b'd + b'cd'$$
$$h = ab + bc'd' + ad' + b'c'd + a'b'c$$

3. For each of the following, find all minimum sum of product expressions. (If there is more than one solution, the number of solutions is given in parentheses.)

   a. $f(a, b, c, d) = \Sigma m(0, 2, 3, 7, 8, 9, 13, 15) + \Sigma d(1, 12)$

   b. $F(W, X, Y, Z) = \Sigma m(1, 3, 5, 6, 7, 13, 14) + \Sigma d(8, 10, 12)$

   (2 solutions)

   c. $f(a, b, c, d) = \Sigma m(3, 8, 10, 13, 15)$
   $+ \Sigma d(0, 2, 5, 7, 11, 12, 14)$ (8 solutions)

a.

c d \ a b	00	01	11	10
00	1		X	1
01	X		1	1
11	1	1	1	
10	1*			

c d \ a b	00	01	11	10
00	1		X	1
01	X		1	1
11	1	1	1	
10	1			

The first map shows the one essential prime implicant, $a'b'$. The remaining 1's can be covered by two additional terms, as shown on the second map. In this example, all don't cares are treated as 1's. The resulting solution is

$$f = a'b' + ac' + bcd$$

Although there are other prime implicants, such as $b'c'$, abd, and $a'cd$, three prime implicants would be needed in addition to $a'b'$ if any of them were chosen.

b.

Y Z \ W X	00	01	11	10
00			X	X
01	1	1	1	
11	1	1		
10		1	1	X

Y Z \ W X	00	01	11	10
00			X	X
01	1*	1	1	
11	1*	1		
10	1	1		X

Y Z \ W X	00	01	11	10
00	1		X	X
01	1	1	1	
11	1	1		
10		1	1	X

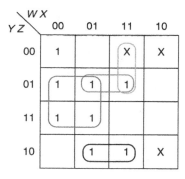

The second map shows all of the prime implicants circled. It is clear that only $W'Z$ is essential, after which three 1's remain uncovered. The prime implicant XYZ' is the only one that can cover two of these and thus appears in both minimum solutions. That leaves a choice of two terms to cover the remaining one—either WXY' (light green) or $XY'Z$ (gray). Note that they treat the don't care at m_{12} differently and thus, although the two solutions shown below both satisfy the requirements of the problem, they are not equal:

$$F = W'Z + XYZ' + WXY'$$
$$F = W'Z + XYZ' + XY'Z$$

Also, the group of four (WZ') is not used; that would require a four term solution.

c. There are no essential prime implicants in this problem. The left map shows the only two prime implicants that cover m_8; they also cover m_{10}. We must choose one of these. The next map shows the only prime implicants that cover m_{13}; both also cover m_{15}. We must choose one of these also. Finally, the last map shows the only two prime implicants that cover m_3.

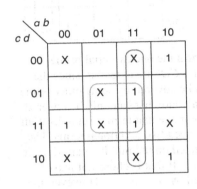

So, our final solution takes one from each group, giving us a total of eight solutions:

$$f = \left\{ \begin{matrix} ad' \\ b'd' \end{matrix} \right\} + \left\{ \begin{matrix} ab \\ bd \end{matrix} \right\} + \left\{ \begin{matrix} cd \\ b'c \end{matrix} \right\}$$

or, written out

$$f = ad' + ab + cd$$
$$f = ad' + ab + b'c$$
$$f = ad' + bd + cd$$
$$f = ad' + bd + b'c$$
$$f = b'd' + ab + cd$$
$$f = b'd' + ab + b'c$$
$$f = b'd' + bd + cd$$
$$f = b'd' + bd + b'c$$

4. For each of the following, find all minimum sum of product expressions. Label the solutions $f_1, f_2, \ldots$ and indicate which solutions are equal.

a. $F(A, B, C, D) = \Sigma m(4, 6, 9, 10, 11, 12, 13, 14)$
$\qquad\qquad + \Sigma d(2, 5, 7, 8)$ \qquad (3 solutions)

b. $f(a, b, c, d) = \Sigma m(0, 1, 4, 6, 10, 14)$
$\qquad\qquad + \Sigma d(5, 7, 8, 9, 11, 12, 15)$ \qquad (13 solutions)

a.

CD \ AB	00	01	11	10
00		1	1	X
01		X	1	1
11		X		1*
10	X	1	1	1

CD \ AB	00	01	11	10
00		1	1	X
01		X	1	1
11		X		1
10	X	1	1	1

CD \ AB	00	01	11	10
00		1	1	X
01		X	1	1
11		X		1
10	X	1	1	1

On the first map, we have shown the one essential prime implicant, AB'. Neither $A'B$ nor CD' are essential, since the 1's covered by them can each be covered by some other prime implicant. (That there is a don't care that can only be covered by one of these terms does not make that term essential.) With five 1's left to be covered, we need two additional terms. The first that stands out is BD', circled on the middle map, since it covers four of the remaining 1's. If that is chosen, it leaves only m_{13}, which can be covered by BC' or AC'. However, the third map shows still another cover, utilizing BC' and CD'. Thus, the three solutions are

$$F_1 = AB' + BD' + BC'$$
$$F_2 = AB' + BD' + AC'$$
$$F_3 = AB' + BC' + CD'$$

Notice that none of the solutions utilize the remaining prime implicant, $A'B$.

Next is the question of whether or not these three solutions are equal. The answer can be determined by examining how the don't cares are treated by each of the functions. The following table shows that:

	2	5	7	8
F_1	0	1	0	1
F_2	0	0	0	1
F_3	1	1	0	1

In all functions, m_7 is treated as 0 (that is, it is not included in any prime implicant used) and m_8 as 1 (since it is included in the essential prime implicant, AB'); but the first two columns show that no two functions treat m_2 and m_5 the same. Thus, none of these is equal to any other.

b. There are no essential prime implicants. The best place to start is with a 1 that can only be covered in two ways; in this problem there is only one, m_1. Any solution must contain either the term $a'c'$ (as shown on the first four maps) or the term $b'c'$ (as shown on the remaining two maps). There is no reason to use both, since $b'c'$ does not cover any 1's that are not already covered by $a'c'$. The first map shows $a'c'$. Note that there are three 1's left, requiring two more terms. At least one of these terms must cover two of the remaining 1's.

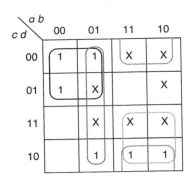

The second map shows two ways of covering m_6 and m_{14}, bc and bd'. In either case, only one 1 is left to be covered. The third map shows the previously covered 1's as don't cares and three ways of covering the last 1, m_{10}. Thus, we have as the first six solutions

$$f_1 = a'c' + bc + ab'$$
$$f_2 = a'c' + bc + ac$$
$$f_3 = a'c' + bc + ad'$$
$$f_4 = a'c' + bd' + ab'$$
$$f_5 = a'c' + bd' + ac$$
$$f_6 = a'c' + bd' + ad'$$

Next, we consider how we may cover both m_{10} and m_{14} with one term (in addition to those already found). That provides two more solutions shown on the left map below. (Other solutions that use these terms have already been listed.)

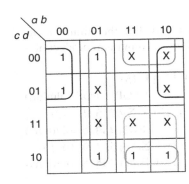

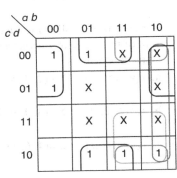

$$f_7 = a'c' + a'b + ad'$$
$$f_8 = a'c' + a'b + ac$$

We next consider the solutions that use $b'c'$. The middle map shows two of these, utilizing $a'b$. The last map shows the final three, utilizing bd', instead; it has the same three last terms as in the first series. Thus, we have

$$f_9 = b'c' + a'b + ad'$$
$$f_{10} = b'c' + a'b + ac$$
$$f_{11} = b'c' + bd' + ab'$$
$$f_{12} = b'c' + bd' + ac$$
$$f_{13} = b'c' + bd' + ad'$$

Finally, the table below shows how each of the functions treats the don't cares:

	5	7	8	9	11	12	15
f_1	1	1	1	1	1	0	1
f_2	1	1	0	0	1	0	1
f_3	1	1	1	0	0	1	1
f_4	1	0	1	1	1	1	0
f_5	1	0	0	0	1	1	1
f_6	1	0	1	0	0	1	0
f_7	1	1	1	0	0	1	0
f_8	1	1	0	0	1	0	1
f_9	1	1	1	1	0	1	0
f_{10}	1	1	1	1	1	0	1
f_{11}	0	0	1	1	1	1	0
f_{12}	0	0	1	1	1	1	1
f_{13}	0	0	1	1	0	1	0

Comparing the rows, the only two pairs that are equal are

$$f_1 = f_{10} \quad \text{and} \quad f_2 = f_8.$$

5. For each of the following functions, find all of the minimum sum of product expressions and all of the minimum product of sums expressions:

a. $f(w, x, y, z) = \Sigma m(2, 3, 5, 7, 10, 13, 14, 15)$

(1 SOP, 1 POS solution)

b. $f(a, b, c, d) = \Sigma m(3, 4, 9, 13, 14, 15) + \Sigma d(2, 5, 10, 12)$

(1 SOP, 2 POS solutions)

c. $f(a, b, c, d) = \Sigma m(4, 6, 11, 12, 13) + \Sigma d(3, 5, 7, 9, 10, 15)$

(2 SOP and 8 POS solutions)

a. The map of f is shown below.

$yz \backslash wx$	00	01	11	10
00				
01		1	1	
11	1	1	1	
10	1		1	1

$yz \backslash wx$	00	01	11	10
00				
01			1*	1*
11	1	1	1	
10	1		1	1

Although there is only one essential prime implicant, there is only one way to complete the cover with two more terms, namely,

$$f = xz + w'x'y + wyz'$$

By replacing all the 1's with 0's and 0's with 1's, or by plotting all the minterms not in f, we get the map for f'

$yz \backslash wx$	00	01	11	10
00	1	1	1	1
01	1			1
11				1
10		1		

$yz \backslash wx$	00	01	11	10
00	1	1	1*	1
01	1*			1
11				1*
10		1*		

There are four essential prime implicants, covering all of f', giving

$$f' = x'y' + y'z' + w'xz' + wx'z$$

Using DeMorgan's theorem, we get

$$f = (x + y)(y + z)(w + x' + z)(w' + x + z')$$

In this case, the sum of products solution requires fewer terms.

b. As indicated on the map below, all of the 1's are covered by essential prime implicants, producing the minimum sum of product expression

$$f_1 = bc' + ab + a'b'c + ac'd$$

Now, replacing all of the 1's by 0's and 0's by 1's and leaving the X's unchanged, we get the map for f'

There is one essential prime implicant, $ab'c$. Although m_6 and m_7 can each be covered in two ways, only $a'bc$ covers them both (and neither of the other terms cover additional 1's). The middle map shows each of these terms circled, leaving three 1's to be covered. There is a group of four, covering two of the 1's (as shown on the third map), $b'd'$. That leaves just m_1, which can be covered in two ways, as shown on the third map in green and light green lines. Thus, the two minimum sum of product expressions for f' are

$$f_2' = ab'c + a'bc + b'd' + a'c'd$$
$$f_3' = ab'c + a'bc + b'd' + a'b'c'$$

producing the two minimum product of sums solutions

$$f_2 = (a' + b + c')(a + b' + c')(b + d)(a + c + d')$$
$$f_3 = (a' + b + c')(a + b' + c')(b + d)(a + b + c)$$

c. The map for f is shown next (on the left). There are two essential prime implicants, leaving only m_{11} to be covered.

188   **Chapter 3**   The Karnaugh Map

There are two groups of four that can be used, as indicated on the right map.

cd \ ab	00	01	11	10
00		1	1	
01		X	1	X
11	X	X	X	1
10		1		X

cd \ ab	00	01	11	10
00		1	1*	
01	X	1		X
11	X	X	X	1
10	1*			X

Thus the two sum of products solutions are

$$f_1 = a'b + bc' + ad$$
$$f_2 = a'b + bc' + cd$$

We then mapped f' and found no essential prime implicants.

cd \ ab	00	01	11	10
00	1			1
01	1	X		X
11	X	X	X	
10	1		1	X

cd \ ab	00	01	11	10
00	1			1
01	1	X		X
11	X	X	X	
10	1		1	X

cd \ ab	00	01	11	10
00	1			1
01	1	X		X
11	X	X	X	
10	1		1	X

We chose as a starting point m_8. It can be covered either by the four corners, $b'd'$ (as shown on the second map) or by $b'c'$, as shown on the third map. Whichever solution we choose, we need a group of two to cover m_{14} (as shown in light green); neither covers any other 1. After choosing one of these (and $b'd'$), all that remains to be covered is m_1. The three green lines show the covers. (Notice that one of those is $b'c'$.) If we don't choose $b'd'$, then we must choose $b'c'$ to cover m_0 and $a'b'$ to cover m_2 (since the only other prime implicant that covers m_2 is $b'd'$ and we have already found all of the solutions using that term). Thus, the eight solutions for f' are

$$f'_3 = b'd' + abc + a'b'$$
$$f'_4 = b'd' + abc + a'd$$
$$f'_5 = b'd' + abc + b'c'$$

$$f_6' = b'd' + acd' + a'b'$$
$$f_7' = b'd' + acd' + a'd$$
$$f_8' = b'd' + acd' + b'c'$$
$$f_9' = b'c' + abc + a'b'$$
$$f_{10}' = b'c' + acd' + a'b'$$

The product of sums solutions for f are thus

$$f_3 = (b + d)(a' + b' + c')(a + b)$$
$$f_4 = (b + d)(a' + b' + c')(a + d')$$
$$f_5 = (b + d)(a' + b' + c')(b + c)$$
$$f_6 = (b + d)(a' + c' + d)(a + b)$$
$$f_7 = (b + d)(a' + c' + d)(a + d')$$
$$f_8 = (b + d)(a' + c' + d)(b + c)$$
$$f_9 = (b + c)(a' + b' + c')(a + b)$$
$$f_{10} = (b + c)(a' + c' + d)(a + b)$$

6. Label the solutions of each part of problem 5 as $f_1, f_2, \ldots$, and indicate which solutions are equal.

   a. Since this problem does not involve don't cares, all solutions are equal.

   b.

	2	5	10	12
f_1	1	1	0	1
f_2'	1	1	1	0
f_2	0	0	0	1
f_3'	1	0	1	0
f_3	0	1	0	1

   All of the solutions are unique. The sum of products solution treats m_2 as a 1; the product of sums treats it as a 0. The two product of sums solutions treat m_5 differently.

   c.

	3	5	7	9	10	15
f_1	0	1	1	1	0	1
f_2	1	1	1	0	0	1
f_3'	1	0	0	0	1	1
f_4'	1	1	1	0	1	1
f_5'	0	0	0	1	1	1
f_6'	1	0	0	0	1	0
f_7'	1	1	1	0	1	0
f_8'	0	0	0	1	1	0
f_9'	1	0	0	1	0	1
f_{10}'	1	0	0	1	1	0

   For one of the sum of product expressions to be equal to one of the product of sum expressions, the pattern must be opposite (since we are showing the values of the don't cares for f' for the POS forms). Thus, $f_1 = f_6$, and $f_2 = f_8$, that is

$$a'b + bc' + ad = (b + d)(a' + c' + d)(a + b)$$
$$a'b + bc' + cd = (b + d)(a' + c' + d)(b + c)$$

7. For each part of problem 5, draw the block diagram of a two-level NAND gate circuit and a two-level NOR gate circuit. (For those parts with multiple solutions, you need only draw one NAND and one NOR solution.)

a.

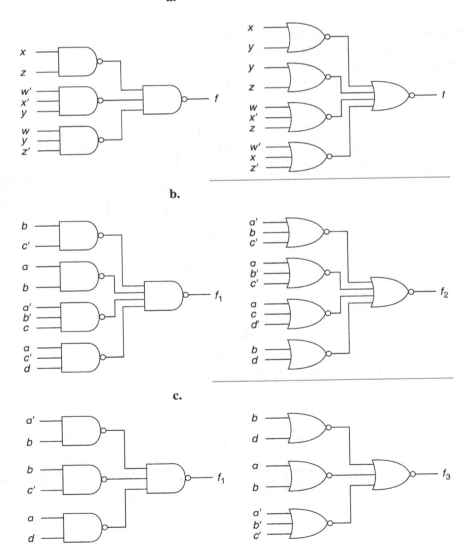

b.

c.

8. Find the minimum sum of products solution(s) for each of the following:

a. $F(A, B, C, D, E) = \Sigma m(0, 5, 7, 9, 11, 13, 15, 18, 19, 22, 23, 25, 27, 28, 29, 31)$

b. $F(A, B, C, D, E) = \Sigma m(0, 2, 4, 7, 8, 10, 15, 17, 20, 21, 23, 25, 26, 27, 29, 31)$

c. $G(V, W, X, Y, Z) = \Sigma m(0, 1, 4, 5, 6, 7, 10, 11, 14, 15, 21, 24, 25, 26, 27)$ (3 solutions)

d. $G(V, W, X, Y, Z) = \Sigma m(0, 1, 5, 6, 7, 8, 9, 14, 17, 20, 21, 22, 23, 25, 28, 29, 30)$ (3 solutions)

e. $H(A, B, C, D, E) = \Sigma m(1, 3, 10, 14, 21, 26, 28, 30)$ $+ \Sigma d(5, 12, 17, 29)$

a. We begin by looking at 1's for which the corresponding position on the other layer is 0. On the first map, all of the essential prime implicants that are totally contained on one layer of the map, $A'B'C'D'E'$, $A'CE$, $AB'D$, and $ABCD'$, are circled.

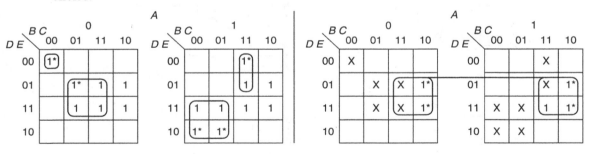

The 1's covered by these essential prime implicants are shown as don't cares on the second map. The remaining 1's are all part of the group of eight, BE, shown on the second map. Thus, the minimum solution is

$$F = A'B'C'D'E' + A'CE + AB'D + ABCD' + BE$$

b. On the left map below, the essential prime implicants are circled. Note that $A'C'E'$ is on the top layer, $AD'E$ is on the lower layer and CDE is split between the layers.

That leaves four 1's to be covered, using two groups of two as shown on the right map. The minimum is thus

$$F = A'C'E' + AD'E + CDE + B'CD'E' + ABC'D$$

c. The map, with essential prime implicants circled, is shown on the left. After choosing $V'W'Y' + VWX' + W'XY'Z$, there are still six 1's uncovered. On the right map, the minterms covered by essential prime implicants are shown as don't cares. Each of the 1's can be covered by two different groups of four, which are shown on the map on the right.

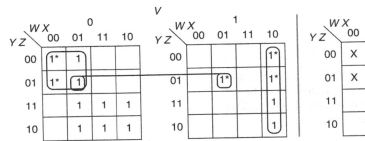

One group that covers four new 1's must be used (or both of them may be used), giving the following solutions:

$$G = V'W'Y' + VWX' + W'XY'Z + V'XY + V'WY$$
$$G = V'W'Y' + VWX' + W'XY'Z + V'XY + WX'Y$$
$$G = V'W'Y' + VWX' + W'XY'Z + V'WY + V'W'X$$

d. On the first map, the two essential prime implicants, $V'X'Y'$ and XYZ', are circled. The term $W'XZ$ is circled on the second map; if it is not used, $W'XY$ would be needed to cover m_7 and m_{23}. But then, three more terms would be needed to cover the function.

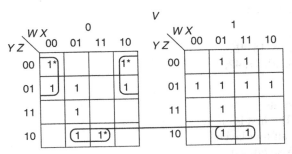

The following maps show the covered terms as don't cares and three ways of covering the remaining 1's. On the left map, the green term, $VY'Z$, is used with either of the other terms, VXY' or VXZ'. On the right map, VXY' and $X'Y'Z$ are used.

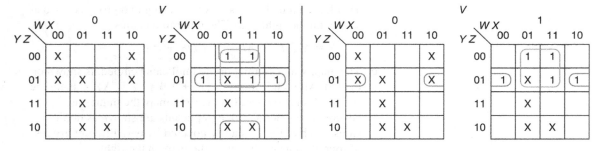

The three minimum solutions are thus

$$G = V'X'Y' + XYZ' + W'XZ + VY'Z + VXY'$$
$$G = V'X'Y' + XYZ' + W'XZ + VY'Z + VXZ'$$
$$G = V'X'Y' + XYZ' + W'XZ + VXY' + X'Y'Z$$

e. The two essential prime implicants, $A'B'C'E$ and BDE', are circled on the first map. Each of the remaining 1's can be covered in two ways, by a group of two contained completely on one layer or by the group of four shown.

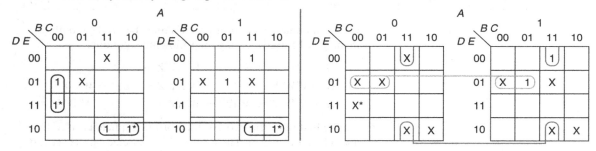

Thus, the minimum solution is

$$H = A'B'C'E + BDE' + BCE' + B'D'E$$

9. Find the four minimum sum of product expressions for the following six-variable function

$$G(A, B, C, D, E, F) = \Sigma m(0, 4, 6, 8, 9, 11, 12, 13, 15, 16,$$
$$20, 22, 24, 25, 27, 28, 29, 31, 32, 34, 36, 38, 40, 41, 42,$$
$$43, 45, 47, 48, 49, 54, 56, 57, 59, 61, 63)$$

On the first map, the three essential prime implicants, $ABD'E'$, CF, and $C'DEF'$, are circled in black. The first is on just the third layer. The other two include 1's on all four layers (and thus do not involve the variable A and B). Also circled (in green) is a group of eight, $A'E'F'$, that is not essential (since each of the 1's is part of some other prime implicant). If that is not used, however, at least two terms would be needed to cover those 1's.

On the next map, the 1's that have been covered are shown as don't cares. The remaining 1's are all on the bottom (10) layer. The four corners, $AB'D'F'$, covers four of the five remaining 1's. Then, either $AB'C'F'$ (on the bottom layer) or $B'C'E'F'$ or $B'C'DF'$ (both half on the top layer and half on the bottom) can be used to cover the remaining 1's. These terms are circled below.

Also, as shown on the map below, $AB'C'F'$ could be used with $AB'CD'$.

Thus, we have the following four solutions

$$H = ABD'E' + CF + C'DEF' + A'E'F' + AB'D'F'$$
$$\qquad + AB'C'F'$$

$$H = ABD'E' + CF + C'DEF' + A'E'F' + AB'D'F'$$
$$\qquad + B'C'E'F'$$

$$H = ABD'E' + CF + C'DEF' + A'E'F' + AB'D'F'$$
$$+ B'C'DF'$$
$$H = ABD'E' + CF + C'DEF' + A'E'F' + AB'C'F'$$
$$+ AB'CD'$$

10. Find a minimum two-level circuit (corresponding to sum of products expressions) using AND gates and one OR gate per function for each of the following sets of functions:

a. $f(a, b, c, d) = \Sigma m(0, 1, 2, 3, 5, 7, 8, 10, 11, 13)$

$g(a, b, c, d) = \Sigma m(0, 2, 5, 8, 10, 11, 13, 15)$

(7 gates, 19 inputs)

b. $f(a, b, c, d) = \Sigma m(1, 2, 4, 5, 6, 9, 11, 13, 15)$

$g(a, b, c, d) = \Sigma m(0, 2, 4, 8, 9, 11, 12, 13, 14, 15)$

(8 gates, 23 inputs)

c. $F(W, X, Y, Z) = \Sigma m(2, 3, 6, 7, 8, 9, 13)$

$G(W, X, Y, Z) = \Sigma m(2, 3, 6, 7, 9, 10, 13, 14)$

$H(W, X, Y, Z) = \Sigma m(0, 1, 4, 5, 9, 10, 13, 14)$

(8 gates, 22 inputs)

d. $f(a, b, c, d) = \Sigma m(0, 2, 3, 8, 9, 10, 11, 12, 13, 15)$

$g(a, b, c, d) = \Sigma m(3, 5, 7, 12, 13, 15)$

$h(a, b, c, d) = \Sigma m(0, 2, 3, 4, 6, 8, 10, 14)$

(10 gates, 28 inputs)

e. $f(a, b, c, d) = \Sigma m(0, 3, 5, 7) + \Sigma d(10, 11, 12, 13, 14, 15)$

$g(a, b, c, d) = \Sigma m(0, 5, 6, 7, 8) + \Sigma d(10, 11, 12, 13, 14, 15)$

(7 gates, 19 inputs)

a. The maps below show the only prime implicant, $a'd$ in f, that covers a 1 not part of the other function.

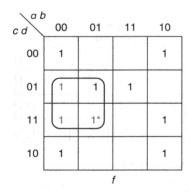

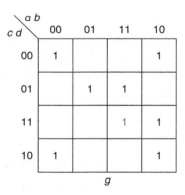

No other 1 (of either f or g) that is not shared makes a prime implicant essential (m_1 or m_3 in f or m_{15} in g). Two other terms,

$b'd'$ and $bc'd$, are essential prime implicants of both f and g and have been thus chosen in the maps below.

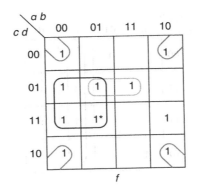

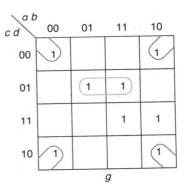

Although the term $ab'c$ could be shared, another term would be needed for g (either abd or acd). This would require seven gates and 20 gate inputs (one input too many). But, if acd is used for g, we could then complete covering both functions using $b'c$ for f as shown on the maps below.

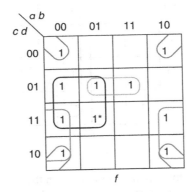

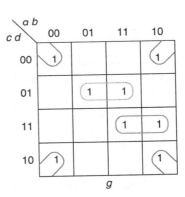

Thus,

$$f = a'd + b'd' + bc'd + b'c$$
$$g = b'd' + bc'd + acd$$

requiring seven gates and 19 inputs.

b. Scanning each function for 1's that are not part of the other function, we find m_1, m_5, and m_6 in f and m_0, m_8, m_{12}, and m_{14}

in g. The only ones that make a prime implicant essential are indicated on the map below.

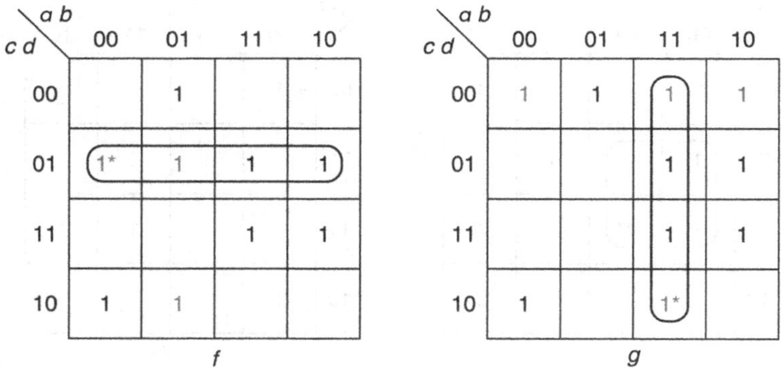

$cd \backslash ab$	00	01	11	10
00		1		
01	1*	1	1	1
11			1	1
10	1	1		

f

$cd \backslash ab$	00	01	11	10
00	1	1	1	1
01			1	1
11			1	1
10	1		1*	

g

Next, we note that ad is an essential prime implicant of both functions, producing the following maps:

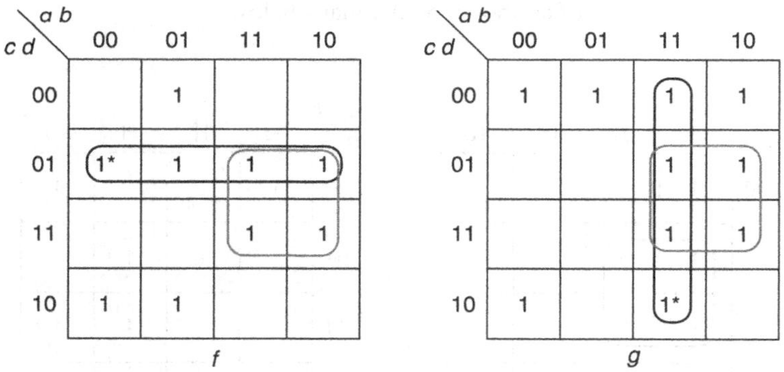

$cd \backslash ab$	00	01	11	10
00		1		
01	1*	1	1	1
11			1	1
10	1	1		

f

$cd \backslash ab$	00	01	11	10
00	1	1	1	1
01			1	1
11			1	1
10	1		1*	

g

Unless we choose $c'd'$ to cover the remaining three 1's in the first row of g, we will need an extra term. Once we have done that, we see that the last 1 (m_2) of g can be covered by the minterm and shared with f. That leaves just two 1's of f that can be covered with the term $a'bd'$. The functions and the maps are shown next:

$$f = c'd + ad + a'b'cd' + a'bd'$$
$$g = ab + ad + c'd' + a'b'cd'$$

for a total of eight gates and 23 inputs.

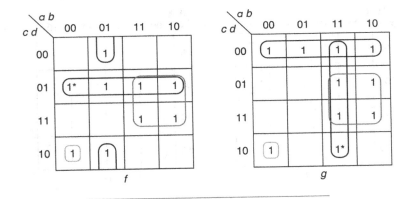

c. When minimizing three functions, we still look for 1's that are only included in one of the functions and that make a prime implicant essential. In this problem, the only ones that satisfy these conditions are m_8 in F and m_0 and m_4 in H, as shown on the map below.

Next, notice that $W'Y$ is an essential prime implicant of both F and G. Once that is chosen, the term $WY'Z$ covers the remaining 1 of F and two 1's in G and H. (That term would be used for both F and G in any case since it is an essential prime implicant of both and is shareable. It is used for H since the remaining 1's in the prime implicant $Y'Z$ are already covered.) Finally, WYZ', an essential prime implicant of H, finishes the cover of G and H. The maps and functions below show the final solution, utilizing eight gates and 22 inputs.

YZ \ WX	00	01	11	10
00				1*
01			1	1
11	1	1		
10	1	1		

F

YZ \ WX	00	01	11	10
00				
01			1	1
11	1	1		
10	1	1	1	1

G

YZ \ WX	00	01	11	10
00	1*	1*		
01	1	1	1	1
11				
10			1	1

H

$$F = WX'Y' + W'Y + WY'Z$$
$$G = W'Y + WY'Z + WYZ'$$
$$H = W'Y' + WY'Z + WYZ'$$

d. On the maps below, the essential prime implicants that cover 1's not part of any other function are circled. In f, m_9 and m_{11} can be covered with any of three prime implicants.

cd \ ab	00	01	11	10
00	1		1	1
01			1	1
11	1		1	1
10	1			1

f

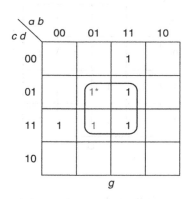

g

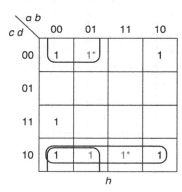

h

Next, we note that m_8 can only be covered by $b'd'$ in h and that $b'd'$ is also an essential prime implicant of f. That leaves only m_3 uncovered in h; by using the minterm for that, it can be shared with both f and g. (Otherwise, a new term would be required in each of those functions.) The resulting maps are shown below.

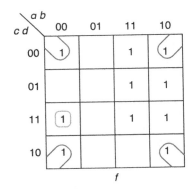

f

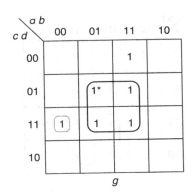

g

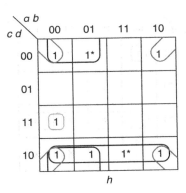

h

The only uncovered 1 in *g* is m_{12}. By using *abc'* for both that and for *f*, we can cover the three remaining 1's in *f* with *ad*, yielding the maps and equations below.

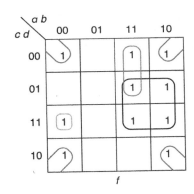

f

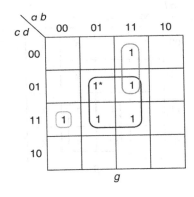

g

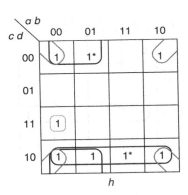

h

$$f = b'd' + a'b'cd + abc' + ad$$
$$g = bd + a'b'cd + abc'$$
$$h = a'd' + cd' + b'd' + a'b'cd$$

e. This example includes a number of don't cares, but that does not change the process significantly. There are two essential prime implicants, *cd* in *f* and *bc* in *g*, that cover 1's that cannot be shared. In addition, *a'b'c'd'* must be used in *f* since it is the only prime implicant that covers m_0. (If a minterm is a prime implicant, we have no choice but to use it.) The maps below show these terms circled.

Map f:

cd \ ab	00	01	11	10
00	(1)		X	
01		1	X	
11	(1*	1	X	X)
10			X	X

Map g:

cd \ ab	00	01	11	10
00	1		X	1
01		1	X	
11		(1	X)	X
10		(1*	X)	X

Next, we use bd to cover m_5 in both functions, and complete the cover of f. The obvious choice is to use $b'c'd'$ for the remaining 1's of g, producing the following maps and equations:

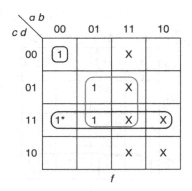

Map f:

cd \ ab	00	01	11	10
00	(1)		X	
01		1	X	
11	(1*	1	X)	X)
10			X	X

Map g:

cd \ ab	00	01	11	10
00	(1)		X	1
01		1	X	
11		(1	X)	X
10		1*	X	X

$$f = cd + a'b'c'd' + bd$$
$$g = bc + bd + b'c'd'$$

But, there is another solution, as illustrated below. By using $a'b'c'd'$ to cover m_0 in g (we already needed that term for f), we can cover the remaining 1 in g with a group of four, ad', producing the solution

$$f = cd + a'b'c'd' + bd$$
$$g = bc + bd + a'b'c'd' + ad'$$

as shown on the following maps. Both solutions require seven gates and 19 inputs.

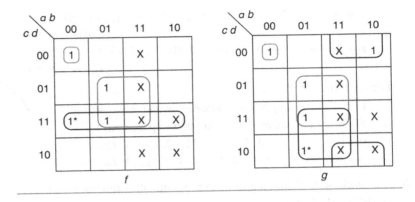

f   g

3.8   EXERCISES

1. For each of the following, find all minimum sum of products expressions. (If there is more than one solution, the number of solutions is given in parentheses.)

   a. $f(a, b, c) = \Sigma m(1, 2, 3, 6, 7)$

   *b. $g(w, x, y) = \Sigma m(0, 1, 5, 6, 7)$ (2 solutions)

   c. $h(a, b, c) = \Sigma m(0, 1, 2, 5, 6, 7)$ (2 solutions)

   d. $f(a, b, c, d) = \Sigma m(1, 2, 3, 5, 6, 7, 8, 11, 13, 15)$

   *e. $G(W, X, Y, Z) = \Sigma m(0, 2, 5, 7, 8, 10, 12, 13)$

   f. $h(a, b, c, d) = \Sigma m(2, 4, 5, 6, 7, 8, 10, 12, 13, 15)$

                                                                  (2 solutions)

   g. $f(a, b, c, d) = \Sigma m(1, 3, 4, 5, 6, 11, 12, 13, 14, 15)$

                                                                  (2 solutions)

   h. $g(w, x, y, z) = \Sigma m(2, 3, 6, 7, 8, 10, 11, 12, 13, 15)$

                                                                  (2 solutions)

   *i. $h(p, q, r, s) = \Sigma m(0, 2, 3, 4, 5, 8, 11, 12, 13, 14, 15)$

                                                                  (3 solutions)

   j. $F(W, X, Y, Z) = \Sigma m(0, 2, 3, 4, 5, 8, 10, 11, 12, 13, 14, 15)$

                                                                  (4 solutions)

   k. $f(w, x, y, z) = \Sigma m(0, 1, 2, 4, 5, 6, 9, 10, 11, 13, 14, 15)$

                                                                  (2 solutions)

   l. $g(a, b, c, d) = \Sigma m(0, 1, 2, 3, 4, 5, 6, 8, 9, 10, 12, 15)$

   *m. $H(W, X, Y, Z) = \Sigma m(0, 2, 3, 5, 7, 8, 10, 12, 13)$

                                                                  (4 solutions)

   *n. $f(a, b, c, d) = \Sigma m(0, 1, 2, 4, 5, 6, 7, 8, 9, 10, 11, 13, 14, 15)$

                                                                  (6 solutions)

 o. $g(w, x, y, z) = \Sigma m(0, 1, 2, 3, 5, 6, 7, 8, 9, 10, 13, 14, 15)$
                  (6 solutions)

 p. $f(a, b, c, d) = \Sigma m(0, 3, 5, 6, 7, 9, 10, 11, 12, 13, 14)$
                  (32 solutions)

2. For the following functions,

 i. List all prime implicants, indicating which are essential.

 ii. Show the minimum sum of products expression(s).

 a. $f(a, b, c, d) = \Sigma m(0, 3, 4, 5, 8, 11, 12, 13, 14, 15)$

*b. $g(w, x, y, z) = \Sigma m(0, 3, 4, 5, 6, 7, 8, 9, 11, 13, 14, 15)$

3. Map each of the following functions and find the minimum sum of products expression:

 a. $F = AD + AB + A'CD' + B'CD + A'BC'D'$

*b. $g = w'yz + xy'z + wy + wxy'z' + wz + xyz'$

4. For each of the following, find all minimum sum of products expressions. (If there is more than one solution, the number of solutions is given in parentheses.) Label the solutions $f_1, f_2, \ldots$.

 a. $f(w, x, y, z) = \Sigma m(1, 3, 6, 8, 11, 14) + \Sigma d(2, 4, 5, 13, 15)$
                  (3 solutions)

 b. $f(a, b, c, d) = \Sigma m(0, 3, 6, 9, 11, 13, 14) + \Sigma d(5, 7, 10, 12)$

*c. $f(a, b, c, d) = \Sigma m(0, 2, 3, 5, 7, 8, 9, 10, 11) + \Sigma d(4, 15)$
                  (3 solutions)

 d. $f(w, x, y, z) = \Sigma m(0, 2, 4, 5, 10, 12, 15) + \Sigma d(8, 14)$
                  (2 solutions)

 e. $f(a, b, c, d) = \Sigma m(5, 7, 9, 11, 13, 14) + \Sigma d(2, 6, 10, 12, 15)$
                  (4 solutions)

*f. $f(a, b, c, d) = \Sigma m(0, 2, 4, 5, 6, 7, 8, 9, 10, 14) + \Sigma d(3, 13)$
                  (3 solutions)

 g. $f(w, x, y, z) = \Sigma m(1, 2, 5, 10, 12) + \Sigma d(0, 3, 4, 8, 13, 14, 15)$
                  (7 solutions)

5. For each of the functions of problem 4, indicate which solutions are equal.

6. For each of the following functions, find all of the minimum sum of products expressions and all of the minimum product of sums expressions:

*a. $f(A, B, C, D) = \Sigma m(1, 4, 5, 6, 7, 9, 11, 13, 15)$

 b. $f(W, X, Y, Z) = \Sigma m(2, 4, 5, 6, 7, 10, 11, 15)$

 c. $f(A, B, C, D) = \Sigma m(1, 5, 6, 7, 8, 9, 10, 12, 13, 14, 15)$
               (1 SOP and 2 POS solutions)

*d. $f(a, b, c, d) = \Sigma m(0, 2, 4, 6, 7, 9, 11, 12, 13, 14, 15)$
               (2 SOP and 1 POS solutions)

   e. $f(w, x, y, z) = \Sigma m(0, 4, 6, 9, 10, 11, 14) + \Sigma d(1, 3, 5, 7)$

   f. $f(a, b, c, d) = \Sigma m(0, 1, 2, 5, 7, 9) + \Sigma d(6, 8, 11, 13, 14, 15)$
                (4 SOP and 2 POS solutions)

   g. $f(w, x, y, z) = \Sigma m(4, 6, 9, 10, 11, 13) + \Sigma d(2, 12, 15)$
                (2 SOP and 2 POS solutions)

   h. $f(a, b, c, d) = \Sigma m(0, 1, 4, 6, 10, 14) + \Sigma d(5, 7, 8, 9, 11, 12, 15)$
                (13 SOP and 3 POS solutions)

  *i. $f(w, x, y, z) = \Sigma m(1, 3, 7, 11, 13, 14) + \Sigma d(0, 2, 5, 8, 10, 12, 15)$
                (6 SOP and 1 POS solutions)

   j. $f(a, b, c, d) = \Sigma m(0, 1, 6, 15) + \Sigma d(3, 5, 7, 11, 14)$
                (1 SOP and 2 POS solutions)

7. Label the solutions of each part of problem 6 as $f_1, f_2, \ldots$ and indicate which solutions are equal.

8. For each part of problem 6, draw the block diagram of a two-level NAND gate circuit and a two-level NOR gate circuit. (For those parts with multiple solutions, you need only draw one NAND and one NOR solution.)

9. For each of the following five variable functions, find all minimum sum of products expressions. (If there is more than one solution, the number of solutions is given in parentheses.)

   a. $F(A, B, C, D, E) = \Sigma m(0, 1, 5, 7, 8, 9, 10, 11, 13, 15, 18, 20,$
                $21, 23, 26, 28, 29, 31)$

   b. $G(A, B, C, D, E) = \Sigma m(0, 1, 2, 4, 5, 6, 10, 13, 14, 18, 21, 22,$
                $24, 26, 29, 30)$

  *c. $H(A, B, C, D, E) = \Sigma m(5, 8, 12, 13, 15, 17, 19, 21, 23, 24, 28, 31)$

   d. $F(V, W, X, Y, Z) = \Sigma m(2, 4, 5, 6, 10, 11, 12, 13, 14, 15, 16,$
                $17, 18, 21, 24, 25, 29, 30, 31)$

   e. $G(V, W, X, Y, Z) = \Sigma m(0, 1, 4, 5, 8, 9, 10, 15, 16, 18, 19, 20,$
                $24, 26, 28, 31)$

  *f. $H(V, W, X, Y, Z) = \Sigma m(0, 1, 2, 3, 5, 7, 10, 11, 14, 15, 16, 18,$
                $24, 25, 28, 29, 31)$ (2 solutions)

   g. $F(A, B, C, D, E) = \Sigma m(0, 4, 6, 8, 12, 13, 14, 15, 16, 17, 18,$
                $21, 24, 25, 26, 28, 29, 31)$ (6 solutions)

   h. $G(A, B, C, D, E) = \Sigma m(0, 3, 5, 7\ 12, 13, 14, 15, 19, 20, 21,$
                $22, 23, 25, 26, 29, 30)$ (3 solutions)

  *i. $H(A, B, C, D, E) = \Sigma m(0, 1, 5, 6, 7, 8, 9, 14, 17, 20, 21, 22,$
                $23, 25, 28, 29, 30)$ (3 solutions)

   j. $F(V, W, X, Y, Z) = \Sigma m(0, 4, 5, 7, 10, 11, 14, 15, 16, 18, 20,$
                $21, 23, 24, 25, 26, 29, 31)$ (4 solutions)

   k. $G(V, W, X, Y, Z) = \Sigma m(0, 2, 5, 6, 8, 10, 11, 13, 14, 15, 16, 17,$
                $18, 19, 20, 21, 22, 24, 26, 29, 31)$
                (3 solutions)

l. $H(V, W, X, Y, Z) = \Sigma m(0, 1, 2, 3, 5, 8, 9, 10, 13, 17, 18, 19,$
$20, 21, 26, 28, 29)$

(3 solutions)

m. $F(A, B, C, D, E) = \Sigma m(1, 2, 5, 8, 9, 10, 12, 13, 14, 15, 16, 18,$
$21, 22, 23, 24, 26, 29, 30, 31)$

(18 solutions)

*n. $G(V, W, X, Y, Z) = \Sigma m(0, 1, 5, 7, 8, 13, 24, 25, 29, 31)$
$+ \Sigma d(9, 15, 16, 17, 23, 26, 27, 30)$

(2 solutions)

o. $H(A, B, C, D, E) = \Sigma m(0, 4, 12, 15, 27, 29, 30) + \Sigma d(1, 5, 9,$
$10, 14, 16, 20, 28, 31)$

(4 solutions)

p. $F(A, B, C, D, E) = \Sigma m(8, 9, 11, 14, 28, 30) + d(0, 3, 4, 6, 7,$
$12, 13, 15, 20, 22, 27, 29, 31)$

(8 solutions)

10. For each of the following six-variable functions, find all minimum sum of products expressions. (The number of terms and literals and, if there is more than one solution, the number of solutions is given in parentheses.)

a. $G(A, B, C, D, E, F) = \Sigma m(4, 5, 6, 7, 8, 10, 13, 15, 18, 20, 21,$
$22, 23, 26, 29, 30, 31, 33, 36, 37, 38,$
$39, 40, 42, 49, 52, 53, 54, 55, 60, 61)$

(6 terms, 21 literals)

*b. $G(A, B, C, D, E, F) = \Sigma m(2, 3, 6, 7, 8, 12, 14, 17, 19, 21, 23,$
$25, 27, 28, 29, 30, 32, 33, 34, 35, 40, 44,$
$46, 49, 51, 53, 55, 57, 59, 61, 62, 63)$

(8 terms, 30 literals)

c. $G(A, B, C, D, E, F) = \Sigma m(0, 1, 2, 4, 5, 6, 7, 9, 13, 15, 17, 19,$
$21, 23, 26, 27, 29, 30, 31, 33, 37, 39,$
$40, 42, 44, 45, 46, 47, 49, 53, 55, 57,$
$59, 60, 61, 62, 63)$

(8 terms, 28 literals, 2 solutions)

11. Find a minimum two-level circuit (corresponding to sum of products expressions) using AND and one OR gate per function for each of the following sets of functions.

*a. $f(a, b, c, d) = \Sigma m(1, 3, 5, 8, 9, 10, 13, 14)$
$g(a, b, c, d) = \Sigma m(4, 5, 6, 7, 10, 13, 14)$ (7 gates, 21 inputs)

b. $f(a, b, c, d) = \Sigma m(0, 1, 2, 3, 4, 5, 8, 10, 13)$
$g(a, b, c, d) = \Sigma m(0, 1, 2, 3, 8, 9, 10, 11, 13)$

(6 gates, 16 inputs)

c. $f(a, b, c, d) = \Sigma m(5, 8, 9, 12, 13, 14)$
$g(a, b, c, d) = \Sigma m(1, 3, 5, 8, 9, 10)$

(3 solutions, 8 gates, 25 inputs)

d. $f(a, b, c, d) = \Sigma m(1, 3, 4, 5, 10, 11, 12, 14, 15)$
 $g(a, b, c, d) = \Sigma m(0, 1, 2, 8, 10, 11, 12, 15)$
 (9 gates, 28 inputs)

*e. $F(W, X, Y, Z) = \Sigma m(1, 5, 7, 8, 10, 11, 12, 14, 15)$
 $G(W, X, Y, Z) = \Sigma m(0, 1, 4, 6, 7, 8, 12)$ (8 gates, 23 inputs)

f. $F(W, X, Y, Z) = \Sigma m(0, 2, 3, 7, 8, 9, 13, 15)$
 $G(W, X, Y, Z) = \Sigma m(0, 2, 8, 9, 10, 12, 13, 14)$
 (2 solutions, 8 gates, 23 inputs)

g. $f(a, b, c, d) = \Sigma m(1, 3, 5, 7, 8, 9, 10)$
 $g(a, b, c, d) = \Sigma m(0, 2, 4, 5, 6, 8, 10, 11, 12)$
 $h(a, b, c, d) = \Sigma m(1, 2, 3, 5, 7, 10, 12, 13, 14, 15)$
 (2 solutions, 12 gates, 33 inputs)

*h. $f(a, b, c, d) = \Sigma m(0, 3, 4, 5, 7, 8, 12, 13, 15)$
 $g(a, b, c, d) = \Sigma m(1, 5, 7, 8, 9, 10, 11, 13, 14, 15)$
 $h(a, b, c, d) = \Sigma m(1, 2, 4, 5, 7, 10, 13, 14, 15)$
 (2 solutions, 11 gates, 33 inputs)

i. $f(a, b, c, d) = \Sigma m(0, 2, 3, 4, 6, 7, 9, 11, 13)$
 $g(a, b, c, d) = \Sigma m(2, 3, 5, 6, 7, 8, 9, 10, 13)$
 $h(a, b, c, d) = \Sigma m(0, 4, 8, 9, 10, 13, 15)$
 (2 solutions for f and g, 10 gates, 32 inputs)

*j. $f(a, c, b, d) = \Sigma m(0, 1, 2, 3, 4, 9) + \Sigma d(10, 11, 12, 13, 14, 15)$
 $g(a, c, b, d) = \Sigma m(1, 2, 6, 9) + \Sigma d(10, 11, 12, 13, 14, 15)$
 (3 solutions for f, 6 gates, 15 inputs)

k. $f(a, c, b, d) = \Sigma m(5, 6, 11) + \Sigma d(0, 1, 2, 4, 8)$
 $g(a, c, b, d) = \Sigma m(6, 9, 11, 12, 14) + \Sigma d(0, 1, 2, 4, 8)$
 (2 solutions for g, 7 gates, 18 inputs)

12. In each of the following sets, the functions have been minimized
 individually. Find a minimum two-level circuit (corresponding to
 sum of products expressions) using AND and one OR gate per
 function for each.

a. $F = B'D' + CD' + AB'C$
 $G = BC + ACD$ (6 gates, 15 inputs)

*b. $F = A'B'C'D + BC + ACD + AC'D'$
 $G = A'B'C'D' + A'BC + BCD'$
 $H = B'C'D' + BCD + AC' + AD$
 (2 solutions for H, 10 gates, 35 inputs)

c. $f = a'b' + a'd + b'c'd'$
 $g = b'c'd' + bd + acd + abc$
 $h = a'd' + a'b + bc'd + b'c'd'$ (10 gates, 31 inputs)

3.9 CHAPTER 3 TEST (100 MINUTES, OR TWO 50-MINUTE TESTS)

1. Find the minimum sum of products expression for each of the following functions (that is, circle the terms on the map and write the algebraic expressions).

a.

yz \ wx	00	01	11	10
00		1		1
01		1		
11		1	1	1
10		1		

b.

cd \ ab	00	01	11	10
00	1	1	1	
01	1	1	1	
11			1	1
10	1	1	1	

2. Find all four minimum sum of product expressions for the following function. (Two copies of the map are given for your convenience.)

cd \ ab	00	01	11	10
00	1	1	1	
01	1		1	1
11	1		1	1
10		1	1	1

cd \ ab	00	01	11	10
00	1	1	1	
01	1		1	1
11	1		1	1
10		1	1	1

3. For the following function (three copies of the map are shown),

   a. List all prime implicants, indicating which, if any, are essential.

   b. Find all four minimum solutions.

Chapter 3 The Karnaugh Map

yz \ wx	00	01	11	10
00		1	1	X
01	X	X		X
11	X			1
10			1	1

yz \ wx	00	01	11	10
00		1	1	X
01	X	X		X
11	X			1
10			1	1

yz \ wx	00	01	11	10
00		1	1	X
01	X	X		X
11	X			1
10			1	1

4. For the following function (three copies of the map are shown),
   a. List all prime implicants, indicating which, if any, are essential.
   b. Find both minimum solutions.

yz \ wx	00	01	11	10
00				
01		1	1	1
11	1	1		1
10	1	1	1	1

yz \ wx	00	01	11	10
00				
01		1	1	1
11	1	1		1
10	1	1	1	1

yz \ wx	00	01	11	10
00				
01		1	1	1
11	1	1		1
10	1	1	1	1

5. For the following four-variable function, f, find both minimum sum of products expressions and both minimum product of sums expressions.

cd \ ab	00	01	11	10
00			X	
01	X	1	X	1
11	1	1		X
10		X		

6. For the following function, f, find all four minimum sum of products expressions and all four minimum product of sums expressions.

yz \ wx	00	01	11	10
00	X		1	
01	X	1	1	
11	X		X	1
10	X		X	

7. For the following five-variable problem, find both minimum sum of products expressions.

A

DE \ BC	00	01	11	10
00	1		1	
01	1	1		
11	1			
10	1			

0

DE \ BC	00	01	11	10
00			1	
01		1	1	
11		1	1	1
10				1

1

8. For the following five-variable problem, find both minimum sum of products expressions. (5 terms, 15 literals)

A

DE \ BC	00	01	11	10
00	1			1
01				1
11		1	1	1
10	1			1

0

DE \ BC	00	01	11	10
00	1	1	1	
01	1			1
11	1	1	1	1
10	1	1	1	

1

Chapter 3 The Karnaugh Map

9. a. For the following two functions, find the minimum sum of products expression for each (treating them as two separate problems).

yz \ wx	00	01	11	10
00		1	1	1
01				1
11				1
10			1	1

f

yz \ wx	00	01	11	10
00				
01	1	1		1
11	1	1		1
10		1		

g

b. For the same two functions, find a minimum sum of products solution (corresponding to minimum number of gates, and among those with the same number of gates, minimum number of gate inputs). (7 gates, 19 inputs)

10. Consider the three functions, the maps of which are shown below.

yz \ wx	00	01	11	10
00				1
01	1	1		
11	1	1	1	1
10	1	1		1

f

yz \ wx	00	01	11	10
00		1	1	1
01				
11			1	
10	1	1	1	

g

yz \ wx	00	01	11	10
00		1		1
01	1	1		
11	1	1	1	
10		1		

h

a. Find the minimum sum of products expression (individually) for each of the three functions. Indicate which, if any, prime implicants can be shared.

b. Find a minimum two-level NAND gate solution. Full credit for a solution using 10 gates and 32 inputs. All variables are available both uncomplemented and complemented. Show the equations *and* a block diagram.

APPENDIX B: ANSWERS TO SELECTED EXERCISES

B.1   Chapter 1 Answers

1.   a. 31   d. 47   h. 0

2.   a. 000001001001

   e. 001111101000

   g. $4200 > 2^{12} = 4096$ Thus, can't represent in 12 bits

3.   a. i. 4553   ii. 96B

   c. i. 1427   ii. 317

4.   b. 544   d. 1023

5.   a. 001111 $3 + 12 = 15$

   d. 000001 $51 + 14 = 65$ overflow

   e. 110010 $11 + 39 = 50$

6.   a. 011001   c. cannot be stored

   e. 110001

7.   c. $+21$ d. -28 h. -32

8.   c. 10001111

   d. cannot store numbers larger than $+127$

9.   a. 000100 $-11 + (+15) = +4$

   d. 010000 $-22 + (-26) =$ overflow

   f. 101101 $-3 + (-16) = -19$

10.   b. 111001   i. $17 - 24 =$ overflow

                ii. $+17 - (+24) = -7$

   c. 110011   i. $58 - 7 = 51$

                ii. $-6 - (+7) = -13$

   d. 001100   i. $36 - 24 = 12$

                ii. $-28 - (+24) =$ overflow

11.   a.   i. 0001 0000 0011

      ii. 0001 0000 0011

      iii. 0001 0000 0011

      iv. 0100 0011 0110

      v. 10100 11000 10001

12.   i.   ii.   iii.   iv.   v.   vi.

   b. no   18   15   no   27 $+27$

   d. 95   no   no   62   149 -107

13.   a. ii. 0100010 1001111 1001011 0100010

   b. iii. $9/3 = 3$

14.   a. ii. 0110011

   b. i. 1010 (no error)

      iii. 1110 (bit 3 error)

16. a.

w	x	y	z	1	2	3
0	0	0	0	1	1	1
0	0	0	1	1	1	1
0	0	1	0	1	1	1
0	0	1	1	1	1	1
0	1	0	0	1	1	1
0	1	0	1	1	1	1
0	1	1	0	1	1	1
0	1	1	1	0	1	1
1	0	0	0	0	1	1
1	0	0	1	0	1	1
1	0	1	0	0	1	1
1	0	1	1	0	0	1
1	1	0	0	0	0	0
1	1	0	1	0	1	0
1	1	1	0	0	0	0
1	1	1	1	0	1	0

d.

A	B	C	D	F
0	0	0	0	1
0	0	0	1	1
0	0	1	0	0
0	0	1	1	0
0	1	0	0	1
0	1	0	1	1
0	1	1	0	1
0	1	1	1	0
1	0	0	0	0
1	0	0	1	1
1	0	1	0	1
1	0	1	1	1
1	1	0	0	0
1	1	0	1	0
1	1	1	0	1
1	1	1	1	1

h.

a	b	c	d	g
0	0	0	0	1
0	0	0	1	0
0	0	1	0	1
0	0	1	1	0
0	1	0	0	1
0	1	0	1	0
0	1	1	0	1
0	1	1	1	1
1	0	0	0	0
1	0	0	1	1
1	0	1	0	0
1	0	1	1	1
1	1	0	0	X
1	1	0	1	X
1	1	1	0	X
1	1	1	1	X

B.2   Chapter 2 Answers

1. a.

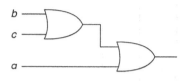 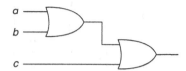

2. a.

X	Y	Z	F
0	0	0	1
0	0	1	0
0	1	0	1
0	1	1	1
1	0	0	1
1	0	1	0
1	1	0	0
1	1	1	1

3. b. $f = h$, but $\neq g$ because of row 011

4. b.   ii. sum of 3 product terms
    d.   iv. product of 2 terms
    f.   i. product of 1 literal   iii. sum of 1 literal
       ii. sum of 1 product term   iv. product of 1 sum term
    g. none

5. b. 4   d. 3   f. 1   g. 6

6. a. $= z$
    d. $= a'b' + ac$
    f. $= x'y' + x'z + xy$
       also $= x'y' + yz + xy$

7. c.

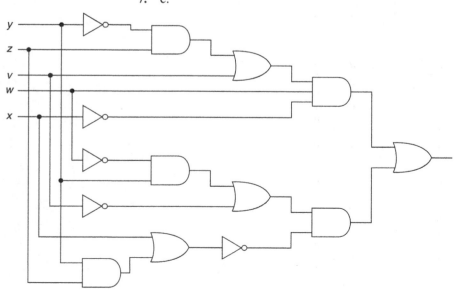

Appendix B   Answers to Selected Exercises

8. c. i. $h = a'c(b + d) + a(c' + bd)$
  ii. $= a'bc + a'cd + ac' + abd$

9. a.

x	y	z	f
0	0	0	0
0	0	1	1
0	1	0	0
0	1	1	1
1	0	0	0
1	0	1	0
1	1	0	1
1	1	1	0

  b. $f = x'y'z + x'yz + xyz'$
  c. $f = x'z + xyz'$
  d. $f'(x, y, z) = \Sigma m(0, 2, 4, 5, 7)$

10. a. $f(a, b, c) = \Sigma m(1, 5, 6, 7)$
    $g(a, b, c) = \Sigma m(0, 1, 4, 5, 6)$
  b. $f = a'b'c + ab'c + abc' + abc$
    $g = a'b'c' + a'b'c + ab'c' + ab'c + abc'$
  c. $f = b'c + ab$
    $g = b' + ac'$
  d. $f'(a, b, c) = \Sigma m(0, 2, 3, 4)$
    $g'(a, b, c) = \Sigma m(2, 3, 7)$

12. a. yes   b. no   c. yes   d. no   e. no   f. yes

13. b.

yz \ wx	00	01	11	10
00			X	X
01	1	1	1	
11	1	1		
10		1	1	X

d.

cd \ ab	00	01	11	10
00		1		
01		1	1	1
11	1	1		1
10	1	1		1

14. a. $f' = (a' + b' + d)(b + c)(a + c' + d')(a + b' + c + d')$

15.   (10.)   a. $f = (a + b + c)(a + b' + c)(a + b' + c')(a' + b + c)$
$g = (a + b' + c)(a + b + c')(a' + b' + c')$
b. $f = (b + c)(a + b')$ $g = (a + b')(b' + c')$

17.   a. $f = a(bc)' + (c + d')' = ab' + ac' + c'd$
f. $f = 1 \oplus (ab + cd) = a'c' + a'd' + b'c' + b'd'$

18.   d.

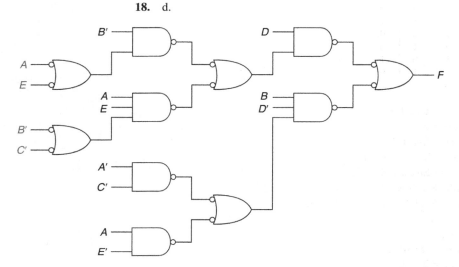

19.   c. $f = b + a'c$

20.   c. $F = W'Z' + Y'Z + WXY$
g. $G = B'D + BC + A'D$
j. $g = bc'd + abc + a'bd'$
$= a'bc' + abd + bcd'$

21.   a. $f = a'b'c' + a'bd + a'cd' + abc + a'c'd$
$+ a'b'd' + a'bc + bcd + bcd'$
$= bc + a'c'd + a'b'd'$

22.   b. $g = x'y'z' + x'y'z + x'yz' + x'yz + xyz + xy'z'$
$g(w, x, y, z) = \Sigma m(0, 1, 2, 3, 4, 7)$

23.   c. $xy + w'z$

24.   c. $(b' + d)(c + d)(a' + b + d')(b' + c' + d')$

25.   a. $f = w(y' + xz') + z(y' + w'x')$

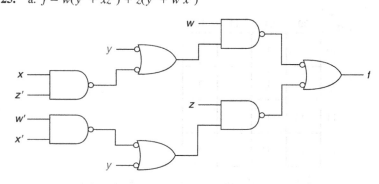

d. $F = B'[D'(A' + CE) + A'C] + B(AC' + C'D)$

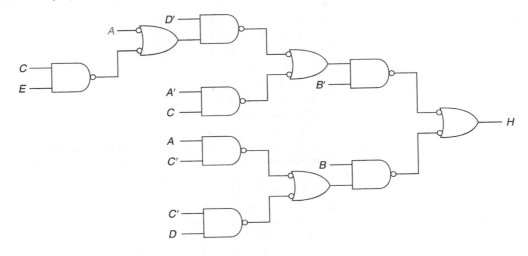

26. a. $F = BE(ACD + C'D' + A'C') + B'(E' + A'C) + CD'E'$

       3   3   3   2   2   3 2   2 2   3   3 packs

    $= BE(C'(A' + D') + ACD) + B'E' + CD'E' + A'B'C$

        3   2   2   2   3   4 2   3   3   3 packs

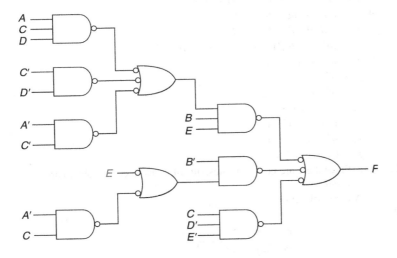

B.3 Chapter 3 Answers

1. b. $g = w'x' + wx + wy$ $g = w'x' + wx + x'y$

   e. $G = X'Z' + W'XZ + WXY'$

   i. $h = pq + qr' + r's' + p'q'r + prs$

      $h = pq + qr' + r's' + p'q'r + q'rs$

      $h = pq + qr' + r's' + q'rs + p'q's'$

m. $H = X'Z' + W'X'Y + W'XZ + WXY'$
$H = X'Z' + W'YZ + W'XZ + WXY'$
$H = X'Z' + W'YZ + XY'Z + WXY'$
$H = X'Z' + W'YZ + XY'Z + WY'Z'$

n. $f = a'c' + ab' + cd' + bd$
$f = b'c' + a'b + cd' + ad$
$f = c'd + ac + a'b + b'd'$
$f = a'c' + ad + bc + b'd'$
$f = b'c' + bd + ac + a'd'$
$f = c'd + bc + ab' + a'd'$

2. b. Prime Implicants: $xy, yz, xz, wz, w'x, w'y'z', x'y'z', wx'y'$
Minimum: $g = yz + xy + w'x + wz + x'y'z'$

3. b. $g = wx + yz + xy + xz + wy + wz$

4. c. $f_1 = ab' + b'd' + cd + a'bc'$
$f_2 = ab' + b'd' + cd + a'bd$
$f_3 = ab' + b'd' + b'c + a'bd$

f. $f_1 = cd' + a'b + b'd' + ac'd$
$f_2 = cd' + a'b + b'd' + ab'c'$
$f_3 = cd' + a'b + a'd' + ab'c'$

5. c. All are different.
f. f_2 and f_3 are equal; f_1 treats m_{13} differently

6. a. $f = A'B + C'D + AD$
$f = (B + D)(A + B + C')(A' + D)$

d. $f_1 = a'd' + ad + bc + ab$
$f_2 = a'd' + ad + bc + bd'$
$f_3 = (a' + b + d)(a + c + d')(a + b + d')$

i. $f_1 = w'z + wy + xz$
$f_2 = w'z + wy + wx$
$f_3 = w'z + wx + x'z$
$f_4 = w'z + wx + yz$
$f_5 = w'x' + wx + yz$
$f_6 = w'x' + wy + xz$
$f_7 = (w + z)(w' + x + y)$

7. a, d. Since there are no don't cares, all solutions to each problem are equal.
i. All are different.

8. a.

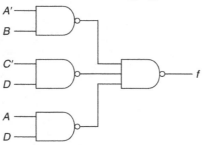
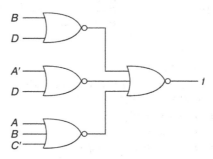

d.

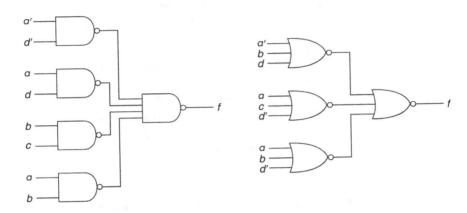

i.

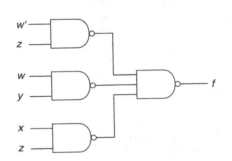   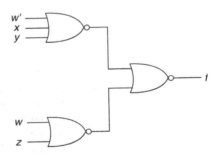

9.   c. $H = AB'E + BD'E' + BCDE + A'CD'E$

f. $H = V'W'Z + V'WY + VWY' + W'X'Z' + VWXZ$
      $H = V'W'Z + V'WY + VWY' + W'X'Z' + WXYZ$

i. $H = A'C'D' + CDE' + B'CE + AD'E + \{ACD'\ \text{or}\ ACE'\}$
      $H = A'C'D' + CDE' + B'CE + ACD' + C'D'E$

n. $G = X'Y' + V'XZ + \{VWZ\ \text{or}\ WXZ\}$

10.   b. $G = B'C'E'F' + BD'F + AB'C'D' + CDEF' + A'B'C'E$
        $+ ABF + BC'F + A'BCDE$

11.   a. $f = a'b'd + ab'c' + bc'd + acd'$
      $g = a'b + bc'd + acd'$

e. $F = WY + WZ' + W'XZ + W'X'Y'Z$
      $G = Y'Z' + W'XY + W'X'Y'Z$

h. $f = c'd' + a'cd + bd$
      $g = bd + a'c'd + ab' + \{abc\ \text{or}\ acd'\}$
      $h = b'cd' + bd + a'c'd + a'bc' + \{abc\ \text{or}\ acd'\}$

j. $f = b'c'd + a'b' + a'c'd'$ or
$f = b'c'd + a'b' + bc'd'$ or
$f = b'c'd + b'c + a'c'd'$
$g = b'c'd + cd'$

12. b. $F = A'B'C'D + AC'D' + ACD + BCD' + A'BCD$
$G = A'B'C'D' + BCD' + A'BCD$
$H = AC'D' + AD + A'BCD + A'B'C'D'$

$F = A'B'C'D + AC'D' + ACD + BCD' + A'BCD$
$G = A'B'C'D' + BCD' + A'BCD$
$H = ACD + AC' + A'BCD + A'B'C'D'$

B.4   Chapter 4 Answers

1., 2. b.

b. $w'x'$	d. $r's'$	f. $a'b$	h. $V'W'X'$
wx	qr'	$b'd'$	$W'X'Z'$
$x'y$	pq	cd'	$V'W'Z$
wy	$p'q's'$	$a'c$	$V'YZ$
	$p'q'r$	$a'd'$	$V'WY$
	prs	$ac'd$	$V'X'Y$
	$q'rs$	$bc'd$	$VX'Y'Z'$
		$ab'c'$	VWY'
			$VWXZ$
			$WXYZ$

3. b. $g = w'x' + wx + wy$
$g = w'x' + wx + x'y$

d. $h = pq + qr' + r's' + p'q'r + prs$
$h = pq + qr' + r's' + p'q'r + q'rs$
$h = pq + qr' + r's' + q'rs + p'q's'$

f. $f_1 = cd' + a'b + b'd' + ac'd$
$f_2 = cd' + a'b + b'd' + ab'c'$
$f_3 = cd' + a'b + a'd' + ab'c'$

h. $H = V'W'Z + V'WY + VWY' + W'X'Z' + VWXZ$
$H = V'W'Z + V'WY + VWY' + W'X'Z' + WXYZ$

4., 5. b. Prime implicants of F: $W'Y'Z, XYZ, WY, WZ', W'XZ$
Prime implicants of G: $Y'Z', W'X'Y', W'XY, W'XZ'$
Shared terms: $W'XYZ, W'X'Y'Z, WY'Z'$

d. Terms for f only: $a'cd, c'd', bc'$
Terms for g only: $c'd, ab', ac, ad$
Term for h only: $b'cd'$
Term for f and g: $ab'c'd'$
Term for f and h: $a'bc'$
Terms for g and h: $a'c'd, abc, acd'$
Term for all three: bd

6. b. $F = WY + WZ' + W'XZ + W'X'Y'Z$
$G = Y'Z' + W'XY + W'X'Y'Z$

d. $f = c'd' + a'cd + bd$
  $g = bd + a'c'd + ab' + \{abc \text{ or } acd'\}$
  $h = b'cd' + bd + a'c'd + a'bc' + \{abc \text{ or } acd'\}$

B.5 Chapter 5 Answers

2. The truth table for this module is

a	b	c	y	s	t
0	0	0	0	1	0
0	0	1	0	1	1
0	1	0	0	1	1
0	1	1	1	0	0
1	0	0	1	0	0
1	0	1	1	0	1
1	1	0	1	0	1
1	1	1	1	1	0

$$y = a + bc \qquad s = a'b' + a'c' + abc \qquad t = b'c + bc'$$

The delay from c to y is 2 for each module. The total delay is $32 + 1$.

7.

a	b	c	X	Y
0	0	0	0	0
0	0	1	0	1
0	1	0	0	0
0	1	1	1	1
1	0	0	0	0
1	0	1	1	1
1	1	0	1	0
1	1	1	1	1

9.

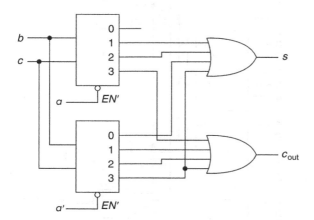

12.

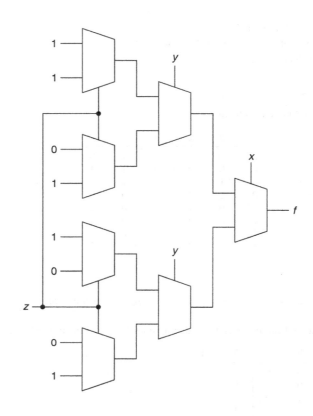

18.   a.

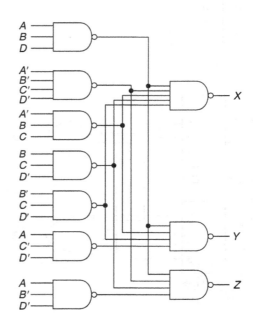

b. The solution is straightforward; the diagram is not shown.

c. We need two decoders. A is connected to the enable of the first. The outputs correspond to the first eight minterms. A' is used to enable the second, producing the other eight minterms. Only three OR gates are needed.

d. The solution of part a. is implemented on a PLA with seven terms

$$X = ABD_1 + A'B'C'D'_2 + A'BC_3 + BCD'_4 + B'CD'_5$$
$$Y = AC'D' + ABD_1 + A'BC_3 + B'CD'_5$$
$$Z = ABD_1 + A'B'C'D'_2 + AB'D' + BCD'_4$$

e. The PAL would be implemented with a solution using only prime implicants of individual functions:

$$X = A'B'D' + CD' + ABD + BC$$
$$Y = AC'D' + ABD + A'BC + B'CD' \quad \text{or}$$
$$\quad = A'CD' + BCD + ABC' + AB'D'$$
$$Z = B'C'D' + ABD + BCD' + \{AB'D' + ACD'\}$$

21. a. $X1 = B'D'_2 + BD + AC'_1 + A'C$

$X2 = B' + C'D' + AD' + AC'_1 + A'CD$

$X3 = D + B'C' + A'B + AC_4 \qquad ***$

or

$\quad = D + A'C' + BC + AB'$

$X4 = B'D'_2 + A'B'C_5 + A'CD'_6 + BC'D + ABD + AC'_1$

$X5 = B'D'_2 + A'CD'_6 + AC'D'$

$X6 = A'BC' + ABC + AB'C' + \{B'C'D' \text{ or } A'C'D'\}$
$\qquad + \{ACD' \text{ or } AB'D'\} + \{BCD' \text{ or } A'BD'\}$

$X7 = BC' + AC'_1 + AB_3 + A'B'C_5 + \{A'CD'^1_6 \text{ or } BD'\}$

$X8 = AB_7 + AC_3$

Package Count

$X1$:	2	2	2	2			4
$X2$:	0	2	2	(2)	3		5
$X3$:	0	2	2	2			4
$X4$:	(2)	3	3	3	3	(2)	6
$X5$:	(2)	(3)	3				3
$X6$:	3	3	3	3	3	3	6
$X7$:	2	(2)	2	(3)	2		5
$X8$:	(2)	(2)					2

2's:	13	7430s:	4	32 gates/95 inputs
3's:	13	7420s:	1	
4's:	2	7410s:	5	(2 left over)
5's	2	7400s:	3	(use one 3-input)
6's:	2			Total: 13 packages

b. $X1 = B'D'_1 + AC'_3 + A'CD_2 + BD$

$\quad X2 = B' + A'CD_2 + AC'_3 + C'D' + ACD'_8$

---

[1]Solving $X7$ alone, you would use BD' in place of $A'CD'$. But, the latter is also a prime implicant and can be shared, saving one gate and three inputs. Gate count is based on BD'.

$$X3 = D + ACD'_8 + B'C'D'_{10} + A'BD'_5$$
$$X4 = A'B'C_4 + B'D'_1 + AC'_3 + A'CD'_7 + A'BC'D_6 + ABCD_9$$
$$X5 = B'D'_1 + A'CD'_7 + \mathbf{AC'D'}$$
$$X6 = ACD'_8 + B'C'D'_{10} + ABCD_9 + A'BC'D_6 + \mathbf{AB'C'} + A'BD'_5$$
$$X7 = A'B'C_4 + AC'_3 + A'BC'D_6 + AB_{11} + A'BD'_5$$
$$X8 = AC + AB_{11}$$

Package Count

X1:	2	2	3	2			4
X2:	0	(3)	(2)	2	3		5
X3:	0	(3)	3	3			4
X4:	3	(2)	(2)	3	4	4	6
X5:	(2)	(3)	3				3
X6:	(3)	(3)	(4)	(4)	3	(3)	6
X7:	(3)	(2)	(4)	2	(3)		5
X8:	2	(2)					2

2's:	7	7430s:	4	24 gates /79 inputs
3's:	9	7420s:	2	
4's:	4	7410s:	3	
5's	2	7400s:	2	
6's:	2	Total: 11 packages		

c. The PLA implementation of part b would require 18 product terms, one for each of the product terms shown, including the single literal terms (B' in X2 and D in X3). We could do this with only 16 product terms if we treated the PLA as a ROM (that is, created the 16 minterms). This would not have worked for part b, since it requires gates of more than eight inputs for those functions with more than eight minterms (all but X5 and X8).

B.6 Chapter 6 Answers

3. c.

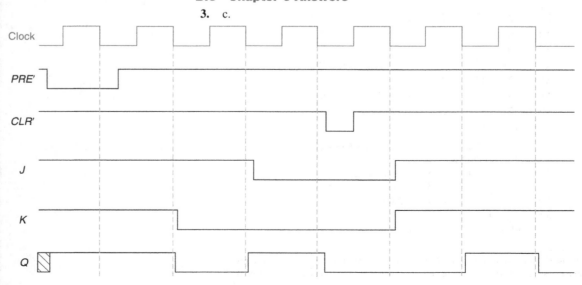

6. b. x 1 1 0 1 0 1 0 1 0 0 1 0 1 1
   q A B B C D C D C D C A B C D B
   z 0 0 0 0 1 0 1 0 1 0 0 0 0 1 0 0

7. b.

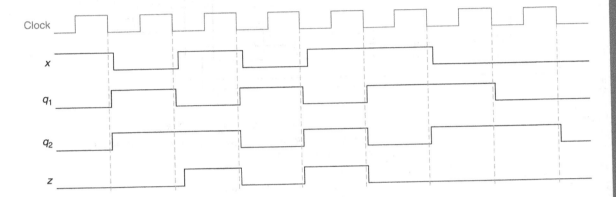

8. a.

$q_1 q_2$	$q_1^* q_2^*$		z
	$x = 0$	$x = 1$	
0 0	1 0	1 0	1
0 1	0 0	1 0	0
1 0	1 1	1 1	1
1 1	0 1	1 1	1

x 0 0 1 1 0 0 1 1 0
q_1 0 1 1 1 1 0 0 1 1 0 ? 1 ?
q_2 0 0 1 1 1 1 0 0 1 1 0 ? 1
z 1 1 1 1 1 0 1 1 1 0 1 1 ?

9. c. x 0 1 1 0 0 1 1 1 0
   A 0 0 0 1 1 1 1 0 1 1 1
   B 0 1 1 1 0 0 0 0 1 0 0 0
   C 0 1 0 0 1 1 0 0 0 1
   z 0 1 0 0 0 0 0 0 0 0 0 0

B.7 Chapter 7 Answers

1. a. The output equation is the same for all types of flip flop:
   $z = x'B + xB'$
   $D_A = x'B' + xA$ $D_B = x' + A$
   $S_A = x'B'$ $R_A = x'B$ (or $x'A$) $S_B = x'$ $R_B = xA'$
        $T_A = x'A + x'B'$ $T_B = x'B' + xA'B$
   $J_A = x'B'$ $K_A = x'$ $J_B = x'$ $K_B = xA'$
   f. $z = A'$
   $D_A = x'A' + xAB'$ $D_B = x'B + xB'$

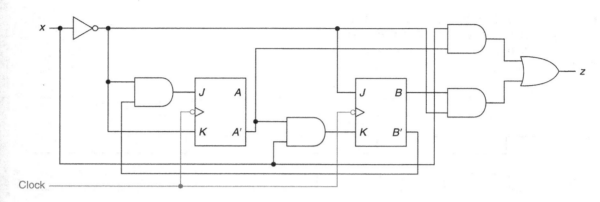

$$J_A = x' \qquad K_A = x' + B \qquad J_B = x \qquad K_B = x$$
$$S_A = x'A' \qquad R_A = x'A + AB \qquad S_B = xB' \qquad R_B = xB$$
$$T_A = x' + AB \qquad T_B = x$$

2. c. $z = q_1'q_2'$
    $$D_1 = x'q_1' + xq_1 \qquad D_2 = xq_1'q_2'$$
    $$J_1 = x' \quad K_1 = x' \qquad J_2 = xq_1' \quad K_2 = 1$$

3. b. (i) $D_1 = xq_1'q_2'$
    $$D_2 = q_1 + x'q_2' + xq_2 = q_1 + x'q_1'q_2' + xq_2$$
    $$z = x'q_1'q_2' + xq_2 = x'q_1'q_2' + xq_2$$
    (ii) $D_1 = xq_2'$
    $$D_2 = q_1 + q_2' + x$$
    $$z = x'q_2' + xq_1'q_2$$
    (iii) $D_1 = x' + q_1' + q_2'$
    $$D_2 = xq_1 + xq_2'$$
    $$z = xq_2 + x'q_1'$$

6. a. $D_D = CBA + DB' + DA'$ $\qquad J_D = CBA \qquad K_D = BA$
    $$D_C = D'C'BA + CB' + CA' \qquad J_C = D'BA \qquad K_C = BA$$
    $$D_B = B'A + BA' \qquad\qquad\quad J_B = K_B = A$$
    $$D_A = A' \qquad\qquad\qquad\qquad J_A = K_A = 1$$

8. b. $D_C = BA + \{CB' \text{ or } B'A'\}$ $\qquad J_C = B \qquad K_C = BA'$
    $$D_B = B' + CA \qquad\qquad\qquad J_B = 1 \qquad K_B = C' + A'$$
    $$D_A = B' + A' \qquad\qquad\qquad J_A = 1 \qquad K_A = B$$

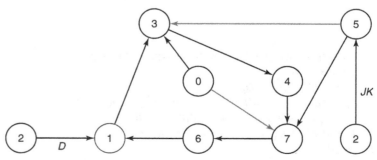

Green path from 0 and 5 when $D_C = BA + B'A'$

10. a. $J_A = B$ $K_A = x + B$ $J_B = x' + A'$ $K_B = 1$
   b. $11 \rightarrow 00$

16. b.   f.

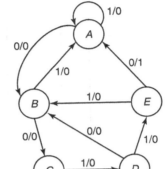

k.   l.

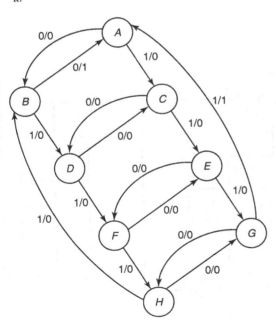

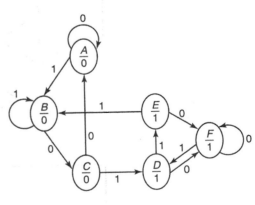

B.8   Chapter 8 Answers

4. a. Assume CLR' is clocked, but does not require counter to be enabled.

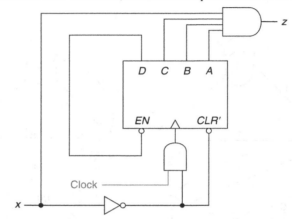

b. $z = x \, q_1' \, q_2' \, q_3' \, q_4' \, q_5' \, q_6' \, q_7' \, q_8$
$= x(q_1 + q_2 + q_3 + q_4 + q_5 + q_6 + q_7)' q_8$

8.

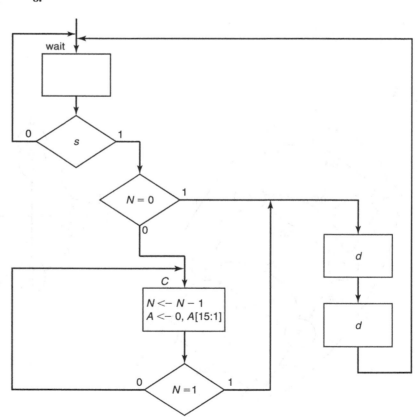

9. a. $J_A = B + C$ $K_A = \{BD + BC \text{ or } BD + CD' \text{ or } BC + C'D\}$
    $J_B = D$ $K_B = C + D$
    $J_C = AD' + B'D$ $K_C = A'D + \{AD' \text{ or } BD'\}$
    $J_D = 1$ $K_D = 1$

In some cases, the next state depends on the choice for K_A or K_C. Those transitions are shown with dashed lines. In any case, the sequence is reached within three clocks.

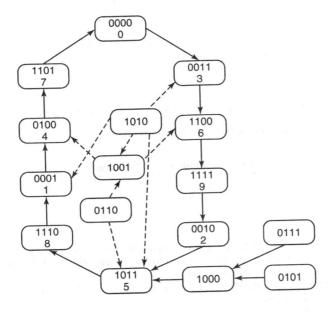

b. A table for the minimal sum of product expressions is shown.

	X1	X2	X3	X4	X5	X6	X7
$A'B'D'$	X			X	X		
$B'CD$	X		X	X			X
ABC	X	X					X
ABD	X	X	X				
$A'C'D'$		X	X			X	
$A'B'C'$		X	X				
$A'B'C$		X					X
ABD'			X	X	X	X	
ACD						X	
$BC'D'$							X
or inputs	4	5	5	3	2	3	4

12. The state table for this counter follows

   a. i. For the D flip flop, we have

$$D_A = A'BC + xAB' + xAC'$$
$$D_B = B'C + BC' + xA'B' + \{AB \text{ or } AC\}$$
$$D_C = x'AC + xA'B' + xAC' + BC' + A'C'$$

The NAND gate requirements are

Size	Number	Packages
1	1 (x')	0 (from 4)
2	4	1
3	6	2
4	1	1
5+	1	1

The cost is thus \$1.25 for gates plus the flip flops.

ii. Using JK flip flops, we get

$$J_A = BC \qquad\qquad K_A = x' + BC$$
$$J_B = C + xA' \qquad K_B = A'C$$
$$J_C = x + A' + B \qquad K_C = x'A' + xA + \{xB \text{ or } A'B\}$$

For this, the NAND gate requirements are

Size	Number	Packages
1	3	1
2	8	2
3	2	1

The two extra NOT gates (1-input) are needed to create the AND for J_A and K_B. The cost is thus \$1.00 for gates plus \$2.00 for the flip flops, a total of \$3.00.

b. Thus, if the D flip flop packages cost less than \$0.875, the first solution is less expensive.

If we can use one D package and one JK package, the best option is to use the JK package for B and C, and one of the Ds for A (using xB and a shared xAB' in place of xA in K_C). That would require

Size	Number	Packages
1	2	0 (from 2's)
2	5	2
3	6	2

This solution would cost \$2.00 plus the cost of the D package. If the D package cost between \$0.75 and \$0.875, this solution would be better.

c. This flip flop will be set when the system is in state 5, 6, or 7 and x is 0, or when in state 0 or 1 and the input is 1. It can be cleared whenever the system is in state 3. Thus, for the new flip flop,

$$J = xA'B' + x'AB + x'AC$$
$$K = A'BC$$

and the output is just the state of that flip flop.

d. All of the outputs come from flip flops. We can compute the inputs for a D flip flop for Q using

$$D = Q^* = JQ' + K'Q$$

Appendix B   Answers to Selected Exercises

and then simplifying the algebra. The result is

$$D = AQ + B'Q + C'Q + xA'B' + x'AB + x'AC$$

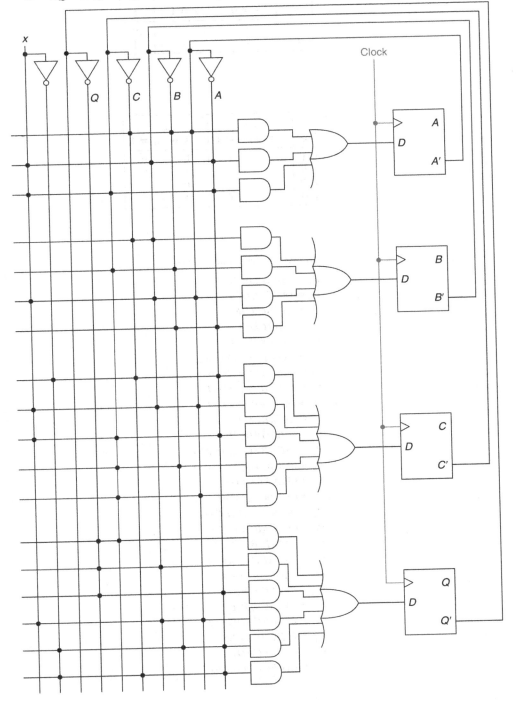

Appendix B Answers to Selected Exercises

B.9 Chapter 9 Answers

1. c.

q	q^*		z
	$x = 0$	$x = 1$	
A	C	A	0
C	C	A	1

h.

q	q^*		z	
	$x = 0$	$x = 1$	$x = 0$	$x = 1$
A	B	D	0	0
B	A	B	1	0
C	B	A	0	0
D	A	C	1	1

k. The system cannot be reduced.

2. c. $P_1 = (AB)(CD)(E)$
   $P_2 = (ABE)(CD)$
   $P_3 = (A)(BC)(DE)$
   $P_4 = (AB)(CDE)$
   $P_5 = (A)(B)(C)(DE)$

   h. $P_1 = (AE)(B)(C)(D)(F)(G)$
   $P_2 = (AEF)(BG)(C)(D)$
   $P_3 = (AE)(BG)(C)(D)(F)$

   k. $P_1 = (ADG)(B)(C)(E)(F)$
   $P_2 = (AE)(BCD)(FG)$
   $P_3 = (AEFG)(BCD)$
   $P_4 = (AG)(B)(C)(D)(E)(F)$
   $P_5 = (A)(BC)(D)(E)(F)(G)$
   $P_6 = (AE)(BCDFG)$
   $P_7 = (A)(B)(C)(DG)(E)(F)$
   $P_8 = (A)(B)(C)(D)(EF)(G)$
   $P_9 = (ADG)(BC)(E)(F)$
   $P_{10} = (ADG)(B)(C)(EF)$
   $P_{11} = (AG)(BC)(D)(E)(F)$
   $P_{12} = (AG)(B)(C)(D)(EF)$
   $P_{13} = (A)(BC)(DG)(E)(F)$
   $P_{14} = (A)(BC)(D)(EF)(G)$
   $P_{15} = (A)(B)(C)(DG)(EF)$
   $P_{16} = (ADG)(BC)(EF)$
   $P_{17} = (AG)(BC)(D)(EF)$
   $P_{18} = (A)(BC)(DG)(EF)$

3. c. i.

q	q^* $x = 0$	$x = 1$	z
A	A	B	0
B	A	B	1

ii.

q	q^* $x = 0$	$x = 1$	z
A	A	B	1
B	E	C	0
C	E	B	1
E	F	A	0
F	E	A	1

iii.

q	q^* $x = 0$	$x = 1$	z
A	A	B	0
B	E	C	0
C	E	B	1
D	A	B	1
E	F	D	1
F	E	D	0

iv.

q	q^* $x = 0$	$x = 1$	z
A	A	B	0
B	E	B	0
E	E	A	1

5. c. The three SP partitions are

$$P_1 = (ABC)(DEF)$$
$$P_2 = (AF)\,(B)\,(C)\,(D)\,(E)$$
$$P_3 = (A)\,(BE)\,(C)\,(D)\,(F)$$

P_1 is the only two-block SP partition; it can be used for the first variable. If we use the output consistent partition, $P_{oc} = (ADE)(BCF)$, for q_3, we need another partition that separates D from E, and B from C. Using P_2, we should keep A and F together, and using P_3, we should keep B and E together. Two such partitions for q_2 use

$$P_4 = (ACDF)(BE)$$
$$P_5 = (ABEF)(CD)$$

producing the assignments

q	q_1	q_2	q_3
A	0	0	0
B	0	1	1
C	0	0	1
D	1	0	0
E	1	1	0
F	1	0	1

q	q_1	q_2	q_3
A	0	0	0
B	0	0	1
C	0	1	1
D	1	1	0
E	1	0	0
F	1	0	1

For the first assignment, the equations are

$$J_1 = x' \qquad\qquad K_1 = 1$$
$$J_2 = xq_1q_3 + xq_1'q_3' \qquad K_2 = x$$
$$J_3 = x' + q_1' + q_2 \qquad K_3 = x'$$
$$z = q_3'$$

using four gates with 11 inputs (plus a NOT).

For the second assignment, the equations are

$$J_1 = x' \qquad\qquad K_1 = 1$$
$$J_2 = xq_1q_3' + xq_1'q_3 \qquad K_2 = xq_1$$
$$J_3 = x' + q_2' \qquad K_3 = x'$$
$$z = q_3'$$

using five gates with 12 inputs (plus a NOT).

Using the first six binary numbers, the solution requires 11 gates with 24 inputs (plus a NOT).

$$J_1 = x'q_2' \qquad\qquad K_1 = 1$$
$$J_2 = xq_1q_3' + xq_1'q_3 \qquad K_2 = xq_3$$
$$J_3 = x' + q_1'q_2' \qquad K_3 = x' + q_1'$$
$$z = q_2'q_3' + q_2q_3$$

5 CHAPTER

Logic Design with MSI Components and Programmable Logic Devices

It is possible to obtain fabricated circuit chips, or packages, that have from a small set of individual gates to a highly complex interconnection of gates corresponding to an entire logic network. The complexity of a single chip is known as the *scale of integration*. As a rough rule of thumb, circuit chips containing from 1 to 10 gates are said to be *small-scale integrated (SSI) circuits*, those having from 10 to 100 gates as *medium-scale integrated (MSI) circuits*, those having 100 to 1,000 gates as *large-scale integrated (LSI) circuits*, and those having more than 1,000 gates as *very-large-scale integrated (VLSI) circuits*.

Chapter 4 was concerned with obtaining optimal logic networks. At that time, emphasis was placed on minimizing the number of gates and the number of gate input terminals. Thus, the realization cost was based on chips having single gates. However, if more than one gate is included on a chip, then the cost more realistically should be associated with the entire package rather than the individual gates. In such a case, a good realization from a cost point of view does not necessarily require the use of a minimal expression according to the previous criteria but rather requires one that does not exceed the capacity of the circuit package.

Another occurring situation in logic design is that certain gate configurations have become so common and useful that manufacturers fabricate these networks on a single chip using medium-scale and large-scale integration. These configurations normally provide a high degree of flexibility, allowing them to be used as logic-design components. Again, good realizations of logic networks are achieved by proper use of these generalized circuits without having to form minimal expressions.

This chapter first introduces some specialized MSI components that have extensive use in digital systems. These include adders, comparators, decoders, encoders, and multiplexers. Their principle of operation and, in some cases, how they can be used as logic-design components are presented.

Unlike the MSI circuits which are designed to perform specific functions, LSI technology introduced highly generalized circuit structures known as *programmable logic devices* (PLDs). In their simplest form, programmable logic devices consist of an array of and-gates and an array of or-gates. However, they must be modified for a specific application. Modification involves specifying the connections within these arrays using a hardware procedure. This procedure is known as *programming*. As a result of programming the arrays, it is possible to achieve realizations of specific functions using generalized components.

In the second part of this chapter, three programmable logic device structures are studied. In particular, the programmable read-only memory (PROM), the programmable logic array (PLA), and the programmable array logic (PAL)* are discussed. ∎

5.1 BINARY ADDERS AND SUBTRACTERS

The most fundamental computational process encountered in digital systems is that of binary addition. In Sec. 2.3 the concept of binary addition was introduced. As was seen at that time, when two binary numbers are added, in general, it is necessary to consider at each bit position an augend bit, x_i, an addend bit, y_i, and a carry-in from the previous bit position, c_i. The result of the addition at each bit position is a sum bit, s_i, and a carry-out bit, c_{i+1}, which is used when adding at the next higher-order bit position. Table 5.1 summarizes the addition process for each bit position, i.e., the values of s_i and c_{i+1} for all the possible assignment of values to x_i, y_i, and c_i.

Although Table 5.1 was constructed as an addition table, it can also be regarded as the truth table for a logic network that performs addition at a single bit position. Such a network is referred to as a *binary full adder*.

Table 5.1 Truth table for a binary full adder

x_i	y_i	c_i	c_{i+1}	s_i
0	0	0	0	0
0	0	1	0	1
0	1	0	0	1
0	1	1	1	0
1	0	0	0	1
1	0	1	1	0
1	1	0	1	0
1	1	1	1	1

---

*PAL is a registered trademark of Advanced Micro Devices, Inc.

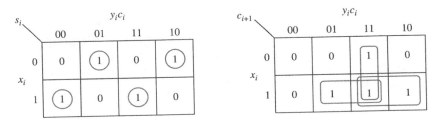

Figure 5.1   Karnaugh maps for the binary full adder.

Having obtained a truth table, let us determine a logic network realization. Karnaugh maps for the sum and carry-out outputs of the binary full adder are shown in Fig. 5.1. The corresponding minimal sums are

$$s_i = \bar{x}_i\bar{y}_ic_i + \bar{x}_iy_i\bar{c}_i + x_i\bar{y}_i\bar{c}_i + x_iy_ic_i$$
$$c_{i+1} = x_iy_i + x_ic_i + y_ic_i \tag{5.1}$$

Although the minimal sum for the sum output is just its minterm canonical formula, a possible simplification of the sum equation is achieved by making use of the exclusive-or operation. In particular,

$$\begin{aligned} s_i &= \bar{x}_i\bar{y}_ic_i + \bar{x}_iy_i\bar{c}_i + x_i\bar{y}_i\bar{c}_i + x_iy_ic_i \\ &= c_i(\bar{x}_i\bar{y}_i + x_iy_i) + \bar{c}_i(\bar{x}_iy_i + x_i\bar{y}_i) \\ &= c_i\overline{(x_i \oplus y_i)} + \bar{c}_i(x_i \oplus y_i) \\ &= c_i \oplus (x_i \oplus y_i) \end{aligned} \tag{5.2}$$

In arriving at Eq. (5.2), it should be noted that the form of the expression on the line above it is $A\bar{B} + \bar{A}B$, where $A = c_i$ and $B = (x_i \oplus y_i)$, which corresponds to $A \oplus B$. The logic diagram for the binary full adder based on Eqs. (5.1) and (5.2) is shown in Fig. 5.2.

The binary full adder is only capable of handling one bit each of an augend and addend along with a carry-in generated as a carry-out from the addition of the previ-

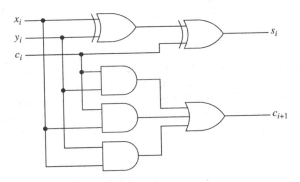

Figure 5.2   A realization of the binary full adder.

Figure 5.3. Parallel (ripple) binary adder.

ous lower-order bit position. Consider now the addition of two binary numbers each consisting of n bits, i.e., $x_{n-1}x_{n-2} \cdots x_1x_0$ and $y_{n-1}y_{n-2} \cdots y_1y_0$. This, in general, results in an $(n + 1)$-bit sum $s_ns_{n-1} \cdots s_1s_0$. A direct approach for designing a binary adder in this case is to write a truth table with 2^{2n} rows corresponding to all the combinations of values assignable to the $2n$ operand bits, and specifying the values for the $n + 1$ sum bits. Clearly, this is a formidable task.

As an alternate approach, n binary full adders, e.g., of the type shown in Fig. 5.2, can be cascaded as illustrated in Fig. 5.3, where c_n, the carry-out from the highest-order bit position, becomes the highest-order sum bit, s_n.* Since for the least-significant-bit position there is no carry-in, a 0 is entered on the corresponding input line. When inputs are applied simultaneously to a logic network, as in Fig. 5.3, it is commonly referred to as a *parallel* input. Thus, the adder network shown in Fig. 5.3 is called a *parallel binary adder*. Although the inputs to this adder are applied simultaneously, the output sum bits do not necessarily occur simultaneously due to the propagation delays associated with the gates. In particular, the network of Fig. 5.3 is prone to a ripple effect in that a carry-out generated at the ith-bit position can affect the sum bits at higher-order bit positions. Hence, the value for a higher-order sum bit is not produced until the carry at its previous order bit position is established. Consequently, this logic network is also referred to as a *ripple binary adder*.

As was discussed in Chapter 2, binary numbers can be signed or unsigned, in which case the output of the adder must be interpreted accordingly as a signed or unsigned result. Another factor affecting the interpretation of the output of the adder is if a final carry-out occurs, i.e., s_n, since it may correspond to an overflow. The reader is referred back to Chapter 2 for the details of binary arithmetic with signed and unsigned numbers and the concept of overflow.

5.1.1 Binary Subtracters

Binary subtraction was also discussed in Sec. 2.3. A binary subtracter can be designed using the same approach as that for a binary adder. The binary subtraction process is summarized in Table 5.2. Again, in general, three bits are involved at each bit order, a minuend bit, x_i, a subtrahend bit, y_i, and a borrow-in bit from the previous bit-order position, b_i. The result of the subtraction is a difference bit, d_i, and a

---

*Networks consisting of a cascade connection of identical subnetworks are frequently referred to as *iterative networks*.

Table 5.2 Truth table for a binary full subtracter

x_i	y_i	b_i	b_{i+1}	d_i
0	0	0	0	0
0	0	1	1	1
0	1	0	1	1
0	1	1	1	0
1	0	0	0	1
1	0	1	0	0
1	1	0	0	0
1	1	1	1	1

borrow-out bit, b_{i+1}. The difference bit at each order is obtained by subtracting both the subtrahend and borrow-in bits from the minuend bit. To achieve this result, however, a borrow-out from the next higher-order bit position may be necessary.

For the purpose of obtaining a realization, Table 5.2 can also be viewed as a truth table for a *binary full subtracter*. Since the d_i column of Table 5.2 is identical to the s_i column of Table 5.1, it is immediately concluded that the difference equation for a binary full subtracter is

$$d_i = x_i \oplus (y_i \oplus b_i)$$

By using a Karnaugh map, the minimal-sum expression for the borrow-out is readily determined as

$$b_{i+1} = \bar{x}_i y_i + \bar{x}_i b_i + y_i b_i$$

These results can be used to construct a logic diagram for a binary full subtracter.

As was done for addition, by cascading n binary full subtracters, a *ripple binary subtracter* is realized for handling two n-bit operands. The structure of such a realization is shown in Fig. 5.4, where $x_{n-1}x_{n-2} \cdots x_1 x_0$ is the n-bit minuend and $y_{n-1}y_{n-2} \cdots y_1 y_0$ is the n-bit subtrahend.

Recalling from Secs. 2.8 and 2.9, subtraction can be replaced by addition through the use of complements. For example, adding the 2's-complement of the subtrahend to the minuend results in the difference between the two numbers.

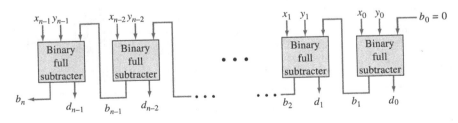

Figure 5.4. Parallel (ripple) binary subtracter.

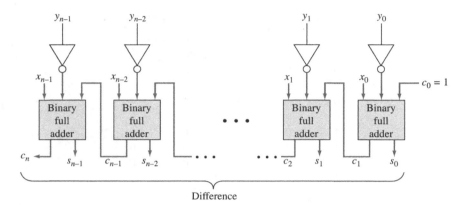

Figure 5.5. Parallel binary subtracter constructed using a parallel binary adder.

Furthermore, the 2's-complement of a binary number is readily obtained by adding one to its 1's-complement. Figure 5.5 shows the design of a subtracter using this approach. The 1's-complement of the subtrahend is formed by inverting each of its bits, and a carry-in of 1 in the least-significant-bit position provides for the addition of 1 to the 1's-complement.

By making use of the fact that $y_i \oplus 1 = \bar{y}_i$, Fig. 5.6 gives a realization of a parallel adder/subtracter. The behavior of this network is determined by the control signal Add/Sub. The subtraction operation is obtained by letting Add/Sub = 1, in which case 1's are appropriately entered into the exclusive-or-gates to provide the 1's-complement of the subtrahend and the initial carry-in of 1. The parallel binary adder then produces the difference. On the other hand, when the two operands are to be added, Add/Sub = 0. The bits of the addend are not modified

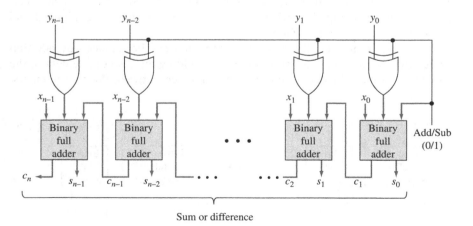

Figure 5.6. Parallel binary adder/subtracter.

by the exclusive-or-gates prior to entering the parallel binary adder and the necessary initial carry-in of 0 is provided.

Since the operands in subtraction can be either signed or unsigned, the output of a binary subtracter must be interpreted appropriately. For example, for unsigned operands, the output from the binary subtracter of Fig. 5.4 is the true difference if the minuend is greater than or equal to the subtrahend. However, the output from the subtracter is the 2's-complement representation of the difference if the minuend is less than the subtrahend. Again the reader is referred back to Chapter 2 for the details of binary arithmetic with signed and unsigned numbers.

5.1.2 Carry Lookahead Adder

In view of the fact that subtraction is readily achievable through the addition of complements, further discussion of the addition/subtraction process is restricted only to the realization of binary adders.

Although the operands are applied in parallel, all the networks illustrated thus far in this section are subject to a ripple effect. The ripple effect dictates the overall speed at which the network operates. To see this, consider the ripple binary adder of Fig. 5.3. It is possible that a carry is generated in the least-significant-bit-position stage, and, owing to the operands, this carry must propagate through all the remaining stages to the highest-order-bit-position stage. For example, such a situation occurs when the two n-bit operands are $01 \cdots 11$ and $00 \cdots 01$ so that the n-bit sum $10 \cdots 00$ is produced. Assuming the binary full adder of Fig. 5.2, two levels of logic are needed to generate the carry at the least-significant-bit-position stage, two levels of logic are needed to propagate the carry through each of the next $n-2$ higher-order stages, and two levels of logic are needed to form the sum or carry at the highest-order-bit-position stage. If each gate is assumed to introduce a unit time of propagation delay, then the maximum propagation delay for the ripple adder becomes $2n$ units of time. Of course, this is a worst-case condition. However, since normally all signals must complete their propagations through a network before new inputs are applied, this worst-case condition becomes a limiting factor in the network's overall speed of operation. To decrease the time required to perform addition, an effort must be made to speed up the propagation of the carries. One approach for doing this is to reduce the number of logic levels in the path of the propagated carries. Adders designed with this consideration in mind are called *high-speed adders*.

Equations (5.1) and (5.2) are the sum and carry equations for the outputs at the ith stage of a binary adder. As seen by these equations, the sum and carry outputs at a given stage are a function of the output carry from the previous stage, which, in turn, is a function of the output carry from still another previous stage, etc. This corresponds to the undesirable ripple effect. If the input carry at a given stage is expressed in terms of the operand variables themselves, i.e., $x_0, x_1, \ldots, x_{n-1}$ and $y_0, y_1, \ldots, y_{n-1}$, then the ripple effect is eliminated and the overall speed of the adder increased.

To see how this is done, again consider Eq. (5.1) for the output carry at the ith stage, i.e.,

$$c_{i+1} = x_i y_i + x_i c_i + y_i c_i$$
$$= x_i y_i + (x_i + y_i) c_i$$

The first term in the last equation, $x_i y_i$, is called the *carry-generate function* since it corresponds to the formation of a carry at the ith stage. The second term, $(x_i + y_i)c_i$, corresponds to a previously generated carry c_i that must propagate past the ith stage to the next stage. The $x_i + y_i$ part of this term is called the *carry-propagate function*. Letting the carry-generate function be denoted by the Boolean variable g_i and the carry-propagate function by p_i, i.e.,

$$g_i = x_i y_i \tag{5.3}$$

$$p_i = x_i + y_i \tag{5.4}$$

the output carry equation for the ith stage is given by

$$c_{i+1} = g_i + p_i c_i$$

Using this general result, the output carry at each of the stages can be written in terms of just the carry-generate functions, the carry-propagate functions, and the initial input carry c_0 as follows:

$$c_1 = g_0 + p_0 c_0 \tag{5.5}$$

$$
\begin{aligned}
c_2 &= g_1 + p_1 c_1 \\
&= g_1 + p_1(g_0 + p_0 c_0) \\
&= g_1 + p_1 g_0 + p_1 p_0 c_0
\end{aligned} \tag{5.6}
$$

$$
\begin{aligned}
c_3 &= g_2 + p_2 c_2 \\
&= g_2 + p_2(g_1 + p_1 g_0 + p_1 p_0 c_0) \\
&= g_2 + p_2 g_1 + p_2 p_1 g_0 + p_2 p_1 p_0 c_0
\end{aligned} \tag{5.7}
$$

$$
\begin{aligned}
c_4 &= g_3 + p_3 c_3 \\
&= g_3 + p_3(g_2 + p_2 g_1 + p_2 p_1 g_0 + p_2 p_1 p_0 c_0) \\
&= g_3 + p_3 g_2 + p_3 p_2 g_1 + p_3 p_2 p_1 g_0 + p_3 p_2 p_1 p_0 c_0
\end{aligned} \tag{5.8}
$$

$$\vdots$$

$$c_{i+1} = g_i + p_i g_{i-1} + p_i p_{i-1} g_{i-2} + \cdots + p_i p_{i-1} \cdots p_1 g_0 + p_i p_{i-1} \cdots p_0 c_0 \tag{5.9}$$

Since each carry-generate function and carry-propagate function is itself only a function of the operand variables as indicated by Eqs. (5.3) and (5.4), the output carry and, correspondingly, the input carry, at each stage can be expressed as a function of the operand variables and the initial input carry c_0. In addition, since the output sum bit at any stage is also a function of the previous stage output carry as indicated by Eq. (5.2), it also can be expressed in terms of just the operand variables and c_0 by the substitution of an appropriate carry equation having the form of Eq. (5.9). Parallel adders whose realizations are based on the above equations are called *carry lookahead adders*. The general organization of a carry lookahead adder is shown in Fig. 5.7a where the carry lookahead network corresponds to a logic network based on Eqs. (5.5) to (5.9). The sigma blocks correspond to the logic needed to form the sum bit, the carry-generate function, and the

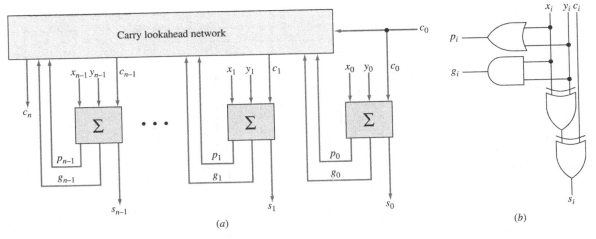

Figure 5.7   A carry lookahead adder. (*a*) General organization. (*b*) Sigma block.

carry-propagate function at each stage. A sigma block based on Eqs. (5.2) to (5.4) is shown in Fig. 5.7*b*.

From the above discussion, the logic diagram of a carry lookahead adder which handles two 4-bit operands is shown in Fig. 5.8. Generalizing from this figure, the path length from the generation of a carry to its appearance as an input at any higher-order stage, i.e., the path length through any stage of the carry lookahead network, is two levels of logic. Thus, with one level of logic to form g_i, two levels of logic for the carry to propagate between any two stages, and one level of logic to have the carry effect a sum output, the maximum propagation delay for a carry lookahead adder is 4 units of time under the assumption that each gate introduces a unit time of propagation delay.

5.1.3 Large High-Speed Adders Using the Carry Lookahead Principle

The basic carry lookahead principle involves minimizing the propagation delay time between the generation of a carry and its utilization at any higher-order stage of an adder. Essentially this is done by having the carry input to each stage be a direct function of the operand bits. Thus, the idea of having sum and carry outputs of the ith stage be a function of x_i, y_i, and c_i is replaced by having these outputs be a function of x_0, x_1, . . . , x_i, y_0, y_1, . . . , y_i, and c_0. In this way, the rippling effect of generated carries to higher-order stages is alleviated.

Although the carry lookahead adder of Fig. 5.8 performs high-speed addition based on the carry lookahead principle, it presents a limitation in the realization of large high-speed adders. The carry lookahead network can get quite large in terms of gates and gate inputs as the number of bits in the operands increases. One approach to circumvent this problem is to divide the bits of the operands into blocks.

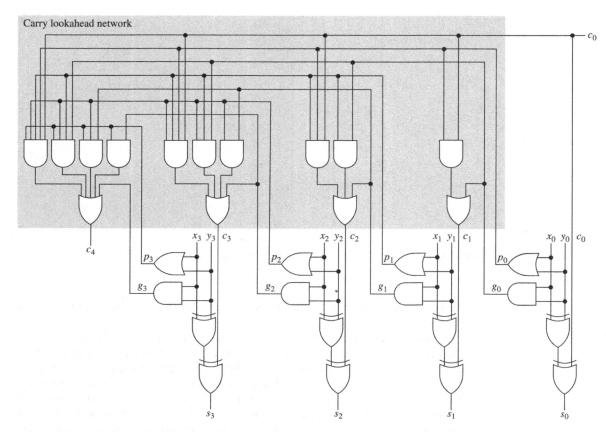

Figure 5.8 A 4-bit carry lookahead adder.

Then, by using carry lookahead adders for each block, their cascade connection results in a large adder. Figure 5.9 illustrates this approach by cascading 4-bit carry lookahead adders. In this case, ripple carries occur between the cascaded 4-bit carry lookahead adders.

Another approach to realizing large high-speed adders again relies on the partitioning of the operands into blocks. However, use is made of generic carry lookahead networks called *carry lookahead generators*. Figure 5.10a shows a possible 4-bit carry lookahead generator. It is the same as the first three stages of the carry lookahead network of Fig. 5.8 with two additional outputs G and P, described by the expressions

$$G = g_3 + p_3 g_2 + p_3 p_2 g_1 + p_3 p_2 p_1 g_0$$

and

$$P = p_3 p_2 p_1 p_0$$

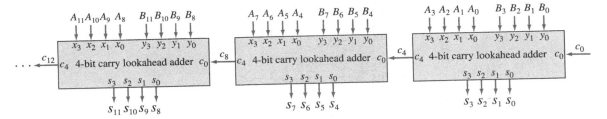

Figure 5.9 Cascade connection of 4-bit carry lookahead adders.

These outputs provide for a block carry-generate signal and a block carry-propagate signal. Using this 4-bit carry lookahead generator, the 16-bit high-speed adder shown in Fig. 5.10b is realized where the Σ-blocks correspond to the network of Fig. 5.7b.

Both of the above two compromises, i.e., cascading carry lookahead adders or utilizing block carry lookahead generators, result in a large parallel adder much faster than that of the ripple parallel adder.

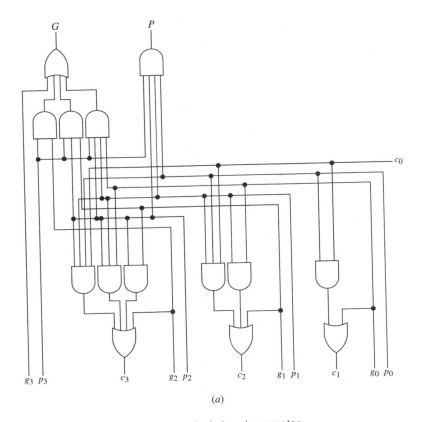

(a)

Figure 5.10 (a) A carry lookahead generator.

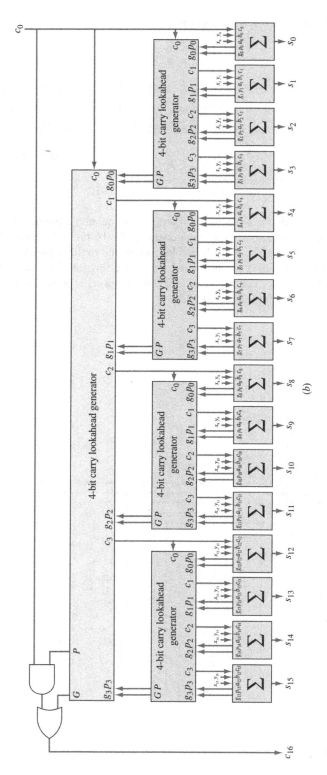

Figure 5.10   (*b*) a 16-bit high-speed adder.

5.2   DECIMAL ADDERS

At times, digital systems are required to handle decimal numbers. As was mentioned in Chapter 2, owing to the availability and reliability of two-valued circuits, the decimal digits are represented by groups of binary digits. Numerous codes for this purpose were given in Sec. 2.10. When performing arithmetic in these digital systems, the system must be capable of accepting the operands in some binary-coded form and producing results also in the same coding scheme.

Again only addition is considered in this section since subtraction can be achieved by means of complements. The use of complements with decimal numbers was also discussed in Chapter 2.

The general form of a single-decade decimal adder, i.e., an adder corresponding to a single-order digit position, is given in Fig. 5.11. In this figure it is assumed that a 4-bit code is used for each decimal digit. Here the two decimal digits serving as operands are denoted by $A_3A_2A_1A_0$ and $B_3B_2B_1B_0$. A carry, denoted by C_{in}, also appears as an input from the addition of the previous decade. The outputs from the adder are a single sum digit, $Z_3Z_2Z_1Z_0$, and a carry, C_{out}. Although the signal values denoting the decimal digits depend upon the code being used, the carries, C_{in} and C_{out}, are only 0 or 1. Thus, only a single line is shown in the figure for each of them.

From Fig. 5.11 it is seen that the five output variables Z_3, Z_2, Z_1, Z_0, and C_{out} are Boolean functions of the nine input variables A_3, A_2, A_1, A_0, B_3, B_2, B_1, B_0, and C_{in}. To design the single-decade adder, a truth table for the output functions can be constructed in which the desired sum digit and output carry are given for each possible pair of input digits and input carry. This truth table has $2^9 = 512$ rows. However, since each of the decimal digits has only 10 code groups and since the carry from the previous decade is only 0 or 1, it follows that the output variables have specified values for only 200 of the 512 rows. Even so, this is an extremely large table with which to work, so an alternate approach should be considered.

The 8421 weighted coding scheme is the most commonly occurring in digital systems and is frequently referred to as simply BCD for binary-coded decimal. When using BCD, a single-decade decimal adder can be constructed by first per-

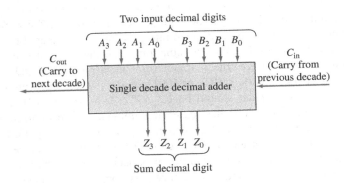

Figure 5.11   Organization of a single-decade decimal adder.

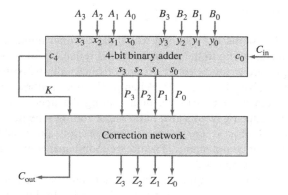

Figure 5.12 Organization of a single-decade BCD adder.

forming conventional binary addition on the two binary-coded operands and then applying a corrective procedure. This approach is illustrated in Fig. 5.12. The code groups for the two decimal digits are added using a 4-bit binary adder as discussed in the previous section to produce intermediate results $KP_3P_2P_1P_0$. These results are then modified so as to obtain the appropriate output carry and code group for the sum digit, i.e., $C_{out}Z_3Z_2Z_1Z_0$. Since each operand digit has a decimal value from 0 to 9 along with the fact that a carry from a previous digit position is at most 1, the decimal sum at each digit position must be in the range from 0 to 19. Table 5.3 summarizes the various outputs from the 4-bit binary adder and the required outputs from the single-decade decimal adder. As shown in the table, if the sum of the two decimal digits and input carry is less than 10, then the code group for the required BCD sum and output carry digits appear at the outputs of the 4-bit binary adder. In this case no corrective procedure is necessary since $KP_3P_2P_1P_0 = C_{out}Z_3Z_2Z_1Z_0$. On the other hand, when the two decimal-digit operands and carry from the previous decade produce an output from the 4-bit binary adder of $KP_3P_2P_1P_0 = 01010$, $01011, \ldots, 10011$, which corresponds to the decimal sums of 10 through 19, corrective action must be taken to get the appropriate values for $C_{out}Z_3Z_2Z_1Z_0$.

The need for a correction is divided into two cases as indicated by the dashed lines in Table 5.3. Consider first the situation when the decimal sums are in the range from 16 to 19. Here, the outputs from the 4-bit binary adder appear as $KP_3P_2P_1P_0 = 10000, 10001, 10010$, or 10011; while the required outputs from the single-decade decimal adder should be $C_{out}Z_3Z_2Z_1Z_0 = 10110, 10111, 11000$, or 11001, respectively. In each of these cases, it is immediately recognized that the occurrence of the carry K indicates that a carry C_{out} also is necessary. Furthermore, if the binary quantity 0110 is added to the output $P_3P_2P_1P_0$, then the correct sum digit, $Z_3Z_2Z_1Z_0$, is obtained. That is, the addition of a decimal 6, i.e., binary 0110, to the output from the 4-bit binary adder is the necessary correction whenever the carry bit K is 1.

Table 5.3 Comparing binary and BCD sums

Decimal sum	Binary sum					Required BCD sum				
	K	P_3	P_2	P_1	P_0	C_{out}	Z_3	Z_2	Z_1	Z_0
0	0	0	0	0	0	0	0	0	0	0
1	0	0	0	0	1	0	0	0	0	1
2	0	0	0	1	0	0	0	0	1	0
3	0	0	0	1	1	0	0	0	1	1
4	0	0	1	0	0	0	0	1	0	0
5	0	0	1	0	1	0	0	1	0	1
6	0	0	1	1	0	0	0	1	1	0
7	0	0	1	1	1	0	0	1	1	1
8	0	1	0	0	0	0	1	0	0	0
9	0	1	0	0	1	0	1	0	0	1
10	0	1	0	1	0	1	0	0	0	0
11	0	1	0	1	1	1	0	0	0	1
12	0	1	1	0	0	1	0	0	1	0
13	0	1	1	0	1	1	0	0	1	1
14	0	1	1	1	0	1	0	1	0	0
15	0	1	1	1	1	1	0	1	0	1
16	1	0	0	0	0	1	0	1	1	0
17	1	0	0	0	1	1	0	1	1	1
18	1	0	0	1	0	1	1	0	0	0
19	1	0	0	1	1	1	1	0	0	1

Now consider the situation when the output from the 4-bit binary adder corresponds to the decimal sums 10 to 15. These outputs appear as $KP_3P_2P_1P_0 = 01010$, $01011, \ldots, 01111$ and the required outputs are $C_{out}Z_3Z_2Z_1Z_0 = 10000, 10001, \ldots, 10101$, respectively. In each of these cases, it is necessary to have $C_{out} = 1$ even though $K = 0$. Again it is immediately recognized that the addition of decimal 6, i.e., binary 0110, to the output from the 4-bit binary adder, $P_3P_2P_1P_0$, results in the correct sum digit. That is, whenever the six binary combinations $P_3P_2P_1P_0 = 1010$, $1011, \ldots, 1111$ occur, the corrective procedure is to add the decimal quantity 6. These six binary combinations correspond to the invalid code groups in the 8421 code. To obtain a Boolean expression to detect these six binary combinations, a Karnaugh map is constructed as shown in Fig. 5.13. Obtaining the minimal sum from the map, it is seen that a correction is needed to the binary sum whenever the Boolean expression $P_3P_2 + P_3P_1$ has the value of 1.

In summary, to design a single-decade BCD adder having the organization of Fig. 5.12, the two decimal digits are added as binary numbers. No correction to the binary sum is necessary when $KP_3P_2P_1P_0 \leq 01001$, but the binary equivalent of the decimal 6 must be added to $P_3P_2P_1P_0$ when $KP_3P_2P_1P_0 > 01001$. The Boolean expression describing the need for a correction is

$$\text{Add } 6 = K + P_3P_2 + P_3P_1 \tag{5.10}$$

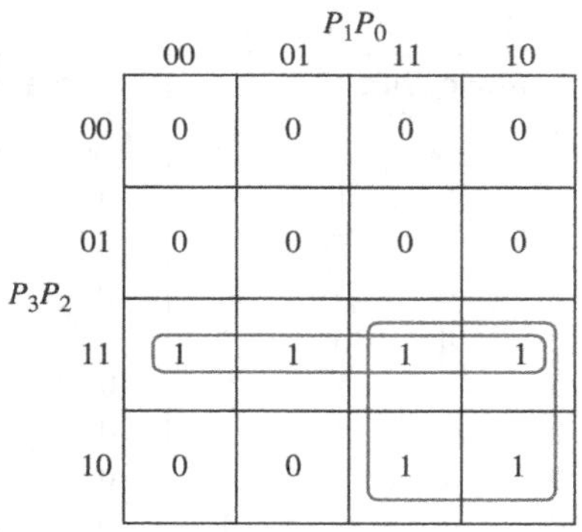

	P_1P_0			
	00	01	11	10
00	0	0	0	0
01	0	0	0	0
11	1	1	1	1
10	0	0	1	1

P_3P_2

Figure 5.13 Karnaugh map to detect the combinations $P_3P_2P_1P_0 = 1010, 1011, \ldots, 1111$.

The first term corresponds to the situation when $10000 \leq KP_3P_2P_1P_0 \leq 10011$, i.e., whenever the carry bit K is 1, and the remaining two terms correspond to the situation when $01010 \leq KP_3P_2P_1P_0 \leq 01111$, i.e., whenever the code group for the sum digit is invalid. It is also noted from Table 5.3 that whenever a corrective action is necessary, a carry C_{out} should be sent to the next decade. Thus, Eq. (5.10) also describes the conditions for the generation of a carry. Figure 5.14 shows the logic diagram of

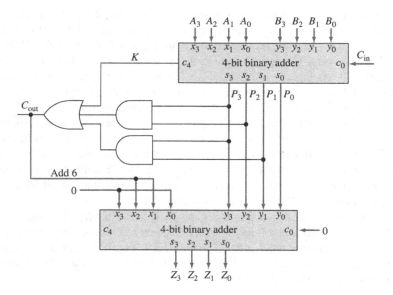

Figure 5.14 A single-decade BCD adder.

a single-decade BCD adder. In this diagram whenever $C_{out} = 0$, the outputs from the upper 4-bit binary adder are sent to the lower 4-bit binary adder and the decimal quantity of zero is added to it, which results in no corrective action. However, whenever $C_{out} = 1$, decimal 6, i.e., binary 0110, is added to the outputs from the upper 4-bit binary adder so that the correct sum digit is obtained.

The above discussion was concerned with the design of a single-decade BCD adder. A decimal adder for two n-digit BCD numbers can be constructed by cascading the network of Fig. 5.14 in much the same way as was done for the ripple binary adder.

5.3 COMPARATORS

A commonly encountered situation in logic design is the need for a network to compare the magnitudes of two binary numbers for the purpose of establishing whether one is greater than, equal to, or less than the other. A conceptually simple approach to the design of such a network, called a *comparator*, makes use of a cascade connection of identical subnetworks in much the same way as was done in the design of the parallel adder.*

To see how such a subnetwork is designed, consider two n-bit binary numbers $A = A_{n-1} \cdots A_i A_{i-1} \cdots A_1 A_0$ and $B = B_{n-1} \cdots B_i B_{i-1} \cdots B_1 B_0$. For the purpose of this design, assume that only one bit of corresponding order from each number is entering the subnetwork, say, A_i and B_i, and that the two binary numbers are to be analyzed from right to left. This subnetwork is called a *1-bit comparator*. The function of the 1-bit comparator is to establish whether $A_i A_{i-1} \cdots A_1 A_0$ is greater than, equal to, or less than $B_i B_{i-1} \cdots B_1 B_0$ given the values of A_i, B_i, and whether $A_{i-1} \cdots A_1 A_0$ is greater than, equal to, or less than $B_{i-1} \cdots B_1 B_0$. The three conditions describing the relative magnitudes of $A_{i-1} \cdots A_1 A_0$ and $B_{i-1} \cdots B_1 B_0$ are assigned to three variables G_i, E_i, and L_i where $G_i = 1$ denotes $A_{i-1} \cdots A_1 A_0 > B_{i-1} \cdots B_1 B_0$, $E_i = 1$ denotes $A_{i-1} \cdots A_1 A_0 = B_{i-1} \cdots B_1 B_0$, and $L_i = 1$ denotes $A_{i-1} \cdots A_1 A_0 < B_{i-1} \cdots B_1 B_0$. Thus, the 1-bit comparator is a 5-input, 3-output network as shown in Fig. 5.15.

Having obtained the organization of the 1-bit comparator, it is now necessary to develop a rule for specifying the values of G_{i+1}, E_{i+1}, and L_{i+1} given the values of A_i, B_i, G_i, E_i, and L_i. Upon a little thought it should become clear that, regardless of

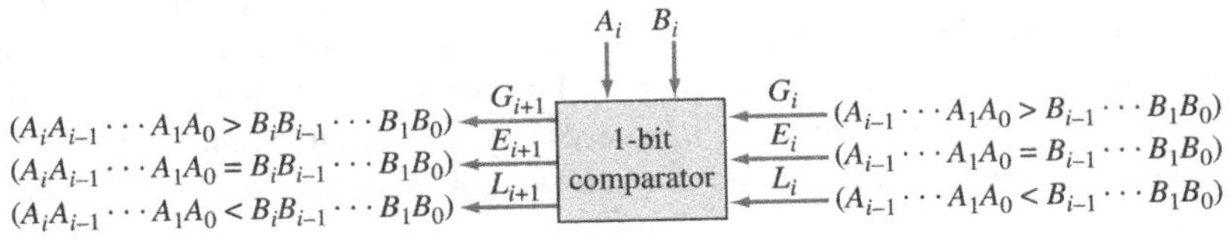

Figure 5.15 Organization of a 1-bit comparator.

_____

*This design of a comparator is another example of an iterative network.

Table 5.4 Truth table for a 1-bit comparator

A_i	B_i	G_i	E_i	L_i	G_{i+1}	E_{i+1}	L_{i+1}	A_i	B_i	G_i	E_i	L_i	G_{i+1}	E_{i+1}	L_{i+1}
0	0	0	0	0	–	–	–	1	0	0	0	0	–	–	–
0	0	0	0	1	0	0	1	1	0	0	0	1	1	0	0
0	0	0	1	0	0	1	0	1	0	0	1	0	1	0	0
0	0	0	1	1	–	–	–	1	0	0	1	1	–	–	–
0	0	1	0	0	1	0	0	1	0	1	0	0	1	0	0
0	0	1	0	1	–	–	–	1	0	1	0	1	–	–	–
0	0	1	1	0	–	–	–	1	0	1	1	0	–	–	–
0	0	1	1	1	–	–	–	1	0	1	1	1	–	–	–
0	1	0	0	0	–	–	–	1	1	0	0	0	–	–	–
0	1	0	0	1	0	0	1	1	1	0	0	1	0	0	1
0	1	0	1	0	0	0	1	1	1	0	1	0	0	1	0
0	1	0	1	1	–	–	–	1	1	0	1	1	–	–	–
0	1	1	0	0	0	0	1	1	1	1	0	0	1	0	0
0	1	1	0	1	–	–	–	1	1	1	0	1	–	–	–
0	1	1	1	0	–	–	–	1	1	1	1	0	–	–	–
0	1	1	1	1	–	–	–	1	1	1	1	1	–	–	–

the relative magnitudes of $A_{i-1} \cdots A_1 A_0$ and $B_{i-1} \cdots B_1 B_0$, if $A_i = 1$ and $B_i = 0$ then $A_i \cdots A_1 A_0 > B_i \cdots B_1 B_0$; while if $A_i = 0$ and $B_i = 1$ then $A_i \cdots A_1 A_0 < B_i \cdots B_1 B_0$. However, if A_i and B_i are the same, then the relative magnitudes of $A_i \cdots A_1 A_0$ and $B_i \cdots B_1 B_0$ are the same as the relative magnitudes of $A_{i-1} \cdots A_1 A_0$ and $B_{i-1} \cdots B_1 B_0$. From this analysis, the truth table shown in Table 5.4 is constructed. The large number of don't-care conditions should be noted. This is a consequence of the fact that one and only one of the three variables G_i, E_i, and L_i has the value of logic-1 at any time. The minimal sum Boolean expressions for Table 5.4 are

$$G_{i+1} = A_i \overline{B}_i + A_i G_i + \overline{B}_i G_i$$
$$E_{i+1} = \overline{A}_i \overline{B}_i \overline{E}_i + A_i B_i E_i$$
$$L_{i+1} = \overline{A}_i B_i + B_i L_i + \overline{A}_i L_i$$

and the corresponding logic network is shown in Fig. 5.16a. Cascading n 1-bit comparators, as shown in Fig. 5.16b, results in a network capable of determining the relative magnitudes of two n-bit binary numbers A and B. Particular attention should be given to the 1-bit comparator having the bit-pair A_0 and B_0 as inputs. In order to commence the comparison process, it is necessary to indicate that no previous digits exist. This is achieved by assigning the values $E_0 = 1$ and $G_0 = L_0 = 0$ to the first 1-bit comparator.

For the purpose of illustrating the concept of binary comparison, the above discussion was based on the design of a 1-bit comparator. Several MSI comparators are commercially available. A typical commercial comparator provides for 4 bits of each number to be compared within each subnetwork. This allows for a more efficient

248   **DIGITAL PRINCIPLES AND DESIGN**

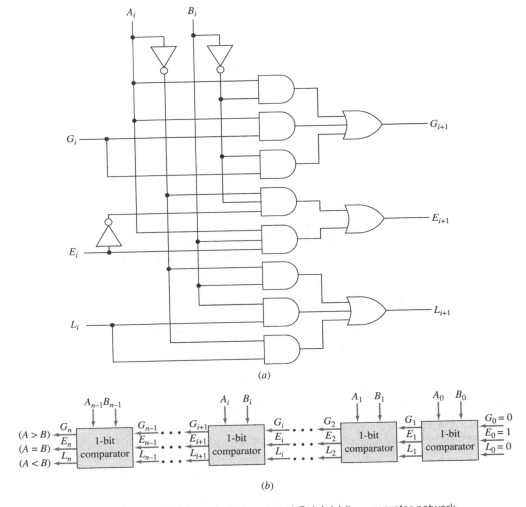

(a)

(b)

Figure 5.16 Comparing two binary numbers *A* and *B*. (*a*) 1-bit comparator network.
(*b*) Cascade connection of 1-bit comparators.

design of the subnetwork. Numbers consisting of more than 4 bits are then compared by cascading these 4-bit comparator subnetworks in the same manner as was illustrated above for the 1-bit comparators.

5.4 DECODERS

Frequently, digital information represented in some binary form must be converted into some alternate binary form. This is achieved by a multiple-input, multiple-output logic network referred to as a *decoder*. The most commonly used decoder is the

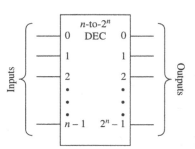

Figure 5.17 An n-to-2^n-line
decoder symbol.

n-to-2^n-*line decoder.* This digital network has n-input lines and 2^n-output lines with the property that only one of the 2^n-output lines responds, say with a logic-1, to a given input combination of values on its n-input lines. A symbol for such a device is shown in Fig. 5.17.

The realization of the n-to-2^n-line decoder is straightforward. Figure 5.18 shows the logic diagram, truth table, and symbol of a 3-to-8-line decoder. In this figure the three input lines are assigned the variables x_0, x_1, and x_2; while the eight output lines are assigned the variables $z_0, z_1, \ldots, z_7$. As shown in the truth table, only one output line responds, i.e., is at logic-1, for each of the input combinations.

To further understand the labels in the symbol of Fig. 5.18c, let a binary 0 be associated with a logic-0 and a binary 1 be associated with a logic-1. In addition, let the ith-input line be weighted by 2^i, for $i = 0,1,2$. In this way, the input combinations can be regarded as binary numbers with the consequence that the jth-output line is at logic-1, for $j = 0, 1, \ldots, 7$, only when input combination j is applied.

The n-to-2^n-line decoder is only one of several types of decoders. *Function-specific decoders* exist having fewer than 2^n outputs. For example, a decoder having 4 inputs and 10 outputs in which a single responding output line corresponds to a combination of the 8421 code is referred to as a BCD-to-decimal decoder. There are also function-specific decoders in which more than one output line responds to a given input combination. For example, there is a four-input-line, seven-output-line decoder that accepts the 4 bits of the 8421 code and is used to drive a seven-segment display. However, the n-to-2^n-line decoders are more flexible than the function-specific decoders. It is now shown that they can be used as a general component for logic design.

5.4.1 Logic Design Using Decoders

In Fig. 5.18, the Boolean expressions describing the outputs of the decoder are also written. Each of these output expressions corresponds to a single minterm.

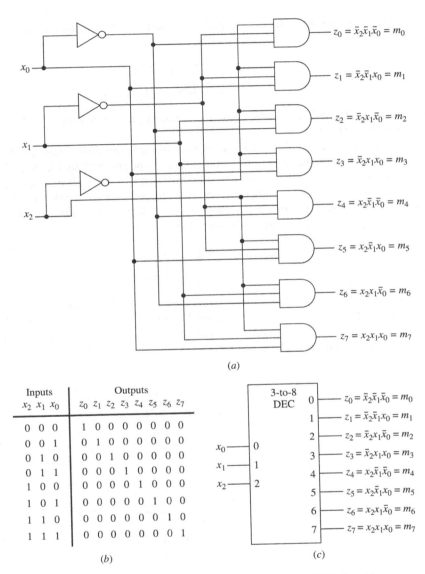

(a)

Inputs	Outputs
x_2 x_1 x_0	z_0 z_1 z_2 z_3 z_4 z_5 z_6 z_7
0 0 0	1 0 0 0 0 0 0 0
0 0 1	0 1 0 0 0 0 0 0
0 1 0	0 0 1 0 0 0 0 0
0 1 1	0 0 0 1 0 0 0 0
1 0 0	0 0 0 0 1 0 0 0
1 0 1	0 0 0 0 0 1 0 0
1 1 0	0 0 0 0 0 0 1 0
1 1 1	0 0 0 0 0 0 0 1

(b)

(c)

Figure 5.18   A 3-to-8-line decoder. (*a*) Logic diagram. (*b*) Truth table.
(*c*) Symbol.

Hence, an n-to-2^n-line decoder is a *minterm generator*. Recall that any Boolean function is describable by a sum of minterms. Thus, by using or-gates in conjunction with an n-to-2^n-line decoder, realizations of Boolean functions are possible. Although these realizations do not correspond to minimal sum-of-products expressions, the realizations are simple to produce due to the nature of the n-to-2^n-line decoder. This is particularly convenient when several functions of the same variables have to be realized. To illustrate this, consider the pair of expressions

$$f_1(x_2,x_1,x_0) = \Sigma m(1,2,4,5)$$
$$f_2(x_2,x_1,x_0) = \Sigma m(1,5,7)$$

Using a single 3-to-8-line decoder and two or-gates, the realization shown in Fig. 5.19 is immediately obtained.

In the realization of Fig. 5.19, the number of input terminals required of each or-gate is equal to the number of minterms that must be summed by the gate. When more than one-half the total number of minterms must be or-ed, it is usually more convenient to use nor-gates rather than or-gates to perform the summing. This results in a net reduction in the total number of input terminals required of the summing gates. For example, consider the pair of expressions

$$f_1(x_2,x_1,x_0) = \Sigma m(0,1,3,4,5,6)$$
$$f_2(x_2,x_1,x_0) = \Sigma m(1,2,3,4,6)$$

It is possible to realize these expressions with a 3-to-8-line decoder and two or-gates having a total of 11 input terminals between them. However, recalling that the complement of a minterm canonical formula is the sum of those minterms not appearing in the original formula, the complementary expressions are written as

$$\bar{f}_1(x_2,x_1,x_0) = \Sigma m(2,7)$$
$$\bar{f}_2(x_2,x_1,x_0) = \Sigma m(0,5,7)$$

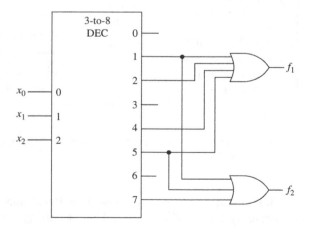

Figure 5.19   Realization of the Boolean expressions
$f_1(x_2,x_1,x_0) = \Sigma m(1,2,4,5)$ and
$f_2(x_2,x_1,x_0) = \Sigma m(1,5,7)$ with a 3-to-8-line decoder and two or-gates.

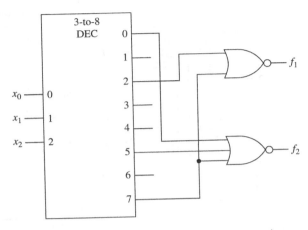

Figure 5.20   Realization of the Boolean expressions
$f_1(x_2,x_1,x_0) = \Sigma m(0,1,3,4,5,6) = \overline{\Sigma m(2,7)}$
and $f_2(x_2,x_1,x_0) = \Sigma m(1,2,3,4,6) =$
$\overline{\Sigma m(0,5,7)}$ with a 3-to-8-line decoder and
two nor-gates.

Finally, complementing these expressions by DeMorgan's law gives

$$\overline{\overline{f}}_1(x_2,x_1,x_0) = f_1(x_2,x_1,x_0) = \overline{\Sigma m(2,7)}$$
$$\overline{\overline{f}}_2(x_2,x_1,x_0) = f_2(x_2,x_1,x_0) = \overline{\Sigma m(0,5,7)}$$

This final pair of expressions corresponds to the realization shown in Fig. 5.20. Here, a total of only five gate-input terminals are required.

It is also possible to obtain realizations of maxterm canonical formulas using n-to-2^n-line decoders. In Chapter 3 it was shown that any maxterm canonical formula can be converted into an equivalent minterm canonical formula. For example, consider the pair of expressions

$$f_1(x_2,x_1,x_0) = \Pi M(0,1,3,5)$$
$$f_2(x_2,x_1,x_0) = \Pi M(1,3,6,7)$$

Using the transformation technique introduced in Sec. 3.6, these expressions are rewritten as

$$f_1(x_2,x_1,x_0) = \Pi M(0,1,3,5) = \Sigma m(2,4,6,7)$$
$$f_2(x_2,x_1,x_0) = \Pi M(1,3,6,7) = \Sigma m(0,2,4,5)$$

These expressions lead to the realization shown in Fig. 5.21a. Alternately, from the above discussion on using nor-gates as summing devices, the expressions can also be written as

$$f_1(x_2,x_1,x_0) = \Pi M(0,1,3,5) = \overline{\Sigma m(0,1,3,5)}$$
$$f_2(x_2,x_1,x_0) = \Pi M(1,3,6,7) = \overline{\Sigma m(1,3,6,7)}$$

which suggests the realization of Fig. 5.21b.

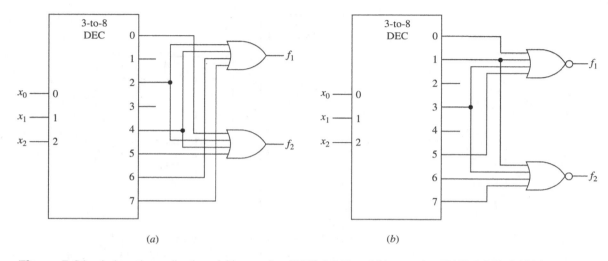

(a)   (b)

Figure 5.21 A decoder realization of $f_1(x_2,x_1,x_0) = \Pi M(0,1,3,5)$ and $f_2(x_2,x_1,x_0) = \Pi M(1,3,6,7)$. (a) Using output or-gates. (b) Using output nor-gates.

Frequently, n-to-2^n-line decoders are constructed from nand-gates. An example of a 3-to-8-line decoder using nand-gates, along with its truth table and symbol, is shown in Fig. 5.22. The Boolean expressions of the outputs are also given in the figure. In this case, for each input combination the single responding output line is associated with a logic-0, as is readily seen by the truth table. Since each output is logic-0 for only one input combination, it follows that each output is describable by a single maxterm. Thus, a nand-gate realization of a decoder is a *maxterm generator*. Particular attention should be given to the output terminals in the symbol of the decoder where bubble notation is used to indicate complementation is occurring. It should also be recalled from Sec. 3.6 that $\overline{m}_i = M_i$.

Since any Boolean function is describable by a product of maxterms, a nand-gate decoder, along with an and-gate, can serve as the basis of a maxterm canonical formula realization. For example, the realization of the pair of maxterm canonical expressions

$$f_1(x_2,x_1,x_0) = \Pi M(0,3,5)$$
$$f_2(x_2,x_1,x_0) = \Pi M(2,3,4)$$

is shown in Fig. 5.23.

When more than one-half of the total possible maxterms occur in a Boolean expression, the output and-gate can be replaced by a nand-gate so as to reduce the number of inputs needed to the output gate. To illustrate this, consider the pair of expressions

$$f_1(x_2,x_1,x_0) = \Pi M(0,1,3,4,7)$$
$$f_2(x_2,x_1,x_0) = \Pi M(1,2,3,4,5,6)$$

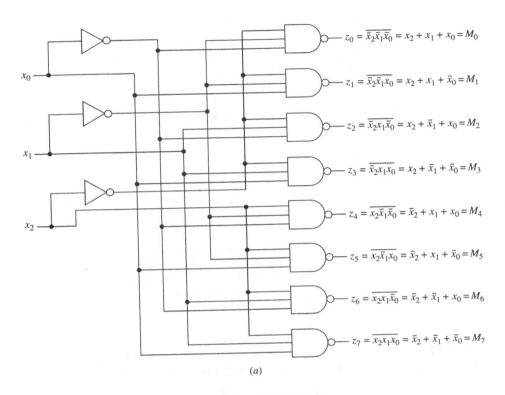

$z_0 = \overline{\overline{x}_2\overline{x}_1\overline{x}_0} = x_2 + x_1 + x_0 = M_0$

$z_1 = \overline{\overline{x}_2\overline{x}_1 x_0} = x_2 + x_1 + \overline{x}_0 = M_1$

$z_2 = \overline{\overline{x}_2 x_1 \overline{x}_0} = x_2 + \overline{x}_1 + x_0 = M_2$

$z_3 = \overline{\overline{x}_2 x_1 x_0} = x_2 + \overline{x}_1 + \overline{x}_0 = M_3$

$z_4 = \overline{x_2 \overline{x}_1 \overline{x}_0} = \overline{x}_2 + x_1 + x_0 = M_4$

$z_5 = \overline{x_2 \overline{x}_1 x_0} = \overline{x}_2 + x_1 + \overline{x}_0 = M_5$

$z_6 = \overline{x_2 x_1 \overline{x}_0} = \overline{x}_2 + \overline{x}_1 + x_0 = M_6$

$z_7 = \overline{x_2 x_1 x_0} = \overline{x}_2 + \overline{x}_1 + \overline{x}_0 = M_7$

(*a*)

Inputs			Outputs							
x_2	x_1	x_0	z_0	z_1	z_2	z_3	z_4	z_5	z_6	z_7
0	0	0	0	1	1	1	1	1	1	1
0	0	1	1	0	1	1	1	1	1	1
0	1	0	1	1	0	1	1	1	1	1
0	1	1	1	1	1	0	1	1	1	1
1	0	0	1	1	1	1	0	1	1	1
1	0	1	1	1	1	1	1	0	1	1
1	1	0	1	1	1	1	1	1	0	1
1	1	1	1	1	1	1	1	1	1	0

(*b*)

3-to-8 DEC

x_0 — 0

x_1 — 1

x_2 — 2

0 $z_0 = \overline{\overline{x}_2\overline{x}_1\overline{x}_0} = x_2 + x_1 + x_0 = M_0$

1 $z_1 = \overline{\overline{x}_2\overline{x}_1 x_0} = x_2 + x_1 + \overline{x}_0 = M_1$

2 $z_2 = \overline{\overline{x}_2 x_1 \overline{x}_0} = x_2 + \overline{x}_1 + x_0 = M_2$

3 $z_3 = \overline{\overline{x}_2 x_1 x_0} = x_2 + \overline{x}_1 + \overline{x}_0 = M_3$

4 $z_4 = \overline{x_2 \overline{x}_1 \overline{x}_0} = \overline{x}_2 + x_1 + x_0 = M_4$

5 $z_5 = \overline{x_2 \overline{x}_1 x_0} = \overline{x}_2 + x_1 + \overline{x}_0 = M_5$

6 $z_6 = \overline{x_2 x_1 \overline{x}_0} = \overline{x}_2 + \overline{x}_1 + x_0 = M_6$

7 $z_7 = \overline{x_2 x_1 x_0} = \overline{x}_2 + \overline{x}_1 + \overline{x}_0 = M_7$

(*c*)

Figure 5.22 A 3-to-8-line decoder using nand-gates. (*a*) Logic diagram. (*b*) Truth table. (*c*) Symbol.

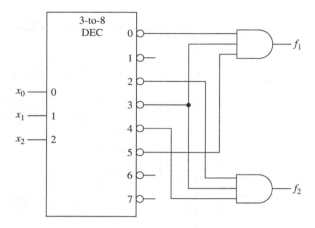

Figure 5.23 Realization of the pair of maxterm canonical expressions $f_1(x_2,x_1,x_0) = \Pi M(0,3,5)$ and $f_2(x_2,x_1,x_0) = \Pi M(2,3,4)$ with a 3-to-8-line decoder and two and-gates.

Using the fact that the complement of a maxterm canonical formula is the product of those maxterms not appearing in the original formula, the complementary formulas are

$$\overline{f}_1(x_2,x_1,x_0) = \Pi M(2,5,6)$$
$$\overline{f}_2(x_2,x_1,x_0) = \Pi M(0,7)$$

Complementing both sides of each equation results in

$$\overline{\overline{f}}_1(x_2,x_1,x_0) = f_1(x_2,x_1,x_0) = \overline{\Pi M(2,5,6)}$$
$$\overline{\overline{f}}_2(x_2,x_1,x_0) = f_2(x_2,x_1,x_0) = \overline{\Pi M(0,7)}$$

These expressions suggest the realization of Fig. 5.24.

Although the nand-gate version of an n-to-2^n-line decoder is a maxterm generator, it can also be used to realize expressions in minterm canonical form. This is done by simply transforming the minterm canonical formula into its equivalent maxterm canonical formula, as was discussed in Sec. 3.6. Again, either and-gates or nand-gates are used to collect the maxterms. For example, the pair of minterm canonical formulas

$$f_1(x_2,x_1,x_0) = \Sigma m(0,2,6,7)$$
$$f_2(x_2,x_1,x_0) = \Sigma m(3,5,6,7)$$

can be written as

$$f_1(x_2,x_1,x_0) = \Sigma m(0,2,6,7) = \Pi M(1,3,4,5)$$
$$f_2(x_2,x_1,x_0) = \Sigma m(3,5,6,7) = \Pi M(0,1,2,4)$$

256 DIGITAL PRINCIPLES AND DESIGN

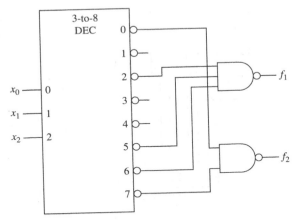

Figure 5.24 Realization of the Boolean expressions
$f_1(x_2,x_1,x_0) = \Pi M(0,1,3,4,7) = \overline{\Pi M(2,5,6)}$
and $f_2(x_2,x_1,x_0) = \Pi M(1,2,3,4,5,6) = \overline{\Pi M(0,7)}$ with a 3-to-8-line decoder and two nand-gates.

which has the realization shown in Fig. 5.25*a,* or written as

$$f_1(x_2,x_1,x_0) = \Sigma m(0,2,6,7) = \overline{\Pi M(0,2,6,7)}$$
$$f_2(x_2,x_1,x_0) = \Sigma m(3,5,6,7) = \overline{\Pi M(3,5,6,7)}$$

which has the realization shown in Fig. 5.25*b.*

5.4.2 Decoders with an Enable Input

Normally decoders have one or more additional input lines that are referred to as *enable inputs.* This is illustrated in Fig. 5.26, where a single enable input, E, is used in an and-gate realization of a 2-to-4-line decoder and in Fig. 5.27, where a single enable input, $\overline{E}$, is used in a nand-gate realization of a 2-to-4-line decoder. In each figure, a truth table and symbol are included. These truth tables are said to be *compressed* since not all input combinations explicitly appear. In compressed truth tables the $\times$'s indicate don't-care conditions. In this way, several rows of a normal truth table are replaced by a single row in a compressed truth table.

To function as the previously explained decoders, a logic-1 is applied to the enable input E of the decoder in Fig. 5.26; while in Fig. 5.27 a logic-0 is applied to the enable input $\overline{E}$. In such cases, the decoders are said to be *enabled.* On the other hand, when the enable inputs are such as to prevent the decoding process, the decoders are said to be *disabled.* In the case of Fig. 5.26, all outputs of the decoder are at logic-0 when it is disabled; while in the case of Fig. 5.27, all outputs of the decoder are at logic-1 when it is disabled. Particular attention should be given to the symbol of Fig. 5.27*c,* where the bubble on the enable input line indicates that the decoder is enabled when the input on this line is at logic-0.

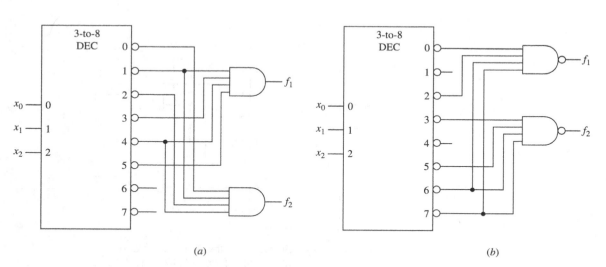

Figure 5.25   A decoder realization of $f_1(x_2,x_1,x_0) = \Sigma m(0,2,6,7)$ and $f_2(x_2,x_1,x_0) = \Sigma m(3,5,6,7)$. (*a*) Using output and-gates. (*b*) Using output nand-gates.

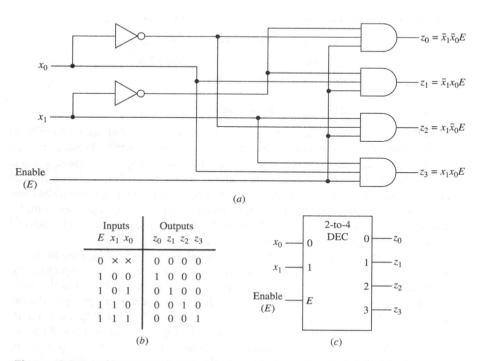

Inputs	Outputs
E x_1 x_0	z_0 z_1 z_2 z_3
0 × ×	0 0 0 0
1 0 0	1 0 0 0
1 0 1	0 1 0 0
1 1 0	0 0 1 0
1 1 1	0 0 0 1

(*b*)

(*c*)

Figure 5.26   And-gate 2-to-4-line decoder with an enable input. (*a*) Logic diagram.
(*b*) Compressed truth table. (*c*) Symbol.

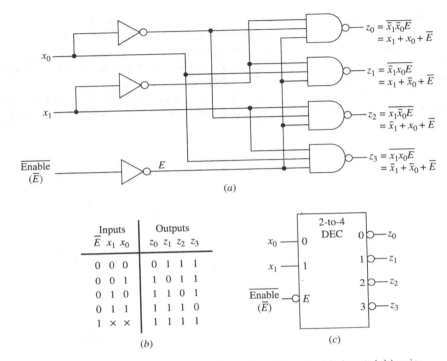

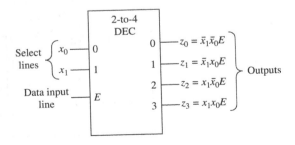

Figure 5.27   Nand-gate 2-to-4-line decoder with an enable input. (*a*) Logic diagram. (*b*) Compressed truth table. (*c*) Symbol.

The enable input provides the decoder with additional flexibility. For example, suppose a digital network is to be designed which accepts data information and must channel it to one of four outputs. This is achieved using a decoder in the configuration shown in Fig. 5.28. Here, the data are applied to the enable input. By entering a binary combination on the other two input lines, labeled as *select lines* in the figure, precisely one output line is selected to receive the information appearing on the data input line. In particular, if $x_1 = 0$ and $x_0 = 1$, then the output line labeled

Figure 5.28   Demultiplexer.

1, which is described by the Boolean expression $\bar{x}_1 x_0 E$, corresponds to $\bar{0} \cdot 1 \cdot E = E$ and hence follows the data on the input line E; i.e., the output line z_1 has the same bit value as on the data input line E. All the other output lines are at logic-0 during this time. This process is known as *demultiplexing*. For this reason, decoders with enable inputs are also referred to as *decoders/demultiplexers*.

Decoders with enable inputs are also used to construct larger decoders from smaller decoders. An example of this is shown in Fig. 5.29, where all the decoder

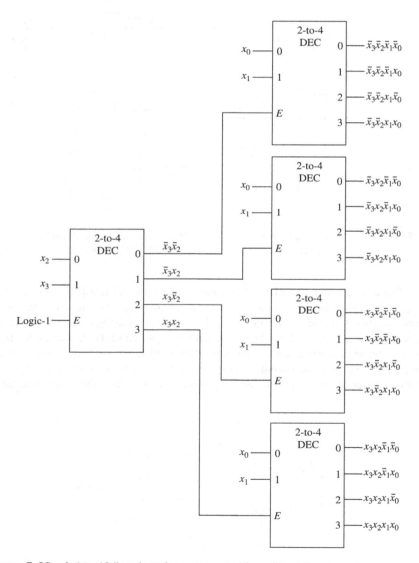

Figure 5.29 A 4-to-16-line decoder constructed from 2-to-4-line decoders.

260   DIGITAL PRINCIPLES AND DESIGN

output lines are labeled with their corresponding Boolean expressions. Here the first-level decoder is used to generate the four combinations of the x_2 and x_3 variables since $E = 1$. Each of these combinations is applied to the enable input at a second-level decoder that introduces the four combinations of the x_0 and x_1 variables. The net result is a network that generates the 16 minterms of four variables or, equivalently, serves as a 4-to-16-line decoder.

5.5 ENCODERS

Like decoders, *encoders* also provide for the conversion of binary information from one form to another. Encoders are essentially the inverse of decoders. Normally decoders have more output lines than input lines. On the other hand, decoders that have more input lines than output lines are usually called encoders.

Perhaps the simplest encoder is the 2^n-*to-n-line encoder* in which an assertive logic value, say, logic-1, on one of its 2^n input lines causes the corresponding binary code to appear at the output lines. If it is assumed that at most one input line is asserted* at any time, then the 2^n-to-n-line encoder is simply a collection of or-gates. Figure 5.30 shows a 2^n-to-n-line encoder symbol and Fig. 5.31 shows the logic diagram for an 8-to-3-line encoder. The equations for the three outputs of Fig. 5.31 are

$$z_0 = x_1 + x_3 + x_5 + x_7$$
$$z_1 = x_2 + x_3 + x_6 + x_7$$
$$z_2 = x_4 + x_5 + x_6 + x_7$$

In general, the Boolean expression for the output z_i is the sum of each input x_j in which the binary representation of j has a 1 in the 2^i-bit position.

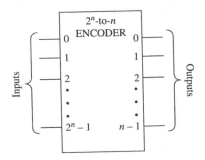

Figure 5.30 A 2^n-to-n-line encoder symbol.

---

*When a named input signal to a logic network is to cause an action when at logic-1, the signal is said to be *active high.* Similarly, when a named input signal to a logic network is to cause an action when at logic-0, the signal is said to be *active low.* When a signal is at its active level, it is said to be *asserted.*

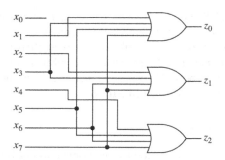

Figure 5.31 An 8-to-3-line encoder.

The assumption that at most a single input to the 2^n-to-n-line encoder is asserted at any time is significant in its operation. For example, in the encoder of Fig. 5.31, assume that both x_3 and x_5 are simultaneously logic-1. Logic-1's then appear at all three output terminals, implying that x_7 must have been logic-1. For this reason, *priority encoders* have been developed. In a priority encoder, a priority scheme is assigned to the input lines so that whenever more than one input line is asserted at any time, the output is determined by the input line having the highest priority. For example, Table 5.5 is a condensed truth table specifying the behavior of a priority encoder where the output is determined by the asserted input having the highest index, i.e., x_i has higher priority than x_j if $i > j$. Thus, referring to Table 5.5, if $x_4 = x_5 = x_6 = x_7 = 0$ and $x_3 = 1$, then $z_2 z_1 z_0 = 011$ regardless of the values of the x_0, x_1, and x_2 inputs.

An output is also included in Table 5.5, labeled *valid*, to indicate that at least one input line is asserted. This is done so as to distinguish the situation that no input line is asserted from when the x_0 input line is asserted, since in both cases $z_2 z_1 z_0 = 000$.

Table 5.5 Condensed truth table for an 8-to-3 line priority encoder

Inputs								Outputs			
x_0	x_1	x_2	x_3	x_4	x_5	x_6	x_7	z_2	z_1	z_0	Valid
0	0	0	0	0	0	0	0	0	0	0	0
1	0	0	0	0	0	0	0	0	0	0	1
×	1	0	0	0	0	0	0	0	0	1	1
×	×	1	0	0	0	0	0	0	1	0	1
×	×	×	1	0	0	0	0	0	1	1	1
×	×	×	×	1	0	0	0	1	0	0	1
×	×	×	×	×	1	0	0	1	0	1	1
×	×	×	×	×	×	1	0	1	1	0	1
×	×	×	×	×	×	×	1	1	1	1	1

5.6 MULTIPLEXERS

Another very useful MSI device is the *multiplexer*. Multiplexers are also called *data selectors*. The basic function of this device is to select one of its 2^n *data input lines* and place the corresponding information appearing on this line onto a single output line. Since there are 2^n data input lines, n bits are needed to specify which input line is to be selected. This is achieved by placing the binary code for a desired data input line onto its n *select input lines*. A symbol for a 2^n-to-1-line multiplexer is shown in Fig. 5.32. Typically an *enable*, or *strobe*, *line* is also included to provide greater flexibility as in the case of decoders. The multiplexer shown in Fig. 5.32 is enabled by applying a logic-1 to the E input terminal. Some commercial multiplexers require a logic-0 for enabling. In such a case an inversion bubble appears in the symbol at the E input terminal.

A realization of a 4-to-1-line multiplexer is given in Fig. 5.33 along with its compressed truth table and symbol. The $\times$'s in the compressed truth table denote irrelevant, i.e., don't-care, conditions. As shown in the figure, each data input line I_i goes to its own and-gate. The select lines are used to uniquely select one of the and-gates. Thus, if the multiplexer is enabled, then the output corresponds to the value on the data input line of the selected and-gate. As in the case of decoders, the 0-1 combinations on the select lines are regarded as binary numbers. The decimal equivalents of these numbers determine which data input lines are selected and serve to identify the corresponding input terminals in the symbol.

Table 5.6 provides an alternate description of the behavior of the 4-to-1-line multiplexer. This description is frequently referred to as a *function table*. Here, rather than listing the functional values on the output lines, the input that appears at the output is listed for each combination of values on the select lines. Again a $\times$ in the table indicates an irrelevant condition. From either the logic diagram or function table, an algebraic description of the multiplexer can immediately be written as

$$f = (I_0 \overline{S}_1 \overline{S}_0 + I_1 \overline{S}_1 S_0 + I_2 S_1 \overline{S}_0 + I_3 S_1 S_0)E \tag{5.11}$$

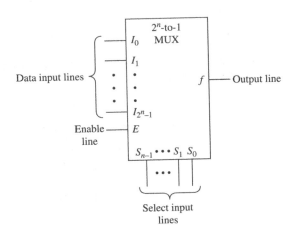

Figure 5.32　A 2^n-to-1-line multiplexer symbol.

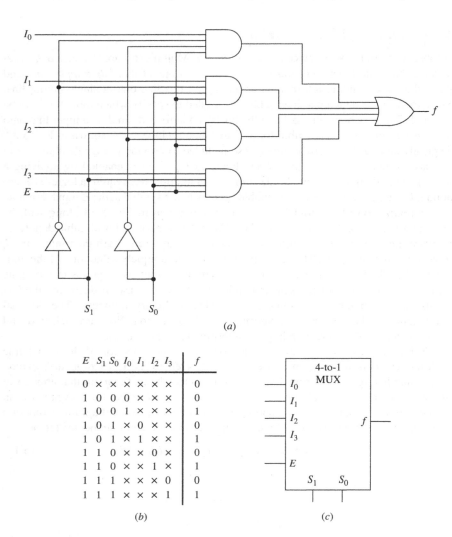

E	S_1	S_0	I_0	I_1	I_2	I_3	f
0	×	×	×	×	×	×	0
1	0	0	0	×	×	×	0
1	0	0	1	×	×	×	1
1	0	1	×	0	×	×	0
1	0	1	×	1	×	×	1
1	1	0	×	×	0	×	0
1	1	0	×	×	1	×	1
1	1	1	×	×	×	0	0
1	1	1	×	×	×	1	1

(b)

(c)

Figure 5.33 A 4-to-1-line multiplexer. (a) Logic diagram. (b) Compressed truth table. (c) Symbol.

Table 5.6 Function table for a 4-to-1-line multiplexer

E	S_1	S_0	f
0	×	×	0
1	0	0	I_0
1	0	1	I_1
1	1	0	I_2
1	1	1	I_3

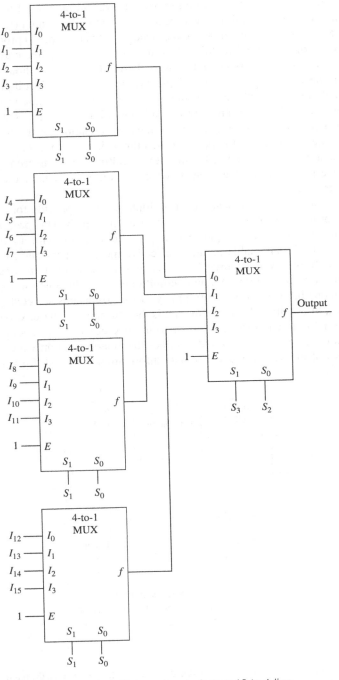

Figure 5.34   A multiplexer tree to form a 16-to-1-line multiplexer.

In addition to the 4-to-1-line multiplexer shown in Fig. 5.33, 2-to-1-line, 8-to-1-line, and 16-to-1-line multiplexers are also commercially available. By interconnecting several multiplexers in a treelike structure, it is possible to produce a larger multiplexer. For example, Fig. 5.34 illustrates how five 4-to-1-line multiplexers are used to construct a 16-to-1-line multiplexer. Particular attention should be given to the select lines. As a 16-to-1-line multiplexer, there are four select inputs S_3, S_2, S_1, and S_0. It should be noted that S_3 is the most significant select line in that its input is most heavily weighted when viewed as a binary digit; while S_0 is the least significant select line. In this way, if i is the binary combination on the $S_3S_2S_1S_0$-lines, then data line I_i is selected to appear at the output. In actuality, the S_1S_0-inputs select one data input from each of the first-level multiplexers. The second-level multiplexer, via its S_3S_2-lines, then selects which data input reaches the output of the multiplexer tree.

One of the primary applications of multiplexers is to provide for the transmission of information from several sources over a single path. This process is known as *multiplexing*. When a multiplexer is used in conjunction with a demultiplexer, i.e., a decoder with an enable input, an effective means is provided for connecting information from several source locations to several destination locations. This basic application of multiplexers and demultiplexers is illustrated in Fig. 5.35.* In this figure, one bit of information from any of four sources is selected according to the source address lines. This information is then placed on a wire, known as a *bus*, that connects to a demultiplexer similar to the one described in Sec. 5.4. The bit-combination on the destination address lines then determines on which of the four output lines of the demultiplexer the data information is placed. By using n of the

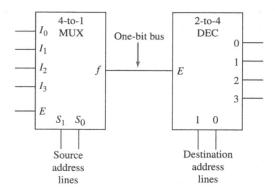

Figure 5.35 A multiplexer/demultiplexer arrangement for information transmission.

---

*In Fig. 5.35 the demultiplexer symbol was modified from Fig. 5.28 to emphasize the multiplexer/demultiplexer arrangement.

266   **DIGITAL PRINCIPLES AND DESIGN**

structures shown in Fig. 5.35 in parallel, an n-bit word from any of four source locations is transferred to any of four destination locations.

5.6.1 Logic Design with Multiplexers

Multiplexers are also used as general logic-design devices for realizing Boolean functions. Let us begin this discussion by considering the most direct way this is done. Consider a three-variable Boolean function and its truth table as shown in Fig. 5.36a. The Boolean expression corresponding to this truth table can be written as

$$f(x,y,z) = f_0 \cdot \bar{x}\bar{y}\bar{z} + f_1 \cdot \bar{x}\bar{y}z + f_2 \cdot \bar{x}y\bar{z} + f_3 \cdot \bar{x}yz$$
$$+ f_4 \cdot x\bar{y}\bar{z} + f_5 \cdot x\bar{y}z + f_6 \cdot xy\bar{z} + f_7 \cdot xyz \quad (5.12)$$

where f_i denotes functional values 0 and 1.* The Boolean expression for a 4-to-1-line multiplexer was previously written as Eq. (5.11). In an analogous manner to Eq. (5.11), an 8-to-1-line multiplexer is described by the Boolean expression

$$f = (I_0\bar{S}_2\bar{S}_1\bar{S}_0 + I_1\bar{S}_2\bar{S}_1S_0 + I_2\bar{S}_2S_1\bar{S}_0 + I_3\bar{S}_2S_1S_0$$
$$+ I_4S_2\bar{S}_1\bar{S}_0 + I_5S_2\bar{S}_1S_0 + I_6S_2S_1\bar{S}_0 + I_7S_2S_1S_0)E \quad (5.13)$$

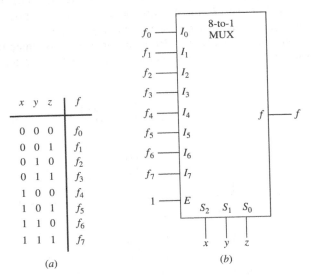

$$\begin{array}{ccc|c} x & y & z & f \\ \hline 0 & 0 & 0 & f_0 \\ 0 & 0 & 1 & f_1 \\ 0 & 1 & 0 & f_2 \\ 0 & 1 & 1 & f_3 \\ 1 & 0 & 0 & f_4 \\ 1 & 0 & 1 & f_5 \\ 1 & 1 & 0 & f_6 \\ 1 & 1 & 1 & f_7 \end{array}$$

(a)   (b)

Figure 5.36 Realization of a three-variable function using an 8-to-1-line multiplexer. (a) Three-variable truth table. (b) General realization.

*Note that f_i denotes a functional value in this presentation and not an entire function as in other sections of this book.

If E is assumed to be logic-1, then Eq. (5.13) is transformed into Eq. (5.12) by replacing I_i with f_i, S_2 with x, S_1 with y, and S_0 with z. In other words, by placing x, y, and z on select lines S_2, S_1, and S_0, respectively, and placing the functional values f_i on data input lines I_i, an enabled 8-to-1-line multiplexer realizes a general three-variable truth table. This realization is shown in Fig. 5.36b.

As a specific example, consider the truth table of Fig. 5.37a. By placing a logic-1 on the enable input line, the eight functional values on the eight data input lines of an 8-to-1-line multiplexer, and connecting the select lines S_2, S_1, S_0 to x, y, z, respectively, the configuration of Fig. 5.37b becomes a realization of the given truth table.

Rather than working from a truth table, one could start with a minterm canonical formula to obtain a realization with a multiplexer. Since each minterm in an expression algebraically describes a row of a truth table having a functional value of 1, the realization is obtained by simply applying a 1 input to the I_i line if minterm m_i appears in the expression and applying a 0 input to the I_j line if m_j does not appear in the expression. For example, consider the minterm canonical formula

$$f(x,y,z) = \Sigma m(0,2,3,5)$$

The realization is obtained by placing x, y, and z on the S_2, S_1, and S_0 lines, respectively, logic-1 on data input lines I_0, I_2, I_3, and I_5, and logic-0 on the remaining data input lines, i.e., I_1, I_4, I_6, and I_7. In addition, the multiplexer must be enabled by setting $E = 1$. This again is the realization shown in Fig. 5.37b.

If at least one input variable of a Boolean function is assumed to be available in both its complemented and uncomplemented form, or, equivalently, a not-gate

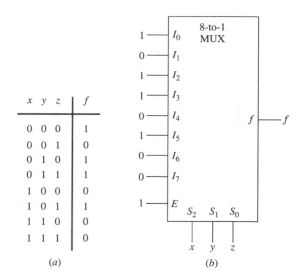

x	y	z	f
0	0	0	1
0	0	1	0
0	1	0	1
0	1	1	1
1	0	0	0
1	0	1	1
1	1	0	0
1	1	1	0

(a)   (b)

Figure 5.37   Realization of $f(x,y,z) = \Sigma m(0,2,3,5)$.
(a) Truth table. (b) 8-to-1-line
multiplexer realization.

is used to generate the complement of a variable, then any n-variable function is realizable with a 2^{n-1}-to-1-line multiplexer. For example, in the case of a three-variable function, this implies that only a 4-to-1-line multiplexer is needed for a realization. To see this, again consider Eq. (5.12). Doing some simple factoring, Eq. (5.12) becomes

$$f(x,y,z) = (f_0 \cdot \bar{z} + f_1 \cdot z)\bar{x}\,\bar{y} + (f_2 \cdot \bar{z} + f_3 \cdot z)\bar{x}y + (f_4 \cdot \bar{z} + f_5 \cdot z)x\bar{y} + (f_6 \cdot \bar{z} + f_7 \cdot z)xy$$

Furthermore, when $E = 1$ Eq. (5.11) has the form

$$f = I_0\bar{S}_1\bar{S}_0 + I_1\bar{S}_1S_0 + I_2S_1\bar{S}_0 + I_3S_1S_0$$

Comparing these last two equations, it immediately follows that a realization of any three-variable Boolean function is obtained by placing the x and y variables on the S_1 and S_0 select lines of a 4-to-1-line multiplexer, the single-variable functions $f_i \cdot \bar{z} + f_j \cdot z$ on the data input lines, and letting $E = 1$ as shown in Fig. 5.38. In any particular situation, the single-variable functions $f_i \cdot \bar{z} + f_j \cdot z$ reduce to 0, 1, z, or $\bar{z}$ depending upon the values of f_i and f_j.

As an illustration, again consider the truth table in Fig. 5.37a. Since $f_0 = 1$ and $f_1 = 0$, $f_0 \cdot \bar{z} + f_1 \cdot z$ evaluates to $\bar{z}$. Similarly, with $f_2 = 1$ and $f_3 = 1$, then $f_2 \cdot \bar{z} + f_3 \cdot z = 1$; with $f_4 = 0$ and $f_5 = 1$, then $f_4 \cdot \bar{z} + f_5 \cdot z = z$; and with $f_6 = 0$ and $f_7 = 0$, then $f_6 \cdot \bar{z} + f_7 \cdot z = 0$. Thus, the realization is obtained by placing x and y on the S_1 and S_0 select lines, respectively, $\bar{z}$ on the I_0 line, logic-1 on the I_1 line, z on the I_2 line, and logic-0 on the I_3 line. In addition, the multiplexer must be enabled. The resulting realization is shown in Fig. 5.39.

Alternatively, the minterm canonical formula for the truth table in Fig. 5.37a is

$$f(x,y,z) = \bar{x}\bar{y}\bar{z} + \bar{x}y\bar{z} + \bar{x}yz + x\bar{y}z$$

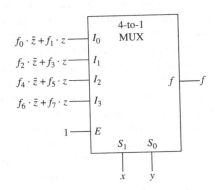

Figure 5.38 A general realization of a 3-variable Boolean function using a 4-to-1-line multiplexer.

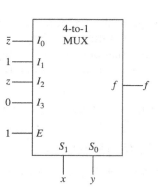

Figure 5.39   Realization of $f(x,y,z) = \Sigma m(0,2,3,5)$ using a 4-to-1-line multiplexer.

When the expression is factored into the following form

$$f(x,y,z) = \bar{x}\,\bar{y}(\bar{z}) + \bar{x}y(\bar{z} + z) + x\bar{y}(z)$$
$$= \bar{x}\,\bar{y}(\bar{z}) + \bar{x}y(1) + x\bar{y}(z) + xy(0)$$

the realization of Fig. 5.39 again results, where the entities in parentheses appear on the data input lines. The last term, $xy(0)$, was included to indicate what input must appear on the I_3 line to provide for the appropriate output when selected with $x = y = 1$.

Although in the above discussion the x and y variables appear on the select lines and functions of z appear on the data lines, by appropriate factoring of Eq. (5.12) realizations are possible where other variables appear on the select and data lines. In this way, if only one variable is available in its complemented and uncomplemented form, then it should be used for the data lines; while the remaining variables are used for the select lines. Furthermore, it should be noted that the order in which variables are assigned to the select lines affects the order in which the single-variable functions appear as inputs to the data input lines.

Karnaugh maps provide a convenient tool for obtaining multiplexer realizations. First it is necessary to establish which variables to assign to the select lines. Once this is done, the inputs for the I_i data lines are read directly from the map. To illustrate this, again consider a three-variable Boolean function of x, y, and z. Assume x is placed on the S_1 line and y is placed on the S_0 line. Figure 5.40a shows a three-variable Karnaugh map along with this assignment indicated by double arrows. Applying this assignment to Eq. (5.11) and letting $E = 1$, Eq. (5.11) becomes

$$f = I_0\bar{x}\,\bar{y} + I_1\bar{x}y + I_2x\bar{y} + I_3xy$$

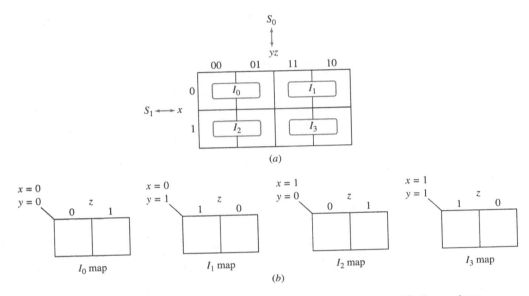

Figure 5.40   Obtaining multiplexer realizations using Karnaugh maps. (a) Cell groupings corresponding to the data line functions. (b) Karnaugh maps for the I_i subfunctions.

Now consider each term in this expression. The first term, $I_0 \bar{x}\,\bar{y}$, corresponds to those cells in which $x = 0$ and $y = 0$. These are the two upper left cells of the Karnaugh map in Fig. 5.40 labeled as I_0. These two cells can be regarded as a submap for the z variable as indicated in Fig. 5.40b. Thus, depending upon the 0-1 entries within this submap, the expression for I_0 is readily obtained. In a similar manner, the second term, $I_1 \bar{x}y$, corresponds to those cells in which $x = 0$ and $y = 1$. These are the two upper right cells of the map. The entries within these cells correspond to the I_1 input. The cells associated with I_2 and I_3 are obtained in a like manner and are also shown in Fig. 5.40a.

As an example, again consider the truth table of Fig. 5.37a. The Karnaugh map is drawn in Fig. 5.41a. For emphasis, the four pairs of cells corresponding to the data inputs are redrawn as single-variable submaps in Fig. 5.41b. It should be noted that the axis labels for the I_1 and I_3 submaps are shown in reverse order to be consistent with the Karnaugh map of Fig. 5.41a. Grouping the 1-cells, the expressions for the subfunctions are now written. In particular, $I_0 = \bar{z}$, $I_1 = 1$, $I_2 = z$, and $I_3 = 0$. This again leads to the realization shown in Fig. 5.39. Although submaps were drawn in Fig. 5.41b, the expressions for the subfunctions are obtained from the original map by noting the patterns within the appropriate pair of cells. When both cells contain 0's or 1's, then the subfunctions are 0 or 1, respectively. When one cell contains a 0 and the other a 1, $I_i = z$ if the 1 occurs in the cell in which $z = 1$; while $I_i = \bar{z}$ if the 1 occurs in the cell in which $z = 0$.

Introduction to Discrete Logic & Digital System

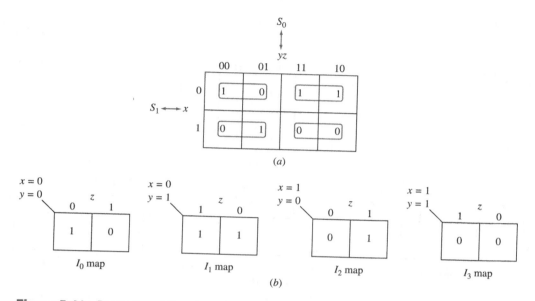

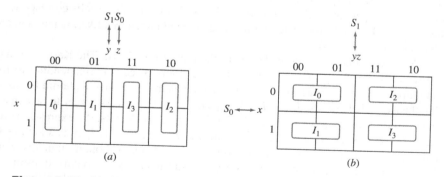

Figure 5.41 Realization of $f(x,y,z) = \Sigma m(0,2,3,5)$. (a) Karnaugh map. (b) I_0, I_1, I_2, and I_3 submaps.

Karnaugh maps can readily handle other assignments of the input variables to the select lines. For example, Fig. 5.42 illustrates the I_i submaps under two additional assignments. In Fig. 5.42a, input variable y is applied to select line S_1 and input variable z is applied to select line S_0. In Fig. 5.42b, input variable x is applied to select line S_0 and input variable y is applied to select line S_1. Depending upon the assignment, the submaps for functions of the third variable are located differently.

Figure 5.42 Using Karnaugh maps to obtain multiplexer realizations under various assignments to the select inputs. (a) Applying input variables y and z to the S_1 and S_0 select lines. (b) Applying input variables x and y to the S_0 and S_1 select lines.

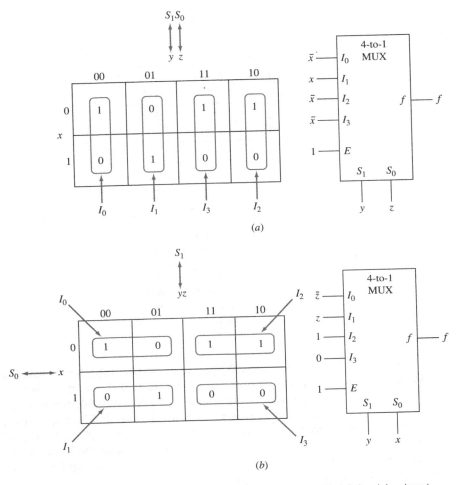

Figure 5.43   Alternative realizations of $f(x,y,z) = \Sigma m(0,2,3,5)$. (a) Applying input variables y and z to the S_1 and S_0 select lines. (b) Applying input variables x and y to the S_0 and S_1 select lines.

However, in each case, the submaps correspond to the four combinations of values to the variables on the select lines. Realizations of the truth table of Fig. 5.37a using the two assignments of Fig. 5.42 are shown in Fig. 5.43.

An 8-to-1-line multiplexer can be used to realize any four-variable Boolean function. Three of the variables are placed on the select lines. The inputs to the data lines are then the possible single-variable functions of the fourth variable, namely, 0, 1, the variable, and its complement. Figure 5.44 shows the relationships between the map cells and the data-line inputs under the assumption that the input variables

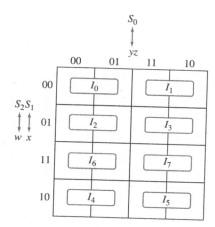

Figure 5.44   A select line assignment and corresponding data line functions for a multiplexer realization of a four-variable function.

w, x, and y are applied to select lines S_2, S_1, and S_0, respectively. In this case, the eight I_i inputs are determined by pairs of cells associated with the eight combination of values to the x, y, and z variables. An example of a four-variable function on a Karnaugh map, along with the multiplexer realization, is given in Fig. 5.45. Particular attention should be given to I_7 since $z = 0$ corresponds to the right cell and $z = 1$ corresponds to the left cell of the I_7 submap. As in the case of the three-variable Karnaugh map, it is a simple matter to reinterpret a four-variable map for different assignments of the input variables to the select lines.

In the above discussion, 2^n-to-1-line multiplexers were used to realize functions of $n + 1$ variables. This was achieved by applying functions of a single variable to the data input lines. By allowing realizations of m variable functions as inputs to the data input lines, 2^n-to-1-line multiplexers can be used in the realization of $(n + m)$-variable functions. To illustrate this, Fig. 5.46 shows a four-variable Karnaugh map in which it is assumed that the input variables w and x are applied to the S_1 and S_0 select inputs, respectively, of a 4-to-1-line multiplexer. This implies that functions of the y and z variables must appear at the data input lines in the overall realization. To determine these functions, it is necessary to consider the four cases corresponding to the four assignments of 0's and 1's to the variables on the select lines. As indicated in Fig. 5.46, there are four cells corresponding to $wx = 00$. These four cells form the submap for the function at the I_0 terminal. Similarly, the input to the I_1 terminal is described by the four cells in which $wx = 01$, the input to the I_2 terminal is

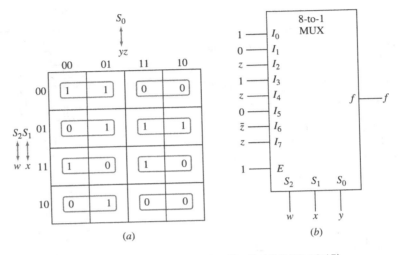

Figure 5.45   Realization of $f(w,x,y,z) = \Sigma m(0,1,5,6,7,9,12,15)$.
(*a*) Karnaugh map. (*b*) Multiplexer realization.

described by the four cells in which $wx = 10$, and the input to the I_3 terminal is described by the four cells in which $wx = 11$. By analyzing these submaps, appropriate logic is readily determined for these input terminals.

As an example, consider the Karnaugh map of Fig. 5.47*a*. Although the four submaps can be interpreted directly on the Karnaugh map itself, they are redrawn in Fig. 5.47*b* to *e* for clarity. These are two-variable Karnaugh maps where it is as-

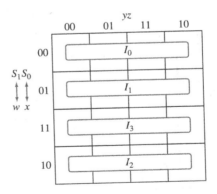

Figure 5.46   Using a four-variable Karnaugh map to obtain a Boolean function realization with a 4-to-1-line multiplexer.

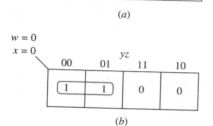

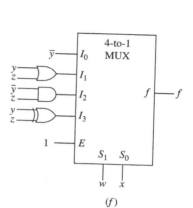

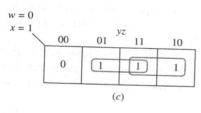

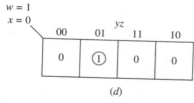

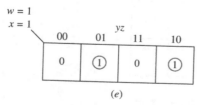

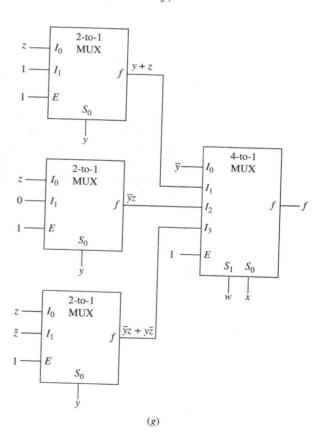

Figure 5.47 Realization of the Boolean function $f(w,x,y,z) = \Sigma m(0,1,5,6,7,9,13,14)$. (a) Karnaugh map. (b) I_0 submap. (c) I_1 submap. (d) I_2 submap. (e) I_3 submap. (f) Realization using a 4-to-1-line multiplexer. (g) Realization using a multiplexer tree.

DIGITAL PRINCIPLES AND DESIGN

sumed that the left and right edges are connected. From the four submaps, it immediately follows that

$$I_0 = \bar{y}$$
$$I_1 = y + z$$
$$I_2 = \bar{y}z$$
$$I_3 = \bar{y}z + y\bar{z} = y \oplus z$$

The realization of the Boolean function is given in Fig. 5.47f.

As a further variation in using multiplexers to realize functions of $n + m$ variables, each of the functions involving the m variables can itself be realized with multiplexers creating a treelike structure of multiplexers. For example, each two-variable function at the data input lines in Fig. 5.47f can be realized with 2-to-1-line multiplexers. This results in the realization shown in Fig. 5.47g.

5.7 PROGRAMMABLE LOGIC DEVICES (PLDs)

With the advent of large-scale integration technology, it has become feasible to fabricate large circuits within a single chip. One such consequence of this technology are the *programmable logic devices* (PLDs). Three such devices are studied in the remainder of this chapter: the *programmable read-only memory* (PROM), the *programmable logic array* (PLA), and the *programmable array logic** (PAL) device.

The general structure of programmable logic devices is illustrated in Fig. 5.48. The inputs to the PLD are applied to a set of buffer/inverters. The logic equivalent of the buffer/inverter is shown in Fig. 5.49. These devices have both the true value of the input as well as the complemented value of the input as its outputs. In addi-

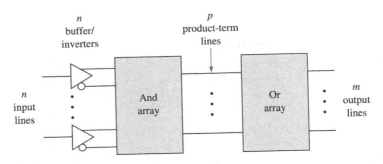

Figure 5.48 General structure of PLDs.

---

*Programmable array logic is a registered trademark of Monolithic Memories, Inc., a division of Advanced Micro Devices, Inc.

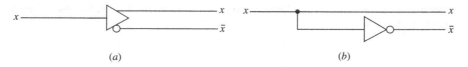

Figure 5.49   Buffer/inverter. (*a*) Symbol. (*b*) Logic equivalent.

tion, these devices produce the necessary drive for the and-array which follows since, in general, the outputs from these devices serve as inputs to a very large number of gates. The array of and-gates accepts the *n* input variables and their complements and is used to generate a set of *p* product terms. These product terms, in turn, serve as inputs to an array of or-gates to realize a set of *m* sum-of-product expressions.

In PLDs, one or both of the gate arrays are programmable in the sense that the logic designer can specify the connections within an array. In this way, PLDs serve as general circuits for the realization of a set of Boolean functions. Table 5.7 summarizes which arrays are programmable for the various PLDs. In the case of the programmable read-only memory (PROM) and the programmable array logic (PAL) devices, only one array is programmable; while both arrays are programmable in the case of the programmable logic array (PLA).

In a programmable array, the connections to each gate can be modified. One simple approach to fabricating a programmable gate is to have each of its inputs connected to a fuse as illustrated in Fig. 5.50*a*. In this figure, the gate realizes the product term *abcd*. Assume, however, that the product term *bc* is to be generated. To do this, the gate is programmed by removing the *a* and *d* connections. This is done by blowing the corresponding fuses. The net result is to have a gate with the desired connections as illustrated in Fig. 5.50*b*. It is assumed in this discussion that an open input to an and-gate is equivalent to a constant logic-1 input and that an

Table 5.7 Types of PLDs

Device	And-array	Or-array
PROM	Fixed	Programmable
PLA	Programmable	Programmable
PAL	Programmable	Fixed

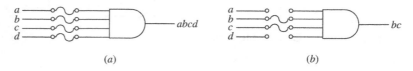

Figure 5.50   Programming by blowing fuses. (*a*) Before programming.
(*b*) After programming.

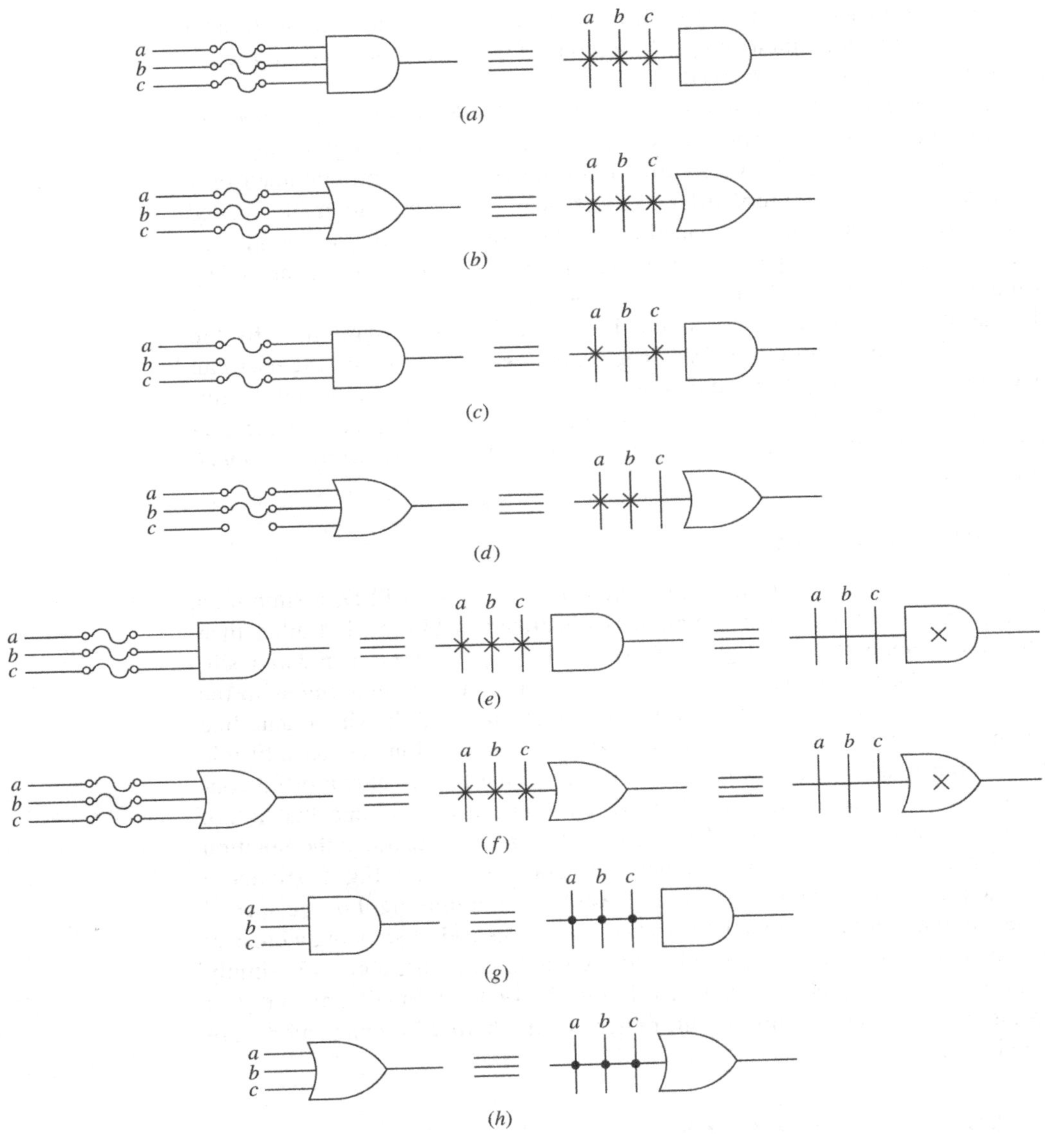

278   **DIGITAL PRINCIPLES AND DESIGN**

(a)

(b)

(c)

(d)

(e)

(f)

(g)

(h)

Figure 5.51   PLD notation. (a) Unprogrammed and-gate. (b) Unprogrammed or-gate.
(c) Programmed and-gate realizing the term ac. (d) Programmed or-gate realizing
the term a + b. (e) Special notation for an and-gate having all its input fuses intact.
(f) Special notation for an or-gate having all its input fuses intact. (g) And-gate with
nonfusible inputs. (h) Or-gate with nonfusible inputs.

open input to an or-gate is equivalent to a constant logic-0 input. Although other schemes are used in addition to simple fuse inputs, for the purpose of this presentation, this simple approach is assumed.

It should be noted that programming is really a hardware procedure. Specialized equipment, called *programmers*, is needed to carry out the programming of a PLD by an end-user. Clearly, fused-programmable devices are programmed only once. However, manufacturers offer devices that are reprogrammable, called *erasable PLDs.* In this case, the connections can be reset to their original conditions and then reprogrammed. Depending upon the type of device, erasing is achieved by exposing the PLD to ultraviolet light or using electrical signals.

In the above discussion it was stated that the PLD is programmed by the user. These PLDs are said to be *field programmable.* Alternatively, the user can specify the desired connections and supply the information to the manufacturer. The manufacturer then prepares an overlay that is used to complete the connections as the last step in the fabrication process. Such PLDs are referred to as *mask programmable.*

5.7.1 PLD Notation

To indicate the connections in the and-array and or-array of a PLD, a simplified notation is frequently used. This notation is illustrated in Fig. 5.51. Rather than drawing all the inputs to the and-gates and or-gates, the gates are drawn with a single input line. The inputs themselves are indicated by lines at right angles to the single gate line. The intersections between the input lines and the single gate line correspond to the types of connections. A cross at the intersection denotes a fusible link that is intact; while the lack of a cross indicates the fuse is blown or no connection exists. The occurrence of a hard-wired connection, i.e., one that is not fusible, is indicated by a junction dot. Figure 5.51a and b illustrates the notation for an and-gate and an or-gate prior to being programmed; while Fig. 5.51c and d shows examples of the notation for these gates after programming. For the special case when all the input fuses to a gate are kept intact, instead of showing a cross at the intersection between each input line and the single gate line, a cross is simply placed inside the gate symbol as indicated in Fig. 5.51e and f. Finally, an and-gate and or-gate with nonfusible inputs, but, rather, having hard-wire connections, are illustrated in Fig. 5.51g and h.

5.8 PROGRAMMABLE READ-ONLY MEMORIES (PROMs)

The basic structure of a programmable read-only memory (PROM) is shown in Fig. 5.52 and its equivalent logic diagram in Fig. 5.53a. As a PLD, it consists of an and-array with a set of buffer/inverters and an or-array. The and-array with buffer/inverters is really an n-to-2^n-line decoder and the or-array is simply a collection of programmable or-gates. The or-array is also called the *memory array.* The decoder serves as a minterm generator. The n-variable minterms appear on the 2^n lines at the

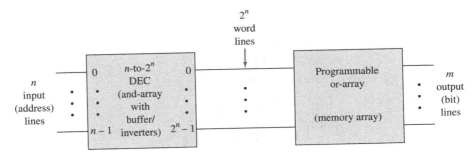

Figure 5.52   Structure of a PROM.

decoder output. These are known as *word lines*. As is seen in Fig. 5.53a, all 2^n outputs of the decoder are connected to each of the m gates in the or-array via programmable fusible links. The n input lines are called the *address lines* and the m output lines the *bit lines*. A PROM is characterized by the number of output lines of the decoder and the number of output lines from the or-array. Hence, the PROM of Fig. 5.53a is referred to as a $2^n \times m$ PROM.

The logic diagram of Fig. 5.53a is redrawn in Fig. 5.53b using the PLD notation introduced in the previous section. Since the and-array is fixed, i.e., not programmable, connections are shown by junction dots. The fusible connections in the or-array, however, are shown by crosses since this array is programmable.

The realization of a set of Boolean expressions using a decoder and or-gates was discussed in Sec. 5.4. The very same approach is applicable in using a PROM since a PROM is a device that includes both the decoder and or-gates within the same network. Given a set of Boolean expressions in minterm canonical form or a set of Boolean functions in truth table form, it is only necessary to determine which programmable links of a PROM to retain and which to open. The programming of the PROM is then carried out by blowing the appropriate fuses. PROMs are typically used for code conversions, generating bit patterns for characters, and as lookup tables for arithmetic functions.

As a simple example of using a PROM for combinational logic design, consider the Boolean expressions

$$f_1(x_2,x_1,x_0) = \Sigma m(0,1,2,5,7)$$
$$f_2(x_2,x_1,x_0) = \Sigma m(1,2,4,6)$$

The corresponding truth table is given in Fig. 5.54a. Since these are functions of three input variables, a PROM having a 3-to-8-line decoder is needed. In addition, since there are two functions being realized, the or-array must consist of two gates. Hence, an 8×2 PROM is needed for the realization. The realization is shown in Fig. 5.54b using the PLD notation. A blown fusible link on the input of an or-gate is equivalent to a logic-0 input. It should be emphasized that this example is for illustrative purposes only. From a practical point of view, PROMs are intended for combinational networks having a large number of inputs and outputs.

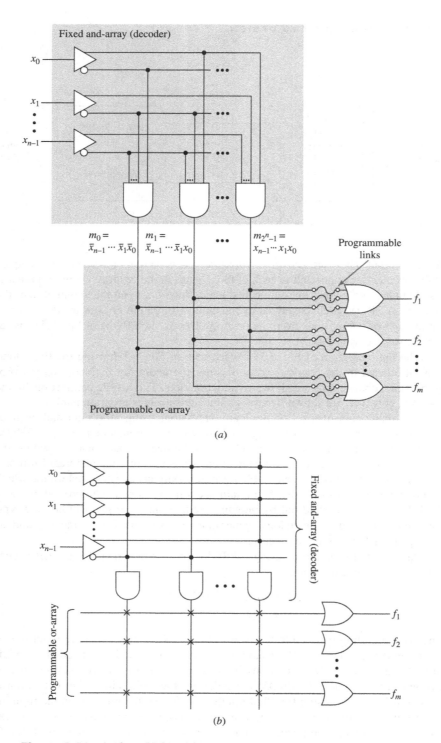

Figure 5.53 A $2^n \times m$ PROM. (*a*) Logic diagram. (*b*) Representation in PLD notation.

x_2	x_1	x_0	f_1	f_2
0	0	0	1	0
0	0	1	1	1
0	1	0	1	1
0	1	1	0	0
1	0	0	0	1
1	0	1	1	0
1	1	0	0	1
1	1	1	1	0

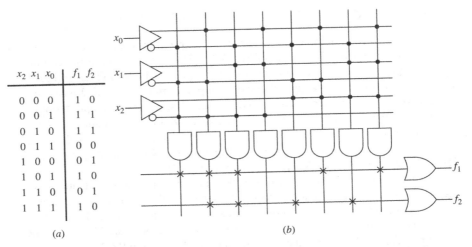

(a)   (b)

Figure 5.54   Using a PROM for logic design. (*a*) Truth table. (*b*) PROM realization.

It may seem strange that the structure of Fig. 5.52, as a logic-design device, is called a read-only memory. Read-only memory devices were originally developed to store permanent data in a digital system. In these devices each piece of data, called a *word*, is accessible by specifying an address.

To see how the structure of Fig. 5.52 is viewed as a memory device, again consider Fig. 5.54. By applying a 3-bit combination to the x_0, x_1, and x_2 lines, precisely one and-gate in the decoder is selected in the sense that its output line, i.e., word line, is logic-1. Thus, each input combination is regarded as an *address* of one of the word lines. As a consequence of selecting a given word line, a pattern of 0's and 1's, i.e., a word, as determined by the fusible connections to the selected word line appears at the output terminals, i.e., the bit lines, of the device. This 0-1 pattern is considered the word *stored* at the address associated with the selected word line. For example, the word stored at address $x_2x_1x_0 = 100$ in Fig. 5.54 is $f_1f_2 = 01$. Finally, the fact that the connections associated with the fusible links normally cannot be altered once they are formed makes the term *read-only* appropriate for this device. Hence, the realization shown in Fig. 5.54 is a read-only memory storing four words each consisting of 2 bits.

For each additional input line to a PROM, the number of gates in the decoder and the number of inputs to each gate in the or-array double. This is because all possible minterms are generated by the decoder and all the minterms appear as inputs to the gates in the or-array. However, in many applications, not all the minterms are necessary. In such cases, the and-array is not utilized efficiently. Also, as was seen in the discussion on minimization, collections of minterms can frequently be replaced by a single product term. If the and-array is made programmable so that only necessary product terms are generated, then its size can be controlled. As is seen in the next two sections, programmable and-arrays occur in the PLA and PAL devices.

5.9 PROGRAMMABLE LOGIC ARRAYS (PLAs)

Another type of programmable logic device is the programmable logic array (PLA). The PLA has the general structure of Fig. 5.48 where both the and-array and the or-array are programmable. A logic diagram for a general PLA is given in Fig. 5.55. For proper operation it is assumed that open input terminals to an and-gate, i.e., terminals connected to blown fuses, behave as logic-1's; while open input terminals to an or-gate behave as logic-0's. PLAs are characterized by three numbers: the number of input lines n, the number of product terms that can be generated p, i.e., the number of and-gates, and the number of output lines m. Consequently, they are designated as $n \times p \times m$ PLAs. A typical PLA is $16 \times 48 \times 8$.

As was mentioned in the previous section, in many logic design situations, not all the minterms are needed for a realization. This is particularly true in problems involving a large number of don't-care conditions, since minterms denoting these conditions do not have to appear in the implementation. For n input variables, there are 2^n minterms. This is also the number of gates in the and-array of a PROM. However, in a PLA the number of gates in the and-array is significantly less than 2^n. To see the extent of the reduction in the size of the and-array, consider functions of 16 input variables.

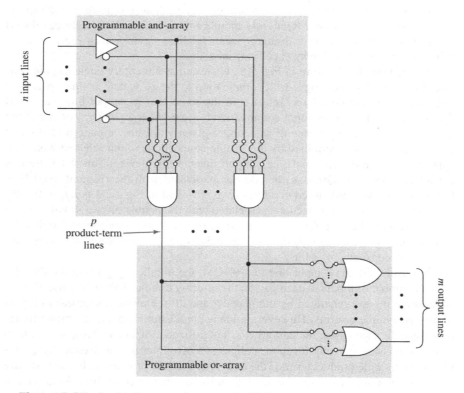

Figure 5.55   Logic diagram of an $n \times p \times m$ PLA.

In this case there are $2^{16} = 65,536$ minterms. However, in a $16 \times 48 \times 8$ PLA, provision is made to realize only 48 product terms. Referring to Fig. 5.55, it should be noted that both complemented and uncomplemented inputs, for a total of $2n$ inputs, appear at each and-gate to provide maximum flexibility in product-term generation.

Since all minterms are generated in a PROM, the realization of a set of Boolean functions is based on minterm canonical expressions. It is never necessary to minimize these expressions prior to obtaining a realization with a PROM. On the other hand, in the case of PLAs, depending upon how the fuses are programmed, the and-gates are capable of generating product terms that are not necessarily minterms. As a consequence, a realization using a PLA is based on sum-of-product expressions that may not be canonical. However, what is significant is that the logic designer is bounded by the number of product terms that are realizable by the and-array. This implies that it is necessary to obtain a set of expressions in which the total number of distinct product terms does not exceed the number of gates in the and-array. Thus, some degree of equation simplification generally is appropriate. Techniques for minimizing a set of Boolean expressions using the criterion of minimal number of distinct terms were previously discussed in Chapter 4.

To illustrate the use of a PLA for combinational logic design, consider the expressions

$$f_1(x,y,z) = \Sigma m(0,1,3,4)$$
$$f_2(x,y,z) = \Sigma m(1,2,3,4,5)$$

Assume that a $3 \times 4 \times 2$ PLA is available for the realization of the expressions. Before continuing, however, the reader should be well aware that this is not a practical application of the use of PLAs due to its simplicity, but it does serve the purpose of showing the concept of PLA combinational logic design. It is now noted that the size of the or-array in the available PLA is sufficient since it has two output or-gates. However, there are six distinct minterms between the two expressions. A realization based on the canonical expressions is therefore not possible with the assumed PLA since only four and-gates appear in the and-array. A formal approach to obtaining a pair of equivalent expressions, hopefully having at most four distinct terms, is to first establish the multiple-output prime implicants using the Quine-McCluskey method and then, using a multiple-output prime-implicant table, to find a multiple-output minimal sum having the fewest terms as discussed in Secs. 4.12 and 4.13. Of course, for real-world problems the minimization mechanics is done by specialized software written for this purpose. However, at this time let us attempt to obtain a solution using simple observations. When dealing with two output functions, it is known from Chapter 4 that the complete set of multiple-output prime implicants consists of all the prime implicants of the individual functions f_1 and f_2 as well as the prime implicants of the product function $f_1 \cdot f_2$. It was also established in Chapter 4 that there exists a multiple-output minimal sum consisting of just multiple-output prime implicants. A subset of the prime implicants of f_1 and $f_1 \cdot f_2$ are used in the multiple-output minimal sum for f_1; while a subset of the prime implicants of f_2 and $f_1 \cdot f_2$ are used in the multiple-output minimal sum for f_2. Figure 5.56a shows the prime implicants of $f_1, f_2,$ and $f_1 \cdot f_2$ as they

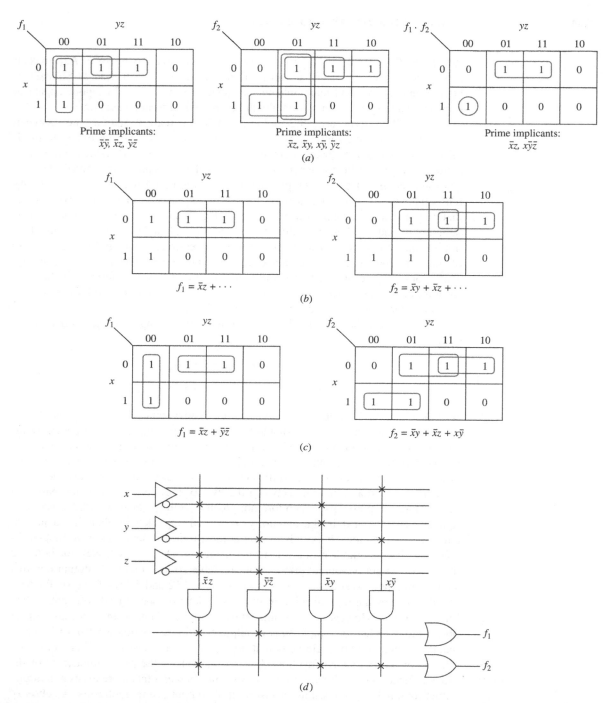

Figure 5.56 Example of combinational logic design using a PLA. (*a*) Maps showing the multiple-output prime implicants. (*b*) Partial covering of the f_1 and f_2 maps. (*c*) Maps for the multiple-output minimal sum. (*d*) Realization using a 3×4×2 PLA.

appear on Karnaugh maps.* There are a total of seven *distinct* prime implicants. Referring to the f_1 and $f_1 \cdot f_2$ maps to determine the terms for the minimized f_1 expression, it is now noted that of the four distinct prime implicants in these maps only prime implicant $\bar{x}z$ covers the $xyz = 011$ 1-cell of f_1. Similarly, referring to the f_2 and $f_1 \cdot f_2$ maps to determine the terms for the minimized f_2 expression, $\bar{x}y$ is the only prime implicant of the five distinct prime implicants in these maps that covers the $xyz = 010$ 1-cell of f_2. Hence, these two prime implicants must occur in the multiple-output minimal sum. Furthermore, it is next noted that prime implicant $\bar{x}z$, which is being used for f_1, can also be used for f_2 to cover the $xyz = 001$ 1-cell. Figure 5.56b shows the covering of the f_1 and f_2 maps at this point, along with the incomplete multiple-output minimal sum having two distinct product terms. From these maps it is immediately seen that using one additional prime implicant subcube for each of the functions, as shown in Fig. 5.56c, results in a multiple-output minimal sum having four distinct terms, i.e.,

$$f_1(x,y,z) = \bar{x}z + \bar{y}\bar{z}$$
$$f_2(x,y,z) = \bar{x}y + \bar{x}z + x\bar{y}$$

The corresponding $3{\times}4{\times}2$ PLA realization is shown in Fig. 5.56d.

Although, in the above example, the final expressions for f_1 and f_2 could have been obtained using the prime implicants of the individual functions and ignoring the product function $f_1 \cdot f_2$, it should not be concluded that simply minimizing the individual expressions always results in a multiple-output minimal sum. A second example illustrates this point. Consider the expressions

$$f_1(x,y,z) = \Sigma m(0,1,3,5)$$
$$f_2(x,y,z) = \Sigma m(3,5,7)$$

Again a realization with a $3{\times}4{\times}2$ PLA is attempted. The Karnaugh maps displaying the multiple-output prime implicants are shown in Fig. 5.57a. Using an analysis similar to the previous example, Fig. 5.57b shows the covering for the multiple-output minimal sum

$$f_1(x,y,z) = \bar{x}\bar{y} + \bar{x}z + x\bar{y}z$$
$$f_2(x,y,z) = yz + x\bar{y}z$$

which consists of only four distinct product terms. Hence, a realization using a $3{\times}4{\times}2$ PLA is possible. An alternative covering, shown in Fig. 5.57c, corresponds to the multiple-output minimal sum

$$f_1(x,y,z) = \bar{x}\bar{y} + \bar{y}z + \bar{x}yz$$
$$f_2(x,y,z) = xz + \bar{x}yz$$

The realization based on the expressions obtained from Fig. 5.57b is shown in Fig. 5.57d using the PLD notation. It should be noted that a realization would not be possible with the assumed $3{\times}4{\times}2$ PLA if the expressions were individually minimized.

---

*Recall that the minterms of the product function $f_1 \cdot f_2$ are the minterms common to both f_1 and f_2.

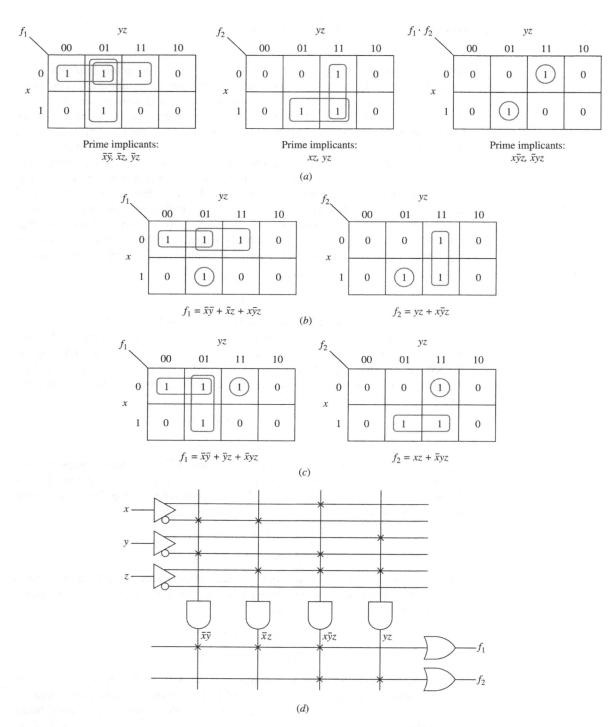

Figure 5.57 Example of combinational logic design using a PLA. (*a*) Maps showing the multiple-output prime implicants. (*b*) A multiple-output minimal sum covering. (*c*) Alternative multiple-output minimal sum covering. (*d*) realization using a 3×4×2 PLA.

288   **DIGITAL PRINCIPLES AND DESIGN**

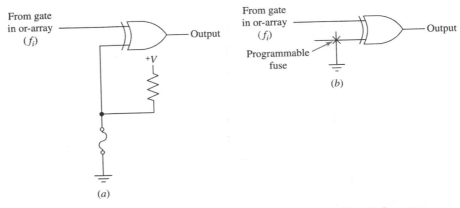

Figure 5.58 Exclusive-or-gate with a programmable fuse. (*a*) Circuit diagram. (*b*) Symbolic representation.

For greater flexibility, PLAs normally make provision for either a true output or a complemented output. One way in which this is achieved is illustrated in Fig. 5.58*a*. The output from each gate in the or-array, f_i, feeds into one input of an exclusive-or-gate. The other input to the exclusive-or-gate, having a programable fuse to ground, is connected to a pull-up resistor as shown in the figure. Assuming positive logic, when the fuse is left intact, the lower input to the exclusive-or-gate is at ground which is equivalent to a logic-0. Since $f_i \oplus 0 = \bar{f}_i$, it follows that the output of the exclusive-or-gate is the same as the upper input. That is, the output corresponds to the true realization of f_i. On the other hand, when the fuse is blown, a positive voltage, i.e., logic-1, is applied to the lower input of the exclusive-or-gate. Since $f_i \oplus 1 = \bar{f}_i$, the net result is that the output of the exclusive-or-gate corresponds to the complemented realization of f_i. The symbolic representation of the programmable exclusive-or-gate is given in Fig. 5.58*b*. The general structure of a PLA with true or complemented output capability is shown in Fig. 5.59.

Now consider the Boolean functions

$$f_1(x,y,z) = \Sigma m(1,2,3,7)$$

$$f_2(x,y,z) = \Sigma m(0,1,2,6)$$

The Karnaugh maps of these functions are given in Fig. 5.60. The upper two maps are used to obtain a multiple-output minimal sum for f_1 and f_2; while the lower two maps are used to obtain the multiple-output minimal sum for $\bar{f}_1$ and $\bar{f}_2$. Again assume a realization of these functions using a 3×4×2 PLA is to be attempted. As in the previous examples, realizations of functions of this simplicity are not justified using PLAs. However, the interest here is to illustrate the use of complemented functions. If a 3×4×2 PLA is to be used, then only four product terms can be generated. Thus, a realization is not possible using the subcubes of 1-cells as indicated in the upper two maps of Fig. 5.60. On the other hand, the indicated

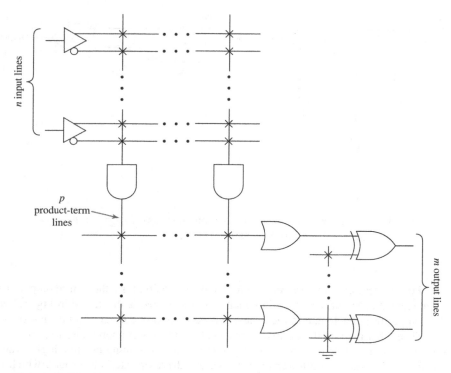

Figure 5.59   General structure of a PLA having true and complemented output capability.

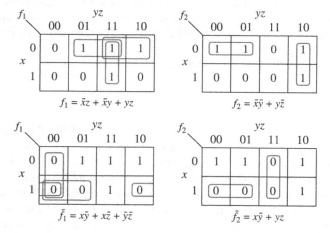

$$f_1 = \bar{x}z + \bar{x}y + yz$$

$$f_2 = \bar{x}\bar{y} + y\bar{z}$$

$$\bar{f}_1 = x\bar{y} + x\bar{z} + \bar{y}\bar{z}$$

$$\bar{f}_2 = x\bar{y} + yz$$

Figure 5.60   Karnaugh maps for the functions $f_1(x,y,z) = \Sigma m(1,2,3,7)$ and $f_2(x,y,z) = \Sigma m(0,1,2,6)$.

290   DIGITAL PRINCIPLES AND DESIGN

subcubes of the 1-cells for f_1 and the subcubes of the 0-cells for f_2 in Fig. 5.60 result in the expressions

$$f_1(x,y,z) = \bar{x}z + \bar{x}y + yz$$
$$\bar{f}_2(x,y,z) = x\bar{y} + yz$$

For these two expressions there are only four distinct product terms: $\bar{x}z$, $\bar{x}y$, yz, and $x\bar{y}$. Thus, the fuses in the and-array and or-array can be programmed for the f_1 and $\bar{f}_2$ expressions. If the $3\times4\times2$ PLA has provisions for complementing its outputs as was illustrated in Fig. 5.58, then by leaving the fuse for the f_1 output exclusive-or-gate intact and blowing the fuse for the f_2 output, the desired realization is possi-

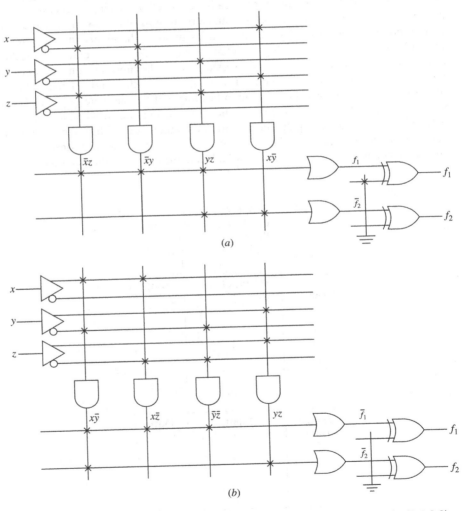

(a)

(b)

Figure 5.61   Two realizations of $f_1(x,y,z) = \Sigma m(1,2,3,7)$ and $f_2(x,y,z) = \Sigma m(0,1,2,6)$. (a) Realization based on f_1 and $\bar{f}_2$ (b) Realization based on $\bar{f}_1$ and $\bar{f}_2$.

ble. This is shown in Fig. 5.61a. It should be noted that $\bar{f}_2$ really occurs at one of the outputs of the or-array. By programming the corresponding exclusive-or-gate fuse, $\bar{\bar{f}}_2 = f_2$ appears at the output of the PLA.

In Fig. 5.60, it is also observed that there are only four distinct product terms in the expressions for $\bar{f}_1$ and $\bar{f}_2$. Hence, an alternative realization using a 3×4×2 PLA with output complementation capability can be based on these expressions. In this case, both output exclusive-or-gate fuses must be blown. This results in complementing the expressions so that the original functions are realized. The corresponding realization is shown in Fig. 5.61b.

A common way of specifying the connections in a PLA is via the *PLA table*. PLA tables for the two realizations of Fig. 5.61 are given in Table 5.8. In general, the PLA table has three sections for indicating connections: an input section, an output section, and a *T/C* section. Each product term is assigned a row in the table. The input section is used to specify the connections between the inputs and the gates in the and-array, thereby describing the connections needed to generate the product terms. The input variables are listed across the top of the input section. A 1 entry in this section indicates that a connection is to exist between the uncomplemented form of the input variable listed in the column heading and the and-gate associated with the row. On the other hand, a 0 entry in the input section indicates that a connection is to exist between the complemented form of the input variable listed in the column heading and the and-gate associated with the row. Finally, a dash indicates that there are no connections for the associated variable and the corresponding and-gate.

Table 5.8   PLA tables for the realizations of the functions given by the Karnaugh maps of Fig. 5.60. (a) PLA table for Fig. 5.61a. (b) PLA table for Fig. 5.61b

Product term	Inputs			Outputs	
	x	y	z	f_1	f_2
$\bar{x}z$	0	–	1	1	–
$\bar{x}y$	0	1	–	1	–
yz	–	1	1	1	1
$x\bar{y}$	1	0	–	–	1
			T/C	T	C

(a)

Product term	Inputs			Outputs	
	x	y	z	f_1	f_2
$x\bar{y}$	1	0	–	1	1
$x\bar{z}$	1	–	0	1	–
$\bar{y}\bar{z}$	–	0	0	1	–
yz	–	1	1	–	1
			T/C	C	C

(b)

The output section of the PLA table is used to specify the connections between the outputs of the and-gates and the inputs to the or-gates. The column headings correspond to the functions being realized. Here a 1 entry indicates that a connection is to exist between the and-gate associated with the row and the or-gate associated with the column. A dash entry in the output section indicates that the and-gate associated with the row is not connected to the or-gate associated with the column.

The *T/C* section indicates how the exclusive-or-gate fuses are programmed. A *T* entry means that the true output is used, thereby implying the fuse should be kept intact; while a *C* entry means that the output should be complemented, implying the fuse should be blown.

The above examples were contrived so that multiple-output minimal expressions were required to obtain the desired PLA realizations. However, PLAs are available in a variety of sizes. Nothing is gained by performing minimization if the minimized and nonminimized expressions result in using the same size PLA. PLAs are intended to provide for convenient realizations. For this reason, complete minimization becomes a secondary consideration when obtaining a PLA realization, since no simplification or only slight simplification of expressions may be sufficient for a realization using a PLA of a specified size. For example, simply minimizing the individual expressions and making use of any common terms might be sufficient to obtain an efficient realization without the need for determining the multiple-output minimal sum that involves the prime implicants of the product functions. In Chapter 8, PLAs are used without regard to determining multiple-output minimal sums. It will be seen that the networks being designed at that time are modeled in a form that immediately suggests a PLA realization.

5.10 PROGRAMMABLE ARRAY LOGIC (PAL) DEVICES

The final PLD to be discussed is the programmable array logic (PAL) device. In this type of device, only the and-array is programmable. The or-array is fixed by the manufacturer of the device. This makes the PAL device easier to program and less expensive than the PLA. On the other hand, since the or-array is fixed, it is less flexible than the PLA.

To illustrate the structure of a PAL device, a simple four-input, three-output PAL device is shown in Fig. 5.62. The reader should be aware that this PAL device is for illustrative purposes only and does not represent one that is commercially available. Commercial PAL devices can handle 10 or more inputs and may provide complemented outputs. In the figure, particular attention should be given to the fixed or-array. Here, two of the or-gates have three inputs each, while the third or-gate has only two inputs. All the input variables and their complements appear at the inputs to each of the and-gates. This allows each and-gate to generate any product term up to four variables. However, the output of each and-gate serves as an input to only one or-gate. For this simple, illustrative PAL device, three Boolean expressions can be realized in which two expressions can have at most three product terms and one expression can have at most two product terms.

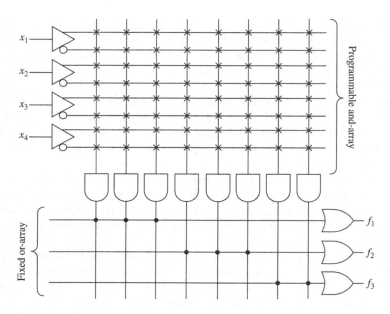

Figure 5.62   A simple four-input, three-output PAL device.

As an illustration of using a PAL device to realize combinational logic, consider the two functions

$$f_1(x,y,z) = \Sigma m(1,2,4,5,7)$$
$$f_2(x,y,z) = \Sigma m(0,1,3,5,7)$$

The corresponding Karnaugh maps are drawn in Fig. 5.63*a* from which the minimal sums are found to be

$$f_1(x,y,z) = x\bar{y} + xz + \bar{y}z + \bar{x}y\bar{z}$$
$$f_2(x,y,z) = z + \bar{x}\,\bar{y}$$

To use the illustrative PAL device of Fig. 5.62, a problem occurs with the realization of f_1 since the minimal expression consists of four product terms, while no or-gate in this device has more than three inputs. However, a realization is achievable if the realization is based upon the three expressions

$$f_1 = f_3 + \bar{y}z + \bar{x}y\bar{z}$$
$$f_2 = z + \bar{x}\,\bar{y}$$
$$f_3 = x\bar{y} + xz$$

This realization is shown in Fig. 5.63*b*. Here the first two product terms of f_1 are generated as the subfunction f_3. The f_3 subfunction is then fed back into an input terminal and combined with the remaining product terms of f_1 to produce the desired realization of f_1. To realize f_2, only two terms need to be generated. Since a three-input or-gate is used, the third input must correspond to a logic-0 so as not

294　　DIGITAL PRINCIPLES AND DESIGN

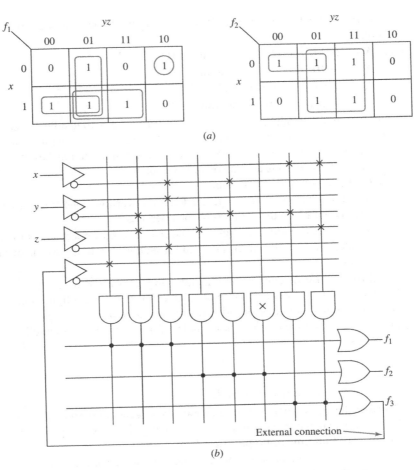

Figure 5.63　An example of using a PAL device to realize two Boolean functions. (*a*) Karnaugh maps. (*b*) Realization.

to affect the f_2 output. This is achieved by keeping all the fuses intact to the and-gate that serves as the third input to the f_2 or-gate. With a variable and its complement as inputs to an and-gate, the output of the gate is always at logic-0. As was mentioned in Sec. 5.7, the $\times$ in the gate symbol indicates that all its fuses are kept intact.

CHAPTER 5　PROBLEMS

5.1　Assume an adder/subtracter of the type shown in Fig. 5.6 is capable of handling two 5-bit operands. For each of the following set of unsigned operands, X and Y, and control input, Add/Sub, determine the output. Check your answers by converting the binary numbers into decimal.

    a. $X = 10111$, $Y = 00110$, Add/Sub = 0

    b. $X = 11010$, $Y = 01101$, Add/Sub = 0

    c. $X = 11001$, $Y = 00101$, Add/Sub = 1

    d. $X = 10011$, $Y = 11010$, Add/Sub = 1

5.2 Assume the binary adder/subtracter shown in Fig. 5.6 is to handle signed binary numbers in which x_{n-1} and y_{n-1} are the sign bits. Two methods were given in Sec. 2.8 for the detection of an overflow condition, one based on the sign bits of the operands and the other based on the carries into and from the sign digit position during addition.

    a. Determine the additional logic needed if an overflow condition is to be detected based on the sign bits of the operands.

    b. Determine the additional logic needed if an overflow condition is to be detected based on the carries into and from the sign digit position during addition.

5.3 Consider the cascade connection illustrated in Fig. 5.9 of 4-bit carry lookahead adders to obtain a large parallel adder. For this configuration, calculate the maximum propagation delay time, assuming each gate introduces a unit time of propagation delay, for a parallel adder handling

    a. 8 bits.

    b. 20 bits.

    c. 40 bits.

    d. n bits where n is divisible by 4.

5.4 Consider the 16-bit adder using carry lookahead generators shown in Fig. 5.10b. Calculate the maximum propagation delay time assuming each gate introduces a unit time of propagation delay.

5.5 a. Using a 4-bit binary adder, design a network to convert a decimal digit in 8421 code into a decimal digit in excess-3 code.

    b. Using a 4-bit binary adder, design a network to convert a decimal digit in excess-3 code into a decimal digit in 8421 code.

5.6 Using an approach similar to that for the design of a single decade 8421 BCD adder, design a single decade 8421 BCD subtracter incorporating 4-bit binary subtracters.

5.7 Using an approach similar to that for the design of a single decade 8421 BCD adder, design a single decade adder in which the operand digits are in excess-3 code.

5.8 Design a specialized comparator for determining if two n-bit numbers are equal. To do this, design the necessary 1-bit comparator that can be cascaded to achieve this task.

5.9 In the design of the 1-bit comparator in Sec. 5.3, conditions $A > B$, $A = B$, and $A < B$ corresponded to $GEL = 100$, 010, and 001, respectively. Another approach to the design of a 1-bit comparator is to code the three conditions.

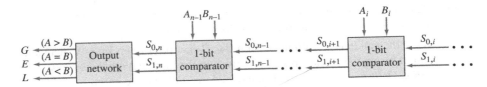

Figure P5.9

One possible code is $S_1S_0 = 10, 00$, and 01 for $A > B, A = B$, and $A < B$, respectively. This implies that only two output lines occur from each 1-bit comparator. However, at the output of the last 1-bit comparator, an additional network must be designed to convert the end result into terms of G, E, and L. This approach is illustrated in Fig. P5.9. Design a 1-bit comparator and output network for this approach.

5.10   Using or-gates and/or nor-gates along with a 3-to-8-line decoder of the type shown in Fig. 5.18, realize the following pairs of expressions. In each case, the gates should be selected so as to minimize their total number of input terminals.

    a. $f_1(x_2,x_1,x_0) = \Sigma m(1,3)$
        $f_2(x_2,x_1,x_0) = \Sigma m(3,6,7)$

    b. $f_1(x_2,x_1,x_0) = \Sigma m(0,1,5,6,7)$
        $f_2(x_2,x_1,x_0) = \Sigma m(1,2,3,6,7)$

    c. $f_1(x_2,x_1,x_0) = \Sigma m(0,2,4)$
        $f_2(x_2,x_1,x_0) = \Sigma m(1,2,4,5,7)$

5.11   Using or-gates and/or nor-gates along with a 3-to-8-line decoder of the type shown in Fig. 5.18, realize the following pairs of expressions. In each case, the gates should be selected so as to minimize their total number of input terminals.

    a. $f_1(x_2,x_1,x_0) = \Pi M(0,3,5,6,7)$
        $f_2(x_2,x_1,x_0) = \Pi M(2,3,4,5,7)$

    b. $f_1(x_2,x_1,x_0) = \Pi M(0,1,7)$
        $f_2(x_2,x_1,x_0) = \Pi M(1,5,7)$

    c. $f_1(x_2,x_1,x_0) = \Pi M(1,2,5)$
        $f_2(x_2,x_1,x_0) = \Pi M(0,1,3,5,7)$

5.12   Using and-gates and/or nand-gates along with a 3-to-8-line decoder of the type shown in Fig. 5.22, realize the pairs of expressions of Problem 5.11. In each case, the gates should be selected so as to minimize their total number of input terminals.

5.13   Using and-gates and/or nand-gates along with a 3-to-8-line decoder of the type shown in Fig. 5.22, realize the pairs of expressions of Problem 5.10. In each case, the gates should be selected so as to minimize their total number of input terminals.

5.14   Using a 4-to-16-line decoder constructed from nand-gates and having an enable input $\overline{E}$, design an excess-3 to 8421 code converter. Select gates so as to minimize their total number of input terminals.

5.15 Using two 2-to-4-line decoders of the type shown in Fig. 5.26 along with any necessary gates, construct a 3-to-8-line decoder.

5.16 Write the condensed truth table for a 4-to-2-line priority encoder with a valid output where the highest priority is given to the input having the highest index. Determine the minimal sum equations for the three outputs.

5.17 Repeat Problem 5.16 where the highest priority is given to the input having the lowest index.

5.18 Figure 5.34 showed the structure of a 16-to-1-line multiplexer constructed from only 4-to-1-line multiplexers. Other structures are possible depending upon the type of multiplexers used. Construct a multiplexer tree for a 16-to-1-line multiplexer

   a.   Using only 2-to-1-line multiplexers.

   b.   Using 2-to-1-line and 4-to-1-line multiplexers. (Note: three different structures are possible.)

   c.   Using 2-to-1-line and 8-to-1-line multiplexers. (Note: two different structures are possible.)

5.19 Determine a Boolean expression in terms of the input variables that correspond to each of the multiplexer realizations shown in Fig. P5.19.

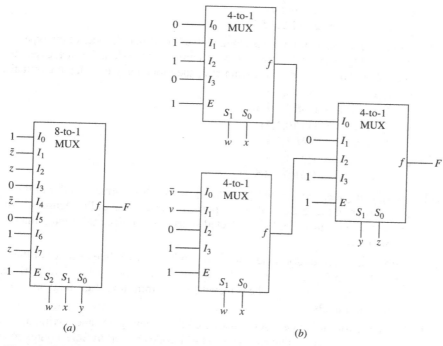

(a)   *(b)*

Figure P5.19

5.20 For each of the following assignments to the select lines of an 8-to-1-line multiplexer, show the location of the I_i submaps, for $i = 0,1, \ldots, 7$, on a 4-variable Karnaugh map having the variables w, x, y, and z.

    a. x, y, and z on select lines S_2, S_1, and S_0, respectively.

    b. w, y, and z on select lines S_2, S_1, and S_0, respectively.

    c. y, x, and w on select lines S_2, S_1, and S_0, respectively.

5.21 Realize each of the following Boolean expressions using an 8-to-1-line multiplexer where w, x, and y appear on select lines S_2, S_1, and S_0, respectively.

    a. $f(w,x,y,z) = \Sigma m(1,2,6,7,9,11,12,14,15)$

    b. $f(w,x,y,z) = \Sigma m(2,5,6,7,9,12,13,15)$

    c. $f(w,x,y,z) = \Sigma m(1,2,4,5,8,10,11,15)$

    d. $f(w,x,y,z) = \Sigma m(0,4,6,8,9,11,13,14)$

5.22 Repeat Problem 5.21 where x, y, and z appear on select lines S_2, S_1, and S_0, respectively.

5.23 For the function given by the Karnaugh map in Fig. 5.47a, determine a realization using a 4-to-1-line multiplexer and external gates if the w and x variables are applied to the S_0 and S_1 select lines, respectively.

5.24 Realize the Boolean expression

$$f(w,x,y,z) = \Sigma m(4,5,7,8,10,12,15)$$

using a 4-to-1-line multiplexer and external gates.

    a.   Let w and x appear on the select lines S_1 and S_0, respectively.

    b.   Let y and z appear on the select lines S_1 and S_0, respectively.

5.25 Realize the Boolean expression

$$f(w,x,y,z) = \Sigma m(0,2,4,5,7,9,10,14)$$

using a multiplexer tree structure. The first level should consist of two 4-to-1-line multiplexers with variables w and z on their select lines S_1 and S_0, respectively, and the second level should consist of a single 2-to-1-line multiplexer with the variable y on its select line.

5.26 A *shifter* is a combinational network capable of shifting a string of 0's and 1's to the left or right, leaving vacancies, by a fixed number of places as a result of a control signal. For example, assuming vacated positions are replaced by 0's, the string 0011 when shifted right by 1 bit position becomes 0001 and when shifted left by 1 bit position becomes 0110. A shifter to handle an n-bit string can be readily designed with n multiplexers. Bits from the string are applied to the data input lines. The control signals for the various actions are applied to the select input lines. The shifted string appears on the output lines. Design a shifter for handling a 4-bit string where Table P5.26 indicates the control signals and the desired actions. Vacated positions should be filled with 0's.

Table P5.26

S_1	S_0	Action
0	0	No change, i.e., pass input string to output
0	1	Shift right 1 bit position
1	0	Shift right 2 bit positions
1	1	Shift left 1 bit position

5.27 For the PROM realization shown in Fig. P5.27, determine the corresponding Boolean expressions for the outputs.

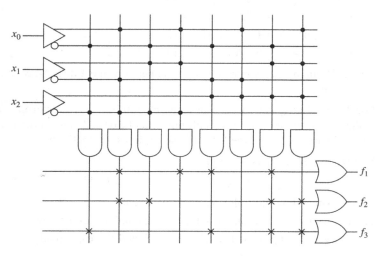

Figure P5.27

5.28 An application of PROMs is to perform code conversion. Using a PROM of an appropriate size, draw the logic diagram in PLD notation for a PROM realization to convert 4-bit binary numbers into Gray code. (Refer to Table 2.9 for the Gray code.)

5.29 An application of PROMs is to realize lookup tables for arithmetic functions. Using a PROM of the smallest appropriate size, draw the logic diagram in PLD notation for a PROM realization of the lookup table corresponding to the decimal arithmetic expression $F(X) = 3X + 2$ for $0 \le X \le 7$ where $F(X)$ and X are expressed in binary.

5.30 The pair of Boolean functions

$$f_1(w,x,y,z) = \Sigma m(2,4,5,10,12,13,14)$$

$$f_2(w,x,y,z) = \Sigma m(2,9,10,11,13,14,15)$$

are to be realized with a PLA having only true outputs. By considering just the prime implicants of each individual function and the product function, determine the minimal number of product terms needed for a realization. Draw the logic diagram of the realization in PLD notation and show the corresponding PLA table.

5.31 The following sets of Boolean functions are to be realized with PLAs having both true and complemented outputs. By considering just the prime implicants of the individual functions and their complements, determine the minimal number of product terms needed for each realization. In each case, draw the logic diagram of the realization in PLD notation and show the corresponding PLA table.

a. $f_1(x,y,z) = \Sigma m(3,6,7)$
   $f_2(x,y,z) = \Sigma m(0,1,2,6,7)$
   $f_3(x,y,z) = \Sigma m(0,1,3,4,5)$

b. $f_1(x,y,z) = \Sigma m(0,1,2,5,7)$
   $f_2(x,y,z) = \Sigma m(3,4,5)$
   $f_3(x,y,z) = \Sigma m(3,4,5,6)$

c. $f_1(x,y,z) = \Sigma m(1,3,4,6)$
   $f_2(x,y,z) = \Sigma m(0,2,4,5,7)$
   $f_3(x,y,z) = \Sigma m(1,3,5,6,7)$

5.32 Using the PAL device in Fig. 5.62, draw the logic diagram of a realization in PLD notation for the following set of Boolean functions.

$$f_1(x,y,z) = \Sigma m(1,2,4,6,7)$$

$$f_2(x,y,z) = \Sigma m(2,4,5,6)$$

$$f_3(x,y,z) = \Sigma m(1,4,6)$$